Pure Mathematics at Advanced Level

THIRD EDITION

Other books by L. Harwood Clarke and F. G. J. Norton
OBJECTIVE TESTS IN ORDINARY LEVEL MATHEMATICS
OBJECTIVE TESTS IN C.S.E. MATHEMATICS
ADDITIONAL APPLIED MATHEMATICS
ADDITIONAL PURE MATHEMATICS (third edition)
ORDINARY LEVEL MATHEMATICS (sixth edition)

By L. Harwood Clarke
A NOTEBOOK IN PURE MATHEMATICS
A NOTEBOOK IN APPLIED MATHEMATICS
TRIGONOMETRY AT ORDINARY LEVEL
MATHEMATICS ONE
MATHEMATICS TWO
MATHEMATICS THREE
MATHEMATICS FOUR
HINTS FOR ORDINARY LEVEL MATHEMATICS
HINTS FOR ADVANCED LEVEL MATHEMATICS
MODERN MATHEMATICS AT ORDINARY LEVEL
FOUR FIGURE MATHEMATICAL TABLES
EXERCISES AND WORKED EXAMPLES IN ORDINARY LEVEL MATHEMATICS

By F. G. J. Norton
ADVANCED LEVEL APPLIED MATHEMATICS

All published by Heinemann Educational Books Ltd

Also by F. G. J. Norton
PAN STUDY AIDS—MATHS
Published by Pan Books Ltd, with Heinemann Educational Books Ltd.

Pure Mathematics at Advanced Level

L. HARWOOD CLARKE

THIRD EDITION

prepared by
F. G. J. NORTON
*formerly Head of the Mathematics Department,
Rugby School*

HEINEMANN EDUCATIONAL BOOKS
LONDON

Heinemann Educational Books Ltd
Halley Court, Jordan Hill, Oxford OX2 8EJ
OXFORD LONDON EDINBURGH MADRID ATHENS
BOLOGNA MELBOURNE SYDNEY AUCKLAND
IBADAN NAIROBI GABORONE HARARE
KINGSTON PORTSMOUTH (NH) SINGAPORE

ISBN 0 435 51188 2

First published 1967
Reprinted once
Second Edition 1971
Reprinted three times
Third Edition 1982
Reprinted 1983, 1987, 1990

British Library Cataloguing in Publication Data

Clarke, L. Harwood
  Pure mathematics at Advanced Level.—3rd ed.
  1. Mathematics—1961–
  I. Title   II. Norton, F. G. J.
  510   QA39.2
  ISBN 0-435-51188-2

Set in 10/11pt Monophoto Times by
Eta Services (Typesetters) Ltd, Beccles, Suffolk
Printed and bound in Great Britain by
Biddles Ltd, Guildford and King's Lynn

Foreword to the Third Edition

Many changes have been made in advanced level syllabuses since this book was written fifteen years ago, but the publication of a common core syllabus for schools now gives a measure of stability, and this has been reflected by both new and proposed A level syllabuses of the G.C.E. Boards. This book covers all the core syllabuses of the G.C.E. Boards for mathematics at advanced level, and all the most popular topics which occur as options in Further Mathematics and in the Special Papers.

In revising this book, a sequel to *Additional Pure Mathematics*, care was taken to cover all the appropriate 'new' topics, and also to rewrite where necessary many of the chapters on 'old' topics, to show how those topics have developed recently. The chapter on 'Choice and Chance', for example, has been replaced by two chapters, one on permutations and combinations and the other on probability, developing that branch of mathematics from the level reached in *Additional Pure Mathematics*. Among others, the chapter on vectors has been rewritten, as vectors are now used more algebraically, with few of the pure geometry applications, such as disguised examples on Ceva's and Menelaus' theorems which were current in the mid-sixties. There are very many easy questions—and some hard ones—on vectors, as confidence in using vectors is only acquired by practice. There is a chapter devoted to curve sketching, and numerical methods are introduced for approximate solutions of equations. Topics that do not at present occur in many syllabuses, such as relations and functions, and matrices, are kept as much as possible on their own and can easily be recognised and omitted if desired.

Acknowledgements

I am most grateful for the following examination boards for permission to use questions from past G.C.E. papers, indicated by the following letters:

Associated Examining Board (A.E.B.)
Cambridge University Local Examination Syndicate (C.)
Joint Matriculation Board (J.M.B.)
University of London Schools Examination Department (L.)
Oxford Delegacy of Local Examinations (O.)
Oxford and Cambridge Schools Examination Board (O. & C.)
  Mathematics in Education and Industry project (M.E.I.)
  Schools Mathematics Project (S.M.P.)

It is a pleasure also to thank the examination boards for the help that they have given over these past years to schools and universities in trying to establish suitable syllabuses and examinations in mathematics in schools.

I should thank once more Graham Taylor and all the staff at Heinemann Educational Books for their help in the production of this new edition.

RUGBY 1982   F. G. J. NORTON

vi

Preface to the First Edition

This book is a continuation of my *Additional Pure Mathematics* and completes the syllabus of Pure Mathematics to Advanced Level. The book contains more than is necessary for any one Board but I hope that sufficient work is included to cover the syllabuses of all Boards.

At this level, a division of the material into the separate subjects of algebra, calculus and trigonometry is virtually impossible and these subjects have been grouped together under the one heading 'analysis'. Two chapters on vectors and complex numbers have been separated because opinions about their correct place in a course differ widely and the teacher is left free to consider this section at his convenience. The section on coordinate geometry is also separated as the inclusion of this into an integrated course seems artificial.

Chapters are included on vectors, complex numbers and co-ordinate geometry of three dimensions which is perhaps unusual at this level but the modern trend is towards these subjects and they are already, or shortly will be, in the requirements of some Boards.

My grateful thanks are due to the Oxford & Cambridge Joint Board (O. & C.), the Joint Matriculation Board (J.M.B.), the University of Cambridge (C.) and the University of London (L.) for permission to use questions set in their Advanced Level examinations. These questions are acknowledged in the text.

BEDFORD, 1967   L.H.C.

Contents

1 Permutations and Combinations

Revision

In *Additional Pure Mathematics* the following results were proved:
1. The number of ways of selecting r objects from n (when the order in which they are selected does not matter) is

$$\frac{n(n-1)(n-2)\ldots\ldots\ldots(n-r+1)}{1 \times 2 \times 3 \ldots\ldots\ldots \times r}.$$

This can be written $\dfrac{n!}{r!(n-r)!}$ or ^nC_r or sometimes $\binom{n}{r}$, care being taken to avoid confusing the last form with matrices.

Example 1. *The number of ways of choosing 3 books from 8 is* $\dfrac{8 \times 7 \times 6}{1 \times 2 \times 3} = 56.$

2. The number of ways in which r objects, chosen from n, can be arranged in order is $n(n-1)(n-2)\ldots\ldots(n-r+1)$. This can be written $\dfrac{n!}{(n-r)!}$ or ^nP_r.

Example 2. *The number of ways in which first, second and third prizes can be awarded in a class of 10 pupils is $10 \times 9 \times 8$, i.e., 720.*

We also established two useful relations between binomial coefficients:
3. $\qquad\qquad\qquad ^nC_r = {}^nC_{n-r}.$
4. $\qquad\qquad ^{n+1}C_{r+1} = {}^nC_r + {}^nC_{r+1}.$

Arrangements subject to given conditions

Suppose that five different books are to be arranged on a shelf, so that two of them, *David Copperfield* and *Silas Marner*, do not come together. In how many different ways can this be done?

Imagine that *David Copperfield* and *Silas Marner* are bound together. We then have this unit and three others, a total of four. These four units can be arranged in 4!, i.e. 24 different ways. But *David Copperfield* and *Silas Marner* can be interchanged in everyone of these arrangements, so that the total number of arrangements in which these two particular books are adjacent is $2 \times 4!$, i.e. 48.

Since the total number of ways of arranging the five books is 120, there are $120 - 48$, i.e. 72 ways in which *David Copperfield* and *Silas Marner* do not come together.

Example 3. *In how many ways can 3 boys and 2 girls be arranged in a straight line if the girls are not to be next to each other?*

This problem is exactly the same as that of arranging the five books, so that we can use the same method and obtain 72 as the solution.

The problem can also be solved in this manner. Suppose that the boys are positioned at A, B and C. The first girl can be put in any one of 4 positions; to the left of A, between A and B, between B and C, or to the right of C. (It often helps to draw a diagram).

$$\ldots\ldots A \ldots\ldots B \ldots\ldots C \ldots\ldots$$
$$\text{G} \quad \text{or G} \quad \text{or G} \quad \text{or G}$$

Suppose that the order is A G B C. The second girl cannot be placed next to G, so that there are only three positions in which she can be placed,

$$\ldots\ldots A\,G\,B \ldots\ldots C \ldots\ldots$$
$$\text{G}_2 \qquad \text{or G}_2 \quad \text{or G}_2$$

This gives 12 ways of placing the girls after the boys have been placed. But there are 3!, i.e. 6 ways of placing the boys, so there are 12 × 6, 72 arrangements altogether.

Example 4. *How many even numbers greater than 4000 can be formed from the digits 2, 3, 4 and 5 (repetitions not allowed)?*

The thousand digit must be either 4 or 5. If it is 5, the unit digit must be 2 or 4, i.e. there are 2 choices. The ten digit also has two possibilities and then the hundred digit is fixed. The number of possibilities is 2 × 2 or 4.

If the thousand digit is 4, the unit digit must be 2. There are two choices for the ten digit and then the hundred digit is fixed. The number of possibilities is 1 × 2 or 2.

Therefore there are 4 + 2, a total of 6 even numbers greater than 4000 that can be formed from these digits.

Arrangements round a circular table

A circular table has no 'head' or other distinguishing feature, and arrangements like those in Fig. 1.1 are considered identical. If n people

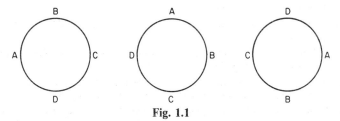

Fig. 1.1

are arranged in a straight line, there are $n!$ different ways in which that can be done. Placed round a circular table, each arrangement will be repeated n times, so there are $(n - 1)!$ different arrangements. Alternatively, we can regard any one person as 'head', and place the other $(n - 1)$ persons in $(n - 1)!$ different ways.

Arrangements of coloured beads around a circular wire

A circular wire differs from a circular table because when we turn it over we see that the other side presents an arrangement of coloured beads different from that on the first side. Thus when the wire on the

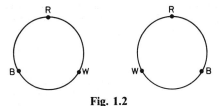

Fig. 1.2

left (where R = red, W = white and B = blue) is turned over we immediately obtain the arrangement on the left. We can see that the only two different arrangements of three coloured beads on a circular wire can be found on opposite sides of the same wire, i.e. there is really only one arrangement. More generally, n beads on a circular wire can be arranged in $\frac{1}{2}(n - 1)!$ different ways.

Exercise 1.1

1. There are 20 seats on a bus. In how many ways can 3 people be seated in the bus?
2. In how many ways can the 20 seats on the bus be filled by persons chosen from a crowd of 23? (Leave your answer in factorials).
3. Find the number of ways of arranging 4 different coats on 6 pegs, if no peg can have more than one coat on it.
4. In how many ways can 5 letters be placed in 5 envelopes?
5. A secretary addresses four envelopes to receive four letters. In how many ways can all 4 letters be placed in wrong envelopes?
6. How many 4-digit numbers can be formed from the digits 2, 3, 4, 5 and 6 if repetitions are not allowed?
7. How many 4-digit numbers are there greater than 2000? How many of these end in 3?
8. In how many ways can 6 boys be arranged in line if two of them, Bob and Jack, cannot sit together?
9. In how many ways can these six boys be arranged round a circular table? In how many of these will Bob and Jack not sit together?
10. In how many ways can the letters NOMAD be arranged if the vowels are not to come together?
11. In how many ways can a red bead, a yellow bead, a green bead and a white bead be arranged on a circular wire? In how many of these will the yellow and the white beads not be together?
12. In how many ways can a tennis four be arranged between four girls? In how many of these will two particular girls play as partners?

13. Two cricket teams of 11 players each are to be chosen from among 22 boys. In how many ways can this be done if two players are to be on opposite sides?

14. In how many ways can 6 boys be divided into two groups of 2 boys and 4 boys?

15. In how many ways can 9 boys be divided into groups of 4 boys, 3 boys and 2 boys?

16. In how many ways can 6 boys be divided into two groups of 3?

17. In how many ways can 9 boys be divided into 3 groups of 3?

18. How many even numbers between 500 and 800 can be formed from the digits 3, 4, 5 and 6 if repetitions are not allowed?

19. In how many ways can the results of 7 football matches be forecast? In how many of these will exactly one result be wrong?

20. In how many ways can a hand of 13 cards be made up with 6 hearts and 7 spades, chosen from 13 hearts and 13 spades?

Number of arrangements of *n* objects not all different

Suppose that we wish to find the number of arrangements of three identical copies of *Robinson Crusoe*, two identical copies of *David Copperfield* and a copy of *Pickwick Papers*, to be placed on a shelf.

If the copies were all different, then there would be 6! different arrangements. The three different copies of *Robinson Crusoe* would be arranged in 3! different ways, and so when the different copies are replaced by identical copies each arrangement is repeated 3! times; similarly when the two different copies of *David Copperfield* are replaced by identical copies, each arrangement is repeated twice, so that the number of different arrangements is $\dfrac{6!}{3!2!}$, i.e. 60.

More generally, if there are *n* objects of which *p* are alike of one kind, *q* alike of another kind and *r* alike of a third kind, they can be arranged in $\dfrac{n!}{p!q!r!}$ different ways.

Exercise 1.2

1. Find the number of different ways of arranging 3 identical pennies and 2 identical half-pennies in a line.

2. Find the number of different ways of arranging 4 black balls, 3 red balls and 2 white balls in a row.

3. Find how many binary numbers can be made from four 1's and three 0's, if all the digits are used.

4. How many six-digit binary numbers are there?

5. How many different arrangements can be made of the letters *a*, *a*, *a*, *b*, *b*, *b*, and *c*?

6. How many of the arrangements in Q.5 end with (i) a, (ii) c?

7. How many arrangements can be made of the letters SIMPLIFY?

8. How many arrangements can be made of the letters INNUMERABLE?

9. In how many of the arrangements in Q.8 are the two letters N adjacent?

10. How many six digit numbers can be made from the digits 3, 3, 3, 4, 4 and 5?

11. How many of the arrangements in Q.10 are even?

12. How many of the numbers formed in Q.10 are multiples of 3?

13. How many different signals can be made using 3 white flags, 3 red flags and 2 green flags?

14. How many different code words can be formed from 4 dashes and 3 dots?

15. If 8 identical coins show 5 heads and 3 tails, in how many ways can they be arranged in a straight line?

16. In how many of the ways in Q.15 will all the heads be together?

17. In how many ways can 4 identical armless chairs and 2 identical arm chairs be arranged in a straight line?

18. In how many ways can the chairs in Q.17 be arranged in a circle?

19. Find the number of arrangements that can be made of the letters IRREGULAR.

20. In how many of the arrangements in Q.19 will the three letters R come together?

Selections any number at a time

Suppose that we are allowed to choose from 8 different books and may take as many or as few as we wish. In how many ways can we make our selection?

We have two choices for each book; we can either accept it or reject it. So the number of choices for 8 books is $2 \times 2 \times 2 \ldots$ to 8 factors, i.e. 2^8. This however includes the selection in which we have rejected every book, so that the number of different selections of books is $2^8 - 1$. More generally, the number of selections from n different objects, if any number can be taken, is $2^n - 1$.

It is interesting to solve this by another method. The number of ways of choosing 1 object from n is $^nC_1$; the number of ways of choosing 2 objects from n is $^nC_2$, and so on. The total number of ways selections is therefore

$$^nC_1 + {}^nC_2 + {}^nC_3 + \ldots {}^nC_n.$$

Consider the expansion of $(1 + x)^n$. Then

$$(1 + x)^n = 1 + {}^nC_1x + {}^nC_2x^2 \ldots + {}^nC_nx^n.$$

Put $x = 1$;

$$2^n = 1 + {}^nC_1 + {}^nC_2 + \ldots + {}^nC_n$$

showing that $2^n - 1 = {}^nC_1 + {}^nC_2 + {}^nC_3 + \ldots {}^nC_n$

thus the two expressions are equal.

Selections made from n objects, not all different

Now suppose that the books are not all different, that there are 3 copies of *Robinson Crusoe*, 2 of *Treasure Island*, and that the other three books are all different.

We may choose to take one copy of *Robinson Crusoe*, or two copies, or three copies, or may refuse to take even a single copy, so we have four choices with this book. Similarly with *Treasure Island*, we have three choices (0, 1 or 2 copies); with each of the others we have two choices.

The number of selections is therefore $4 \times 3 \times 2 \times 2 \times 2$, but again this includes the case where we refuse them all, so that the number of different selections of books is $4 \times 3 \times 2^3 - 1$, i.e. 95.

In general, if there are p objects of one kind, q of another kind and r different objects, the number of different selections that can be made is $(p + 1)(q + 1)2^r - 1$.

Miscellaneous worked examples

Example 5. *How many selections, any number at a time, can be made from 4 red flags, 3 green flags and 2 white flags?*

There are 5 choices with the red flags, 4 with the green flags and three with the white flags, so the total number of different selections of flags is $5 \times 4 \times 3 - 1$, i.e. 59.

Example 6. *Eight different books include 'Julius Caesar' and 'Hamlet'. Find the number of selections, any number at a time, which include:*

(*i*) *'Julius Caesar' but not 'Hamlet'*,
(*ii*) *'Hamlet' but not 'Julius Caesar'*,
(*iii*) *both 'Julius Caesar' and 'Hamlet'.*

(i) If *Julius Caesar* but not *Hamlet* is chosen, we must find the number of selections from the other 6 books. This is 2^6 and since we have already chosen *Julius Caesar*, there is no need to consider the case of total refusal.

The number of selections is 2^6 or 64.

(ii) Similarly the number of selections is again 64.

(iii) Here we take both books and any others. We have to choose any number at a time from 6. The number of selections is again 2^6 or 64.

The number of selections which include neither *Julius Caesar* nor *Hamlet* is the number of selections from 6 objects but this time the case of total refusal must be considered. The number of selections is $2^6 - 1$ or 63.

The total number of selections should therefore be $64 + 64 + 64 + 63$ or 255 which is $2^8 - 1$.

Example 7. *Find how many different four-digit numbers can be made using the digits 1, 2, 3, 4, 5 and 6. Find also how many of these numbers are such that*

(*i*) *no digit is repeated*,
(*ii*) *one digit occurs twice*,

(*iii*) *two digits occur twice,*
(*iv*) *one digit occurs three times,*
(*v*) *one digit occurs four times.*

First, we can use any digit as many times as we wish, so that the first digit can be chosen in 6 ways, the second in six ways, the third and fourth likewise in six ways. Thus there are 6 × 6 × 6 × 6, 1296 numbers that can be formed from these digits.

The second part of the example classifies all these numbers, so that the five answers should total 1296. It is often a useful check on our accuracy if we can find two alternative ways of solving harder problems like this one.

(i) These are numbers like 1234. The first digit can be chosen in 6 ways, the next in 5 ways, and so on. Thus the total number of ways is 6 × 5 × 4 × 3, 360 ways.

(ii) These are numbers like 1123 or 1213. The digit to be repeated we can choose in 6 ways, the other two digits in $\dfrac{5 \times 4}{1 \times 2}$, i.e. 10 ways, so we have 60 ways of choosing the digits. Suppose the digits chosen are the digits 1123.
These can be arranged in $\dfrac{4!}{2!}$ ways (the 2! occurring because two digits are the same), i.e. 12 ways. Thus there are 60 × 12 different numbers in which one digit is repeated, i.e. 720.

(iii) These are numbers like 1122. Choose the two digits to be used in $\dfrac{6 \times 5}{1 \times 2}$, 15 different ways. These digits, say 1122 can be arranged into $\dfrac{4!}{2!2!}$ (i.e. 6) different orders, since there are four digits in two pairs. Thus there are 15 × 6, i.e. 90, numbers in which two digits are repeated.

(iv) Numbers like 1112. Choose the digit to be repeated in 6 ways and the other digit in 5 ways. There are now four digits, of which three are the same, so they can be arranged in $\dfrac{4!}{3!}$, i.e. 4 ways. Thus there are 30 × 4, 120, numbers in which one digit occurs three times.

(v) Numbers like 1111. Clearly there are only 6 ways of choosing the digit to be used, so there are only six such numbers.

Checking the total of answers to the five parts (i) to (v), 360 + 720 + 90 + 120 + 6 = 1296.

Exercise 1.3

1. How many different sums of money can be made from 3 £1 notes, 1 50p coin, 4 10p coins and 3 2p coins?

2. How many different selections of letters can be made from the letters a, a, a, a, b, b, c?

3. How many of the selections of letters in Q.2 contain the letter b?

4. How many selections can be made from 7 different books if any number of books can be taken?

5. How many of the selections in Q.4 will contain one particular book?

6. How many selections can be made from 5 apples, 3 pears and 2 bananas if any number can be taken?

7. How many of the selections in Q.6 contain (i) exactly one apple, (ii) at least one apple?

8. How many factors are there of 144, excluding 1 and 144?

9. How many factors are there of 720?

10. In how many ways can (i) 256 (ii) 512 be expressed as a product?

Exercise 1.4: Miscellaneous

1. How many selections of two cards can be made from a pack of 52, if at least one of the cards must be a King?

2. In how many ways can a team of 6 boys be chosen from 8, if one particular boy must be chosen?

3. How many different numbers can be formed using all the digits 3, 4, 5, 8? How many of these numbers are even?

4. How many three-digit numbers can be made from 3, 4, 5 and 8 if
   (i) no repetitions are allowed
   (ii) repetitions are allowed?

5. How many different numbers can be formed using some of the digits 3, 3, 4, 5 and 6?

6. How many different arrangements can be made of the letters STRESS?

7. How many different selections of three letters can be made from the letters STRESS?

8. How many different arrangements can be made of three letters chosen from STRESS?

9. In how many ways can a committee of two men and two women be chosen from 4 men and 5 women?

10. In how many ways can a committee of 3 schoolmasters, 3 businessmen and 3 professors be chosen from 5 schoolmasters, 4 businessmen and 6 professors?

11. In how many ways can 4 people be divided into 2 groups of 2?

12. In how many ways can 6 people be divided into (i) 2 groups of 3, (ii) 3 groups of 2?

13. In how many ways can 8 people be divided into 4 pairs?

14. In how many ways can $2m$ people be divided into m pairs?

15. In how many ways can 8 boys be divided into 4 pairs, if Bill must be paired with Harry?

16. Ten different books are placed on a shelf. Four are red, four white and two blue. In how many ways can they be arranged if
   (i) the red books must be placed together in a given order,
   (ii) the red books must be placed together but in any order,
   (iii) the red books must be placed together in any order and the white books must be placed together in any order?

17. Four points lie in a plane, but no three of them are in one straight line. How many triangles can be drawn using three of these points as vertices?

18. Eight points lie in a plane. What is the greatest number of triangles that can be drawn using three of these points as vertices?

19. Twelve points are chosen in a plane such that 6 of them lie on one straight line but no other selection of three points are collinear. How many triangles can be drawn using these points as vertices?

20. How many diagonals has a regular n-sided polygon? (A diagonal is any straight line joining two non-adjacent vertices.) Is the answer different if the polygon is not regular?

21. What is the greatest possible number of points of intersection of 8 straight lines and 4 circles?

22. How many circles can be drawn passing through 3 points out of 6 given points, when one and only one set of 4 of these points are concyclic?

Prove the following results (i) by considering suitable selections, (ii) by considering binomial expansions of expressions like $(1 + x)^k$ for differing k.

23. $^{n+1}C_{r+1} = {}^nC_{r+1} + {}^nC_r$.

24. $^{n+2}C_{r+2} = {}^nC_r + 2\,{}^nC_{r+1} + {}^nC_{r+2}$.

25. $^{n+1}C_{r+1} = {}^nC_r + {}^{n-1}C_r + {}^{n-2}C_r + \ldots {}^nC_r$.

2 Further Probability

Revision summary

In *Additional Pure Mathematics* we found the following definitions and results.

1. The probability of a particular outcome was defined as

$$\frac{\text{the number of equiprobable favourable outcomes}}{\text{the total number of equiprobable outcomes}}.$$

We noticed that these outcomes must be equiprobable.

2. The addition law says that if two events A and B are mutually exclusive, which means that both A and B cannot happen, then

$$\Pr(A \text{ or } B) = \Pr(A) + \Pr(B),$$

but if A and B are not mutually exclusive,

$$\Pr(A \text{ or } B \text{ or both}) = \Pr(A) + \Pr(B) - \Pr(\text{both } A \text{ and } B).$$

We saw that we could express this in set notation

$$\Pr(A \cup B) = \Pr(A) + \Pr(B) - \Pr(A \cap B).$$

3. The multiplication law says that if two events A and B are independent, that is, the outcome of one does not affect the outcome of the other, $\Pr(A \text{ and } B) = \Pr(A)\Pr(B)$. If the events are not independent, $\Pr(A \text{ and } B) = \Pr(A|B)\Pr(B) = \Pr(B|A)\Pr(A)$, where $\Pr(B|A)$ means 'the probability of B, given that A has already happened'.

Example 1. *Two fair dice are thrown. What is the probability that both show a '4'?*

These events are independent, since one die does not affect the other, and the probability that each shows a '4' is $\frac{1}{6}$, so that the probability that both show '4' is $\frac{1}{6} \times \frac{1}{6}$ i.e. $\frac{1}{36}$.

Example 2. *A card is drawn from a well-shuffled pack of 52, examined, and not replaced. A second card is then drawn and examined. What is the probability that they are both Aces?*

These events are not independent, for the probability that the second card is an Ace is clearly affected by whether the first card is an Ace or not. Denote the event 'the first card is an Ace' by A, the event 'the second card is an Ace' by B. Then $\Pr(A) = \frac{4}{52}$. The probability that the second card is an Ace given that the first card is an Ace we write $\Pr(B|A)$, and is $\frac{3}{51}$, so that

$$\Pr(A \text{ and } B) = \Pr(A)\Pr(B|A) = \frac{4}{52} \times \frac{3}{51} = \frac{1}{221},$$

i.e.

$$\Pr(A \cap B) = \Pr(A)\Pr(B|A) = \frac{1}{221}.$$

4. If a trial can have only one of two possible outcomes, which we can call 'success' and 'failure', if the probability of success is p, the probability of failure is $(1 - p)$. The probability of r successes in n trials is

$$\frac{n!}{(n - r)!r!} p^r(1 - p)^{n-r}$$

which can be abbreviated $_nC_r\, p^r(1 - p)^{n-r}$ or $\binom{n}{r} p^r(1 - p)^{n-r}$. This is called a *binomial* distribution.

Example 3. *The probability that a biased coin shows 'heads' is 4/5. The probability that when thrown five times, three of the throws will show 'heads' is* $\frac{5!}{3!2!} (4/5)^3(1/5)^2$, i.e. 0.2048.

5. If a sequence of trials finishes as soon as a failure is recorded, the probability of $n - 1$ successes in n trials is $p^{n-1}(1 - p)$. This is called a *geometric* distribution.

Example 4. *The probability that a student fails to solve a problem at any one attempt is constant and is 0.8. The probability that he solves the problem at the fifth attempt is* $(0.8)^4$ (0.2), *since he will have four failures before succeeding at the fifth attempt.*

Applications of the definition

We can use our ability to apply permutations and combinations to find all the equiprobable outcomes to a problem, find how many of these are favourable, and so calculate the probability of a particular outcome.

Example 5. *Three boys and two girls are to be arranged in random order in a straight line. Find the probability that the girls are not next to each other.*

In Chapter 1, Example 3 we saw that there are 72 ways in which the girls are not next to each other, i.e. there are 72 equiprobable favourable outcomes. The five children can be arranged in 5!, i.e. 120 ways, so that there are 120 equiprobable outcomes, thus the probability that the girls are not next to each other is $\frac{72}{120}$, i.e. 0.6.

Example 6. *The digits 2, 3, 4 and 5 are used to form a four-digit number, all numbers being equiprobable. Find the probability that the number formed is even and greater than 4000.*

In Chapter 1, Example 4 we saw that there are 6 even numbers greater than 4000 that can be formed from these digits. There are 4! (i.e. 24) numbers altogether that can be formed from the four digits, so that the probability that a number so formed is even and greater than 4000 is $\frac{6}{24}$, i.e. $\frac{1}{4}$.

Exercise 2.1

1. A four-digit number is selected at random from all those greater than 2000. Find the probability that the number
   (i) ends in the digit 3,
   (ii) is divisible by 3.

2. Twenty-four code words are made from the letters BEAR. When one of these is chosen at random, what is the probability that it
   (i) begins with a vowel,
   (ii) begins with a B and ends with an R?

3. A five digit number is made by arranging in random order the digits 1, 2, 3, 4, 5. What is the probability that the number
   (i) ends with a 3,
   (ii) is divisible by 5,
   (iii) is divisible by 3?

4. Two letters are chosen at random from BRISTOL and written down in order. What is the probability that
   (i) only one is a vowel,
   (ii) both are vowels,
   (iii) neither is a vowel?

5. Six boys are to be seated in random order on a bench. What is the probability that two of them, Bob and Jack, sit together?

6. What is the probability that the vowels are not adjacent when the letters NOMAD are arranged in random order?

7. Four girls Kate, Linda, Mary and Naomi agree to play tennis, and spin for partners. What is the probability that Kate and Linda will be partners?

8. Each football match can be described as a win for the home team (1), a win for the away team (2) or a draw (X). A man forecasts the results of four matches by writing down 1, 2 or X at random. Assuming that all outcomes of each match are equiprobable what is the probability that
   (i) all four of his forecasts are correct,
   (ii) none of his forecasts are correct,
   (iii) exactly one of his forecasts is correct?

9. A team of 11 boys is chosen at random from a class of 20. Find the probability that one particular boy of the 20 is chosen.

10. In how many ways can a selection be made from 3 red balls, 4 white balls and 2 green balls, if any number of balls can be selected? What is the probability that a selection made at random will include exactly one green ball?

Conditional probability: application of Venn diagrams

We have been accustomed to use Venn diagrams to illustrate probability results problems, and for example Fig. 2.1 illustrates the addition law that $\Pr(A \text{ or } B \text{ or both}) = \Pr(A) + \Pr(B) - \Pr(\text{both } A$

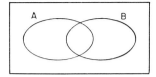

Fig. 2.1

and *B*). We can also use Venn diagrams to illustrate problems involving conditional probability.

Two friends Bill and Chris often play football on Saturday. The probability that Bill plays any one day, written Pr(*B*) is 0.9, the probability that Chris plays, Pr(*C*), is 0.8, and the probability that both play, Pr(*B* ∩ *C*), is 0.75. We can display these probabilities* in a

Fig. 2.2

Venn diagram and see that the probability that Bill plays but not Chris is 0.15, that Chris plays but not Bill is 0.05. The probability that neither plays is 0.05. We can extend our use of set notation to write

Pr(Bill does not play) = Pr(*B′*) = 0.1

Pr(Chris does not play) = Pr(*C′*) = 0.2

Pr(both Bill and Chris play) = Pr(*B* ∩ *C*) = 0.75

Pr(neither Bill nor Chris plays) = Pr(*B′* ∩ *C′*) = 0.05

Pr(Bill plays, given that Chris is playing) = Pr(*B*|*C*) = $\dfrac{0.75}{0.8}$ = 0.9375

Pr(Chris plays, given that Bill is playing) = Pr(*C*|*B*) = $\dfrac{0.75}{0.9}$ ≃ 0.83.

To find Pr(*B*|*C*) we had to choose from the elements of the set ε, and the favourable elements were those in which Bill was playing, represented

---

* *The probabilities are proportional to the number of elements in the appropriate sets.*

Since Pr(*B*) = $\dfrac{n(B)}{n(\varepsilon)}$ = 0.9, *if we take n(ε) as 1, then n(B) = 0.75. We may prefer to take, say*

n(ε) = 100 then n(B) = 75.

by $B \cap C$, so that

$$\Pr(B|C) = \frac{\Pr(B \cap C)}{\Pr(C)} = \frac{0.75}{0.8} = 0.9375.$$

Similarly $\qquad \Pr(C|B) = \dfrac{\Pr(B \cap C)}{\Pr(B)} \simeq 0.83.$

Example 7. *Two events A and B are such that* $Pr(A) = 0.4$, $Pr(A' \cap B) = 0.3$ *and* $Pr(B|A) = 0.6$. *Find*

(i) $Pr(A \cap B)$ (ii) $Pr(B)$ (iii) $Pr(A|B)$.

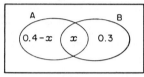

Fig. 2.3

When we start to complete the Venn diagram, we can insert 0.3 in the region representing $A' \cap B$, but then face the difficulty that we do not know how much of the 0.4 is in $A \cap B$ and how much in $A \cap B'$. Call the part in $A \cap B$, x. Then since $\Pr(B|A)$ is 0.6,

$$\frac{x}{0.4} = 0.6$$

i.e. $x = 0.24$, and we can proceed immediately to Fig. 2.4, from which

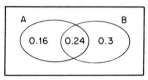

Fig. 2.4

we can write down $\qquad \Pr(A \cap B) = 0.24,$

$$\Pr(B) = 0.3 + 0.24 = 0.54$$

and $\qquad \Pr(A|B) = \dfrac{\Pr(A \cap B)}{\Pr(B)} = \dfrac{0.24}{0.54} \simeq 0.44.$

Exercise 2.2

1. Two events X and Y are such that $\Pr(X) = 0.7$, $\Pr(Y) = 0.8$ and $\Pr(X \cap Y) = 0.6$. Find

(i) $\Pr(X \cup Y)$ (ii) $\Pr(X|Y)$ (iii) $\Pr(Y|X)$.

2. Two events A and B are such that $\Pr(A) = 0.8$, $\Pr(B) = 0.6$ and $\Pr(A \cup B) = 0.95$. Find

(i) $\Pr(A \cap B)$ (ii) $\Pr(A|B)$ (iii) $\Pr(B|A)$.

3. Two events A and B are such that $\Pr(A) = 0.8$, $\Pr(B) = 0.6$ and $\Pr(A \cap B) = 0.48$. Find

(i) $\Pr(A|B)$ (ii) $\Pr(B|A)$ (iii) $\Pr(A|B')$.

Say, with reason, whether A and B are independent.

4. Two events A and B are such that $\Pr(A) = 0.8$, $\Pr(B) = 0.7$ and $\Pr(A \cap B) = 0.5$. Find

(i) $\Pr(A|B)$ (ii) $\Pr(A|B')$

and say whether A and B are independent.

5. Two events A and B are such that $\Pr(A) = a$ and $\Pr(B) = b$. Prove that $\Pr(A \cap B) = ab$ if and only if $\Pr(A|B) = \Pr(A|B')$.

6. Two events A and B are such that $\Pr(A) = 0.5$, $\Pr(A' \cap B) = 0.4$ and $\Pr(B|A) = 0.6$. Find

(i) $\Pr(A \cap B)$ (ii) $\Pr(B)$ (iii) $\Pr(A|B)$.

7. Two events A and B are such that $\Pr(A' \cap B) = 0.16$, $\Pr(A \cap B') = 0.3$ and $\Pr(A|B) = 0.6$. Find

(i) $\Pr(A \cap B)$ (ii) $\Pr(A \cup B)$ (iii) $\Pr(B|A)$.

8. In a certain examination, the probability that a candidate passes in mathematics is 0.9, that a candidate passes in physics is 0.8 and that a candidate passes both mathematics and physics is 0.7. Find

(i) the probability that a candidate passes maths or physics or both,

(ii) the probability that a candidate passes maths, given that he passes physics.

Are the two events, passing in maths and passing in physics, independent?

9. In a certain house the probability that there are eggs for breakfast is 0.8, that there is bacon for breakfast is 0.7 and that there are both eggs and bacon for breakfast is 0.6. Find the probability that

(i) there is bacon for breakfast, given that there are eggs for breakfast,

(ii) there are eggs for breakfast, given that there is bacon for breakfast.

10. Two friends Xantippe and Yvonne often go to the hairdressers on Friday afternoons. If Yvonne goes, the probability that Xantippe also goes is 0.96; if Xantippe goes, the probability that Yvonne also goes is 0.8; the probability that neither goes is 0.07. Find the probability that both girls go to the hairdresser.

Bayes' theorem

'Every morning I have cornflakes or porridge for breakfast; the probability that I have cornflakes is 0.6. If I have cornflakes, the probability that I have coffee is 0.8, otherwise I have tea; if I have porridge, the probability that I have coffee is 0.3, that I have tea is 0.7. If my wife sees that I am drinking coffee, can she find the probability that I had previously had cornflakes?'

First we must find the probability that I have coffee each morning, and we can draw a tree diagram (Fig. 2.5). We see that the probability that I have coffee is $0.6 \times 0.8 + 0.4 \times 0.3$, i.e. 0.6, and checking the other branches the probability that I have tea is 0.4, making a total of 1, as expected. The probability that I have coffee is 0.6, and that is made up of 0.48 from the branch on which I had cornflakes and 0.12 on the

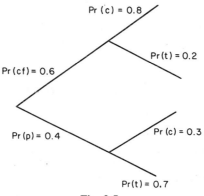

Pr (c) = 0.8

Pr (t) = 0.2

Pr (cf) = 0.6

Pr (p) = 0.4

Pr (c) = 0.3

Pr (t) = 0.7

Fig. 2.5

branch on which I had porridge. Thus the probability that I had cornflakes is four times the probability that I had porridge, so that given I am having coffee, the probability that I had cornflakes is 0.8. This can be seen to have been obtained from

$$\frac{0.8 \times 0.6}{0.8 \times 0.6 + 0.3 \times 0.4}$$

and can be written

$$\text{Pr(cornflakes|coffee)} = \frac{\text{Pr}(c|cf)\text{Pr}(cf)}{\text{Pr}(c|cf)\text{Pr}(cf) + \text{Pr}(c|p)\text{Pr}(p)}$$

or more generally, if A = having cornflakes,
A' = not having cornflakes,
B = having coffee,
B' = not having coffee,

$$\text{Pr}(A|B) = \frac{\text{Pr}(B|A)\text{Pr}(A)}{\text{Pr}(B|A)\text{Pr}(A) + \text{Pr}(B|A')\text{Pr}(A')}.$$

This is called Bayes' Theorem, and can be seen in this form to be only an application of ratio to probability. The value $\text{Pr}(A|B)$ is sometimes called the *a posteriori* (or posterior) probability of A, given B, in contrast to $\text{Pr}(A)$, the *a priori* (or prior) probability of A when nothing is known of B.

Exercise 2.3

1. The probability that a certain football team loses the first match of the season is 0.9; if it loses that match, the probability that it loses the second match is 0.3, but if it does not lose the first match the probability that it loses the second match is 0.8. Given that it loses the second match, find the probability that it lost the first match.

2. One wet afternoon a man settles down to make soufflés. The probability that the first soufflé rises is 0.7. If this rises, the probability that the second soufflé also rises is 0.6, whereas if the first soufflé does not rise he takes much more care with the second, and the probability that this rises is 0.9. Given that the second soufflé rises, what is the probability that the first soufflé rose?

3. John washes up after lunch three times a week, and his sister Mary washes up the other four times. John's days are chosen at random each week. The probability that he will break one or more dishes during a washing is 0.1 and the probability that Mary will is 0.05. One day after lunch Dad, hearing a dish crash said, 'Apparently this is John's day for doing the washing up'. What is the probability that he was right? (S.M.P.)

4. A company advertises a professional vacancy in three national daily newspapers A, B, C which have readerships in the proportions 2, 3, 1 respectively. From a survey of the occupations of the readers of these papers it is thought that the probabilities of an individual reader replying are 0.002, 0.001, 0.005 respectively.

   (i) If the company receives one reply, what are the probabilities that the applicant is a reader of papers A, B, C respectively?

   (ii) If two replies are received, what is the probability that both applicants are readers of paper A?

   (You may assume that each reader sees only one paper.) (M.E.I.)

5. Half the population of the city of Ekron are Philistines and the other half are Canaanites. A Philistine never tells the truth, but a Canaanite speaks truthfully with a probability $\frac{2}{5}$ and falsely with a probability $\frac{3}{5}$. What is the probability that a citizen encountered at random will give a correct answer to a question? Tabulate the probabilities that 0, 1, 2 or 3 men out of a sample of 3 citizens taken at random from Ekron will affirm a proposition;

   (i) when it is true   (ii) when it is false.

   The proposition has a prior probability $\frac{3}{4}$ of being true. What is the posterior probability of it being true conditional on it being affirmed by only one out of the three? (C.)

6. A bag A contains 5 similar balls, of which 3 are red and 2 black, and a bag B contains 4 red and 5 black balls. A ball is drawn at random from A and placed in B; subsequently a ball is drawn at random from B and placed in A. What is the chance that if a ball is now drawn from A it will be red? If this ball is in fact red, what is the probability that the first two balls drawn were also red? (M.E.I.)

Exercise 2.4: Miscellaneous

1. Find the probability of a total of 7 when two fair die are thrown.

2. Find the probability of a total of 7 when three fair die are thrown.
3. Find the probability of a total of 7 when four fair dice are thrown.
4. Find the coefficient of x^7 in the expansion of

   (i) $\left(\dfrac{x}{6}\right)^2 (1 - x)^{-2}$,

   (ii) $\left(\dfrac{x}{6}\right)^3 (1 - x)^{-3}$,

   (iii) $\left(\dfrac{x}{6}\right)^4 (1 - x)^{-4}$,

   in ascending powers of x. (See *Additional Pure Mathematics*, page 60.) Comment on the relation between these answers and the answers to Q.1–3.

5. Three families are being entertained by a conjuror. The Smith family consists of three boys and two girls, the Jones family of one boy and three girls, and the Browns of two boys and one girl. In order to choose a child to assist in a conjuring trick, the conjuror can either choose a child at random from the twelve children in front of him, or he can choose a family at random, and then choose a child at random from that family. Find the probability that he will choose a boy if he uses the second method, and so decide which of the two methods is more likely to find a boy to assist with the trick.

6. Medical records show that 60% of the population of a large city have had measles. What is the probability that of five citizens selected at random, not more than two have suffered from the disease?　(S.M.P.)

7. The probability of a given light-bulb failing in any one month is 0.3. What is the probability that none of the 15 bulbs in my house will fail during the next three months?　(S.M.P.)

8. In a game, two ordinary fair dice are thrown. What is the probability that
   (i) both show sixes,
   (ii) neither shows a six,
   (iii) at least one of the two shows a six,
   (iv) the sum of the two numbers shown is six?　(A.E.B.)

9. (a) Two players A and B, each have one throw with a fair die. Find the probability that
   (i) one or the other, but not both, throws a six,
   (ii) their two throws give scores adding up to six.

   (b) In a game, A and B throw a single fair die alternately, A, throwing first. Find the probability that A will throw a six before B.　(A.E.B.)

10. The probabilities of two events A and B are $\frac{2}{3}$ and $\frac{3}{4}$. Show that the probability of both occurring lies between $\frac{5}{12}$ and $\frac{2}{3}$. Describe the relationships between the events for these limiting values to be taken. What is the probability of A and B (or both) occurring if the events are independent?　(A.E.B.)

11. Assuming a population in which equal numbers of births occur in each of the twelve months of the year, calculate the probabilities that, of four persons taken at random,

(i) no two will be found to have birthdays in the same month,

(ii) exactly two will have birthdays in the same month and the others are in different months.   (M.E.I.)

12. A and B are two events and B' is the complementary event to B (i.e. not B). Show that $\Pr(A)$ lies between $\Pr(A|B)$ and $\Pr(A|B')$.   (M.E.I.)

13. In an examination the respective probabilities of three candidates solving a certain problem are $\frac{4}{5}$, $\frac{3}{4}$ and $\frac{2}{3}$.

Calculate the probability that the examiner will receive from these candidates

(i) one, and only one correct solution,

(ii) not more than one correct solution,

(iii) at least one correct solution.   (J.M.B.)

14. Three people each have an ordinary pack of 52 playing cards. Each draws one card from his pack. Find the probabilities that

(i) all three cards drawn are black,

(ii) exactly two of the cards drawn are hearts,

(iii) at least one ace is drawn,

(iv) the three cards are from different suits.   (M.E.I.)

15. A secretary types four letters and addresses correctly the four corresponding envelopes. She then places the letters at random, one into each envelope. Find the probability that

(i) every letter goes into the correct envelope,

(ii) no letter is in the correct envelope.

16. The secretary of Q.15 repeats the procedure with five letters and five envelopes. What is now the probability that

(i) every letter goes into the correct envelope,

(ii) no letter goes into the correct envelope?

17. A man drives to work each day, and may be delayed at two road junctions. The probability of delay at junction A is 0.8, at junction B is 0.5, and these delays are independent of each other. If he is delayed at either junction he is late for work.

(i) Given that he is late one day, what is the probability that he was delayed at junction A?

(ii) Given that he was delayed at one and only one junction, what is the probability that he was delayed at A?

18. A bus journey contains stops at three intermediate places. The probabilities of delays at these stops are 0.3, 0.5 and 0.7.

(i) Find the probability that there are no delays at these stops.

(ii) Find the probability that there is exactly one delay.

(iii) Given that there is exactly one delay, find the probability that it occurs at the first stop.

19. In a certain examination 1000 candidates took geography and history. 640 passed geography, 720 passed history and 480 passed both. If a candidate is selected at random, find the probability

(i) that he passed geography, given that he passed history,

(ii) that he passed history, given that he passed geography,

(iii) that he failed history, given that he failed geography.

20. A game is played with two fair dice; these are thrown at the same time, and the sum of the numbers gives the score.

(i) Show that the probability of scoring 5 is $\frac{1}{9}$ and that the probability of scoring 9 is also $\frac{1}{9}$. Find also the probability of scoring 7.

(ii) If a player throws until he scores 5 or 7, show that the probability of scoring 5 before scoring 7 is $\frac{2}{5}$.

(iii) In the American game of crap-shooting the thrower wins if he scores 7 or 11 at the first throw and loses if he scores 2, 3 or 12. If the first score is 4, 5, 6, 8, 9 or 10 he continues to throw until he scores either the same number as on the first throw or 7. If he scores the same number he wins, if he scores 7 he loses.

Show that the probability of winning is $\dfrac{244}{495}$.

3 Induction and Finite Series

The Σ notation

Consider the series $1^2 + 2^2 + 3^2 + \ldots + n^2$; the general term in the series is r^2 and to obtain the terms in the series we take successively the values 1 to n for r. The series is written $\sum_1^n r^2$, meaning the sum of all terms like r^2 from 1^2 up to n^2.*

Examples

(i) $\sum_1^n r = 1 + 2 + 3 + 4 \ldots + n.$

(ii) $\sum_1^{2n} r = 1 + 2 + 3 \ldots + 2n.$

(iii) $\sum_4^{10} r^3 = 4^3 + 5^3 + \ldots 10^3.$

The method of induction

Consider the following:

$$1 = 1 = 1^2$$
$$1 + 3 = 4 = 2^2$$
$$1 + 3 + 5 = 9 = 3^2$$
$$1 + 3 + 5 + 7 = 16 = 4^2.$$

We see that the sum of the first two odd numbers is 2^2, the sum of the first three odd numbers is 3^2, and the sum of the first four odd numbers is 4^2. Is this true for all, however many odd numbers we sum, so that the sum of the first 100 odd numbers may be 100^2?

If only we knew the sum of the first 99 odd numbers, we could easily find the sum of the first hundred odd numbers, by adding the hundredth odd number, i.e. adding 199. Suppose that the sum of the first 99 odd numbers *is* 99^2, then the sum of the first hundred odd numbers is $99^2 + 199$, i.e. $9801 + 199$, $10\,000$, which is 100^2. So that *if* the sum of the first 99 odd numbers is 99^2, then the sum of the first hundred odd numbers is 100^2. But of course the sum of the first 99 odd numbers may not be 99^2. . . .

---

* If there is any ambiguity, we write $\sum_{r=1}^{r=n}$, e.g. $\sum_{r=1}^{r=n} rs = s + 2s + 3s \ldots + ns.$

The method of induction is this. We need to have some idea of the result that we are trying to prove, which may be guessed from some special observations, or is more likely at this stage to be given in a textbook or examination question. We then investigate to see *if* it is true for some one specific value of our unknown (usually n), whether we can prove it for the 'next' value of that unknown. If this can be proved, we then try to find a starting value for n, that is a value of n for which we can prove our conjecture by routine calculations. Having found that the conjecture is true for that one value, we proved earlier that it is always true for the next, so that our conjecture is true for all values of n obtainable from the first, usually for all positive integer values of n.

Example 1. *Find the sum of the series* $\sum_{1}^{n} r^3$, *i.e.* $1^3 + 2^3 + 3^3 \ldots n^3$

We notice that
$$1^2 = 1 = 1^2$$
$$1^3 + 2^3 = 9 = 3^2$$
$$1^3 + 2^3 + 3^3 = 36 = 6^2$$
$$1^3 + 2^3 + 3^3 + 4^3 = 100 = 10^2.$$

We may also notice that $10 = \frac{1}{2} \times 4 \times 5$, $6 = \frac{1}{2} \times 3 \times 4$, $3 = \frac{1}{2} \times 2 \times 3$, $1 = \frac{1}{2} \times 1 \times 2$, and if we do, it may suggest that perhaps
$$1^3 + 2^3 + 3^3 \ldots n^3 = [\tfrac{1}{2}n(n + 1)]^2.$$

Now we can begin the proof by induction.

Suppose that this result is true for any one particular value of n, and call that value k. This means that
$$1^3 + 2^3 + 3^3 \ldots + k^3 = [\tfrac{1}{2}k(k + 1)]^2.$$

To find the sum of the first $(k + 1)$ cubes, we need to add $(k + 1)^3$ to each side of the equation, so that
$$
\begin{aligned}
1^3 + 2^3 + 3^3 \ldots + k^3 + (k + 1)^3 &= [\tfrac{1}{2}k(k + 1)]^2 + (k + 1)^3 \\
&= (k + 1)^2 \{\tfrac{1}{4}(k^2) + (k + 1)\} \\
&= (k + 1)^2 \{\tfrac{1}{4}(k^2 + 4k + 4)\} \\
&= [\tfrac{1}{2}(k + 1)(k + 2)]^2,
\end{aligned}
$$

which is what we should expect if we used our original conjecture to find the sum of the first $(k + 1)$ cubes. So that *if* our conjecture was correct for the one value of n we started with, it is true for the next. But we have already seen that $1^3 = 1 = \frac{1}{2} \times 1 \times 2$ so that the conjecture is correct when $n = 1$. Since it is true when $n = 1$, it is true for the next value of n, i.e. $n = 2$. Since it is true for $n = 2$, it is true for $n = 3$, so that we can see that it is true for all positive integral values of n,

i.e.
$$\sum_{1}^{n} r^3 = [\tfrac{1}{2}n(n + 1)]^2.$$

Example 2. *Prove by induction that*
$$1 \times 2 + 2 \times 3 + 3 \times 4 + \ldots + n \times (n + 1) = \tfrac{1}{3}n(n + 1)(n + 2).$$

If this is true for some one value of n, say $n = k$, then
$$1 \times 2 + 2 \times 3 + \ldots + k(k + 1) = \tfrac{1}{3}k(k + 1)(k + 2).$$

Adding $(k + 1)(k + 2)$ to both sides,

$$1 \times 2 + 2 \times 3 \ldots + k(k + 1) + (k + 1)(k + 2)$$
$$= \tfrac{1}{3}k(k + 1)(k + 2) + (k + 1)(k + 2)$$
$$= (k + 1)(k + 2)(\tfrac{1}{3}k + 1)$$
$$= \tfrac{1}{3}(k + 1)(k + 2)(k + 3)$$

which we should expect, using our formula to find the sum of the first $(k + 1)$ terms of the series.

Consider now the first term, 1×2. If we use the formula to find the 'sum' of the first 'one terms', we obtain $\tfrac{1}{3} \times 1 \times 2 \times 3$ which equals 2, the first term in the series, so that the formula is true when $n = 1$. Since it is true for $n = 1$, it is true for $n = 2$, and so it is true for all positive integral values of n.

Example 3. *Use the method of induction to find the sum of the interior angles of a polygon with n sides.*

We may remember that the sum of the interior angles of a triangle is 2 right angles; of a quadrilateral is 4 right angles, of a pentagon is 6 right angles; if so, we may conjecture that the angle sum of a polygon with n sides is $2(n - 2)$ right angles.

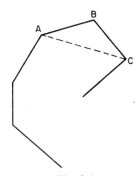

Fig. 3.1

Any polygon P_{n+1} with $n + 1$ sides can be related to a polygon P_n by drawing the line AC (as in Fig. 3.1), making it into a polygon with n sides and a triangle. If our conjecture is true for some one value of n, say k, a k-sided polygon will contain $2(k - 2)$ right angles and a $(k + 1)$ sided polygon will contain $2(k - 2)$ right angles plus the two more from the triangle, i.e. $2(k - 2) + 2$, i.e. $2k - 2$, which can be written $2(k + 1) - 2$ as we should expect from the conjecture. But a triangle (3-sided polygon) has 2 right angles, and from the formula we have $2 \times 3 - 4$, also 2 right angles, so it is true when $n = 3$. Since it is true for $n = 3$, it is true for the next value, $n = 4$, and so on for all positive integral values of n. Notice that in this case it was meaningless to consider the case $n = 1$, as we cannot have a polygon with only one side.

Exercise 3.1

1. Express in Σ notation
    (i) $1 + 3 + 5 \ldots \ldots (2n + 1)$,
    (ii) $a + (a + d) \ldots \ldots a + (n - 1)d$,
    (iii) $1^3 + 3^3 + 5^3 + \ldots \ldots (2n - 1)^3$,
    (iv) $\tan \theta + \tan 2\theta + \ldots \ldots \tan n\theta$,
    (v) $\tan \alpha + \tan (\alpha + \beta) + \tan (\alpha + 2\beta) \ldots \ldots \tan \{\alpha + (n - 1)\beta\}$.

2. Prove the following by induction

    (i) $\sum_{1}^{n} r \equiv 1 + 2 + 3 + \ldots \ldots n = \frac{1}{2}n(n + 1)$,

    (ii) $\sum_{1}^{n} (3r - 1) = 2 + 5 + 8 + \ldots \ldots (3n - 1) = \frac{1}{2}n(3n + 1)$,

    (iii) $\sum_{1}^{n} (3r + 2) = 5 + 8 + \ldots \ldots (3n + 2) = \frac{1}{2}n(3n + 7)$,

    (iv) $\sum_{1}^{n} r^2 = 1^2 + 2^2 \ldots \ldots + n^2 = \frac{1}{6}n(n + 1)(2n + 1)$.

3. Prove that $\sum_{1}^{n} 2^r \equiv 2 + 2^2 + 2^3 \ldots \ldots 2^n = 2(2^n - 1)$.

4. Prove that $\sum_{2}^{n+1} r(2^{r-2}) = n \times 2^n$.

5. Prove that $1 \times 2 \times 3 + 2 \times 3 \times 4 \ldots \ldots n(n + 1)(n + 2)$
$$= \frac{1}{4}n(n + 1)(n + 2)(n + 3).$$

6. Prove that $1(1!) + 2(2!) + 3(3!) + \ldots \ldots n(n!) = (n + 1)! - 1$.

7. Prove that $\sum_{1}^{n} \frac{1}{r(r + 1)} = \frac{n}{(n + 1)}$.

8. Prove by induction that when £P is invested for t years at $r\%$ per annum Compound Interest added yearly, the value of the investment £A is given by $A = P\left(1 + \dfrac{r}{100}\right)^t$.

9. Prove by induction

    (i) $\sum_{1}^{n} r(r + 2) = \frac{1}{6}n(n + 1)(2n + 7)$,

    (ii) $\sum_{1}^{n} r(r + 3) = \frac{1}{3}n(n + 1)(n + 5)$.

10. Prove by induction $\sum_{1}^{n} r^4 = \frac{1}{30}n(n + 1)(2n + 1)(3n^2 + 3n - 1)$.

Other examples of proofs by induction

Almost all the examples so far have referred to the summation of series, so that to find the sum of $(k + 1)$ terms, we merely added the $(k + 1)$th term to the previous k terms. We noticed though that we could use the idea of induction in some other contexts; to find the angle-sum of a polygon and to find the formula for Compound Interest. We now look at other examples where we can use the idea of induction.

To find $\dfrac{d^n}{dx^n}(\sin 2x)$

We notice that

$$\frac{d}{dx}(\sin 2x) = 2\cos 2x = 2\sin(2x + \pi/2)$$

$$\frac{d^2}{dx^2}(\sin 2x) = -4\sin 2x = 2^2\sin(2x + 2\pi/2)$$

and $\qquad \dfrac{d^3}{dx^3}(\sin 2x) = -8\cos 2x = 2^3\sin(2x + 3\pi/2).$

Is it true that $\dfrac{d^n}{dx^n}(\sin 2x) = 2^n\sin(2x + n\pi/2)$?

If this is true for some one value of n, say $n = k$,

$$\frac{d^k}{dx^k}(\sin 2x) = 2^k\sin(2x + k\pi/2)$$

We must now differentiate $\dfrac{d^k}{dx^k}(\sin 2x)$ to obtain $\dfrac{d^{k+1}}{dx^{k+1}}(\sin 2x)$, i.e.

$$\frac{d^{k+1}}{dx^{k+1}}(\sin 2x) = \frac{d}{dx}\{2^k\sin(2x + k\pi/2)\}$$
$$= 2^{k+1}\cos(2x + k\pi/2) = 2^{k+1}\sin(2x + (k+1)\pi/2),$$

so that if the conjecture is true for any one value, it is true for the next. But we saw at the very beginning that $\dfrac{d}{dx}(\sin 2x) = 2\sin(2x + \pi/2)$, so that it is true when $n = 1$; therefore it is true for $n = 2$, for $n = 3$ and so on for all positive integer values of n. In this case, if we interpret negative values of n as referring to integrals, then it can be shown to be true for all negative integer values of n as well.

Tests for divisibility

It is easily seen that $9 + 7 = 16$, $81 + 7 = 88$, $729 + 7 = 736$, and that 16, 88 and 736 are all multiples of 8. Is it true that all numbers of the form $9^n + 7$ are multiples of 8?

If the conjecture is true for some one value of n, say $n = k$, then $9^k + 7$ is a multiple of 8, i.e., $9^k + 7 = 8m$, where m is an integer. Then $9^{k+1} + 7 = 9(8m - 7) + 7 = 72m - 56$, a multiple of 8. Thus if one number in the sequence $9^n + 7$ is a multiple of 7, then the next number also is. But we have seen that the first number, $9 + 7$, is a multiple of 8, so that all later numbers of this form $9^n + 7$ are also multiples of 8.

Notice that we could express both the conjecture and the proof in terms of numbers mod 8.

If it is true that
$$9^k + 7 = 0 \bmod 8,$$
$$9^{k+1} + 63 = 0 \bmod 8,$$
i.e.
$$9^{k+1} + 7 = 0 \bmod 8, \text{ as expected.}$$

Application to inequalities

To prove by induction that $4^n > 3n^2 + 1$ for all values of $n > 2$, first suppose that it is true for some one value of n, say $n = k$, so that
$$4^k > 3k^2 + 1.$$
Then
$$4^{k+1} > 4(3k^2 + 1)$$
$$> 3(k + 1)^2 + 1,$$
since
$$12k^2 + 4 > 3k^2 + 6k + 4$$
since
$$9k^2 - 6k > 0$$
when
$$k > 2/3.$$
So if the inequality is satisfied for one value of n, it is satisfied by the 'next'. But when $n = 2$, $4^2 > 3 \times 2^2 + 1$, so that the inequality is true when $n = 2$. Since we have found a starting-point $n = 2$ for the induction, it is true for $n = 3$; since it is true for $n = 3$ it is true for $n = 4$, and so on for all positive integral values of n.

Proof of the binomial theorem

When n is a positive integer, the binomial theorem
$$(x + a)^n = x^n + {}_nC_1 x^{n-1}a + {}_nC_2 x^{n-2}a^2 + \dots$$
$${}_nC_r x^{n-r}a^r \dots + a^n$$
can be proved using induction.

Suppose this is true for some one value of n, say $n = k$. Then
$$(x + a)^k = x^k + {}_kC_1 x^{k-1}a + \dots {}_kC_r x^{k-r}a^r + \dots a^k.$$
Multiplying by $(x + a)$,
$$(x + a)^{k+1} = (x + a)(x^k + {}_kC_1 x^{k-1}a + \dots {}_kC_r x^{k-r}a^r \dots a^k)$$
$$= x^{k+1} + x^k a(1 + {}_kC_1) \dots$$
$$+ x^{k+1-r}a^r({}_kC_r + {}_kC_{r-1}) \dots + a^{k+1}$$
$$= x^{k+1} + {}_{k+1}C_1 x^k a \dots {}_{k+1}C_r x^{k+1-r}a^r \dots + {}^{k+1},$$
since $1 + {}_kC_1 = 1 + k = {}_{k+1}C_1$ and ${}_kC_r + {}_kC_{r-1} = {}_{k+1}C_r$. Thus if the theorem is true for any one value of n, it is true for the next. But $(x + a)^2 = x^2 + {}_2C_1 xa + a^2$, so that the theorem is true when $n = 2$. Since it is true when $n = 2$, it is true when $n = 3$, and so by induction is true for all positive integral values of n.

Application to matrices

The last example that we give shows the method of Induction applied to find the nth power of a matrix.

Example 4.

If
$$\mathbf{M} = \begin{pmatrix} 2 & -1 \\ 1 & 0 \end{pmatrix},$$

prove by induction that
$$\mathbf{M}^n = \begin{pmatrix} n+1 & -n \\ n & 1-n \end{pmatrix}.$$

If this is true for some one value of n, say $n = k$,
$$\mathbf{M}^k = \begin{pmatrix} k+1 & -k \\ k & 1-k \end{pmatrix}.$$

Multiplying by $\mathbf{M}$,
$$\mathbf{M}^{k+1} = \begin{pmatrix} 2 & -1 \\ 1 & 0 \end{pmatrix}\begin{pmatrix} k+1 & -k \\ k & 1-k \end{pmatrix}$$
$$= \begin{pmatrix} k+2 & -(k+1) \\ k+1 & -k \end{pmatrix}$$
$$= \begin{pmatrix} k+2 & -(k+1) \\ k+1 & 1-(k+1) \end{pmatrix}$$

which we expect.

But
$$\mathbf{M} = \begin{pmatrix} 2 & -1 \\ 1 & 0 \end{pmatrix}$$
$$= \begin{pmatrix} 1+1 & -1 \\ 1 & 1-1 \end{pmatrix}$$

so that it is true when $n = 1$. Since it is true when $n = 1$, it is true when $n = 2$, and so on for all positive integral values of n.

Exercise 3.2

1. Prove by induction

   (i) $\dfrac{d^n}{dx^n}(x^m) = \dfrac{m!}{(m-n)!}x^{m-n}, \ m \geqslant n,$

   (ii) $\dfrac{d^n}{dx^n}(\cos x) = \cos(x + n\pi/2),$

   (iii) $\dfrac{d^n}{dx^n}(\sin ax) = a^n \sin(x + n\pi/2).$

2. Prove by induction
   (i) $2^{n+2} + 3^{2n+1}$ is a multiple of 7,
   (ii) $6^n + 8^n$ is a multiple of 7 if n is odd,
   (iii) $8^n - 6^n$ is a multiple of 7 if n is even,
   (iv) $n^3 - n$ is a multiple of 6,
   (v) $(3n+1)7^n + a$ is a multiple of 9 for some one value of a, which should be found.

3. Prove by induction that

$$\begin{pmatrix} 1 & 0 & 0 \\ 0 & 0 & -1 \\ 0 & -1 & 0 \end{pmatrix}^{2n+1} = \begin{pmatrix} 1 & 0 & 0 \\ 0 & 0 & -1 \\ 0 & -1 & 0 \end{pmatrix}$$

when n is any positive integer.

4. Prove by induction that if

$$A = \begin{pmatrix} 1 & 1 & 1 \\ 0 & 1 & 1 \\ 0 & 0 & 1 \end{pmatrix},$$

$$A^n = \begin{pmatrix} 1 & n & \frac{1}{2}n(n+1) \\ 0 & 1 & n \\ 0 & 0 & 1 \end{pmatrix}.$$

5. Straight lines are said to be in general position in a plane if no two are parallel and no three meet in a point. Prove by induction that n straight lines in general position divide a plane into

$$^nC_0 + {}^nC_1 + {}^nC_2$$

regions.

The difference method

Suppose we wish to sum the series $u_1 + u_2 + \ldots + u_n$ and are able to find a function $f(x)$ such that

$$f(n) - f(n-1) = u_n.$$

It follows that

$$f(n-1) - f(n-2) = u_{n-1},$$
$$f(n-2) - f(n-3) = u_{n-2}$$
$$\ldots\ldots\ldots\ldots\ldots$$
$$f(1) - f(0) = u_1.$$

Adding these equations,

$$f(n) - f(0) = u_1 + u_2 + \ldots u_n = S.$$

By this method we are able to find $\sum\limits_{1}^{n} u_r$; the difficulty is to find the function $f(x)$. The following examples give illustrations of the use of this method.

Example 5. *Consider $f(n) = n^2$.*

Then
$$n^2 - (n-1)^2 = 2n - 1.$$

Therefore
$$(n-1)^2 - (n-2)^2 = 2n - 3$$

and
$$(n-2)^2 - (n-3)^2 = 2n - 5.$$

$$\ldots\ldots\ldots\ldots\ldots$$

Eventually
$$1^2 - 0^2 = 1.$$

Adding:
$$n^2 = 1 + 3 + 5 + \ldots + (2n-1),$$

so the sum of the first n odd numbers is n^2.

Example 6. *Let* $f(n) = n^3$.

$$n^3 - (n-1)^3 = 3n^2 - 3n + 1$$
$$(n-1)^3 - (n-2)^3 = 3(n-1)^2 - 3(n-1) + 1$$
$$(n-2)^3 - (n-3)^3 = 3(n-2)^2 - 3(n-2) + 1$$
$$\cdots\cdots\cdots\cdots\cdots$$
$$1^3 - 0^3 = 3(1)^2 - 3(1) + 1.$$

Adding:
$$n^3 = 3\sum_1^n r^2 - 3\sum_1^n r + \sum_1^n 1.$$

Now
$$\sum_1^n 1 = 1 + 1 + 1 \ldots \text{to } n \text{ terms} = n.$$

$$\sum_1^n r = \tfrac{1}{2}n(n+1) \text{ by the sum of an A.P.}$$

$$\therefore \quad n^3 = 3\sum_1^n r^2 - \frac{3n(n+1)}{2} + n.$$

Rearranging:
$$3\sum_1^n r^2 = n^3 + \frac{3n(n+1)}{2} - n$$
$$= n(n^2 - 1) + \frac{3n(n+1)}{2}$$
$$= \frac{n(n+1)}{2}\{2n - 2 + 3\}$$
$$= \frac{n(n+1)(2n+1)}{2}.$$

$$\therefore \quad \sum_1^n r^2 = \frac{n(n+1)(2n+1)}{6}.$$

This gives a formula for the sum of the squares of the first n natural numbers.

Example 7. *Let* $f(n) = n^4$.

$$n^4 - (n-1)^4 = 4n^3 - 6n^2 + 4n - 1$$
$$\therefore \quad (n-1)^4 - (n-2)^4 = 4(n-1)^3 - 6(n-1)^2 + 4(n-1) - 1$$
$$\cdots\cdots\cdots\cdots\cdots$$
$$1^4 - 0^4 = 4(1)^3 - 6(1)^2 + 4(1) - 1.$$

Adding:
$$n^4 = 4\sum_1^n r^3 - 6\sum_1^n r^2 + 4\sum_1^n r - \sum_1^n 1.$$

Putting in values for $\sum_1^n 1$, $\sum_1^n r$ and $\sum_1^n r^2$ already found, we have

$$4\sum_1^n r^3 = n^4 + 6\frac{n(n+1)(2n+1)}{6} - 4\frac{n(n+1)}{2} + n$$
$$= n(n^3 + 1) + n(n+1)(2n+1) - 2n(n+1)$$
$$= n(n+1)\{n^2 - n + 1 + 2n + 1 - 2\}$$
$$= n(n+1)(n^2 + n)$$
$$= \{n(n+1)\}^2.$$

$$\therefore \quad \sum_1^n r^3 = \left\{\frac{n(n+1)}{2}\right\}^2.$$

This is the formula for the sum of the cubes of the first n natural numbers. It is an easy formula to remember because the sum of the cubes is the square of the sum of the first n natural numbers.

It is possible to proceed in this way and find $\sum_1^n r^4, \sum_1^n r^5$ but these are not so frequently needed; the formulae for $\sum_1^n r, \sum_1^n r^2$ and $\sum_1^n r^3$, however, are often useful and worth remembering.

Example 8. *Let $f(n) = n(n + 1)(n + 2)$.*

$$n(n + 1)(n + 2) - (n - 1)n(n + 1)$$
$$= n(n + 1)\{(n + 2) - (n - 1)\}$$
$$= 3n(n + 1).$$

Similarly
$$(n - 1)(n)(n + 1) - (n - 2)(n - 1)n$$
$$= 3(n - 1)n,$$
$$(n - 2)(n - 1)n - (n - 3)(n - 2)(n - 1)$$
$$= 3(n - 2)(n - 1)$$
$$\dots\dots\dots\dots\dots$$
$$1.2.3 - 0.1.2 = 3(1.2).$$

Adding
$$n(n + 1)(n + 2) = 3\sum_1^n r(r + 1).$$

$$\therefore \quad \sum_1^n r(r + 1) = \frac{n(n + 1)(n + 2)}{3}.$$

This is a particular case of a more general property, namely

$$\sum_1^n r(r + 1)(r + 2) \dots (r + k) = \frac{n(n + 1) \dots (n + k + 1)}{k + 2}.$$

The sum is written down by multiplying the nth term by the next highest factor and dividing by the number of factors in the expression written down.

Example. *Sum the series $1 \times 2 \times 3 + 2 \times 3 \times 4 + \dots + n(n + 1)(n + 2)$.*

$$\sum_1^n r(r + 1)(r + 2) = \frac{n(n + 1)(n + 2)(n + 3)}{4}.$$

The formulae for $\sum_1^n r^2$ and $\sum_1^n r^3$ provide one general method of summing algebraic series; the formula given in example 8 above provides an alternative method. The two methods are illustrated in the following worked examples.

Worked examples

Example 9. *Sum $1 \times 2 \times 4 + 2 \times 3 \times 5 + 3 \times 4 \times 6 + \dots + n(n + 1)(n + 3)$.*
First method

$$\sum_1^n r(r + 1)(r + 3) = \sum_1^n (r^3 + 4r^2 + 3r)$$
$$= \sum_1^n r^3 + 4\sum_1^n r^2 + 3\sum_1^n r$$

$$= \left\{ \frac{n(n+1)}{2} \right\}^2 + 4\frac{n(n+1)(2n+1)}{6} + \frac{3n(n+1)}{2}$$

$$= \frac{n(n+1)}{24} \{6n(n+1) + 16(2n+1) + 36\}$$

$$= \frac{n(n+1)(6n^2 + 38n + 52)}{24}$$

$$= \frac{n(n+1)(3n^2 + 19n + 26)}{12}$$

$$= \frac{n(n+1)(n+2)(3n+13)}{12}.$$

Second method

Express the general term as the sum of expressions each of which is the product of consecutive integers.

$$r(r+1)(r+3) = r(r+1)\{(r+2) + 1\}$$
$$= r(r+1)(r+2) + r(r+1)$$

$$\sum_1^n r(r+1)(r+3) = \sum_1^n r(r+1)(r+2) + \sum_1^n r(r+1)$$

$$= \frac{n(n+1)(n+2)(n+3)}{4} + \frac{n(n+1)(n+2)}{3}$$

$$= \frac{n(n+1)(n+2)}{12}(3n + 9 + 4)$$

$$= \frac{n(n+1)(n+2)(3n+13)}{12}.$$

Example 10. *Sum $1 \times 3 + 3 \times 5 + 5 \times 7 + \ldots + (2n-1)(2n+1)$.*

First method

$$\sum_1^n (2r-1)(2r+1) = \sum_1^n (4r^2 - 1)$$

$$= 4\sum_1^n r^2 - \sum_1^n 1$$

$$= \frac{4n(n+1)(2n+1)}{6} - n \quad \left[\text{Remember that } \sum_1^n 1 = n.\right]$$

$$= \frac{n}{3}\{2(n+1)(2n+1) - 3\}$$

$$= \frac{n}{3}\{4n^2 + 6n - 1\}.$$

Second method

$$4r^2 - 1 = 4r(r + 1) - 4r - 1.$$

$$\sum_1^n (4r^2 - 1) = 4\sum_1^n r(r + 1) - 4\sum_1^n r - \sum_1^n 1$$

$$= \frac{4n(n + 1)(n + 2)}{3} - \frac{4n(n + 1)}{2} - n$$

$$= \frac{n}{3}\{4(n + 1)(n + 2) - 6(n + 1) - 3\}$$

$$= \frac{n}{3}\{4n^2 + 12n + 8 - 6n - 6 - 3\}$$

$$= \frac{n}{3}\{4n^2 + 6n - 1\}.$$

Exercise 3.3

1. Write down the nth term of each of the following series:
   (i) $1 \times 3 + 2 \times 4 + 3 \times 5\ldots\ldots$
   (ii) $3 \times 4 + 4 \times 5 + 5 \times 6\ldots\ldots$
   (iii) $1 \times 4 + 2 \times 5 + 3 \times 6\ldots\ldots$
   (iv) $1 \times 4 + 4 \times 6 + 7 \times 8\ldots\ldots$
   (v) $1 \times 2 \times 4 + 2 \times 3 \times 6 + 3 \times 4 \times 8\ldots\ldots$

2. Find the sum of each of the following:
   (i) $1 \times 3 + 2 \times 4 + 3 \times 5\ldots\ldots n(n + 2)$,
   (ii) $1^2 + 2^2 + 3^2 + \ldots\ldots 10^2$,
   (iii) $11^2 + 12^2 + 13^2\ldots\ldots 20^2$,
   (iv) $1^2 + 3^2 + 5^2 + 99^2$,
   (v) $1^3 + 2^3 + 3^3 + \ldots\ldots 8^3$,
   (vi) $8^3 + 9^3 + 10^3 + \ldots\ldots 20^3$,
   (vii) $(m + 1)^2 + (m + 2)^2 + \ldots\ldots (2m)^2$,
   (viii) $(m + 1)^3 + (m + 2)^3 + \ldots\ldots (2m)^3$,
   (ix) $1 \times 2^2 + 2 \times 3^2 + 3 \times 4^2\ldots\ldots n(n + 1)^2$,
   (x) $1 \times 2^2 + 2 \times 3^2 + \ldots\ldots (n + 1)(n + 2)^2$.

3. Find the sum of the first n terms of each of the following series:
   (i) $1 \times 2 + 2 \times 3 + 3 \times 4\ldots\ldots$
   (ii) $2 \times 4 + 4 \times 6 + 6 \times 12\ldots\ldots$
   (iii) $1 \times 2 + 3 \times 4 + 5 \times 6\ldots\ldots$
   (iv) $1 \times 3 + 3 \times 5 + 5 \times 7\ldots\ldots$
   (v) $2 \times 3 + 4 \times 5 + 6 \times 7\ldots\ldots$

4. How many terms of the series $1^3 + 2^3 + 3^3 \ldots$ must be taken for the sum to exceed $10\,000$?

5. Find $\sum_1^n (n^2 - r^2)$.

6. Find $\sum_1^n r(r + 3)(r + 5)$.

7. Find $\sum_1^n (r + 2)(r + 3)$.

8. Find the first three terms of the series whose sum to n terms is $n(n + 1)(n + 3)$.

9. Find the first three terms of the series whose sum to n terms is $n^2(n + 1)$.

10. Find the first three terms of the series whose sum to n terms is n^3.

11. Sum to n terms the series $1 \times 3 \times 5 + 2 \times 4 \times 6 + 3 \times 5 \times 7 + \ldots$

12. Sum to n terms the series $1 \times 3 \times 4 + 2 \times 4 \times 5 + 3 \times 5 \times 6 + \ldots$

Power series

A series such as
$$S = a_0 + a_1x + a_2x^2 + \ldots + a_rx^r + \ldots + a_nx^n,$$
in which each term is a multiple of a power of x is called a power series. The most familiar example of a power series is the geometric progression
$$1 + x + x^2 + \ldots + x^{n-1}$$
whose sum we know to be $\dfrac{1 - x^n}{1 - x}$.

Power series are met later in probability, e.g. as probability generating functions. They are usually summed in the same way as the geometric progression, or by differentiating a suitable series.

Example. *Find the sum of n terms of the series*
$$1 + 2x + 3x^2 + \ldots$$

First method

Let
$$S = 1 + 2x + 3x^2 + \ldots + nx^{n-1}.$$
Then
$$xS = x + 2x^2 + \ldots + (n-1)x^{n-1} + nx^n.$$
Subtracting:
$$S(1 - x) = (1 + x + x^2 + \ldots + x^{n-1}) - nx^n.$$
$$= \frac{1 - x^n}{1 - x} - nx^n$$
$$= \frac{1 - x^n - nx^n + nx^{n+1}}{1 - x}$$
$$\therefore \quad S = \frac{1 - x^n(n + 1) + nx^{n+1}}{(1 - x)^2}.$$

Second method

The series may also be summed by considering first the series
$$x + x^2 + x^3 + \ldots + x^n.$$
The sum of this series is $x \dfrac{1 - x^n}{1 - x}$ (G.P.)
$$\therefore \quad x + x^2 + x^3 + \ldots + x^n = \frac{x - x^{n+1}}{1 - x}.$$

Differentiate both sides of this equation. Then

$$1 + 2x + 3x^2 + \ldots + nx^{n-1}$$
$$= \frac{(1-x)\{1-(n+1)x^n\} - (-1)(x - x^{n+1})}{(1-x)^2}$$
$$= \frac{1 - (n+1)x^n - x + (n+1)x^{n+1} + x - x^{n+1}}{(1-x)^2}$$
$$= \frac{1 - (n+1)x^n + nx^{n+1}}{(1-x)^2}.$$

Exercise 3.4: Miscellaneous

1. Prove by induction

   (i) $\displaystyle\sum_1^n \frac{1}{r(r+1)} = \frac{n}{n+1}$,

   (ii) $\displaystyle\sum_1^n \frac{1}{4r^2 - 1} = \frac{n}{2n+1}$.

2. Prove by induction that $17^n - 1$ is a multiple of 16, when n is a positive integer.

3. Prove by induction that $x^n - 1$ is divisible by $x - 1$, when n is a positive integer,

   (*Hint: use* $x^{k+1} - 1 \equiv x^{k+1} - x^k + x^k - 1$
   $\equiv x^k(x-1) + x^k - 1.$

4. Prove by induction that $x^n - y^n$ is divisible by $x - y$, when n is a positive integer.

5. How many different pairs of numbers can be made from the first n integers?

   Show by induction that the sum of the products of pairs of the first n integers is $\frac{1}{24}n(n^2 - 1)(3n + 2)$.

6. Show that $\displaystyle\frac{1}{2}\left\{\frac{1}{r} - \frac{1}{r+2}\right\} = \frac{1}{r(r+2)}$.

   Hence find $\displaystyle\sum_1^n \frac{1}{r(r+2)}$.

7. Show that $\displaystyle\frac{1}{r} - \frac{1}{r+1} = \frac{1}{r(r+1)}$.

   Hence find $\displaystyle\sum_1^n \frac{1}{r(r+1)}$.

8. Sum to n terms the series $1 + 2(2) + 3(2)^2 + 4(2)^3 + \ldots$

9. Sum to n terms the series $1 + 2(3) + 3(3)^2 + 4(3)^3 + \ldots$

10. Show that $r^2(r+1)^2 - r^2(r-1)^2 = 4r^3$ and hence deduce the value of $\displaystyle\sum_1^n r^3$.

11. Find the sum of $2n$ terms of the series
$$1^2 - 2^2 + 3^2 - 4^2 + \ldots$$

12. Show that $\sum_{1}^{n} r(r+2)(r+4) = \dfrac{n(n+1)(n+4)(n+5)}{4}$.

13. Show that $C_0 + C_1 x + 2C_2 x^2 + \ldots + nC_n x^n = 1 + nx(1+x)^{n-1}$.

14. Sum $1^3 + 3^3 + 5^3 + \ldots + (2^n - 1)^3$.

15. The sum of n terms of a series is n^2 for all values of n. Find the rth term of the series.

16. The sum of n terms of a series is n^3 for all values of n. Find the rth term of the series

17. Evaluate $\sum_{1}^{k} (r-1)(r^2+1)$.

18. Show that the sum of n terms of the series $1 - 2 + 3 - 4\ldots$ is $\frac{1}{4}\{1 + (-1)^{n-1}(2n+1)\}$.

19. Show that the sum of n terms of the series $1^2 - 2^2 + 3^2 - 4^2 \ldots$ is $(-1)^{n-1}\dfrac{n(n+1)}{2}$.

20. The nth term of the series $3 + 5x + 11x^2 + 29x^3 + \ldots$ is $2x^{n-1} + (3x)^{n-1}$. Sum the series to n terms.

21. Show that $\sum_{1}^{n} r(2r-1) = \dfrac{n(n+1)(4n-1)}{6}$.

22. Find the sum of the series $2^2 + 4^2 + 6^2 + \ldots + (2m)^2$.

23. Find the sum of the series $2^3 + 4^3 + 6^6 + \ldots + (2m)^3$.

24. Show that $1 + 2\cos\theta + 3\cos^2\theta + \ldots + n\cos^{n-1}\theta$
$$= \dfrac{1 - (n+1)\cos^n\theta + n\cos^{n+1}\theta}{(1-\cos\theta)^2}.$$

25. Show that the sum of n terms of the series
$$1 - 1 + 1 - 1 + \ldots \text{ is } \tfrac{1}{2}\{1 + (-1)^{n+1}\}.$$

26. Given that $(1 + x + x^2)^n = a_0 + a_1 x + a_2 x^2 + \ldots + a_{2n} x^{2n}$, find the values of (i) $a_0 + a_1 + a_2 + \ldots + a_{2n}$; (ii) $(a_0 - a_1 + a_2 \ldots + a_{2n})$.

27. Show that $5^{6n} + 2^{3n+1} - 3$ is a multiple of 7 for all positive integral values of n.

28. Show that $5^{2n} - 3^{2n}$ is a multiple of 8 for all positive integral values of n.

29. Show that $3^{4n+3} + 53$ is a multiple of 80 for all positive integral values of n.

30. Find the sum of n terms of the series
$$1(n) + 2(n-1) + 3(n-2) + \ldots + n(1).$$

4 Mappings: Relations and Functions

Revision

We are probably familiar with the following:

Cartesian product

The cartesian product of two sets A and B, written $A \times B$ is the set of all possible ordered pairs obtained by selecting the first element from A and the second element from B.

Example 1. *If $A = \{1, 2, 3\}$ and $B = \{a, b\}$, the elements in the cartesian product $A \times B$ are*

$$(1, a), (1, b), (2, a), (2, b), (3, a), (3, b)$$

while those in the cartesian product $B \times A$ are

$$(a, 1), (a, 2), (a, 3), (b, 1), (b, 2), (b, 3).$$

Since these are ordered pairs, the elements are all different, and this will always be so if A and B do not have any elements in common.

If $\mathbb{R}$ is the set of all real numbers, the cartesian product $\mathbb{R} \times \mathbb{R}$, written $\mathbb{R}^2$, is the set of all ordered pairs (x, y), where x and $y \in \mathbb{R}$, and there is a one-one correspondence between the elements of $\mathbb{R}^2$ and the points in the cartesian plane.

Relation

A relation associates some elements of one set—the domain—with some elements of a second set (which may be the same set as the first set)—called the codomain.

Example 2. *If the domain is the set of positive integers $\mathbb{Z}_+$ and the codomain is also the set $\mathbb{Z}_+$, the relation 'is greater than' associates some members of $\mathbb{Z}_+$ with other members of $\mathbb{Z}_+$.*

Function

A function* associates with every element of the domain one and only one element of the codomain, called its image. The set of images

---

* Function and mapping should mean exactly the same. Since some writers use mapping to be the same as relation, to avoid confusion we shall rarely use the term mapping though the verb 'maps' is sometimes useful.

of all elements in the domain is called the range of the function. If the range is the same as the codomain, the function is said to be 'onto'; if the range is a proper subset of the codomain, the function is said to be 'into'.

Example 2. *If the domain is the set of all real numbers* $\mathbb{R}$, *and the codomain is also the set* $\mathbb{R}$, *then the function* $f : x \mapsto x^2$ *is 'into', whereas the function* $g : x \mapsto 2x$ *is onto, since every element of the codomain is an element of the range of* g, *but at least one element in the codomain is not in the range of* f.

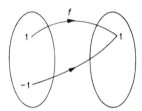 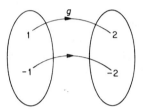

Fig. 4.1

Invariant element

An element k is invariant under a function f if $f(k) = k$. For example, every element is invariant under the function $f : x \mapsto x$, only the element 1 is invariant under $f : x \mapsto x^2$, and only the element $3/2$ is invariant under the function $f : x \mapsto 3 - x$, since $x = 3 - x \Rightarrow x = 3/2$.

One-one functions

If every element x in the domain corresponds to only one element in the range, the function is called a one-one function. The following terms are sometimes found:

a function that is one-one is called *injective*,
a function that is one-one and onto is called *bijective*,
a function that is one-one or many-one and onto is called *surjective*.

Example 3. *If the domain and codomain are the set of all positive integers* $\mathbb{Z}_+$ $\{1, 2, 3, \ldots\}$ *then the function* $f : x \mapsto x + 1$ *is one-one and into (since the element 1 in the codomain is not the image of any element in the domain). If however the codomain is restricted to the set of integers greater than 1, i.e.* $\{2, 3, \ldots\}$ *the function is one-one and onto.*

If the domain and codomain are $\mathbb{Z}$ the function $f : x \mapsto x^2$ is not 'onto', because e.g. 2 is not the image of any element in the domain. But if the domain and codomain are $\mathbb{R}$, the set of all real numbers, then the function is surjective.

Inverse functions

If a function f maps an element x in the domain into an element y in the range, the function f^{-1} that maps y back into x is called the inverse function. Since there must be a unique image under a function, only one-one functions have inverse functions. We may find it convenient to restrict the domain of a function so that we have an inverse function, e.g. if the domain is $\mathbb{R}$, the function $f : x \mapsto x^2$ does not have an inverse, but if the function is $\mathbb{R}_+$ then there is a unique square root of every number, so that the inverse function exists.

The graph of a function will show whether one value of x corresponds to one and only one value of y.

Example 4. *If the function f is such that the inverse function f^{-1} exists, find a possible domain and range for each of the following.*

(i) $f : x \mapsto x^2$,
(ii) $f : x \mapsto \sin x$,
(iii) $f : x \mapsto \cos x$.

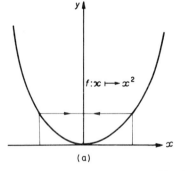 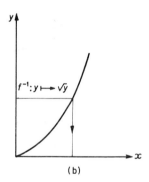

(a)   (b)

Fig. 4.2

(i) Figure 4.3(a) shows the graph of $y = x^2$. For every real value of x there is an image y, but for every positive value of y there are two possible images, one negative and one positive (the non-negative number 0 has only one image). If however we define the domain as the set of all non-negative real numbers, then the range is also the set of all non-negative numbers, and the function has an inverse. The function f is now one-one and onto, i.e. bijective.

(ii) We can see from Fig. 4.4 that if the domain is $\{x : -\pi/2 \leqslant x \leqslant \pi/2\}$ and the range is $\{y : -1 \leqslant y \leqslant 1\}$, then the function $f : x \mapsto \sin x$ has an inverse. The function again is one-one and onto, bijective. The values of x in this case are called the principal values.

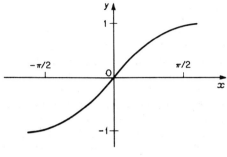

Fig. 4.3

One can see the restrictions on the domain built into any calculator; use of e.g. the inv sin button produces one and only one image because the domain is restricted by the calculator.

(iii) Considering the function $f: x \mapsto \cos x$, Fig. 4.5 shows that if the domain is $\{x: 0 \leqslant x \leqslant \pi\}$ and the range $\{y: -1 \leqslant y \leqslant 1\}$, then the function is one-one and onto, and there is an inverse function.

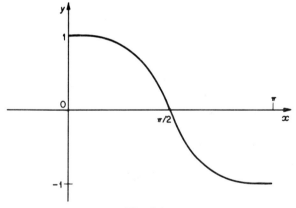

Fig. 4.4

Composite functions

If $f: x \mapsto 2x$ and $g: x \mapsto \sin x$, $gf(\pi/6)$ means that we first find the image of $\pi/6$ under f, i.e. $f(\pi/6) = \pi/3$, then* the image of $\pi/3$ under g, i.e., $g(\pi/3) = \sin(\pi/3) = \frac{1}{2}\sqrt{3}$. This is not the same as $fg(\pi/6)$, for $fg(\pi/6) = f(\frac{1}{2}) = 1$, since $g(\pi/6) = \sin \pi/6 = \frac{1}{2}$ and $f(\frac{1}{2}) = 2 \times \frac{1}{2} = 1$.

* Some writers use $f^{\circ}g$ or $f.g$, but all agree that $fg(x)$ means first apply g, then f.

To find the inverse of this composite function we must first find the image under g^{-1}, then under f^{-1}, e.g., $f^{-1}g^{-1}(\frac{1}{2}) = f^{-1}(\pi/6) = \pi/12$. Thus $(gf)^{-1} = f^{-1}g^{-1}$.

Example 5. *If $f:x \to 1 + x$ and $g:x \to 1/x$, $x \in \mathbb{R}$, $x \neq 0$, find*

(i) $gf(\frac{1}{2})$ (ii) $fg(\frac{1}{2})$ (iii) $f^{-1}g^{-1}(2/3)$
  (iv) $g^{-1}f^{-1}(2/3)$.

(i) $f(\frac{1}{2}) = 1 + \frac{1}{2} = 3/2$ and $g(3/2) = \dfrac{1}{3/2} = 2/3$

$$\therefore \quad gf(\tfrac{1}{2}) = 2/3$$

(ii) $g(\frac{1}{2}) = \dfrac{1}{\frac{1}{2}} = 2$ and $f(2) = 3$

$$\therefore \quad fg(\tfrac{1}{2}) = 3,$$

(iii) $g^{-1}(2/3) = \dfrac{1}{2/3} = \dfrac{3}{2}$ and $f^{-1}(3/2) = \dfrac{3}{2} - 1 = \tfrac{1}{2}$

$$\therefore \quad f^{-1}g^{-1}(2/3) = \tfrac{1}{2},$$

whereas
(iv) $g^{-1}f^{-1}(2/3) = g^{-1}(-1/3) = -3.$

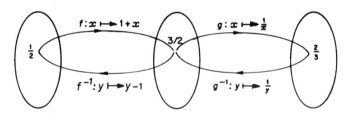

Fig. 4.5

The composite function gf can be written as a single function h where $h:x \mapsto \dfrac{1}{x+1}$ whereas fg is the single function H where $H:x \mapsto \dfrac{1}{x} + 1$.

Even and odd functions

If $f(x)$ denotes the image of x under f, a function f such that $f(-x) = f(x)$ for all x is called an even function. The graph of an even function is symmetrical about the line $y = 0$. Examples of even functions are $f:x \mapsto x^2 - 1$, $f:x \mapsto \cos x$ and $f:x \mapsto 2^{-x^2}$ (Fig. 4.6).

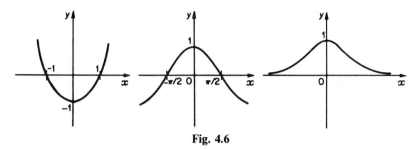

Fig. 4.6

A function f such that $f(x) = -f(-x)$ for all x is called an odd function. The graph of an odd function is symmetrical about the origin. Examples of odd functions are $f: x \mapsto x$, $f: x \mapsto x^3$ and $f: x \mapsto \sin x$ (Fig. 4.7).

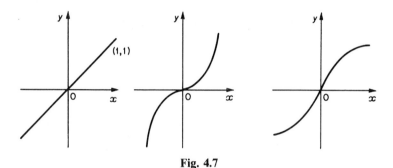

Fig. 4.7

Periodic functions

A function f such that $f(x + a) = f(x)$ for all x is said to be periodic, period a where a is the smallest positive constant for which this is true. The most important periodic functions are the trigonometric functions, e.g., $f: x \mapsto \sin x$ and $f: x \mapsto \cos x$ (period 2π) and $f: x \mapsto \tan x$ (period π). Figure 4.8 shows two other periodic functions:

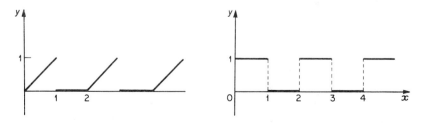

Fig. 4.8

Example 6. *Find whether the function $f: x \mapsto \sin (x^2)$ is odd or even, and whether or not it is periodic.*

Since $f(-x) = \sin (-x)^2 = \sin (x^2) = f(x)$, the function f is even, though the sin function is odd.

To see whether the function is periodic, the sin function itself is periodic, period 2π, but unequal intervals of x are required to give equal intervals of x^2, so that this function is not periodic. These properties are illustrated in Fig. 4.9.

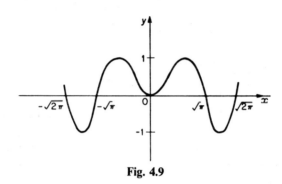

Fig. 4.9

Exercise 4

1. Sketch the function f defined by
$$f: x \rightarrow \begin{cases} -1 & \text{if} & x \leqslant -1 \\ x & \text{if} & -1 < x \leqslant 1 \\ 1 & \text{if} & 1 < x \end{cases}$$
(a) Is there an inverse function?
(b) Is f odd or even or neither?

2. Sketch the function $f:x \mapsto 2^x$
(a) over the domain $\mathbb{R}$ (b) over the domain $\mathbb{R}_+$.
Show that an inverse function exists, and find this inverse function.

3. Functions f and g are defined over $\mathbb{R}$ $(x \neq 0)$ by
$$f:x \mapsto 4 - x \quad \text{and} \quad g:x \mapsto \frac{4}{x} \cdot$$
Show that each of the functions is its own inverse and verify that $(fg)^{-1}$ is gf. Find the invariant value(s) under each function.

4. Functions f and g are defined over $\mathbb{R}$ by
$$f:x \mapsto e^x \quad \text{and} \quad g:x \mapsto \sin x.$$
Find the range of
(a) f (b) g (c) gf (d) fg.

5. Decide which of the following functions defined over $\mathbb{R}$ is one-one, and find the range of each function.

(i) $f : x \mapsto x + 2$.

(ii) $f : x \mapsto x^2 + 2x$.

(iii) $f : x \mapsto \dfrac{1}{x^2 + 2}$.

6. The following functions are defined over $x \in \mathbb{R}_+$, $x \neq 0$. Which has an inverse function? Give the inverse function where it exists.

(i) $f : x \mapsto x^2$.

(ii) $f : x \mapsto x^2 + 1$.

(iii) $f : x \mapsto x^2 - 1$.

(iv) $f : x \mapsto (x - 1)^2$.

(v) $f : x \mapsto x^2 - 2x$.

Where an inverse function does not exist, give an alternative domain over which the function is defined so that there is an inverse.

7. If the domain is $\{x : -1 \leqslant x \leqslant 1\}$ and $f : x \mapsto x\sqrt{(1 - x^2)}$ sketch f to show that there is no inverse function.

8. If $f : x \mapsto \sin x$ and $g : x \mapsto 3x$, find single functions h, H such that $h = gf$ and $H = fg$. Find also h^{-1}, H^{-1}, restricting the domain over which the functions are defined so that the inverse functions exist.

9. If $f : x \mapsto \cos x$ and $g : x \mapsto x + \pi/4$, find single functions h, H such that $h = gf$ and $H = fg$. Find also h^{-1} and H^{-1} restricting the domain over which the functions are defined so that inverse functions exist.

10. Use the definition of a periodic function to show that each of the following functions is periodic, and find the value of the period a in each case.

(i) $f : x \mapsto \sin 2x$.   (ii) $f : x \mapsto \cos 4x$.

(iii) $f : x \mapsto \tan 2x$.   (iv) $f : x \mapsto \sec 4x$.

(v) $f : x \mapsto \sin (x + \pi/4)$.   (vi) $f : x \mapsto \sin (4x + \pi)$.

11. One and only one of the following functions is periodic. Find its period and the range, if $x \in \mathbb{R}$, $x \neq 0$.

(i) $f : x \mapsto \sin \sqrt{x}$ (ii) $f : x \mapsto \sin \dfrac{1}{x}$

(iii) $f : x \mapsto \sin 2^x$.   (iv) $f : x \mapsto \sin (\sin x)$.

12. A function f is periodic, and is defined by

$$f : x \mapsto \begin{cases} x - 2k & \text{if} \quad 2k < x \leqslant 2k + 1 \\ 2 - x + 2k & \text{if} \quad 2k + 1 < x \leqslant 2k + 2 \end{cases},$$

for all integers k. Sketch f over the domain $\mathbb{R}$, and find the period from the sketch. Is f odd or even?

13. Are the following functions, defined over $\mathbb{R}$, odd or even? Find their period, if they are periodic.

(i) $f : x \mapsto e^x$.   (ii) $f : x \mapsto e^{x^2}$.

(iii) $f : x \mapsto 1/x$, $x \neq 0$.   (iv) $f : x \mapsto \sin 2x$.

(v) $f : x \mapsto \sin (x - \pi/2)$.   (vi) $f : x \mapsto \cos (\pi - x)$.

14. Functions f and g are defined by

$f : x \mapsto \sin x,\ x \in \mathbb{R}$

$g : x \mapsto \tan x,\ x \in \mathbb{R} \quad x \neq (k + \tfrac{1}{2})\pi$ where k is an integer.

(a) Write down the periods of f and g, and find the period of fg and gf.

(b) Find the range of the functions fg and gf.

15. A function f is defined from $\mathbb{R}$ to $\mathbb{R}$, i.e., both the domain and codomain are $\mathbb{R}$. Which of the following functions is into and which onto? Which are injective, bijective or surjective?

(i) $f : x \mapsto 2x$.

(ii) $f : x \mapsto x^2$.

(iii) $f : x \mapsto 10^x$.

(iv) $f : x \mapsto \sin x$.

(v) $f : x \mapsto \tan x$.

(vi) $f : x \mapsto 0$.

5 Limits and Approximations

Value of $\dfrac{f(x)}{g(x)}$ **for some one value of** x

To find the value of $f(x)/g(x)$ for some one value of x, say $x = a$, if $f(a) \neq 0$ and $g(a) \neq 0$, there is clearly no problem, and the value is merely $f(a)/g(a)$. Difficulty only arises when either $f(x)$ or $g(x)$ or both becomes very small as x approaches the value a, and $f(a)$ or $g(a)$ or both is zero. We say that as x tends to a, $f(x)$ tends to zero.

To find the value of bx/c, (where $b \neq 0$, $c \neq 0$) as $x \to 0$, bx/c becomes as small as we wish when x becomes small, and so we say $bx/c \to 0$, which we may write $\mathrm{Lt}_{x \to 0}\, bx/c = 0$.

To find the value of b/cx, as $x \to 0$, we must emphasise that we are not trying to 'divide by zero', which is meaningless. As x becomes small, b/cx becomes large, e.g.

when	$x = 0.1$,	$b/cx = 10b/c$,
when	$x = 0.01$,	$b/cx = 1000b/c$,
when	$x = 0.000001$,	$b/cx = 1\,000\,000b/c$.

The smaller x, the larger b/cx and we can make b/cx greater than any specified value, say G, by taking x sufficiently small. We may say that b/cx 'tends to infinity' as x tends to 0, i.e.

$$\mathrm{Lt}_{x \to 0} \frac{b}{cx} \text{ is infinite.}$$

$\mathrm{Lt}_{x \to 0} \dfrac{ax + bx^2 + \ldots}{Ax + Bx^2 + \ldots}$

To find the limit of $\dfrac{ax + bx^2 + \ldots}{Ax + Bx^2 + \ldots}$ as x tends to zero, we are concerned with values of x near zero but not with the value zero itself.

$$\therefore \quad \frac{ax + bx^2 + \ldots}{Ax + Bx^2 + \ldots} = \frac{a + bx + \ldots}{A + Bx + \ldots} \quad \text{(since } x \neq 0\text{)}.$$

The limit of this expression as x tends to zero is $\dfrac{a}{A}$.

If each of a and A is zero, the limit is $\dfrac{b}{B}$.

If a is zero but A is not zero, the value of the limit is 0.

If A is zero but a is not zero, the expression tends to infinity.

We write,

$$\text{Lt}_{x\to 0} \frac{ax + bx^2 + \dots}{Ax + Bx^2 + \dots} = \frac{a}{A}$$

or

$$\frac{ax + bx^2 + \dots}{Ax + Bx^2 + \dots} \to \frac{a}{A} \quad \text{as } x \to 0.$$

Example 1.

$$\text{Lt}_{x\to 0} \frac{3 + 4x + 2x^2}{5 - x - x^2} = \frac{3}{5}$$

Example 2.

$$\text{Lt}_{y\to \infty} \frac{3 + 4y + 2y^2}{5 - y - y^2}$$

Put $y = \dfrac{1}{x}$ so that $x \to 0$.

$$\frac{3 + 4y + 2y^2}{5 - y - y^2} = \frac{3 + 4/x + 2/x^2}{5 - 1/x - 1/x^2} = \frac{3x^2 + 4x + 2}{5x^2 - x - 1}$$

$$\therefore \quad \text{Lt}_{y\to \infty} \frac{3 + 4y + 2y^2}{5 - y - y^2} = \text{Lt}_{x\to 0} \frac{3x^2 + 4x + 2}{5x^2 - x - 1} = -2.$$

$\text{Lt}_{x\to 0} \dfrac{\sin x}{x}$

As seen in Chapter 20 of *Additional Pure Mathematics*,

$$\frac{\sin x}{x} \to 1 \text{ as } x \to 0 \quad \text{provided } x \text{ is in radians.}$$

This is an important limit used in proving that

$$\frac{d}{dx} (\sin x) = \cos x$$

and

$$\frac{d}{dx} (\cos x) = -\sin x.$$

We may deduce the value of $\text{Lt}_{x\to 0} \dfrac{\sin x^0}{x}$.

Suppose $x^0 = y$ radians. Then $x = \dfrac{180y}{\pi}$.

$$\therefore \quad \frac{\sin x^0}{x} = \frac{\pi \sin y}{180y}.$$

$$\therefore \quad \text{Lt}_{x\to 0} \frac{\sin x^0}{x} = \text{Lt}_{y\to 0} \frac{\pi \sin y}{180y} = \frac{\pi}{180} \text{Lt}_{y\to 0} \frac{\sin y}{y} = \frac{\pi}{180}.$$

$\mathrm{Lt}_{n \to \infty} \left(1 + \dfrac{1}{n}\right)^n$

Consider the value of the expression $\left(1 + \dfrac{1}{n}\right)^n$ as n takes values which become increasingly large.

n	$\left(1 + \dfrac{1}{n}\right)$	$\log_{10}\left(1 + \dfrac{1}{n}\right)$	$n \log_{10}\left(1 + \dfrac{1}{n}\right)$	$\left(1 + \dfrac{1}{n}\right)^n$
1	2			2
2	1.5	0.1761	0.3522	2.250
5	1.2	0.0792	0.3960	2.489
10	1.1	0.0414	0.414	2.594
100	1.01	0.0043	0.430	2.692

When $n = 1000$, the value of the expression is about 2.716 92.
When $n = 10\,000$, the value of the expression is about 2.718 15.
So we may say that

$$\mathrm{Lt}_{n \to \infty} \left(1 + \frac{1}{n}\right)^n = 2.718 \text{ approximately.}$$

This is one of the most important numbers in mathematics and is called the base of natural logarithms e.

Putting $n = \dfrac{1}{x}$ so that $x \to 0$, we see that

$$\mathrm{Lt}_{x \to 0} (1 + x)^{1/x} = \mathrm{e}.$$

Now consider $\mathrm{Lt}_{n \to \infty} \left(1 + \dfrac{x}{n}\right)^n$.

Put $\dfrac{x}{n} = \dfrac{1}{m}$ so that $m \to \infty$.

Then $n = mx$.

$$\therefore \quad \mathrm{Lt}_{n \to \infty} \left(1 + \frac{x}{n}\right)^n = \mathrm{Lt}_{m \to \infty} \left(1 + \frac{1}{m}\right)^{mx}$$

$$= \left\{ \mathrm{Lt}_{m \to \infty} \left(1 + \frac{1}{m}\right)^m \right\}^x = \mathrm{e}^x.$$

$$\therefore \quad \mathrm{Lt}_{n \to \infty} \left(1 + \frac{x}{n}\right)^n = \mathrm{e}^x.$$

The differential coefficient as a limit

Let P and Q be two points on the curve $y = f(x)$ as shown in Fig. 5.1.

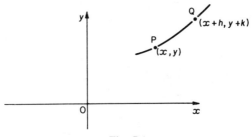

Fig. 5.1

Suppose the coordinates of P are (x, y) and those of Q $(x + h, y + k)$.

Then $$y = f(x)$$
and $$y + k = f(x + h),$$
since both P and Q lie on the curve.

Subtracting $$k = f(x + h) - f(x).$$

The gradient of the chord PQ

$$= \frac{(y + k) - y}{(x + h) - x} = \frac{k}{h}$$

$$= \frac{f(x + h) - f(x)}{h}.$$

As $h \to 0$, the point Q approaches P and the chord PQ becomes more nearly the tangent at P. The gradient of the chord becomes the gradient of the tangent at P, i.e. the value of the differential coefficient at that point.

$$\therefore \quad \frac{d}{dx} f(x) = \text{Lt}_{h \to 0} \frac{f(x + h) - f(x)}{h}.$$

Example 1. *Find from first principles* $\dfrac{d}{dx} (x^3)$.

$$\frac{d}{dx} (x^3) = \text{Lt}_{h \to 0} \frac{(x + h)^3 - x^3}{h}$$

$$= \text{Lt}_{h \to 0} \frac{3x^2 h + 3xh^2 + h^3}{h}$$

$$= 3x^2.$$

Example 2. *Find from first principles $\dfrac{d}{dx}(\sin 3x)$.*

$$\frac{d}{dx}(\sin 3x) = \text{Lt}_{h \to 0} \frac{\sin 3(x + h) - \sin 3x}{h}$$

$$= \text{Lt}_{h \to 0} \frac{2 \cos \dfrac{6x + 3h}{2} \sin \dfrac{3h}{2}}{h}$$

But

$$\text{Lt}_{h \to 0} \frac{\sin 3h/2}{3h/2} = 1.$$

$$\therefore \quad \text{Lt}_{h \to 0} \frac{\sin 3h/2}{h} = \frac{3}{2}.$$

As $h \to 0$,

$$\frac{6x + 3h}{2} \to 3x.$$

$$\therefore \quad \frac{d}{dx}\left(\sin 3x\right) = 2 \cos 3x \left(\frac{3}{2}\right) = 3 \cos 3x.$$

Differential coefficient of x^n

$$\frac{d}{dx}(x^n) = \text{Lt}_{h \to 0} \frac{(x + h)^n - x^n}{h}$$

$$= \text{Lt}_{h \to 0} \frac{x^n(1 + h/x)^n - x^n}{h}$$

Since $\dfrac{h}{x}$ is small, $\left(1 + \dfrac{h}{x}\right)^n$ may be expanded by the binomial theorem.

$$\therefore \quad \frac{d}{dx}(x^n) = \text{Lt}_{h \to 0} \frac{x^n\left(1 + \dfrac{nh}{x} + \text{higher powers of } h\right) - x^n}{h}$$

$$= \text{Lt}_{h \to 0} \frac{nhx^{n-1} + \text{higher powers of } h}{h}$$

$$= nx^{n-1}$$

Limits when $x \to a$

If an expression is indeterminate when $x = a$, its limit as $x \to a$ is often best found by writing $y = x - a$ so that $y \to 0$. The expression is then put in terms of y and the limit found as before.

Example 1. *Find* $Lt_{x \to 1} \dfrac{x^2 - 2x + 1}{x^2 - 3x + 2}$

Put $y = x - 1$ so that $x = y + 1$.

$$\frac{x^2 - 2x + 1}{x^2 - 3x + 2} = \frac{(y + 1)^2 - 2(y + 1) + 1}{(y + 1)^2 - 3(y + 1) + 2} = \frac{y^2}{y^2 - y}$$

$$\therefore \quad Lt_{x \to 1} \frac{x^2 - 2x + 1}{x^2 - 3x + 2} = Lt_{y \to 0} \frac{y^2}{y^2 - y} = 0.$$

Alternatively, $\dfrac{x^2 - 2x + 1}{x^2 - 3x + 2} = \dfrac{(x - 1)^2}{(x - 1)(x - 2)} = \dfrac{x - 1}{x - 2} \quad (x \neq 1)$

The value of $\dfrac{x - 1}{x - 2}$ when $x = 1$ is 0 and so the limit is 0.

Example 2. *Find* $Lt_{x \to a} \dfrac{\sin x \cos a - \cos x \sin a}{x - a}$

Put $y = x - a$ so that $x = y + a$.

$$\frac{\sin x \cos a - \cos x \sin a}{x - a} = \frac{\sin (y + a) \cos a - \cos (y + a) \sin a}{y}$$

$$= \frac{\cos a(\sin y \cos a + \cos y \sin a) - \sin a(\cos y \cos a - \sin y \sin a)}{y}$$

$$= \frac{\sin y(\cos^2 a + \sin^2 a)}{y} = \frac{\sin y}{y}.$$

$$\therefore \quad Lt_{x \to a} \frac{\sin x \cos a - \cos x \sin a}{x - a} = Lt_{y \to 0} \frac{\sin y}{y} = 1.$$

It would have been simpler to say that

$$Lt_{x \to a} \frac{\sin x \cos a - \cos x \sin a}{x - a} = Lt_{x \to a} \frac{\sin (x - a)}{x - a} = 1.$$

Exercise 5.1

1. Write down the limits of the following expressions as $x \to 0$;

(i) $\dfrac{x^2 + x}{x^2 - x}$,

(ii) $\dfrac{x^3 + x}{x^3 + x^2 + x}$,

(iii) $\dfrac{x^3 - 3x^2 - 5x}{x^3 - 2x^2}$,

(iv) $\dfrac{x^3 - 3x^2}{x^3 - 2x^2 - x}$.

2. Write down the limits of the following expressions as $y \to \infty$;

(i) $\dfrac{y^2 - y}{y^2 + y}$,

(ii) $\dfrac{2y^3 + y^2 + y + 1}{y^3 + 1}$,

(iii) $\dfrac{y^3 - 1}{y^2 + 1}$,

(iv) $\dfrac{y^2 - 1}{y^3 + 1}$.

3. Find the value of $Lt_{x \to a} \dfrac{x^3 - a^3}{x^2 - a^2}$.

4. Find the value of $\text{Lt}_{x\to 0} \dfrac{\sin x - x}{\sin x}$.

5. Find $\text{Lt}_{h\to 0} \dfrac{\pi(r+h)^2 - \pi r^2}{h}$.

Explain the significance of your result.

6. Find $\text{Lt}_{h\to 0} \dfrac{\frac{4}{3}\pi(r+h)^3 - \frac{4}{3}\pi r^3}{h}$.

Explain the significance of your result.

7. Find $\text{Lt}_{n\to\infty}\left(1 + \dfrac{1}{2n}\right)^n$.   **8.** Find $\text{Lt}_{x\to 0}(1 + x)^{3/x}$.

9. Find $\text{Lt}_{n\to\infty}\left(1 + \dfrac{x}{n}\right)^{n/2}$.   **10.** Find $\text{Lt}_{n\to 0}(1 + nx)^{2/n}$.

11. Differentiate from first principles (i) $\sin 3x$, (ii) $\cos 4x$, (iii) $\sqrt{x}$.

12. When h is small, show that $f(x + h) \simeq f(x) + hf'(x)$.

13. Find $\text{Lt}_{x\to 2} \dfrac{x^3 - 8}{x^2 - 4}$.   **14.** Find $\text{Lt}_{x\to a} \dfrac{(x-a)^3}{x^2 - a^2}$.

15. Find $\text{Lt}_{y\to\infty}\, y\sin\left(\dfrac{1}{y}\right)$.   **16.** Find $\text{Lt}_{x\to 0} \dfrac{\tan 2x}{\sin x}$.

17. Find $\text{Lt}_{x\to 0} \dfrac{\sin 3x}{x}$.   **18.** Find $\text{Lt}_{z\to 1} \dfrac{z^n - 1}{z - 1}$.

19. Find $\text{Lt}_{t\to 1} \dfrac{t^n - t}{t - 1}$.   **20.** Find $\text{Lt}_{x\to 2} \dfrac{x^n - 2^n}{x^2 - 4}$.

Approximations

Since

$$f'(x) = \text{Lt}_{h\to 0} \frac{f(x + h) - f(x)}{h},$$

it follows that when h is small,

$$f'(x) \simeq \frac{f(x + h) - f(x)}{h}$$

or that

$$f(x + h) \simeq f(x) + hf'(x).$$

Let $f(x) = \sqrt{x}$, for example, when $f'(x) = \dfrac{1}{2\sqrt{x}}$.

Then

$$\sqrt{(x + h)} \simeq \sqrt{x} + \frac{h}{2\sqrt{x}}.$$

This may be used to find approximations for square roots. Let $x = 25,\ h = 0.1$.

$$\sqrt{25.1} \simeq \sqrt{25} + \frac{0.1}{2\sqrt{25}}$$

$$= 5 + 0.01.$$

$$\therefore \quad \sqrt{25.1} \simeq 5.01.$$

Example 1. *Find an approximation for* $\sqrt[3]{220}$.

If $f(x) = \sqrt[3]{x}$, $f'(x) = \frac{1}{3}x^{-\frac{2}{3}} = \dfrac{1}{3\sqrt[3]{x^2}}$.

$$\therefore \quad \sqrt[3]{(x + h)} \simeq \sqrt[3]{x} + \frac{h}{3\sqrt[3]{x^2}}.$$

Let $x = 216$, $h = 4$.

$$\sqrt[3]{220} \simeq \sqrt[3]{216} + \frac{4}{3\sqrt[3]{(216)^2}}$$

$$= 6 + \frac{4}{3 \times 36}$$

$$= 6 + \frac{1}{27} \simeq 6.04.$$

Example 2. *Find the value of* $\cos 30.05°$.

$$\cos (x + h) \simeq \cos x - h \sin x.$$
$$\therefore \quad \cos 30.05° \simeq \cos 30° - h \sin 30°.$$

h must be measured in radians since we have assumed that

$$\frac{d}{dx}(\cos x) = -\sin x.$$

$$\therefore \quad h = 0.05 \times \frac{\pi}{180}$$

$$\therefore \quad \cos 30.05° \simeq \cos 30° - 0.05 \times \frac{\pi}{180} \times 0.5$$

$$\simeq 0.8660 - 0.0004$$

$$\simeq 0.8656.$$

de l'Hôpital's method of finding limits

Suppose we wish to find the limit of a fraction $\dfrac{f(x)}{\varphi(x)}$ when $x \to a$, given that $f(a) = \varphi(a) = 0$.

Let us put $x = a + h$, so that $h \to 0$ as $x \to a$.

$$\text{Lt}_{x \to a} \frac{f(x)}{\varphi(x)} = \text{Lt}_{h \to 0} \frac{f(a + h)}{\varphi(a + h)}$$

$$= \text{Lt}_{h \to 0} \frac{f(a) + hf'(a)}{\varphi(a) + h\varphi'(a)} \quad \begin{array}{l}\text{(by the approximation}\\ \text{used previously)}\end{array}$$

$$= \frac{f'(a)}{\varphi'(a)} \quad \text{since } f(a) = \varphi(a) = 0.$$

So to find the limit of a fraction in which both numerator and denominator become zero when $x = a$, differentiate numerator and denominator *separately*, and then put $x = a$. If the numerator and denominator are still both zero, repeat the process.

Example 1. Find $Lt_{x \to 1} \dfrac{x^2 - 3x + 2}{x^2 - 4x + 3}$.

When $x = 1$, $\qquad x^2 - 3x + 2 = x^2 - 4x + 3 = 0$.

$$\therefore \quad Lt_{x \to 1} \frac{x^2 - 3x + 2}{x^2 - 4x + 3} = Lt_{x \to 1} \frac{2x - 3}{2x - 4} = \frac{-1}{-2} = \frac{1}{2}.$$

Example 2. Find $Lt_{x \to 0} \dfrac{sin^2\, x}{1 - cos\, x}$.

$$sin^2\, 0 = 1 - cos\, 0 = 0.$$

$$\therefore \quad Lt_{x \to 0} \frac{sin^2\, x}{1 - cos\, x} = Lt_{x \to 0} \frac{2 \sin x \cos x}{\sin x} = Lt_{x \to 0} 2 \cos x = 2.$$

Example 3. Find $Lt_{x \to 2} \dfrac{x^3 - 4x^2 + 4x}{x^3 - 5x^2 + 8x - 4}$.

When $x = 2$, $\qquad x^3 - 4x^2 + 4x = x^3 - 5x^2 + 8x - 4 = 0$.

$$\therefore \quad Lt_{x \to 2} \frac{x^3 - 4x^2 + 4x}{x^3 - 5x^2 + 8x - 4} = Lt_{x \to 2} \frac{3x^2 - 8x + 4}{3x^2 - 10x + 8}.$$

When $x = 2$, $\qquad 3x^2 - 8x + 4 = 3x^2 - 10x + 8 = 0$.

$$\therefore \quad Lt_{x \to 2} \frac{3x^2 - 8x + 4}{3x^2 - 10x + 8} = Lt_{x \to 2} \frac{6x - 8}{6x - 10}$$

$$= \frac{4}{2} = 2.$$

Exercise 5.2

1. Find the following limits:

(i) $\dfrac{x^2 - 1}{x^3 - 1}$ as $x \to 1$;

(ii) $\dfrac{1 - \cos x}{x^2}$ as $x \to 0$;

(iii) $\dfrac{2 \cos x - 1}{x - \pi/3}$ as $x \to \dfrac{\pi}{3}$;

(iv) $\dfrac{(x - 2)^3}{x^3 - 4x^2 + 4x}$ as $x \to 2$;

(v) $\dfrac{x^2 - 1}{x^2 - x}$ as $x \to 1$;

(vi) $\dfrac{x^n - a^n}{x - a}$ as $x \to a$;

(vii) $\dfrac{x^n - a^n}{(x - a)^n}$ as $x \to a$;

(viii) $\dfrac{x^n - a^n}{x(x - a)}$ as $x \to a$.

2. Find approximations for

(i) $\sqrt{37}$;   (ii) $\tan 45.05°$;   (iii) $\sqrt[3]{126}$;   (iv) $\dfrac{1}{10.1}$;

(v) $(33)^{1/5}$;   (vi) $\sin 0.02°$;   (vii) $\cos 89° 55'$;   (viii) $\sin 30° 5'$.

Exercise 5.3: Miscellaneous

1. If $Lt_{x \to 0} \dfrac{ax + bx^2}{4x - 8x^2} = 3$, find the value of a.

2. Find the limit as x tends to zero of $\dfrac{3x - 4x^2}{2x - 3x^2}$.

Find also the limit of the same expression as x tends to infinity.

3. Find $\text{Lt}_{x \to 1} \dfrac{3(x - 1) + 4(x - 1)^2}{2(x - 1) + 5(x - 1)^2}$.

4. Find $\text{Lt}_{x \to a} \dfrac{3(x - a) + 2(x - a)^2}{(x - a) + 3(x - a)^2}$.

5. Differentiate $\tan 2x$ from first principles.

6. Find $\text{Lt} \left(1 + \dfrac{4}{n}\right)^n$ as $n \to \infty$.

7. Find $\text{Lt} \left(1 + \dfrac{x}{3}\right)^{1/x}$ as $x \to 0$.

8. Differentiate $(1 + 3x)^5$ from first principles.

9. Find $\text{Lt}_{x \to 0} \dfrac{(1 + x)^3 - 1}{(1 + x)^4 - 1}$.

10. Find $\text{Lt}_{y \to 1} \dfrac{y^3 - 1}{y^4 - 1}$.

11. Find $\text{Lt}_{y \to 1} \dfrac{y^4 - 1}{y^5 - 1}$.

12. Find $\text{Lt}_{t \to 2} \dfrac{t^4 - 2^4}{t^5 - 2^5}$.

13. Find the limit of $a \dfrac{1 - r^n}{1 - r}$ as $n \to \infty$ when $r < 1$.

14. Find the limit of $\dfrac{1 - r^n}{1 - r}$ as $r \to 1$.

15. Find the limit of $\dfrac{x^2}{1 - \cos 2x}$ as x tends to zero.

16. Find the limit of $\dfrac{x - \sin x}{x - \tan x}$ as x tends to zero.

17. Find $\text{Lt}_{x \to 0} \dfrac{\tan x - x}{x^3}$.

18. Find the value of $\sqrt[3]{65}$ correct to 3 significant figures.

19. Find the value of $\tan 45.01°$.

20. Find $\text{Lt}_{x \to 0} \dfrac{1 - \cos x}{x}$.

6 General Solution of Trigonometric Equations

A trigonometrical equation has an infinite number of solutions. For example, if $\sin \theta = 0.5$, one solution is $\theta = \dfrac{\pi}{6}$. The only other solution between 0 and 2π is $\dfrac{5\pi}{6}$. But any multiples of 2π may be added to these values for θ without altering the value of $\sin \theta$. So $2n\pi + \dfrac{\pi}{6}$ and $2n\pi + \dfrac{5\pi}{6}$ give the general solution of the equation $\sin \theta = 0.5$.

The general solution of sin θ = sin α

Obviously $\theta = \alpha$ is a solution of the equation $\sin \theta = \sin \alpha$ and so $\theta = 2n\pi + \alpha$ is a solution for all integral values of n.

Another solution which does not differ from α by a multiple of 2π is $(\pi - \alpha)$ and so $2n\pi + \pi - \alpha$ or $(2n + 1)\pi - \alpha$ is a solution for all integral values of n.

The complete solution is
$$\theta = 2n\pi + \alpha \quad \text{or} \quad (2n + 1)\pi - \alpha.$$
These may be combined into the single formula
$$\theta = n\pi + (-1)^n \alpha.$$

Example. *Find the general solution of the equation* $\sin \theta = \dfrac{\sqrt{3}}{2}$.

Find any angle whose sine is $\dfrac{\sqrt{3}}{2}$. One such angle is $\dfrac{\pi}{3}$. The general solution of the equation $\sin \theta = \sin \dfrac{\pi}{3}$ is

$$\theta = n\pi + (-1)^n \frac{\pi}{3}$$

or

$$\theta = \left(2n\pi + \frac{\pi}{3}\right) \quad \text{and} \quad (2n + 1)\pi - \frac{\pi}{3},$$

i.e.

$$\left(2n\pi + \frac{\pi}{3}\right) \quad \text{and} \quad \left(2n\pi + \frac{2\pi}{3}\right).$$

N.B. When the particular solution is a multiple of $\dfrac{\pi}{2}$, it is generally simpler to write down the solution by common sense. For example, if $\sin \theta = 1$, the angle is represented in Fig. 6.1 by the radius OB.

The complete solution of the equation $\sin \theta = 1$ is $2n\pi + \dfrac{\pi}{2}$.

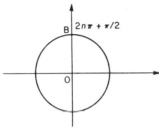

Fig. 6.1

The general solution of cos θ = cos α

A particular solution is $\theta = \alpha$. Therefore $\theta = 2n\pi + \alpha$ is a solution for all integral values of n.

Another solution which does not differ from α by a multiple of 2π is $-\alpha$.

$$\therefore \quad (2n\pi - \alpha) \text{ is also a solution.}$$

The general solution is $\theta = 2n\pi \pm \alpha$.

Example 1. *Find the general solution of the equation* $\cos \theta = 0.5$.

A particular solution is $\theta = \dfrac{\pi}{3}$.

The general solution is $2n\pi \pm \dfrac{\pi}{3}$.

Example 2. *Find the general solution of the equation* $\cos \theta = -0.8$.

A particular solution is
$$\begin{aligned} \theta &= 180° - 36.9° \\ &= 143.1° \end{aligned}$$

The general solution is $\quad 360n° \pm 143.1°$.

N.B. Be careful not to mix degrees and radians.

Example 3. *Find the general solution of the equation* $\sin 2\theta = \cos 3\theta$. *Deduce the exact value of* $\sin 18°$.

The equation may be put in the form

$$\cos 3\theta = \cos\left(\frac{\pi}{2} - 2\theta\right).$$

N.B. It is advisable to put the equation in terms of cosines rather than sines as the general formula for cosines is easier.

From the equality of the two cosines, we deduce

$$3\theta = 2n\pi \pm \left(\frac{\pi}{2} - 2\theta\right).$$

$$\therefore \quad 5\theta = 2n\pi + \frac{\pi}{2} \quad \text{or} \quad \theta = \left(2n\pi - \frac{\pi}{2}\right).$$

The general solution is

$$\theta = \frac{(4n + 1)\pi}{10} \quad \text{or} \quad \frac{(4n - 1)\pi}{2}.$$

The equation $\sin 2\theta = \cos 3\theta$ may be put in the form

$$2 \sin \theta \cos \theta = 4 \cos^3 \theta - 3 \cos \theta,$$

from which $\qquad \cos \theta = 0 \quad \text{or} \quad 2 \sin \theta = 4 \cos^2 \theta - 3.$

If $\cos \theta = 0$, $\qquad\qquad \theta = 2n\pi \pm \dfrac{\pi}{2}.$

If $2 \sin \theta = 4 \cos^2 \theta - 3$,

$$2 \sin \theta = 4(1 - \sin^2 \theta) - 3$$
$$\therefore \quad 4 \sin^2 \theta + 2 \sin \theta - 1 = 0.$$
$$\therefore \quad \sin \theta = \frac{-2 \pm \sqrt{(4 + 16)}}{8} = \frac{-1 \pm \sqrt{5}}{4}.$$

If $\theta = 2n\pi \pm \dfrac{\pi}{2}$,

$$\sin \theta = \pm 1.$$

The general value of θ is $\dfrac{(4n + 1)\pi}{10} \quad \text{or} \quad \dfrac{(4n - 1)\pi}{2}.$

Putting $n = 0$, we see that a possible value of θ is $\dfrac{\pi}{10}$ and so a possible value

of $\sin \theta$ is $\sin \dfrac{\pi}{10}$.

But $\sin \dfrac{\pi}{10}$ is positive and is not equal to ± 1.

$$\therefore \quad \sin \frac{\pi}{10} = \frac{\sqrt{5} - 1}{4},$$

and so $\qquad\qquad \sin 18° = \dfrac{\sqrt{5} - 1}{4}.$

The general solution of $\tan \theta = \tan \alpha$

A particular solution is $\theta = \alpha$. Therefore $\theta = 2n\pi + \alpha$ is a solution for all integral values of n.

Another solution which does not differ from α by a multiple of 2π is $(\pi + \alpha)$.

$$\therefore \quad 2n\pi + \pi + \alpha \quad \text{or} \quad (2n + 1)\pi + \alpha \text{ is a solution.}$$

These two formulae may be combined into the general solution

$$\theta = n\pi + \alpha.$$

Example 1. *Solve the equation tan 3θ = cot θ.*

The equation may be written

$$\tan 3\theta = \tan\left(\frac{\pi}{2} - \theta\right).$$

$$\therefore \quad 3\theta = n\pi + \frac{\pi}{2} - \theta$$

or

$$\theta = \frac{(2n + 1)\pi}{8}.$$

Example 2. *Solve the equation tan 3θ = 1 and hence find the exact value of tan 15°.*

tan 3θ = 1 may be written in the form

$$\tan 3\theta = \tan\frac{\pi}{4}.$$

$$\therefore \quad 3\theta = n\pi + \frac{\pi}{4}$$

or

$$\theta = \frac{(4n + 1)\pi}{12}.$$

Putting $n = 0$, we see that one value of tan θ is $\tan\frac{\pi}{12}$ or tan 15°.

Putting $n = 2$, we see that one value of tan θ is $\tan\frac{3\pi}{4}$ or -1.

$$\tan 3\theta = \tan(2\theta + \theta) = \frac{\tan 2\theta + \tan\theta}{1 - \tan 2\theta \tan\theta}$$

$$= \frac{\dfrac{2\tan\theta}{1 - \tan^2\theta} + \tan\theta}{1 - \tan\theta \dfrac{2\tan\theta}{1 - \tan^2\theta}}$$

$$= \frac{3\tan\theta - \tan^3\theta}{1 - 3\tan^2\theta}.$$

But tan 3θ = 1.

$$\therefore \quad \frac{3\tan\theta - \tan^3\theta}{1 - 3\tan^2\theta} = 1$$

or

$$\tan^3\theta - 3\tan^2\theta - 3\tan\theta + 1 = 0.$$

The values of tan θ are the roots of the equation $t^3 - 3t^2 - 3t + 1 = 0$. One root is -1 and so $(t + 1)$ is a factor.

$$(t + 1)(t^2 - 4t + 1) = 0.$$

$$\therefore \quad \tan 15° \text{ must be a root of } t^2 - 4t + 1 = 0.$$

The roots are $\dfrac{4 \pm \sqrt{12}}{2}$ or $2 \pm \sqrt{3}$.

Since tan 15° < tan 45°,

$$\tan 15° = 2 - \sqrt{3}.$$

Exercise 6.1

Find the general solutions of the following equations:

1. $\sin \theta = \frac{1}{2}$.

2. $\cos \theta = \frac{1}{\sqrt{2}}$.

3. $\tan \theta = \sqrt{3}$.

4. $\operatorname{cosec} \theta = \frac{2}{\sqrt{3}}$.

5. $\sec \theta = 2$.

6. $\cot \theta = \sqrt{3}$.

7. $\sin \theta = -\frac{1}{2}$.

8. $\cos \theta = -\frac{1}{\sqrt{2}}$.

9. $\tan \theta = -\sqrt{3}$.

10. $\sin \theta = 0.6$.

11. $\cos \theta = 0.8$.

12. $\tan \theta = 0.4$.

13. $\sin \theta = -0.8$.

14. $\cos \theta = -0.6$.

15. $\tan \theta = -0.5$.

16. $\sin \theta = \cos 2\theta$.

17. $\sin \theta = -\cos 2\theta$.

18. $\tan \theta = \cot 2\theta$.

19. $\tan \theta = -\cot 2\theta$.

20. $\sin 2\theta = -\cos 3\theta$.

21. $\tan 2\theta = -\cot 3\theta$.

22. $\tan \theta + \tan 2\theta = 0$.

23. $\sin \theta + \sin 3\theta = 0$.

24. $\sin 3\theta + \cos 3\theta = 0$.

25. $\sin 2\theta + \cos 2\theta = 0$.

26. $\tan 2\theta + \cot 3\theta = 0$.

27. $\tan 2\theta \tan 4\theta = 1$.

28. $\tan \theta \tan 3\theta = -1$.

29. $\operatorname{cosec} \theta = \operatorname{cosec} 2\theta$.

30. $\tan \theta + \frac{1}{\tan 3\theta} = 0$.

Equations of the type $a \cos x + b \sin x = c$

These equations were considered in *Additional Pure Mathematics* for values of x between $0°$ and $360°$. There are two methods: the auxiliary angle method and expressing the equation in terms of the tangent of the half angle. The second of these methods is usually the safer of the two.

Example. *Find the general solution of the equation $3 \cos x + 4 \sin x = 2$.*

Method (i)

Draw a triangle with sides 3, 4 and 5 as shown in Fig. 6.2.

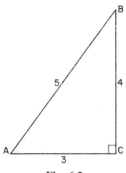

Fig. 6.2

Then $3 = 5 \cos A; \quad 4 = 5 \sin A.$

The equation becomes

$$5 \cos A \cos x + 5 \sin A \sin x = 2$$

or $\qquad\qquad 5 \cos (x - A) = 2.$

$$\therefore \quad \cos (x - A) = \tfrac{2}{5} = \cos 66.42°.$$

$$\therefore \quad x - A = 360n° \pm 66.42°.$$

The value of A is $\tan^{-1} \tfrac{4}{3}$ or $53.13°$. (There is nothing to be gained by finding the general value for A.)

$$\therefore \quad x = 360n° + 53.13° \pm 66.42°$$
$$= 360n° + 119.6° \quad \text{or} \quad 360n° - 13.3°.$$

Method (ii)

Use the formulae

$$\sin x = \frac{2t}{1 + t^2}, \quad \cos x = \frac{1 - t^2}{1 + t^2}$$

where $t = \tan \tfrac{1}{2}x$.

The equation becomes

$$\frac{3(1 - t^2)}{1 + t^2} + \frac{8t}{1 + t^2} = 2$$

or $\qquad\qquad 3 - 3t^2 + 8t = 2 + 2t^2$

i.e. $\qquad\qquad 5t^2 - 8t - 1 = 0.$

$$\therefore \quad t = \frac{8 \pm \sqrt{84}}{10} = \frac{8 \pm 9.165}{10}.$$

$$\therefore \quad \tan \frac{\theta}{2} = 1.7165 \quad \text{or} \quad -0.1165$$

$$= \tan 59.78° \quad \text{or} \quad \tan 173.35°.$$

$$\therefore \quad \frac{\theta}{2} = 180n° + 59.78° \quad \text{or} \quad 180n° + 173.35°.$$

$$\therefore \quad \theta = 360n° + 119.6° \quad \text{or} \quad 360n° + 346.7°.$$

N.B. $\qquad 360n° + 346.7° = 360n° + 360° - 13.3°$

$$= 360(n + 1)° - 13.3°.$$

Exercise 6.2

Find the general solutions of the following equations:

1. $\cos \theta + \sin \theta = \sqrt{2}.$ 2. $2 (\cos \theta + \sin \theta) = \sqrt{3} + 1.$
3. $3 \cos \theta + 4 \sin \theta = 4.$ 4. $5 \cos \theta + 12 \sin \theta = 10.$
5. $8 \cos \theta + 15 \sin \theta = 12.$

Equations in one ratio only

An equation in terms of one ratio only may be solved in the same way as an algebraic equation.

Example. *Find the general solution of the equation* $2 \sin^2 x - 3 \sin x + 1 = 0$.

If $2 \sin^2 x - 3 \sin x + 1 = 0$,
$$(2 \sin x - 1)(\sin x - 1) = 0.$$

$$\therefore \quad \sin x = \tfrac{1}{2} = \sin \frac{\pi}{6} \quad \text{or} \quad \sin x = 1.$$

If $\sin x = \sin \dfrac{\pi}{6}$,

$$x = n\pi + (-1)^n \frac{\pi}{6}.$$

If $\sin x = 1$,

$$x = 2n\pi + \frac{\pi}{2}.$$

The solution is $\quad 2n\pi + \dfrac{\pi}{2} \quad$ or $\quad n\pi + (-1)^n \dfrac{\pi}{6}$.

The identities $\sin^2 x + \cos^2 x = 1$, $\sec^2 x - \tan^2 x = 1$, $\operatorname{cosec}^2 x - \cot^2 x = 1$, $\tan x = \dfrac{\sin x}{\cos x}$ may often be used to express an equation in terms of one ratio only.

Example 1. *Find the general solution of the equation* $2 \cos^2 \theta = 3(1 - \sin \theta)$.

Using $\cos^2 \theta = 1 - \sin^2 \theta$, we have

$$2(1 - \sin^2 \theta) = 3(1 - \sin \theta)$$

or
$$2(1 + \sin \theta)(1 - \sin \theta) = 3(1 - \sin \theta).$$

$$\therefore \quad \text{either } \sin \theta - 1 = 0 \quad \text{or} \quad 2(1 + \sin \theta) = 3$$

i.e.
$$\sin \theta = 1 \quad \text{or} \quad \tfrac{1}{2}.$$

The general solution is $2n\pi + \dfrac{\pi}{2}$ or $n\pi + (-1)^n \dfrac{\pi}{6}$.

Example 2. *Find the general solution of the equation* $6 \sin^2 \theta + 4\cos^2 \theta = 5 \tan \theta$.

Divide throughout by $\cos^2 \theta$.

$$6 \tan^2 \theta + 4 = \frac{5 \tan \theta}{\cos^2 \theta}$$

$$= 5 \tan \theta \sec^2 \theta.$$
$$= 5 \tan \theta \, (1 + \tan^2 \theta).$$

Putting $\tan \theta = t$, we have

$$6t^2 + 4 = 5t + 5t^3.$$
$$\therefore \quad 5t^3 - 6t^2 + 5t - 4 = 0.$$

$t = 1$ satisfies this equation and so $(t - 1)$ is a factor of the left-hand side.

$$\therefore \quad (t - 1)(5t^2 - t + 4) = 0.$$

$5t^2 - t + 4 = 0$ has no real roots and so the only solution is

$$\tan \theta = 1 = \tan \frac{\pi}{4}.$$

The general solution is $n\pi + \dfrac{\pi}{4}$.

Exercise 6.3

Find the general solutions of the following equations:

1. $\sin^2 \theta + 2 \cos^2 \theta = 1\frac{1}{4}$.
2. $\sec^2 \theta + \tan^2 \theta = 3$.
3. $\operatorname{cosec}^2 \theta + 2 \cot^2 \theta = 4$.
4. $\sin \theta + \cos \theta = 2 \tan \theta \cos \theta$.
5. $\sin^2 \theta + 2 \cos^2 \theta = \cos^2 \theta + 4 \sin^2 \theta$.
6. $3 \sin^2 \theta + 2 \cos^2 \theta = 2\frac{3}{4}$.
7. $2 \sin^2 \theta = 4 - 5 \cos \theta$.
8. $3 \cot^2 \theta + 5 = 7 \operatorname{cosec} \theta$.
9. $\tan \theta = 2 \sec^2 \theta - 3$.
10. $\tan \theta + \cot \theta = 2$.

Equations containing sums and differences of sines and cosines

Equations such as $\cos x + \cos 3x = 2 \cos 2x$ and $\sin x + \sin 5x = \sin 2x + \sin 4x$ may be solved using the formulae expressing the sum of two sines or cosines as a product and factorizing.

Example 1. *Find the general solution of the equation $\cos x + \cos 3x = 2 \cos 2x$.*

$$\cos x + \cos 3x = 2 \cos 2x \cos x.$$
$$\therefore \quad 2 \cos 2x \cos x = 2 \cos 2x.$$

Either $\qquad \cos 2x = 0 \quad \text{or} \quad \cos x = 1$.

If $\cos 2x = 0$, $\qquad 2x = (2n + 1)\dfrac{\pi}{2} \quad \text{and} \quad x = (2n + 1)\dfrac{\pi}{4}$.

If $\cos x = 1$, $\qquad\qquad\qquad \pi = 2n\pi$.

The general solution is $2n\pi \quad \text{or} \quad (2n + 1)\dfrac{\pi}{4}$.

Example 2. *Find the general solution of the equation $\sin x + \sin 5x = \sin 2x + \sin 4x$.*

$$\sin x + \sin 5x = 2 \sin 3x \cos 2x.$$
$$\sin 2x + \sin 4x = 2 \sin 3x \cos x.$$
$$\therefore \quad 2 \sin 3x \cos 2x = 2 \sin 3x \cos x.$$

So either $\qquad \sin 3x = 0 \quad \text{or} \quad \cos 2x = \cos x$.

If $\sin 3x = 0$,

$$3x = n\pi \quad \text{and} \quad x = \frac{n\pi}{3}.$$

If $\cos 2x = \cos x$,

$$2x = 2n\pi \pm x.$$
$$\therefore \quad 3x = 2n\pi \quad \text{or} \quad x = 2n\pi$$

i.e.

$$x = \frac{2n\pi}{3} \quad \text{or} \quad 2n\pi.$$

The solutions $x = \dfrac{2n\pi}{3}$ are all contained in $\dfrac{n\pi}{3}$. For example the value obtained by putting $n = 5$ in $\dfrac{2n\pi}{3}$ is also obtained by putting $n = 10$ in $\dfrac{n\pi}{3}$.

Similarly $x = \dfrac{n\pi}{3}$ contains the solutions $2n\pi$.

So the general solution is $x = \dfrac{n\pi}{3}$.

Exercise 6.4

Find the general solutions of the following equations:

1. $\sin x + \sin 5x = \sin 3x$.
2. $\cos x + \cos 5x = \cos 3x$.
3. $\sin 5x - \sin x = \cos 3x$.
4. $\cos x - \cos 5x = \sin 3x$.
5. $\sin 2x + \sin 6x = \sin 4x$.
6. $\sin 6x - \sin 2x = \cos 4x$.
7. $\cos 2x + \cos 6x = \cos 4x$.
8. $\cos 2x - \cos 6x = \sin 4x$.
9. $\cos x + \cos 2x = 2 \cos \dfrac{3x}{2}$.
10. $\cos x - \cos 2x = 2 \sin \dfrac{3x}{2}$.
11. $\sin x + \sin 2x = 2 \sin \dfrac{3x}{2}$.
12. $\sin 2x - \sin x = 2 \cos \dfrac{3x}{2}$.
13. $\sin x + \sin 2x + \sin 4x + \sin 5x = 0$.
14. $\cos \alpha + \cos 2x + \cos 4x + \cos 5x = 0$.
15. $\sin x + \sin 5x = \sin 2x + \sin 4x$.
16. $\cos x + \cos 5x = \cos 2x + \cos 4x$.
17. $\sin x + \sin 3x + \sin 5x + \sin 7x = 0$.
18. $\cos x + \cos 3x + \cos 5x + \cos 7x = 0$.
19. $\sin x + \sin 7x = \sin 3x + \sin 5x$.
20. $\cos x + \cos 7x = \cos 3x + \cos 5x$.

Exercise 6.5: Miscellaneous

1. Find the general solutions of the equations
   (i) $\cos \theta = -\frac{1}{2}$, (ii) $\cos 2\theta = -\frac{1}{2}$.
2. Find the general solution of the equation $3 \sin x = 8 \cot x$.
3. Find the general solution of the equation $\sin \theta = -\cos 22°$.
4. Solve generally the equation $\sin 2\theta = \tan \theta$.
5. Using the formula $\tan 3\theta = \dfrac{3 \tan \theta - \tan^3 \theta}{1 - 3 \tan^2 \theta}$, show that the roots of the equation $t^3 - 3t^2 - 3t + 1 = 0$ are $\tan \dfrac{\pi}{12}$, and $\tan \dfrac{5\pi}{12}$ and $\tan \dfrac{3\pi}{4}$. Hence find the value of $\tan \dfrac{\pi}{12}$.
6. Find the roots to $t^3 + 3t^2 - 3t - 1 = 0$ in terms of the tangents of angles.
7. Find the general solution of the equation $24 \sin x + 7 \cos x = 10$.
8. Find the general solution of the equation
   $$\cos x + \cos 2x + \cos 3x = 0.$$
9. If α and β are solutions of the equation $a \cos x + b \sin x = c$, which do not differ by a multiple of 2π, find the value of $\tan \dfrac{\alpha + \beta}{2}$.
10. With the information given in question 9, show that $\sin (\alpha + \beta) = \dfrac{2ab}{a^2 + b^2}$ and find the value of $\cos (\alpha + \beta)$.

11. Find the general solution of $\cot \theta = \cot 280°$.

12. Find the general solution of $6 \sin \theta - \cos \theta = 2$.

13. Find the general value of θ given that $\cos \theta = \frac{3}{5}$ and $\sin \theta = \frac{4}{5}$.

14. Find the general value of θ given that $\cos \theta = -\frac{3}{5}$ and $\sin \theta = \frac{4}{5}$.

15. Find all the values of θ which satisfy the equation
$$\cos \left(\theta - \frac{\pi}{3} \right) = \sin \left(\theta + \frac{\pi}{3} \right)$$

16. Find all the values of θ which satisfy the equation $\cos \theta + \sin \theta = 1$.

17. Prove that $\tan 4\theta = \dfrac{4 \tan \theta (1 - \tan^2 \theta)}{1 - 6 \tan^2 \theta + \tan^4 \theta}$.

Hence find the roots of the equation $t^4 + 4t^3 - 6t^2 + 1 = 0$.

18. Using the result of question 17, show that
$$\tan \frac{\pi}{16} + \tan \frac{5\pi}{16} - \tan \frac{3\pi}{16} - \tan \frac{7\pi}{16} = -4.$$

19. Show that $\tan \dfrac{\pi}{16} \tan \dfrac{5\pi}{16} \tan \dfrac{3\pi}{16} \tan \dfrac{7\pi}{16} = 1$.

20. If $\sin A = \cos (B + C)$, express A in terms of B and C.

21. If $\sin A = -\cos (B + C)$, express A in terms of B and C.

22. Prove that $\sin 4\theta = \dfrac{4 \tan \theta (1 - \tan^2 \theta)}{(1 + \tan^2 \theta)^2}$.

Hence find the roots of the equation $t^4 + 8t^3 + 2t^2 - 8t + 1 = 0$.

23. Using the result of question 22, show that
$$\tan \frac{\pi}{24} \tan \frac{5\pi}{24} \tan \frac{7\pi}{24} \tan \frac{11\pi}{24} = 1.$$

24. Find the general solution of the equation $4 \sin^3 \theta - 3 \sin \theta + 1 = 0$.

25. Find the general solution of the equation $4 \cos^3 \theta - 3 \cos \theta + 1 = 0$.

26. Find the general solution of the equation
$$(\cos \theta + \sin \theta)(1 - 2 \sin 2\theta) = 2(\cos 3\theta - \sin 3\theta).$$

27. Find the general solution of the equation
$$\sin \theta + \cos \theta = \sec \theta + \operatorname{cosec} \theta.$$

28. Given that $\cos 3\theta = \cos 3\alpha$, express θ in terms of α. What are the possible values of $\cos \theta$?

29. Given that $\sin 3\theta = \sin 3\alpha$, express θ in terms of α. What are the possible values of $\sin \theta$?

30. Solve generally the equation $\tan 5\theta - \tan \theta = 1 + \tan 5\theta \tan \theta$.

Revision Paper A1

1. Write down the first four terms in the expansion of $(1 + x)^8$ in ascending powers of x.

   Evaluate $(1.001)^8 - (0.999)^8$ to 8 significant figures. (C.)

2. With $\log_{10} 2$ denoted by p, write in terms of p

   (i) $\log_{10} 8$, (ii) $\log_2 10$, (iii) $\log_2 5$, (iv) $\log_5 2$, (v) $\log_{125} 128$. (A.E.B.)

3. Find all solutions in the interval $0 < x < 2\pi$ of the equation $\sin x = \cos 2x$.

4. Find the set of values of x for which

$$x^2 - 6x + 10 < 2.$$

5. Given that $y = x(300 - x^2)$, find the maximum value of y. Show that your value is a maximum by

   (a) considering the sign of dy/dx,
   (b) considering d^2y/dx^2.

6. Calculate the area of the finite region bounded by the curve $y = x(3 - x)$ and the straight line $y = x$.

7. Given that $x - 1$ is a factor of the polynomial

$$2x^3 + kx^2 - x - 6$$

   find k. What are the other linear factors of the polynomial for this value of k? (S.M.P.)

8. Given that

$$A = \begin{pmatrix} 2 & 1 \\ 3 & 4 \end{pmatrix} \quad \text{and} \quad I = \begin{pmatrix} 1 & 0 \\ 0 & 1 \end{pmatrix},$$

   find real numbers t and x such that

$$A(A - tI) = xI. \qquad \text{(M.E.I.)}$$

9. Find the values of the scalar α if the two vectors $\mathbf{p} = (2, -3, 5)$, $\mathbf{q} = (3, \alpha, -3)$ are inclined to each other at an angle of

   (i) $\frac{1}{2}\pi$, (ii) $\frac{2}{3}\pi$. (M.E.I.)

10. In one diagram, sketch three lines

$$x + y - 3 = 0, \quad y - 2x - 4 = 0, \quad y - \frac{x}{2} + 2 = 0.$$

   Indicate, by shading on your diagram, the region in which the following three inequalities are all satisfied, marking this region with a large X:

$$x + y - 3 > 0, \quad y - 2x - 4 > 0, \quad y - \frac{x}{2} + 2 > 0. \qquad \text{(L.)}$$

Revision Paper A2

1. Given that
$$y = ax^2 + bx + c,$$
that $y = 8$ when $x = 1$ and that $y = 2$ when $x = -1$, show that $b = 3$ and find a in terms of c.
   Find the range of values of c for which $y > 0$ for all real values of x.

   (J.M.B.)

2. The equations $ax^2 + bx + c = 0$ and $bx^2 + ax + c = 0$, where $a \neq b$, $c \neq 0$, have a common root. Prove that $a + b + c = 0$.   (L.)

3. Establish the formula
$$\log_y x = \frac{1}{\log_x y}.$$
   Solve the simultaneous equations
$$\log_x y + 2 \log_y x = 3,$$
$$\log_9 y + \log_9 x = 3.$$
   (J.M.B.)

4. Use Simpson's rule with five ordinates to estimate $\int_1^2 (x^3 + 1)^{\frac{1}{2}}\, dx$, giving your answer to 3 decimal places.   (A.E.B.)

5. (i) Find the term independent of x in the expansion of
$$\left(\frac{1}{3x} - \frac{3}{2}x^2\right)^9.$$
   (ii) If x^3 and higher powers of x may be neglected, express
$$\left(1 + \frac{5x}{2} - \frac{3x^2}{2}\right)^8$$
   in the form $1 + ax + bx^2$.   (L.)

6. Write down the sum to n terms, S_n, and the sum to infinity, S, of the geometric series
$$a + ar + ar^2 + \ldots$$
   and state the range of values of r for which S exists.
   Show that, if $a > 0$, then $S > 4ar$ except for one value of r and state this exceptional value.
   Find all the real values of a and r for which $S_4 = 40$ and $S = \frac{81}{2}$.
   (M.E.I.)

7.

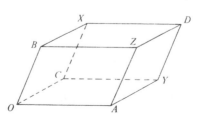

The origin of position vectors is O, and points A, B, C are given by

$$\mathbf{OA} = 5\mathbf{i}, \quad \mathbf{OB} = \mathbf{i} + 3\mathbf{k}, \quad \mathbf{OC} = \mathbf{i} + 4\mathbf{j}.$$

A parallelepiped has OA, OB, OC as three edges, and the remaining vertices are X, Y, Z and D as shown in the diagram.

(i) Write down the position vectors of X, Y, Z and D in terms of $\mathbf{i}$, $\mathbf{j}$, $\mathbf{k}$, and calculate the length of OD.

(ii) Calculate the size of angle OZY.

(iii) The point P divides CZ in the ratio $\lambda:1$. Write down the position vector of P, and evaluate λ if OP is perpendicular to CZ.   (C.)

8. Of the following equations, which represent lines and which represent planes?

(i) $\dfrac{x-2}{1} = \dfrac{y-1}{2} = \dfrac{z-3}{-1}$;

(ii) $x + 2y - z = 1$;

(iii) $\begin{pmatrix} x \\ y \\ z \end{pmatrix} = \begin{pmatrix} 2 \\ 1 \\ 3 \end{pmatrix} + t\begin{pmatrix} 1 \\ -1 \\ -1 \end{pmatrix}.$

Describe, or show in a clear diagram, how these lines and planes are related to each other.   (S.M.P.)

9. Find the solutions of the equation

$$\cos(40° + x) = 3\sin(50° + x)$$

between $0°$ and $360°$.   (L.)

10. Find all the angles between $0°$ and $360°$ which satisfy the following equations:

(i) $\sin\theta = \tan 340°$;

(ii) $\cos 2\theta = \sin\theta$;

(iii) $10\sin\theta - 24\cos\theta = 13$.   (O. & C.)

Revision Paper A3

1. Find in how many ways a jury of 12 may be chosen from 8 men and 9 women. Show that the number of juries on which women are in the majority is rather more than $\frac{3}{7}$ of the total. (L.)

2. The probability that a blue-eyed person is left-handed is $\frac{1}{7}$. The probability that a left-handed person is blue-eyed is $\frac{1}{3}$. The probability that a person has neither of these attributes is $\frac{4}{5}$. What is the probability that a person has both? (S.M.P.)

3. If $A = \begin{pmatrix} 2 & a \\ 0 & 1 \end{pmatrix}$, prove by induction that for every positive integer n

$$A^n = \begin{pmatrix} 2^n & (2^n - 1)a \\ 0 & 1 \end{pmatrix}.$$

   Determine whether this is true when $n = -1$.

4. Find the general solutions in radians of the following equations
   (i) $2 \sin 3\theta - 7 \cos 2\theta + \sin \theta + 1 = 0$,
   (ii) $\cos \theta - \sin 2\theta + \cos 3\theta - \sin 4\theta = 0$. (C.)

5. Find the coefficient of x^5, and the term independent of x, in the binomial expansion of $\left(\dfrac{x^2}{2} - \dfrac{3}{x^3} \right)^{10}$. (L.)

6. How many numbers greater than one million can be formed using as digits the figures 5, 5, 5, 5, 4, 4, 2? How many of these numbers are divisible by 4? (J.M.B.)

7. Obtain the expansion of $(1 + x)^{10}(1 - 2x)^2$ in ascending powers of x up to and including the term in x^4. Evaluate the expression $(1.02)^{10}(0.96)^2$ to four decimal places. (C.)

8. Find all solutions between $0°$ and $360°$ of the equations
   (i) $\cos x + \cos 3x = \cos 2x$;
   (ii) $3 \cos x + 4 \sin x = 4.2$. (J.M.B.)

9. Find $\operatorname{Lt}_{x \to 0} \dfrac{1 - \cos 2x}{x^2}$.

10. The functions f, g are defined for $x > 0$ by
$$f : x \to x^2,$$
$$g : x \to \ln x.$$

   Sketch and label the graphs of g, fg and g^{-1} on the same axes, using the same scale. (A.E.B.)

Revision Paper A4

1. A box contains 9 discs, of which 4 are red, 3 are white and 2 are blue. Three discs are to be drawn at random without replacement from the box. Calculate:
   (i) the probability that the discs, in the order drawn, will be coloured red, white and blue, respectively,
   (ii) the probability that one disc of each colour will be drawn,
   (iii) the probability that the third disc drawn will be red,
   (iv) the probability that no red disc will be drawn,
   (v) the most probable number of red discs that will be drawn. (J.M.B.)

2. An analysis of the other subjects taken by A-level Mathematics candidates in a certain year showed that 20 per cent of them took Further Mathematics, 50 per cent took Physics and 5 per cent took both Further Mathematics and Physics. A candidate is chosen at random from those who took A-level Mathematics.
   (i) Calculate the probability that the chosen candidate took neither Further Mathematics nor Physics.
   (ii) Given that the chosen candidate took at least one of Further Mathematics and Physics, calculate the probability that the candidate took Further Mathematics. (J.M.B.)

3. (i) From a bag containing 4 red, 5 white, 6 blue and 7 black balls four are drawn at random without replacement.
   Find the probability of their being

   (a) all of the same colour,
   (b) all of different colours.

   (ii) Two six-faced dice with faces numbered 1 to 6 respectively are thrown together. What is the most likely value of the total score and what is the probability of the score being greater than this value?
   (O. & C.)

4. Prove by induction that the sum of n terms of the series whose rth term is $r(r + 2)(r + 4)$ is $\dfrac{n(n + 1)(n + 4)(n + 5)}{4}$.

5. Find $\mathrm{Lt}_{x \to 1} \dfrac{x^n - x}{x^m - x}$.

6. Find how many different numbers between 100 and 999 can be formed from the digits 0, 4, 5, 6, 7, 8, no digit being used more than once. How many of these are odd? (C.)

7. Find values of a, b, c, d, independent of r such that
$$5r^4 + r^2 \equiv ar^2(r + 1)^3 + br^3(r + 1)^2 + cr^2(r - 1)^3 + dr^3(r - 1)^2.$$
Hence or otherwise prove that
$$\sum_{r=1}^{n} r^4 = \tfrac{1}{30}n(n + 1)(2n + 1)(3n^2 + 3n - 1).$$
(C.)

8. Solve the equations:
   (i) $\sin^2 2\theta = 0.04$,
   (ii) $\sin \theta + \cos \theta + \sec \theta + \csc \theta = 0$,
   stating the solutions of (i) which lie between $90°$ and $270°$, and the solutions of (ii) which lie between $-180°$ and $+180°$.   (O. & C.)

9. Find (in radian measure) all the values of θ which satisfy the equation $\cos 3\theta = \sin 2\theta$.

   Prove that one of the values of $\sin \theta$ is $\sin \dfrac{\pi}{10}$ and find the remaining values of $\sin \theta$.

   Prove that $\sin \dfrac{\pi}{10} = \tfrac{1}{4}(\sqrt{5} - 1)$

   and find the corresponding expression for $\sin \dfrac{3\pi}{10}$.   (O. & C.)

10. Determine whether each of the three functions, f, g, h defined in $\mathbb{R}$ is an even function, an odd function or neither, given that
$$f(x) = \pi/2 - \sin(x/2),$$
$$g(x) = \pi/2 - \cos(x/3),$$
$$h(x) = \cos(\sin x).$$
   Determine the period, if it exists, of each of the two functions
$$G(x) = g(x) - f(x),$$
$$H(x) = g(x) - h(x) + \sin[f(2x)].$$ (L.)

Revision Paper A5

1. An experiment is performed with a die and two packs of cards. The die is thrown, and if it shows 1, 2, 3 or 4 a card is drawn at random from the first pack, which contains the usual 52 cards; if the score on the die is 5 or 6 a card is drawn from the second pack, which contains only 39 cards, all the clubs having been removed. X denotes the event 'The first pack with 52 cards is used', and Y denotes the event 'The card drawn is a diamond'. Calculate the probabilities

   (i) $P(X)$, (ii) $P(X \cap Y)$, (iii) $P(Y)$, (iv) $P(Y|X)$, (v) $P(X|Y)$. (C.)

2. A and B are events, and A' denotes the complementary event to A (i.e. A' is the event that occurs whenever A does not occur). The following probabilities are given: $P(A) = 0.4$, $P(B|A) = 0.7$, $P(A' \cap B) = 0.3$. Find the probabilities (i) $P(A \cap B)$, (ii) $P(B)$, (iii) $P(A \cup B)$, (iv) $P(A|B)$.

   State, with a reason, whether or not A and B are independent events.   (C.)

3. A faulty gas-lighter works successfully, on average, once in three attempts. When using it one goes on trying until it does work and the gas lights.

   What is the probability that the gas lights (i) first time, (ii) second time, (iii) at the fifth attempt?

   What is the probability that it will not have worked after five attempts?

   The sellers of the lighter promise that if one is returned, they will pay 25p for each time it fails to work before the gas is lit. What is one's expectation in taking up this offer? What is the probability of getting one's money back (or more) if the original price was £1?

   If four people take up this offer, what is the probability that at least two get their money back (or more)?   (A.E.B.)

4. Prove by induction
$$3^{4n} + 2^{4n+1} \equiv 3 \pmod 5.$$

5. A pack of 52 playing cards contains 20 honours. Show that a selection of three cards from the pack can be made in 22 100 different ways and that 4960 of these contain no honour. Deduce the probability that a particular selection of three cards contains at least one honour.   (C.)

6. Find how many three-letter code words can be made with the 26 letters of the alphabet
   (i) when no letter is used more than once in the word,
   (ii) when any letter may be repeated two or three times in the same word,
   (iii) when every word contains exactly one vowel and no letter more than once.   (C.)

7. Prove by induction that
$$\sum_1^n \frac{r^2 + 3r + 1}{r^2(r+1)^2} = \frac{n(2n+3)}{(n+1)^2}.$$

8. (i) Prove that $\dfrac{\sin \alpha + \sin \beta}{\cos \alpha - \cos \beta} = \cot \dfrac{\beta - \alpha}{2}$.

(ii) If $\dfrac{\sin (\alpha + \beta)}{\sin (\alpha - \beta)} = \dfrac{3}{2}$, prove that $\tan \alpha = 5 \tan \beta$.   (C.)

9. The functions f and g are defined over the real numbers by

$$f : x \to 2 - x,$$

$$g : x \to \frac{2}{x} \quad (x \neq 0).$$

Show that each of the functions is its own inverse and verify that the inverse of $f \circ g$ is $g \circ f$.

Show that there are no invariant values of $f \circ g$.   (A.E.B.)

10. The functions f and g are defined by

$$f : x \to \cos x \quad (0 \leqslant x \leqslant \pi),$$
$$g : x \to \tan x \quad (0 \leqslant x \leqslant \tfrac{1}{2}\pi).$$

Sketch separate graphs of each of f, g and f^{-1}.

State, giving your reasons, whether $f^{-1}g$ and $g^{-1}f$ exist.

Solve the equation $f(x) = g(x)$, giving two decimal places in your answer.   (C.)

7 Logarithmic and Exponential Functions

Revision

The following formulae connecting logarithms were proved in *Additional Pure Mathematics*.

1. $\log_a x + \log_a y = \log_a xy.$

2. $\log_a x - \log_a y = \log_a \dfrac{x}{y}.$

3. $\log_a x^n = n \log_a x.$

4. $\log_b x = \dfrac{\log_a x}{\log_a b}.$

The graph of $\log_{10} x$

Values of $\log_{10} x$ can easily be found for the following values of x:

x	10	$10^{\frac{3}{4}}$ (5.62)	$10^{\frac{1}{2}}$ (3.16)	$10^{\frac{1}{4}}$ (1.78)	1	0.1	0.01
$\log_{10} x$	1	0.75	0.5	0.25	0	-1	-2

From these values the graph of $\log_{10} x$ can be drawn and a sketch is given in Fig. 7.1.

Remember that $\log_{10} x$ does not exist for negative values of x.

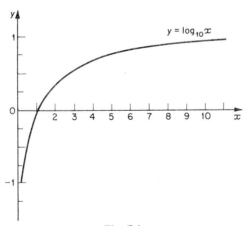

Fig. 7.1

The differential coefficient of $\log_{10} x$

From the definition of a differential coefficient given on page 48,

$$\frac{d}{dx}(\log_{10} x) = \text{Lt}_{h\to 0} \frac{\log_{10}(x+h) - \log_{10} x}{h}$$

$$= \text{Lt}_{h\to 0} \frac{\log_{10}\left(\dfrac{x+h}{x}\right)}{h}$$

$$= \text{Lt}_{h\to 0} \frac{1}{h}\log_{10}\left(1 + \frac{h}{x}\right)$$

$$= \text{Lt}_{h\to 0} \log_{10}\left(1 + \frac{h}{x}\right)^{1/h}.$$

Put $\dfrac{h}{x} = k$ so that $k \to 0$ as $h \to 0$ and $h = kx$.

Then
$$\frac{d}{dx}(\log_{10} x) = \text{Lt}_{k\to 0} \log_{10}(1+k)^{1/kx}$$

$$= \text{Lt}_{k\to 0} \frac{1}{x}\log_{10}(1+k)^{1/k}$$

But we have already seen (page 47) that $(1+k)^{1/k} \to e$ as $k \to 0$.

$$\therefore \quad \frac{d}{dx}(\log_{10} x) = \frac{1}{x}\log_{10} e.$$

The differential coefficient of $\log_a x$

$$\log_a x = \frac{\log_{10} x}{\log_{10} a}$$

by the formula for change of base.

$$\therefore \quad \frac{d}{dx}(\log_a x) = \frac{\dfrac{1}{x}\log_{10} e}{\log_{10} a}$$

$$= \frac{1}{x}\log_a e.$$

In the special case when $a = e$, since $\log_e e = 1$, we have

$$\frac{d}{dx}(\log_e x) = \frac{1}{x}.$$

Logarithms to base e are called natural logarithms or Napierian logarithms after John Napier (1550–1617) who in his *Mirifici Logarithmorum Canonis Descriptio* inspired Briggs to develop the system of common logarithms with the decimal base. Throughout the remainder of this book $\log_e$ will be abbreviated ln.

It follows that
$$\int \frac{1}{x} \, dx = \ln x + c.*$$

Example 1. *Differentiate* $\ln (x^2 + x + 1)$.

The answer may be written down as the differential coefficient of a function of a function but is done from first principles as a reminder.

Let
$$y = \ln (x^2 + x + 1)$$
and let
$$x^2 + x + 1 = z.$$

Then
$$y = \ln z \quad \text{and so} \quad \frac{dy}{dz} = \frac{1}{z}.$$

Also
$$\frac{dz}{dx} = 2x + 1.$$

$$\therefore \quad \frac{dy}{dx} = \frac{dy}{dz} \cdot \frac{dz}{dx} = \frac{2x + 1}{z} = \frac{2x + 1}{x^2 + x + 1}.$$

The differential coefficient is written down by differentiating $\ln (x^2 + x + 1)$ with respect to $(x^2 + x + 1)$ and multiplying the result by the differential coefficient of $(x^2 + x + 1)$ with respect to x.

It follows that
$$\int \frac{2x + 1}{x^2 + x + 1} \, dx = \ln (x^2 + x + 1) + c.$$

Notice here that we are integrating a fraction in which the numerator is the differential of the denominator. Whenever this occurs, the integral is the log of the denominator.

Example 2. *Differentiate* $\ln f(x)$, *where* $f(x)$ *is a function of* x, *and hence write down the value of* $\int \frac{f'(x)}{f(x)} \, dx$.

By the rule for differentiating a function of a function,
$$\frac{d}{dx} \ln f(x) = \frac{1}{f(x)} \times \frac{d}{dx} f(x)$$
$$= \frac{f'(x)}{f(x)}.$$

From this follows the general statement
$$\int \frac{f'(x)}{f(x)} \, dx = \ln f(x) + c.$$

---

* We have taken x positive, and strictly
$$\int \frac{1}{x} \, dx = \ln |x| + C.$$

Example 3. *Find* $\int \dfrac{x^2}{1 + x^3}\, dx.$

$$\int \frac{x^2}{1 + x^3}\, dx = \frac{1}{3} \int \frac{3x^2}{1 + x^3}\, dx.$$

The numerator of this fraction is the differential of the denominator and so the integral is $\frac{1}{3} \ln (1 + x^3) + c$.

Example 4. *Differentiate* $\ln \sqrt[3]{(1 + 5x)}.$

$$\ln \sqrt[3]{(1 + 5x)} = \ln (1 + 5x)^{1/3} = \frac{1}{3} \ln (1 + 5x)$$

$$\therefore \quad \frac{d}{dx} \ln \sqrt[3]{(1 + 5x)} = \frac{1}{3} \cdot \frac{5}{1 + 5x} = \frac{5}{3(1 + 5x)}.$$

Integrals of tan *x* and cot *x*

We are now able to integrate tan x and cot x.

$$\int \tan x \, dx = \int \frac{\sin x}{\cos x}\, dx = - \int \frac{d(\cos x)}{\cos x} = - \ln \cos x + c$$

$$= \ln \sec x + c.$$

$$\int \cot x \, dx = \int \frac{\cos x}{\sin x}\, dx = \int \frac{d(\sin x)}{\sin x} = \ln \sin x + c.$$

If x is replaced by $(ax + b)$, we have

$$\int \tan (ax + b) \, d(ax + b) = \ln \sec (ax + b) + c.$$

But $$d(ax + b) = a \, dx.$$

$$\therefore \quad a \int \tan (ax + b) \, dx = \ln \sec (ax + b) + c.$$

$$\therefore \quad \int \tan (ax + b) \, dx = \frac{1}{a} \ln \sec (ax + b) + c.$$

Similarly $$\int \cot (ax + b) \, dx = \frac{1}{a} \ln \sin (ax + b) + c.$$

Example 1. *Find* $\int \tan 2x \, dx.$

$$\int \tan 2x \, dx = \tfrac{1}{2} \ln \sec 2x + c.$$

Example 2. *Find* $\int \cot (1 - 3x) \, dx.$

$$\int \cot (1 - 3x) \, dx = - \tfrac{1}{3} \ln \sin (1 - 3x) + c.$$

Exercise 7.1

Differentiate with respect to x:

1. $\ln (x^3 + 1)$. **2.** $\ln \sin x$. **3.** $\ln \operatorname{cosec} x$.

4. $\ln (x^n + 1)$. **5.** $\ln (1 + x)(1 + 2x)$. **6.** $\log_{10} x^2$.

7. $\log_a x^3$. **8.** $\ln (1 - x)^3$. **9.** $\ln \sqrt{(1 + 2x)}$.

10. $\ln \sqrt[3]{(1 - x)}$. **11.** $\ln \sqrt{\sin x}$. **12.** $\ln \sqrt{\cos x}$.

13. $\ln \sqrt{(x^2 + x + 1)}$. **14.** $\ln (a + bx)$. **15.** $(\ln x)^2$.

16. $(\ln x)^3$. **17.** $\sqrt{\ln x}$. **18.** $\dfrac{1}{\ln x}$.

19. $\dfrac{1}{(\ln x)^2}$. **20.** $(\ln \sin x)^2$.

Integrate with respect to x:

21. $\dfrac{1}{x + 1}$. **22.** $\dfrac{1}{2x + 1}$. **23.** $\dfrac{1}{3x + 2}$.

24. $\dfrac{1}{1 - x}$. **25.** $\dfrac{1}{1 - 3x}$. **26.** $\dfrac{x^3}{x^4 + 1}$.

27. $\dfrac{x + 1}{x^2 + 2x + 5}$. **28.** $\tan 2x$. **29.** $\cot (x + 1)$.

30. $\tan (1 - 2x)$. **31.** $\dfrac{x + 2}{x^2 + 4x + 1}$. **32.** $\dfrac{1}{x} - \dfrac{1}{x + 1}$.

33. $\dfrac{x}{x + 1}$. **34.** $\dfrac{x}{x^2 + 1}$. **35.** $\dfrac{\cos x}{1 + \sin x}$.

36. $\dfrac{1}{x \log x}$. **37.** $\dfrac{x - 1}{x + 1}$. **38.** $\dfrac{\sin x}{1 - \cos x}$.

39. Evaluate $\displaystyle\int_1^2 \dfrac{1}{1 + x}\, dx$. **40.** Evaluate $\displaystyle\int_2^3 \dfrac{x}{1 + x^2}\, dx$.

The exponential function

The function $f : x \mapsto a^x$ where a is a constant is called an exponential function although the term is most often used in dealing with the particular case $f : x \mapsto e^x$.

If $$y = a^x,$$

then $$\ln y = x \ln a \quad \text{(taking logs to base e)}.$$

$$\therefore \quad \frac{1}{y} \frac{dy}{dx} = \ln a$$

or $$\frac{dy}{dx} = y \ln a = a^x \ln a.$$

$$\therefore \quad \frac{d}{dx} (a^x) = a^x \ln a.$$

Putting $a = e$, we have

$$\frac{d}{dx}(e^x) = e^x, \quad \text{since } \ln e = 1.$$

$f : x \mapsto k\,e^x$ is the only function which remains unaltered on differentiation. This may be proved as follows.

If
$$\frac{dy}{dx} = y,$$

$$\frac{dy}{y} = dx \quad \text{and} \quad \int \frac{dy}{y} = \int dx.$$

$$\therefore \quad \ln y = x + c$$

and
$$y = e^{x+c} = e^x \cdot e^c \quad \text{or} \quad A\,e^x.$$

More generally, if the rate of change of a function is always directly proportional to the function, we have

$$\frac{dy}{dt} = ky \quad \text{or} \quad \frac{dy}{y} = k\,dt.$$

Integrating, $\ln y = kt + c \quad \text{or} \quad y = A\,e^{kt}.$

Examples of this law are:

1. Newton's Law of Cooling

This states that the rate of temperature loss of a cooling body is proportional to the difference of temperature between the body and its surroundings. This involves a 'decay' factor e^{-kt}.

2. Leakage in an electric condenser

The leakage from a condenser under charge is proportional to the charge.

3. Growth of a colony

The growth of a biological colony is proportional to the population.

Example 1. $\dfrac{d}{dx}(e^{ax^2}) = e^{ax^2} \times \dfrac{d}{dx}(ax^2) = 2ax\,e^{ax^2}.$

Example 2. $\dfrac{d}{dx}(e^{\sin x}) = e^{\sin x} \times \dfrac{d}{dx}(\sin x) = \cos x\,e^{\sin x}.$

Example 3. $\dfrac{d}{dx}(e^{\tan 3x}) = e^{\tan 3x} \times \dfrac{d}{dx}(\tan 3x)$

$$= e^{\tan 3x} \sec^2 3x \times \frac{d}{dx}(3x)$$

$$= 3\sec^2 3x\,e^{\tan 3x}$$

Example 4. $\dfrac{d}{dx}(x^2\,e^x) = x^2\,\dfrac{d}{dx}(e^x) + e^x\,\dfrac{d}{dx}(x^2) = e^x(x^2 + 2x).$

The integral of e^{kx}

Since $\dfrac{d}{dx}(e^x) = e^x,$ it follows that $\displaystyle\int e^x\,dx = e^x + c.$

Since $\dfrac{d}{dx}(e^{kx}) = k\,e^{kx},$ it follows that $\displaystyle\int e^{kx}\,dx = \dfrac{e^{kx}}{k} + c.$

Example 1. *Integrate* $\displaystyle\int e^{\sin x}\cos x\,dx.$

Put $\sin x = y$ so that $\cos x\,dx = dy.$

Then $\displaystyle\int e^{\sin x}\cos x\,dx = \int e^y\,dy = e^y + c = e^{\sin x} + c.$

Example 2. *Integrate* $\displaystyle\int x\,e^{1+x^2}\,dx.$

Put $1 + x^2 = z$ so that $dz = 2x\,dx.$

$$\int x\,e^{1+x^2}\,dx = \tfrac{1}{2}\int e^z\,dz = \tfrac{1}{2}e^z + c = \tfrac{1}{2}e^{1+x^2} + c.$$

Exercise 7.2

Differentiate with respect to x:

1. $e^{\sqrt{x}}$.
2. $e^{\cos x}$.
3. $e^{\tan x}$.
4. e^{5x}.

5. $x\,e^x$.
6. $\sin x\,e^x$.
7. $\dfrac{e^x}{x}$.
8. $x\,e^{4x}$.

9. $x\,e^{\sin x}$.
10. $(x + 1)e^x$.
11. a^{4x}.
12. $a^{\sin x}$.

13. 3^x.
14. $3^{\cos x}$.
15. $e^x \ln x$.
16. $x\,e^x \ln x$.

17. e^{1-x}.
18. e^{a-bx}.
19. $x^2\,e^{-x}$.
20. $\sin x\,e^{-x}$.

Integrate with respect to x:

21. e^{4x}.
22. e^{ax+b}.
23. e^{-x}.
24. e^{1-x}.

25. $x^2\,e^{1+x^2}$.
26. $\dfrac{1}{\sqrt{x}}\,e^{\sqrt{x}}$.
27. $\sec^2 x\,e^{\tan x}$.
28. 4^x.

29. a^x.
30. 4^{1-x}.
31. $(1 + x)\,e^{x^2+2x}$.

32. $\dfrac{1}{x}\,e^{\log x}$.
33. e^{5x-3}.
34. $x\,e^{x^2}$.
35. $\dfrac{e^{1/x}}{x^2}$.

36. Evaluate $\displaystyle\int_1^2 e^{2x}\,dx.$

37. Evaluate $\displaystyle\int_2^3 x\,e^{x^2}\,dx.$

38. If $\dfrac{dy}{dx} = 3y$ and $y = 1$ when $x = 0$, show that $y = e^{3x}$.

39. If $\dfrac{dy}{dx} = -2y$ and $y = 2$ when $x = 0$, show that $y = 2e^{-2x}$.

40. If $\dfrac{dy}{dx} = ky$, show that $y = y_0\, e^{kx}$ where y_0 is the value of y when $x = 0$.

Logarithmic differentiation

Complicated products and quotients are often best differentiated by taking logarithms before differentiation.

Example 1. *Differentiate* $\dfrac{(1 + 2x)\sqrt{(1 + x)}}{1 - x}$.

Let
$$y = \frac{(1 + 2x)\sqrt{(1 + x)}}{1 - x}.$$

Then
$$\ln y = \ln(1 + 2x) + \tfrac{1}{2}\ln(1 + x) - \ln(1 - x).$$

$$\frac{1}{y}\frac{dy}{dx} = \frac{2}{1 + 2x} + \frac{1}{2(1 + x)} + \frac{1}{1 - x}$$

$$= \frac{4(1 + x)(1 - x) + (1 + 2x)(1 - x) + 2(1 + 2x)(1 + x)}{2(1 + 2x)(1 + x)(1 - x)}$$

$$= \frac{7 + 7x - 2x^2}{2(1 + 2x)(1 + x)(1 - x)}$$

$$\therefore \quad \frac{dy}{dx} = \frac{7 + 7x - 2x^2}{2(1 + 2x)(1 + x)(1 - x)} \times \frac{(1 + 2x)\sqrt{(1 + x)}}{1 - x}$$

$$= \frac{7 + 7x - 2x^2}{2(1 - x)^2\sqrt{(1 + x)}}.$$

Example 2. *Differentiate* $x^{\sin x}$.

This cannot be differentiated by applying the rules for differentiating x^n or a^x.

Let
$$y = x^{\sin x}.$$
$$\ln y = \sin x \ln x.$$

$$\therefore \quad \frac{1}{y}\frac{dy}{dx} = \cos x \ln\, x + \frac{\sin x}{x}.$$

$$\therefore \quad \frac{dy}{dx} = \left(\cos x \ln x + \frac{\sin x}{x}\right) x^{\sin x}.$$

Exercise 7.3

Differentiate with respect to x:

1. $\dfrac{x - 1}{x + 1}$. **2.** $\sqrt{\dfrac{x - 1}{x + 1}}$. **3.** $\dfrac{x^2 - 1}{x^2 + 1}$. **4.** $\sqrt{\dfrac{x^2 - 1}{x^2 + 1}}$.

5. $\dfrac{(x-1)(x-2)}{x-3}$. **6.** $\sqrt{\dfrac{(x-1)(x-2)}{x-3}}$. **7.** x^x.

8. $x^{\ln x}$. **9.** $(\ln x)^x$. **10.** x^{1-x}.

Exercise 7.4: Miscellaneous

1. Find the maximum value of $\dfrac{\ln x}{x}$.

2. The distance s metres travelled by a particle in time t seconds is given by $s = t \, e^{-\frac{1}{2}t^2}$. Show that the velocity in m s^{-1} is given by
$$e^{-\frac{1}{2}t^2}(1 - t^2).$$

3. Differentiate $e^{ax} \sin bx$ with respect to x.

4. If $y = (1 + x)^2 \ln (1 + x)$, find $\dfrac{dy}{dx}$.

5. If $y = e^{2x} \cos x$, show that $\dfrac{d^2 y}{dx^2} - 4\dfrac{dy}{dx} + 5y = 0$.

6. If x, y, z are consecutive terms of a geometric progression, show that $\log x + \log z = 2 \log y$.

7. If $y = \dfrac{e^x}{1 + x^2}$, show that $(x^2 + 1)\dfrac{dy}{dx} = y(x - 1)^2$.

8. The distance of a point moving in a straight line from a fixed point of the line after t seconds is given by $x = e^{-t} \sin t$. Show that it is instantaneously at rest at times $t = \left(n\pi + \dfrac{\pi}{4}\right)$.

9. Differentiate $(\sin x)^x$ with respect to x.

10. Differentiate $e^{ax}(\cos bx + \sin bx)$ with respect to x.

11. Differentiate $\ln \{x + \sqrt{(x^2 + 1)}\}$ with respect to x.

12. Sketch the graph of e^{-x}.

13. Sketch the graph of $\frac{1}{2}(e^x - e^{-x})$.

14. If $y = \frac{1}{2}(e^x + e^{-x})$ and $z = \frac{1}{2}(e^x - e^{-x})$, show that $\dfrac{dy}{dx} = z$ and $\dfrac{dz}{dx} = y$.

Show also that $\displaystyle\int y \, dx = z$ and $\displaystyle\int z \, dx = y$.

15. Find $\displaystyle\int \dfrac{\sin x + \cos x}{\cos x - \sin x} dx$.

16. Sketch the graph of $e^t \sin t$ between 0 and π.

17. Given that $y = \sin(e^x - 1)$, show that $\dfrac{d^2 y}{dx^2} - \dfrac{dy}{dx} + y \, e^{2x} = 0$.

18. When the room temperature is 15°C, liquid cools from 35°C to 25°C in 5 minutes. Find how much longer it will take to cool to 20°C.

19. Find the area bounded by the axes, the curve $y = \frac{1}{2}(e^x + e^{-x})$ and the ordinate $x = 2$.

20. Find the possible values of n if $y = A\,e^{nx}$ satisfies the equation $\dfrac{d^2y}{dx^2} - 4\dfrac{dy}{dx} + 3y = 0$.

21. Find the minimum value of $\dfrac{e^x}{x}$.

22. If $e^x \sin x = \dfrac{d}{dx}\{e^x(A \sin x + B \cos x)\}$, find the values of A and B.

Hence find $\displaystyle\int e^x \sin x\, dx$.

23. Find the y-coordinate of the centroid of the region enclosed by the curve $y = e^x$, the axes and the ordinate $x = 1$.

24. Differentiate $\dfrac{(x + 1)^2(x + 2)}{(x + 3)^3}$.

25. Find the maximum value of $\dfrac{(x + 1)^2(x + 2)}{(x + 3)^3}$.

26. Differentiate logarithmically $x\,e^{ax} \sin bx$.

27. Find the area enclosed between the x-axis, the curve $xy = c^2$ and the ordinates $x = 1$ and $x = 2$.

28. Differentiate $(x - 1)\,e^x$ and hence find $\displaystyle\int x\,e^x\, dx$.

29. Find the values of A and B if

$$\frac{d}{dx}\{(x^2 + Ax + B)e^x\} = x^2\,e^x.$$

Hence find $\displaystyle\int x^2\,e^x\, dx$.

30. Using the result of question 28, find the x-coordinate of the centroid of the region enclosed by the curve $y = e^x$, the axes and the ordinate $x = 1$.

8 Partial Fractions

Linear factors in the denominator

The operation of adding fractions such as $\dfrac{2}{x + 1}$ and $\dfrac{3}{x + 2}$ is familiar to us all. We see that

$$\frac{2}{x + 1} + \frac{3}{x + 2} = \frac{2(x + 2) + 3(x + 1)}{(x + 1)(x + 2)}$$
$$= \frac{5x + 7}{(x + 1)(x + 2)}.$$

Is it possible to reverse the process, i.e. to express $\dfrac{5x + 7}{(x + 1)(x + 2)}$ as the sum of two fractions? Obviously the denominators will be $(x + 1)$ and $(x + 2)$, so let us assume the fraction is equal to $\dfrac{A}{x + 1} + \dfrac{B}{x + 2}$, where A and B are constants. Then

$$\frac{5x + 7}{(x + 1)(x + 2)} \equiv \frac{A}{x + 1} + \frac{B}{x + 2}$$

or
$$5x + 7 = A(x + 2) + B(x + 1).$$

By equating coefficients, we get two linear equations in A and B and so there is a unique solution.

The equations are
$$5 = A + B,$$
$$7 = 2A + B$$

from which
$$A = 2 \quad \text{and} \quad B = 3.$$

This process is called expressing $\dfrac{5x + 7}{(x + 1)(x + 2)}$ in its partial fractions, which are $\dfrac{2}{x + 1} + \dfrac{3}{x + 2}$.

If there were a higher power of x in the numerator, the method would fail, as the highest power of x in the numerator of the sum of $\dfrac{2}{x + 1}$ and $\dfrac{3}{x + 2}$ is unity. *If the degree of the numerator is not less than the degree of the denominator, we must first divide, then express the remainder in partial fractions (see Example 3).*

Use of identities

Notice that $5x + 7 \equiv A(x + 2) + B(x + 1)$ is an identity and so is true for all values of x. When $x = -1$, $2 = A$, and when $x = -2$, $-3 = -B$, so that $A = 2$, $B = 3$ and

$$5x + 7 = 2(x + 2) + 3(x + 1),$$

whence $\dfrac{5x + 7}{(x + 1)(x + 2)} = \dfrac{2}{(x + 1)} + \dfrac{3}{(x + 2)}$ as before.

This suggests a short cut. We can find the value of A by covering up the factor $(x + 1)$ in the original expression and giving x the value which makes this factor zero, i.e. here $x = -1$ in the remainder of the fraction.

$$\frac{5x + 7}{(\quad)(x + 2)} = \frac{2}{1}$$

so that $A = 2$. Similarly, putting $x = -2$,

$$\frac{5x + 7}{(x + 1)(\quad)} = \frac{-3}{-1}$$

so that $B = 3$. This method can always be used when there are linear factors in the denominator, providing of course that the degree of the numerator is less than that of the denominator. It is particularly useful when there are three or more linear factors in the denominator (see Example 2).

Example 1. *Express* $\dfrac{3x + 2}{(x - 1)(x + 1)}$ *in partial fractions.*

Putting $x = 1$ in $\dfrac{3x + 2}{(\quad)(x + 1)}$ gives $\dfrac{5}{2}$.

Putting $x = -1$ in $\dfrac{3x + 2}{(x - 1)(\quad)}$ gives $\dfrac{-1}{-2} = \dfrac{1}{2}$.

The partial fractions are $\dfrac{5}{2(x - 1)} + \dfrac{1}{2(x + 1)}$.

Check $\dfrac{5}{2(x - 1)} + \dfrac{1}{2(x + 1)} = \dfrac{5x + 5 + x - 1}{2(x - 1)(x + 1)} = \dfrac{6x + 4}{2(x - 1)(x + 1)}$

$$= \dfrac{3x + 2}{(x - 1)(x + 1)}.$$

Example 2. *Express* $\dfrac{x^2}{(x - 1)(x - 2)(x - 3)}$ *in its partial fractions.*

First make sure that the degree of the numerator is less than that of the denominator.

Putting $x = 1$ in $\dfrac{x^2}{(x - 2)(x - 3)}$ gives $\dfrac{1}{(-1)(-2)}$ or $\dfrac{1}{2}$.

Putting $x = 2$ in $\dfrac{x^2}{(x-1)(x-3)}$ gives $\dfrac{4}{(1)(-1)}$ or -4.

Putting $x = 3$ in $\dfrac{x^2}{(x-1)(x-2)}$ gives $\dfrac{9}{(2)(1)}$ or $\dfrac{9}{2}$.

The partial fractions are $\dfrac{1}{2(x-1)} - \dfrac{4}{x-2} + \dfrac{9}{2(x-3)}$.

Check $\dfrac{1}{2(x-1)} - \dfrac{4}{x-2} + \dfrac{9}{2(x-3)}$

$$= \frac{(x-2)(x-3) - 8(x-1)(x-3) + 9(x-1)(x-2)}{2(x-1)(x-2)(x-3)}$$

$$= \frac{2x^2}{2(x-1)(x-2)(x-3)} = \frac{x^2}{(x-1)(x-2)(x-3)}.$$

Example 3. *Express* $\dfrac{2x^2 + x + 1}{(x-1)(x+1)}$ *in partial fractions.*

Both numerator and denominator are of degree two. The denominator is $x^2 - 1$, so that division can be carried out by using the identity

$$2x^2 + x + 1 \equiv 2(x^2 - 1) + x + 3,$$

i.e. $\qquad \dfrac{2x^2 + x + 1}{(x-1)(x+1)} = 2 + \dfrac{x+3}{(x-1)(x+1)}.$

Continuing as in Examples 1 and 2, we have

$$\frac{2x^2 + x + 1}{(x-1)(x+1)} = 2 + \frac{2}{(x-1)} - \frac{1}{(x+1)}.$$

Exercise 8.1

Express in partial fractions:

1. $\dfrac{3}{(x-2)(x-3)}$.

2. $\dfrac{x}{(x-2)(x-3)}$.

3. $\dfrac{2x+1}{(x-2)(x-3)}$.

4. $\dfrac{x+1}{(x-1)(x-2)}$.

5. $\dfrac{x-3}{(x-1)(x+1)}$.

6. $\dfrac{x}{(x-1)(x-2)(x-3)}$.

7. $\dfrac{x+2}{x(x-1)(x+1)}$.

8. $\dfrac{x-1}{x(x+2)(x-2)}$.

9. $\dfrac{3x+7}{(x-2)(x+4)}$.

10. $\dfrac{x(x-1)}{(x+1)(x+2)(x+3)}$.

11. $\dfrac{x^2}{(x-1)(x-2)}$.

12. $\dfrac{x^2 + x + 1}{(x-1)(x-3)}$.

13. $\dfrac{x}{(2x-1)(2x-3)}$.

14. $\dfrac{x^2}{(x-1)(x-2)(x-3)}$.

15. $\dfrac{30x^2}{(2x-1)(3x+1)}$.

A quadratic factor in the denominator

Suppose that one factor in the denominator is linear and another is quadratic, so that we wish, for example, to write $\dfrac{3x + 1}{(x + 1)(x^2 + 1)}$ in partial fractions. It will not in general be true that

$$\frac{ax + b}{(x + 1)(x^2 + 1)} \equiv \frac{A}{(x + 1)} + \frac{B}{x^2 + 1}.$$

We know that the degree of the numerator of our given fraction is always less than the degree of the denominator (for if it is not, then we divide) and we can call such an expression a 'proper fraction', and both the fractions into which we are going to resolve our original fractions must be proper fractions. (This can be proved quite easily.) Thus we can only assume that the numerator of the second fraction must be of degree less than two, so that there *may* be a term in x, i.e., we must suppose that

$$\frac{3x + 1}{(x + 1)(x^2 + 1)} \equiv \frac{A}{(x + 1)} + \frac{Bx + C}{x^2 + 1}.$$

Write $\qquad \dfrac{3x + 1}{(x + 1)(x^2 + 1)} \equiv \dfrac{A}{x + 1} + \dfrac{Bx + C}{x^2 + 1}.$

Then $\qquad\qquad 3x + 1 \equiv A(x^2 + 1) + (Bx + C)(x + 1).$ $\qquad$ (i)

Equating coefficients of x^2: $\qquad 0 = A + B.$
Equating coefficients of x: $\qquad 3 = B + C.$
Equating coefficients of unity: $\qquad 1 = A + C.$

$$\therefore \quad A = -1, \quad B = 1, \quad C = 2.$$

The partial fractions are $-\dfrac{1}{x + 1} + \dfrac{x + 2}{x^2 + 1}.$

The value of A could have been found easily by putting $x = -1$ in the equation (i). This gives

$$(-3) + 1 = A(2) \quad \text{or} \quad A = -1.$$

Check $\qquad \dfrac{x + 2}{x^2 + 1} - \dfrac{1}{x + 1} = \dfrac{(x + 1)(x + 2) - (x^2 + 1)}{(x + 1)(x^2 + 1)}$

$$= \frac{3x + 1}{(x + 1)(x^2 + 1)}.$$

Provided that the degree of the numerator is less than that of the denominator, assume the numerator of each partial fraction to be the most general expression of one degree lower than the numerator. With a linear denominator, the numerator is a constant; with a quadratic denominator, the numerator is of the form $Ax + B$; with a cubic denominator, the numerator is of the form $Ax^2 + Bx + C$.

Example 1. *Express in partial fractions* $\dfrac{3x + 4}{(x - 2)(x^2 + x + 1)}$.

The degree of the numerator is less than that of the denominator. Assume

$$\frac{3x + 4}{(x - 2)(x^2 + x + 1)} \equiv \frac{A}{x - 2} + \frac{Bx + C}{x^2 + x + 1}.$$

Then
$$3x + 4 \equiv A(x^2 + x + 1) + (x - 2)(Bx + C).$$

First method by equating coefficients

Equating coefficients of x^2: $0 = A + B.$
Equating coefficients of x: $3 = A + C - 2B.$
Equating coefficients of unity: $4 = A - 2C.$
$$\therefore \quad 3A + C = 3 \quad \text{and} \quad A - 2C = 4,$$

from which
$$C = -\tfrac{9}{7} \quad \text{and} \quad A = \tfrac{10}{7}.$$
$$\therefore \quad B = -\tfrac{10}{7}$$

and the partial fractions are

$$\frac{10}{7(x - 2)} - \frac{10x + 9}{7(x^2 + x + 1)}.$$

Second method

From the identity $3x + 4 \equiv A(x^2 + x + 1) + (x - 2)(Bx + C)$, it is often easier to proceed as follows.

Put $x = 2$ to find A. We get
$$10 = 7A \quad \text{or} \quad A = \tfrac{10}{7}.$$

Substituting this value of A:
$$3x + 4 \equiv \tfrac{10}{7}(x^2 + x + 1) + (x - 2)(Bx + C).$$

Rearranging:
$$(x - 2)(Bx + C) \equiv -\tfrac{10}{7}(x^2 + x + 1) + 3x + 4$$
$$\equiv \frac{-10x^2 + 11x + 18}{7}.$$

Since $(x - 2)$ is a factor of the left-hand side, it must also be a factor of the right-hand side.

$$-10x^2 + 11x + 18 \equiv (x - 2)(-10x - 9).$$
$$\therefore \quad (x - 2)(Bx + C) \equiv \tfrac{1}{7}(x - 2)(-10x - 9).$$
$$\therefore \quad Bx + C \equiv \tfrac{1}{7}(-10x - 9),$$

from which
$$B = -\tfrac{10}{7}, \quad C = -\tfrac{9}{7}.$$

Exercise 8.2

Express in partial fractions

1. $\dfrac{3x + 1}{x(x^2 + 1)}$.

2. $\dfrac{x}{(x + 1)(x^2 + 4)}$.

3. $\dfrac{x + 1}{x(x^2 + 4)}$.

4. $\dfrac{2x - 1}{(x + 1)(x^2 + 2)}$

5. $\dfrac{2x - 1}{(x + 2)(x^2 + 1)}$.

6. $\dfrac{x + 1}{x(x^2 + x + 1)}$.

7. $\dfrac{3}{(x - 1)(x^2 + 2)}$.

8. $\dfrac{2x + 3}{(x - 2)(x^2 + 3)}$.

9. $\dfrac{3x}{(x - 1)(x^2 + x + 1)}$.

10. $\dfrac{1}{(x - 1)(x^2 - x + 1)}$.

11. $\dfrac{3x}{x^3 + 1}$.

12. $\dfrac{3}{x^3 - 1}$.

Repeated linear factor in the denominator

If there is a repeated factor in the denominator, e.g. $(x - 1)^2$, the method above can still be used, but will not give the simplest—or the most useful—alternative expression.

Let us consider the fraction $\dfrac{1 - 8x - x^2}{(x + 1)(x - 1)^2}$. The degree of the numerator is less than that of the denominator, so assume that

$$\frac{1 - 8x - x^2}{(x + 1)(x - 1)^2} \equiv \frac{A}{x + 1} + \frac{Bx + C}{(x - 1)^2}.$$

Then $1 - 8x - x^2 \equiv A(x - 1)^2 + (x + 1)(Bx + C)$.

Putting $x = -1$ gives $8 = 4A$ or $A = 2$.

Equating coefficients of x^2 gives $A + B = -1$. $\therefore$ $B = -3$.

Equating coefficients of unity gives $A + C = 1$. $\therefore$ $C = -1$.

The fraction therefore equals $\dfrac{2}{x + 1} - \dfrac{3x + 1}{(x - 1)^2}$ which is correct but may not be the most useful form.

The fraction $\dfrac{3x + 1}{(x - 1)^2}$ may be expressed as $\dfrac{3(x - 1) + 4}{(x - 1)^2}$ or as $\dfrac{3}{x - 1}$

$+ \dfrac{4}{(x - 1)^2}$.

$$\therefore \quad \frac{1 - 8x - x^2}{(x + 1)(x - 1)^2} \equiv \frac{2}{x + 1} - \frac{3}{x - 1} - \frac{4}{(x - 1)^2},$$

and these are the accepted partial fractions.

The method is shortened if, corresponding to a factor $(x - a)^2$ of the denominator, we assume $\dfrac{A}{x - a} + \dfrac{B}{(x - a)^2}$; corresponding to a factor $(x - a)^3$, we assume $\dfrac{A}{x - a} + \dfrac{B}{(x - a)^2} + \dfrac{C}{(x - a)^3}$ and so on.

The example is now re-worked using the method normally used.

Assume $\dfrac{1 - 8x - x^2}{(x + 1)(x - 1)^2} \equiv \dfrac{A}{x + 1} + \dfrac{B}{x - 1} + \dfrac{C}{(x - 1)^2}$.

Then $1 - 8x - x^2 \equiv A(x - 1)^2 + B(x + 1)(x - 1) + C(x + 1).$

Putting $x = 1$ gives $\qquad\qquad -8 = 2C.$ $\qquad\qquad \therefore\quad C = -4.$
Putting $x = -1$ gives $\qquad\qquad 8 = 4A.$ $\qquad\qquad \therefore\quad A = 2.$
Equating coefficients of x^2 gives $A + B = -1.$ $\qquad \therefore\quad B = -3.$

The partial fractions are

$$\frac{2}{x + 1} - \frac{3}{x - 1} - \frac{4}{(x - 1)^2}.$$

Example 1. *Express in partial fractions* $\dfrac{x + 1}{(x + 2)(x - 1)^2}.$

Write $\qquad \dfrac{x + 1}{(x + 2)(x - 1)^2} \equiv \dfrac{A}{(x + 2)} + \dfrac{B}{(x - 1)} + \dfrac{C}{(x - 1)^2}.$

Using the 'cover up' method, we find that

$$A = \frac{-1}{(-3)^2} = \frac{-1}{9}.$$

We can use the 'cover up' method to find C, for covering up $(x - 1)^2$, we have
$C = \dfrac{2}{3}.$ Notice that we find C, not B, for we cover up $(x - 1)^2$. If we covered
up only $(x - 1)$, we should still have a factor 0 in the denominator, so we
should not be able to find the value of the fraction.

To find B, we see that

$$x + 1 \equiv A(x - 1)^2 + B(x + 2)(x - 1) + C(x + 2).$$

Since we have already found that $A = -\dfrac{1}{9}$ and $C = \dfrac{2}{3},$

$$\therefore \quad x + 1 = -\frac{1}{9}(x - 1)^2 + B(x - 1)(x + 2) + \frac{2}{3}(x + 2).$$

We can now equate the coefficients on each side of any convenient power of x,
say x^2—since there are fewer terms containing x^2 than x—so that

$$0 = -\frac{1}{9} + B,$$

$$B = \frac{1}{9}.$$

Alternatively, we can give x any convenient value, say $x = 0$.

Then $\qquad\qquad\qquad 1 = -\dfrac{1}{9} - 2B + \dfrac{4}{3},$

i.e. $\qquad\qquad\qquad B = \dfrac{1}{9}.$

Thus $\qquad \dfrac{x + 1}{(x + 2)(x - 1)^2} = \dfrac{-1}{9(x + 2)} + \dfrac{1}{9(x - 1)} + \dfrac{2}{(3x - 1)^2}.$

Example 2. *Express in partial fractions* $\dfrac{3x^2 - x - 1}{(x - 1)^5}.$

When a factor of the denominator is raised to a high power, the partial
fractions are often best found by substitution.

Put $x - 1 = y$ so that $x = y + 1$.

$$\frac{3x^2 - x - 1}{(x - 1)^5} = \frac{3(y + 1)^2 - (y + 1) - 1}{y^5}$$

$$= \frac{3y^2 + 5y + 1}{y^5}$$

$$= \frac{3}{y^3} + \frac{5}{y^4} + \frac{1}{y^5}$$

$$= \frac{3}{(x - 1)^3} + \frac{5}{(x - 1)^4} + \frac{1}{(x - 1)^5}.$$

Exercise 8.3

Express in partial fractions:

1. $\dfrac{x}{(x - 1)^2}.$ **2.** $\dfrac{x + 3}{(x + 1)(x - 1)^2}.$ **3.** $\dfrac{1}{(x^2 + 1)(x - 1)^2}.$

4. $\dfrac{x}{(x - 1)^3}.$ **5.** $\dfrac{x}{(x + 1)(x - 1)^3}.$ **6.** $\dfrac{x + 1}{(x + 2)(x - 1)^2}.$

7. $\dfrac{x^3}{(x - 2)^5}.$ **8.** $\dfrac{x^2 + x + 1}{(x - 1)(x + 1)^2}.$ **9.** $\dfrac{x^2}{(x + 1)^4}.$

10. $\dfrac{x^2 + 1}{(x - 1)(x + 1)^3}.$

Applications of partial fractions

By far the most important use of partial fractions is in integration.

Example 1. *Integrate* $\dfrac{4 - 3x}{(1 - x)(2 - x)}.$

$$\frac{4 - 3x}{(1 - x)(2 - x)} = \frac{1}{1 - x} + \frac{2}{2 - x}.$$

$$\therefore \quad \int \frac{4 - 3x}{(1 - x)(2 - x)} \, dx = \int \frac{1}{1 - x} \, dx + \int \frac{2}{2 - x} \, dx$$

$$= -\ln(1 - x) - 2 \ln(2 - x) + C.$$

Example 2. *Integrate* $\dfrac{4x^2 - 2x + 3}{(x^2 + 1)(x - 2)}.$

Let $\qquad \dfrac{4x^2 - 2x + 3}{(x^2 + 1)(x - 2)} \equiv \dfrac{Ax + B}{x^2 + 1} + \dfrac{C}{x - 2}.$

Then $\qquad 4x^2 - 2x + 3 \equiv (Ax + B)(x - 2) + C(x^2 + 1).$

Putting $x = 2$ gives $\qquad 16 - 4 + 3 = 5C.$ $\qquad\qquad \therefore \quad C = 3.$

Equating coefficients of x^2 gives $\qquad 4 = A + C.$ $\qquad\qquad \therefore \quad A = 1.$

Equating coefficients of unity gives $\quad 3 = -2B + C.$ $\qquad\qquad \therefore \quad B = 0.$

The partial fractions are

$$\frac{x}{x^2 + 1} + \frac{3}{x - 2}.$$

$$\therefore \int \frac{4x^2 - 2x + 3}{(x^2 + 1)(x - 2)}\, dx = \int \frac{x}{x^2 + 1}\, dx + \int \frac{3}{x - 2}\, dx$$

$$= \tfrac{1}{2} \int \frac{2x}{x^2 + 1}\, dx + 3 \int \frac{dx}{x - 2}$$

$$= \tfrac{1}{2} \ln (x^2 + 1) + 3 \ln (x - 2) + C.$$

Whenever we are asked to integrate a fraction whose denominator factorizes, use partial fractions.

Partial fractions can also be used to sum a series whose general term is a fraction.

Example 1. *Sum the series* $\displaystyle\sum_1^n \frac{1}{r(r + 1)}$.

$$\frac{1}{r(r + 1)} = \frac{1}{r} - \frac{1}{r + 1}.$$

Express each term in its partial fractions.

$$\frac{1}{1.2} = \frac{1}{1} - \frac{1}{2}$$

$$\frac{1}{2.3} = \frac{1}{2} - \frac{1}{3}$$

$$\cdots\cdots\cdots$$

$$\frac{1}{n(n + 1)} = \frac{1}{n} - \frac{1}{n + 1}.$$

Adding, the terms cancel diagonally;

$$\therefore \sum_1^n \frac{1}{r(r + 1)} = 1 - \frac{1}{n + 1} = \frac{n}{n + 1}.$$

The sum to infinity is the limit of the sum to n terms as n tends to infinity. The sum to infinity is 1.

Example 2. *Sum the series* $\displaystyle\sum_1^n \frac{1}{r(r + 1)(r + 3)}$.

$$\frac{1}{r(r + 1)(r + 3)} = \frac{1}{3r} - \frac{1}{2(r + 1)} + \frac{1}{6(r + 3)}.$$

$$\frac{1}{1.2.4} = \frac{1}{3}\left(\frac{1}{1}\right) - \frac{1}{2}\left(\frac{1}{2}\right) + \frac{1}{6}\left(\frac{1}{4}\right).$$

$$\frac{1}{2.3.5} = \frac{1}{3}\left(\frac{1}{2}\right) - \frac{1}{2}\left(\frac{1}{3}\right) + \frac{1}{6}\left(\frac{1}{5}\right).$$

$$\frac{1}{3.4.6} = \frac{1}{3}\left(\frac{1}{3}\right) - \frac{1}{2}\left(\frac{1}{4}\right) + \frac{1}{6}\left(\frac{1}{6}\right).$$

$$\frac{1}{4.5.7} = \frac{1}{3}\left(\frac{1}{4}\right) - \frac{1}{2}\left(\frac{1}{5}\right) + \frac{1}{6}\left(\frac{1}{7}\right).$$

....

$$\frac{1}{(n-2)(n-1)(n+1)} = \frac{1}{3}\left(\frac{1}{n-2}\right) - \frac{1}{2}\left(\frac{1}{n-1}\right) + \frac{1}{6}\left(\frac{1}{n+1}\right)$$

$$\frac{1}{(n-1)n(n+2)} = \frac{1}{3}\left(\frac{1}{n-1}\right) - \frac{1}{2}\left(\frac{1}{n}\right) + \frac{1}{6}\left(\frac{1}{n+2}\right).$$

$$\frac{1}{n(n+1)(n+3)} = \frac{1}{3}\left(\frac{1}{n}\right) - \frac{1}{2}\left(\frac{1}{n+1}\right) + \frac{1}{6}\left(\frac{1}{n+3}\right).$$

Keep the factors of the partial fractions separate, i.e. write $\frac{1}{3}(\frac{1}{3})$ and not $\frac{1}{9}$. Any term which appears in all three columns cancels, e.g. $\frac{1}{6}(\frac{1}{4}) - \frac{1}{2}(\frac{1}{4}) + \frac{1}{3}(\frac{1}{4})$. The sum to n terms is

$$\frac{1}{3} - \frac{1}{4} + \frac{1}{6} - \frac{1}{6} + \frac{1}{9} + \frac{1}{6(n+1)} + \frac{1}{6(n+2)} - \frac{1}{2(n+1)} + \frac{1}{6(n+3)}$$

or

$$\frac{7}{36} - \frac{1}{3(n+1)} + \frac{1}{6(n+2)} + \frac{1}{6(n+3)}.$$

The sum to infinity is $\frac{7}{36}$.

Other applications of partial fractions include expansion of series (Ch. 10) and solution of differential equations (Ch. 18).

Exercise 8.4

Integrate

1. $\dfrac{3x - 4}{(x - 1)(x - 2)}$.

2. $\dfrac{1}{2x^2 - 3x + 1}$.

3. $\dfrac{x^2}{(x - 1)^2}$.

4. $\dfrac{5x - 2}{6x^2 - 5x + 1}$.

5. $\dfrac{3x + 1}{2x^2 + x}$.

6. $\dfrac{2x^2 + x + 1}{(x^2 + 1)(x + 1)}$.

7. $\dfrac{x}{(x^2 + 1)(x^2 + 2)}$.

8. $\dfrac{4x^2 - x + 1}{x^3 + 1}$.

9. $\dfrac{x}{(x - 2)^2}$.

10. $\dfrac{3}{(x - 1)(2x - 1)}$.

Sum to n terms and to infinity the series whose rth terms are

11. $\dfrac{1}{r(r + 1)(r + 2)}$.

12. $\dfrac{1}{(2r - 1)(2r + 1)}$.

13. $\dfrac{1}{r(r + 2)}$.

14. $\dfrac{2r + 1}{r^2(r + 1)^2}$.

15. Find $\displaystyle\sum_{n}^{2n} \frac{1}{r(r + 1)}$ and find the value of the sum as $n \to \infty$.

Exercise 8.5: Miscellaneous

1. Express $\dfrac{3(x-1)}{(1-2x)(1+x)}$ in partial fractions and hence find

$$\int \frac{3(x-1)}{(1-2x)(1+x)}\,dx.$$

2. Express $\dfrac{1}{x(2x+1)}$ in partial fractions and hence find the area of the region

bounded by the curve $y = \dfrac{1}{x(2x+1)}$, the x-axis and the lines $x = 1$, $x = 2$.

3. Evaluate $\displaystyle\int_{2}^{3} \frac{dx}{(x+1)(x+2)}$.

4. Find the value of $\displaystyle\sum_{1}^{n} \frac{1}{(3r-1)(3r+2)}$.

5. Find the area of the region bounded by the curve $y = \dfrac{1}{x(x+1)}$, the x-axis

and the ordinates $x = 1$ and $x = 2$.

6. Find $\displaystyle\int \frac{x-1}{(x+1)^2(x-2)}\,dx$.

7. Differentiate with respect to x

$$\frac{x-1}{(x+1)^2(x-2)}.$$

8. Show that $\dfrac{1}{r^3} - \dfrac{1}{(r+1)^3} = \dfrac{3r^2+3r+1}{r^3(r+1)^3}$.

Hence find $\displaystyle\sum_{1}^{n} \frac{3r^2+3r+1}{r^3(r+1)^3}$.

9. Express in partial fractions $\dfrac{y}{(y-1)^4}$.

10. Find $\displaystyle\int \frac{x}{(x-1)^4}\,dx$.

11. Find the sum of

$$\frac{1}{1\times3\times5} + \frac{1}{3\times5\times7} + \ldots + \frac{1}{(2n-1)(2n+1)(2n+3)}.$$

12. Find $\displaystyle\sum_{1}^{\infty} \frac{1}{(2n-1)(2n+1)(2n+3)}$.

13. Evaluate $\displaystyle\int_{0}^{1} \frac{dx}{(x+1)(x+2)^2}$.

14. Integrate $\dfrac{x}{(1-x)(1-2x)}$ with respect to x.

15. Integrate $\dfrac{1}{x(x+1)^3}$ with respect to x.

16. Integrate $\dfrac{1 + x^2 + x^3}{x^2(1 + x^2)}$ with respect to x.

17. Show that $\dfrac{1}{r(r + 1)} - \dfrac{1}{(r + 1)(r + 2)} = \dfrac{2}{r(r + 1)(r + 2)}$.

Hence find $\sum\limits_{1}^{n} \dfrac{1}{r(r + 1)(r + 2)}$.

18. Integrate with respect to x:

(i) $\dfrac{x^2}{x + 1}$ (ii) $\dfrac{x - 1}{x + 1}$.

19. Express $\dfrac{2x^2 + 1}{(x + 2)(x - 1)^2}$ in partial fractions.

20. Evaluate $\displaystyle\int_{2}^{3} \dfrac{2x^2 + 1}{(x + 2)(x - 1)^2}\, dx$.

9 Trigonometry: Circular Functions and their Inverses

Revision

We recall that $\dfrac{d}{dx}(\sin x) = \cos x$ and $\dfrac{d}{dx}(\cos x) = -\sin x$. We saw that from these, and from the rules for differentiating products and quotients, we could deduce

$$\frac{d}{dx}(\tan x) = \frac{d}{dx}\left(\frac{\sin x}{\cos x}\right) = \frac{\cos x (\cos x) - \sin x (-\sin x)}{\cos^2 x}$$

$$= \frac{1}{\cos^2 x} = \sec^2 x.$$

$$\frac{d}{dx}(\operatorname{cosec} x) = \frac{d}{dx}(\sin x)^{-1} = -\frac{\cos x}{\sin^2 x} = -\operatorname{cosec} x \cot x.$$

$$\frac{d}{dx}(\sec x) = \frac{d}{dx}(\cos x)^{-1} = \frac{\sin x}{\cos^2 x} = \sec x \tan x.$$

$$\frac{d}{dx}(\cot x) = \frac{d}{dx}(\tan x)^{-1} = -\frac{\sec^2 x}{\tan^2 x} = -\operatorname{cosec}^2 x.$$

Using the method for differentiating a function of a function, we have

$$\frac{d}{dx}(\sin 2x) = 2 \cos 2x,$$

$$\frac{d}{dx}\left[\tan\left(3x + \frac{\pi}{4}\right)\right] = 3 \sec^2\left(3x + \frac{\pi}{4}\right), \text{ etc.}$$

From these we can deduce certain integrals, e.g.

$$\int \sin x \, dx = -\cos x + C,$$

$$\int \cos 2x \, dx = \tfrac{1}{2} \sin 2x + C,$$

$$\int \sec^2\left(x + \frac{\pi}{4}\right) dx = \tan\left(x + \frac{\pi}{4}\right) + C.$$

Using the logarithmic integrals of Chapter 7, we saw

$$\int \tan x \, dx = \int \frac{\sin x}{\cos x} \, dx = -\int \frac{(-\sin x)}{\cos x} \, dx$$

$$= -\ln \cos x + C$$

$$= \ln \sec x + C,$$

and
$$\int \cot x \, dx = \int \frac{\cos x}{\sin x} \, dx$$
$$= \ln \sin x + C,$$

in each case writing the numerator as the derivative of the denominator, and using

$$\int \frac{f'(x)}{f(x)} \, dx = \ln f(x) + C.$$

Example 1. *Differentiate* $\cot^3 (2x + 1)$ *with respect to x.*

$$\frac{d}{dx} \cot^3 (2x + 1) = 3 \cot^2 (2x + 1) \times \frac{d}{dx} \cot (2x + 1)$$

$$= -3 \cot^2 (2x + 1) \operatorname{cosec}^2 (2x + 1) \times \frac{d}{dx} (2x + 1)$$

$$= -6 \cot^2 (2x + 1) \operatorname{cosec}^2 (2x + 1).$$

Example 2. *Differentiate* $e^{2x} \operatorname{cosec} 3x$ *with respect to x.*

$$\frac{d}{dx} (e^{2x} \operatorname{cosec} 3x) = \frac{d}{dx} (e^{2x}) \operatorname{cosec} 3x + e^{2x} \frac{d}{dx} (\operatorname{cosec} 3x)$$

$$= 2e^{2x} \operatorname{cosec} 3x - 3e^{2x} \operatorname{cosec} 3x \cot 3x$$

$$= e^{2x} \operatorname{cosec} 3x(2 - 3 \cot 3x).$$

Example 3. *Find* $\int \tan^2 \tfrac{1}{2}x \, dx.$

$$\int \tan^2 \tfrac{1}{2}x \, dx = \int (\sec^2 \tfrac{1}{2}x - 1) \, dx$$

$$= 2 \tan \tfrac{1}{2}x - x + C.$$

Example 4. *Find* $\int \sec x \, dx.$

$$\int \sec x \, dx = \int \frac{\sec^2 x + \sec x \tan x}{\tan x + \sec x} \, dx$$

$$= \ln (\sec x + \tan x) + C,$$

having multiplied the numerator and denominator of $\dfrac{\sec x}{1}$ by $\sec x + \tan x$, so that the numerator is the derivative of the denominator.

Exercise 9.1

Differentiate with respect to x:

1. $\tan^2 x.$ **2.** $\sec^2 x.$ **3.** $\cos^2 (\tfrac{1}{3}x).$ **4.** $\tan^2 \left(x + \dfrac{\pi}{3}\right).$

5. $\cot \left(2x + \dfrac{\pi}{6}\right).$ **6.** $x \sin x.$ **7.** $\ln \sin 2x.$ **8.** $\ln \sin^2 x.$

9. $(\ln \sin x)^2.$ **10.** $\ln \tan \tfrac{1}{2}x.$

Integrate with respect to x:

11. $\csc^2 2x$.   **12.** $\cot^2 \frac{1}{2}x$.   **13.** $\cot 4x$.

14. $\cot^2\left(x + \frac{\pi}{3}\right)$.   **15.** $\cot\left(2x + \frac{\pi}{6}\right)$.   **16.** $\tan x \sec^2 x$.

17. $\sin^3 2x \cos 2x$.   **18.** $x \sin (x^2)$.   **19.** $\dfrac{\sin x}{1 - \cos x}$.

20. $\dfrac{\cos 2x}{1 + 2 \sin 2x}$.

The inverse sine relation

The 'sine function' f is such that $f : x \mapsto \sin x$, e.g., $\sin\left(\dfrac{\pi}{6}\right) = 0.5$,

$\sin\left(\dfrac{\pi}{2}\right) = 1$, $\sin \pi = 0$. The image of an element y under the inverse relation is written $\sin^{-1} y$ or arc $\sin y$ or inv $\sin y$, and can be thought of as 'the angle whose sine is y', e.g.

$$\text{inv } \sin 0.5 = \left(\frac{-7\pi}{6}\right) \quad \text{or} \quad \frac{\pi}{6} \quad \text{or} \quad \frac{5\pi}{6} \quad \text{or} \quad \frac{13\pi}{6} \quad \text{or} \dots$$

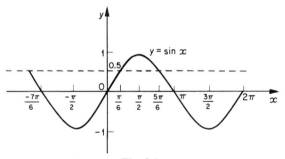

Fig. 9.1

Fig. 9.1 illustrates that for any value of x there is a unique $\sin x$, but for any y there is not a unique inv $\sin y$. The relation $f : y \mapsto$ inv $\sin y$ is one-many, and inv $\sin y$ is said to be *many-valued*.

In order that the inverse relation should be a function, we restrict the range. The range taken for the inverse sine is the set of values $\left\{x : -\dfrac{\pi}{2} \leqslant x \leqslant \dfrac{\pi}{2}\right\}$; these are called the principal values of x; calculators of course give these values of the inv sin. We shall take a different range for the other inverse functions. Figure 9.2 shows the graphs of $y = \sin x$ and $y = \sin^{-1} x$; in the latter, the part of the graph not corresponding to the principal values is shown hatched - - - -.

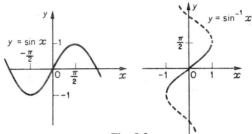

Fig. 9.2

The inverse cosine relation

The relation $f:y \mapsto \text{inv} \cos y$ can be thought of again as 'the angle whose cosine is . . .'. We can also use the notation $\cos^{-1} y$ or arc cos y. Again we have the same problem of a one-many relation, and again we restrict the domain so that the relation becomes a function. The range that we choose is $\{x: 0 \leqslant x \leqslant \pi\}$.

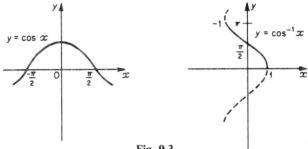

Fig. 9.3

The inverse tangent relation

The relation $f:y \mapsto \text{inv} \tan y$ can be thought of as 'the angle whose tangent is', and we can also use the notation $\tan^{-1} y$ or arc tan y. This time we restrict the range so that it is $\left\{x: \dfrac{-\pi}{2} < x \leqslant \dfrac{\pi}{2}\right\}$.

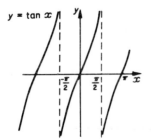
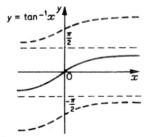

Fig. 9.4

Principal values

In choosing the range of values of x that will be the principal values, the criterion that we use is 'the smallest possible numerical value, positive if there is a choice', e.g.

$$\sin\left(\frac{-7\pi}{6}\right) = \sin\left(\frac{\pi}{6}\right) = \sin\left(\frac{5\pi}{6}\right) = 0.5$$

so inv sin $(0.5) = \frac{\pi}{6}$;

$$\cos\left(\frac{-\pi}{3}\right) = \cos\left(\frac{\pi}{3}\right) = \cos\left(\frac{5\pi}{3}\right) = 0.5,$$

so inv cos $(0.5) = \frac{\pi}{3}$, choosing the positive value;

$$\tan\left(\frac{\pi}{4}\right) = \tan\left(\frac{5\pi}{4}\right) = 1$$

so inv tan $(1) = \frac{\pi}{4}$

and

$$\tan\left(\frac{-\pi}{4}\right) = \tan\left(\frac{3\pi}{4}\right) = -1,$$

so inv tan $(-1) = \frac{-\pi}{4}$, this value being numerically smaller than the positive value $\frac{3\pi}{4}$.

Relations connecting inverse functions

1. Suppose that x is positive and less than 1. Then $\sin^{-1} x$ and $\cos^{-1} x$ are both between 0 and $\frac{\pi}{2}$. If, in triangle ABC, right-angled at B, angle BAC $= \sin^{-1} x$, angle ACB will be $\cos^{-1} x$, so that

$$\sin^{-1} x + \cos^{-1} x = \frac{\pi}{2}.$$

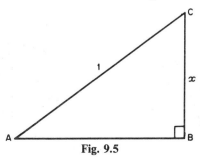

Fig. 9.5

This relation still holds if x is negative and between -1 and 0, though $\sin^{-1} x$ is now negative and $\cos^{-1} x$ between $\dfrac{\pi}{2}$ and π. The proof is left as an exercise.

2. Let $\qquad \tan^{-1} x = \theta \quad$ and $\quad \tan^{-1} y = \varphi$.

Then $\qquad\qquad \tan \theta = x \quad$ and $\quad \tan \varphi = y$.

$$\tan (\theta + \varphi) = \frac{\tan \theta + \tan \varphi}{1 - \tan \theta \tan \varphi}$$

$$= \frac{x + y}{1 - xy}.$$

$$\therefore \quad \theta + \varphi = \tan^{-1} \frac{x + y}{1 - xy},$$

or $\qquad \tan^{-1} x + \tan^{-1} y = \tan^{-1} \dfrac{x + y}{1 - xy}.$

Putting $x = y$ gives $\qquad 2 \tan^{-1} x = \tan^{-1} \dfrac{2x}{1 - x^2}.$

Similarly it may be proved that

$$\tan^{-1} x - \tan^{-1} y = \tan^{-1} \frac{x - y}{1 + xy}.$$

The proof is left as an exercise.

Example. *Show that* $\tan^{-1} \frac{1}{2} + \tan^{-1} \frac{1}{3} = \dfrac{\pi}{4}.$

$$\tan^{-1} \tfrac{1}{2} + \tan^{-1} \tfrac{1}{3} = \tan^{-1} \frac{\tfrac{1}{2} + \tfrac{1}{3}}{1 - \tfrac{1}{6}}$$

$$= \tan^{-1} 1$$

$$= n\pi + \frac{\pi}{4}.$$

Since each of $\tan^{-1} \frac{1}{2}$ and $\tan^{-1} \frac{1}{3}$ is positive and less than $\dfrac{\pi}{2}$, their sum is less than π and so $\tan^{-1} \frac{1}{2} + \tan^{-1} \frac{1}{3} = \dfrac{\pi}{4}.$

3. Identities connecting inverse ratios are best proved by appealing to first principles.

Example. *Simplify* $\sin (2 \tan^{-1} x)$

Let $\qquad\qquad \tan^{-1} x = \theta \quad$ so that $\quad \tan \theta = x.$

$$\sin (2 \tan^{-1} x) = \sin 2\theta$$

$$= \frac{2 \tan \theta}{1 + \tan^2 \theta}$$

$$= \frac{2x}{1 + x^2}.$$

$$\therefore \quad \sin (2 \tan^{-1} x) = \frac{2x}{1 + x^2}.$$

Exercise 9.2

1. Find expressions for the general value in radians of:
   (i) $\sin^{-1} 0$; $\sin^{-1} (1)$; $\sin^{-1} (-1)$,
   (ii) $\cos^{-1} 0$; $\cos^{-1} (1)$; $\cos^{-1} (-1)$,
   (iii) $\tan^{-1} 0$; $\tan^{-1} \left(\frac{\pi}{3} \right)$; $\tan^{-1} \left(\frac{-\pi}{3} \right)$.

2. Without using calculators, find the principal value in radians of:
   (i) $\sin^{-1} 0$; $\sin^{-1} (1)$; $\sin^{-1} (-1)$,
   (ii) $\cos^{-1} 0$; $\cos^{-1} (1)$; $\cos^{-1} (-1)$,
   (iii) $\tan^{-1} 0$; $\tan^{-1} \left(\frac{\sqrt{3}}{3} \right)$; $\tan^{-1} \left(\frac{-\sqrt{3}}{3} \right)$.

Do not use calculators in solving Q. 3–20.

3. Simplify $\sin^{-1} (\cos x)$.

4. Show that $\tan^{-1} x + \tan^{-1} \dfrac{1}{x} = \dfrac{\pi}{2}$.

5. Show that $\tan^{-1} 3 + \tan^{-1} 2 = \dfrac{3\pi}{4}$.

6. Solve the equation $\tan^{-1} 2 + \tan^{-1} x = \tan^{-1} 4$.

7. Show that $2 \tan^{-1} \frac{1}{3} = \tan^{-1} \frac{3}{4}$.

8. Show that $4 \tan^{-1} \frac{1}{2} + \tan^{-1} \frac{24}{7} = \pi$.

9. Find $\tan (\sin^{-1} \frac{3}{5} + \sin^{-1} \frac{5}{13})$.

10. Find the value of $\sin^{-1} \dfrac{\sqrt{3}}{2} + \tan^{-1} \sqrt{3}$.

11. Evaluate $\sin \left(\dfrac{\pi}{2} + \tan^{-1} \dfrac{3}{4} \right)$.

12. Show that $\tan^{-1} x + \cot^{-1} x = \dfrac{\pi}{2}$.

13. Evaluate $\sin (2 \tan^{-1} x + \cot^{-1} x)$.

14. Simplify $\cos (2 \tan^{-1} x)$.

15. If $\theta = \frac{1}{2} \sin^{-1} \frac{3}{4}$, show that $\sin \theta - \cos \theta = \pm \frac{1}{2}$.

16. Find $\tan (\tan^{-1} \frac{1}{2} + \tan^{-1} \frac{1}{3} + \tan^{-1} \frac{1}{4})$.

17. Find the value of $\tan^{-1} \frac{1}{3} + \tan^{-1} \frac{1}{5} + \tan^{-1} \frac{1}{7} + \tan^{-1} \frac{1}{8}$.

18. Simplify $\tan (2 \tan^{-1} x)$.

19. Show that $2 \tan^{-1} \frac{1}{2} = \sin^{-1} \frac{4}{5}$.

20. Solve the equation $\tan^{-1} x = \sin^{-1} \frac{1}{2}$.

Differential coefficients of the inverse ratios

Let $\qquad y = \sin^{-1} x \quad$ so that $\quad \sin y = x.$

Then $\qquad \dfrac{dx}{dy} = \cos y \quad$ and so $\quad \dfrac{dy}{dx} = \dfrac{1}{\cos y}.$

Since $\qquad \sin y = x \quad$ and $\quad \cos^2 y + \sin^2 y = 1,$

$\qquad\qquad \cos y = \pm \sqrt{(1 - \sin^2 y)} = \pm \sqrt{(1 - x^2)}.$

$\qquad \therefore \quad \dfrac{dy}{dx} = \pm \dfrac{1}{\sqrt{(1 - x^2)}}.$

From the graph of $\sin^{-1} x$ (Fig. 9.2), we see that the differential coefficient of the principal value of $\sin^{-1} x$ is always positive.

$$\therefore \quad \frac{d}{dx} \sin^{-1} x = \frac{1}{\sqrt{(1 - x^2)}}.$$

From the relation

$$\sin^{-1} x + \cos^{-1} x = \frac{\pi}{2},$$

it follows that

$$\frac{d}{dx} (\sin^{-1} x) + \frac{d}{dx} (\cos^{-1} x) = 0$$

$$\therefore \quad \frac{d}{dx} (\cos^{-1} x) = -\frac{1}{\sqrt{(1 - x^2)}}.$$

Let $\qquad y = \tan^{-1} x \quad$ so that $\quad x = \tan y.$

Then $\dfrac{dx}{dy} = \sec^2 y \quad$ and $\quad \dfrac{dy}{dx} = \dfrac{1}{\sec^2 y} = \dfrac{1}{1 + \tan^2 y} = \dfrac{1}{1 + x^2}.$

$$\therefore \quad \frac{d}{dx} (\tan^{-1} x) = \frac{1}{1 + x^2}.$$

We can generalise these to give

$$\frac{d}{dx} \left(\sin^{-1} \frac{x}{a} \right) = \frac{1}{\sqrt{(a^2 - x^2)}};$$

$$\frac{d}{dx} \left(\cos^{-1} \frac{x}{a} \right) = \frac{-1}{\sqrt{(a^2 - x^2)}}$$

and $\qquad \dfrac{d}{dx} \left(\tan^{-1} \dfrac{x}{a} \right) = \dfrac{a}{a^2 + x^2}.$

We have now completed the differentiation of the most important functions and a table showing these is given.

y	$\dfrac{dy}{dx}$
x^n	nx^{n-1}
$\sin x$	$\cos x$
$\cos x$	$-\sin x$
$\tan x$	$\sec^2 x$
$\operatorname{cosec} x$	$-\operatorname{cosec} x \cot x$
$\sec x$	$\sec x \tan x$
$\cot x$	$-\operatorname{cosec}^2 x$
e^x	e^x
$\ln x$	$\dfrac{1}{x}$
a^x	$a^x \log a$
$\log_a x$	$\dfrac{1}{x \ln a}$
uv	$u\dfrac{dv}{dx} + v\dfrac{du}{dx}$
$\dfrac{u}{v}$	$\dfrac{v\dfrac{du}{dx} - u\dfrac{dv}{dx}}{v^2}$
$\sin^{-1}\left(\dfrac{x}{a}\right)$	$\dfrac{1}{\sqrt{(a^2 - x^2)}}$
$\cos^{-1}\left(\dfrac{x}{a}\right)$	$-\dfrac{1}{\sqrt{(a^2 - x^2)}}$
$\tan^{-1}\left(\dfrac{x}{a}\right)$	$\dfrac{a}{a^2 + x^2}$

Example 1. *Differentiate with respect to* x:

$$(i)\ \sin^{-1}(3x);\ (ii)\ \tan^{-1}(\tfrac{1}{2}x);\ (iii)\ \cos^{-1}(2x).$$

(i) Regarding this as a 'function of a function', we have

$$\frac{d}{dx}(\sin^{-1}(3x)) = \frac{1}{\sqrt{(1 - 9x^2)}} \times 3 = \frac{3}{\sqrt{(1 - 9x^2)}}$$

or we can use the formula for $\sin^{-1}\left(\dfrac{x}{a}\right)$, where $a = \dfrac{1}{3}$.

(ii)

$$\frac{d}{dx}(\tan^{-1}(\tfrac{1}{2}x)) = \frac{1}{1 + (\tfrac{1}{2}x)^2} \times \frac{1}{2} = \frac{2}{4 + x^2}$$

or again we can use the formula for $\tan^{-1}\left(\dfrac{x}{a}\right)$, where $a = 2$.

(iii)

$$\frac{d}{dx}(\cos^{-1}(2x)) = \frac{-1}{\sqrt{(1 - 4x^2)}} \times 2,$$

remembering that the differential coefficient of $\cos^{-1} x$ is negative,

$$= \frac{-2}{\sqrt{(1 - 4x^2)}}$$

or again we can use the formula for $\cos^{-1}\left(\dfrac{x}{a}\right)$, where $a = \frac{1}{2}$.

Example 2. *Differentiate* $\tan^{-1} \dfrac{2x}{1 - x^2}$ *with respect to* x.

$$\frac{d}{dx} \tan^{-1} \frac{2x}{1 - x^2} = \frac{\dfrac{d}{dx}\left(\dfrac{2x}{1 - x^2}\right)}{1 + \left(\dfrac{2x}{1 - x^2}\right)^2}$$

$$= \frac{\dfrac{(1 - x^2)2 - 2x(-2x)}{(1 - x^2)^2}}{1 + \left(\dfrac{2x}{1 - x^2}\right)^2}$$

$$= \frac{2 - 2x^2 + 4x^2}{1 - 2x^2 + x^4 + 4x^2}$$

$$= \frac{2(1 + x^2)}{(1 + x^2)^2}$$

$$= \frac{2}{1 + x^2}.$$

The differential coefficient could have been found more easily using the identity $\tan^{-1} \dfrac{2x}{1 - x^2} = 2 \tan^{-1} x$.

Example 3. *Differentiate* $\ln (\sin^{-1} 2x)$ *with respect to* x.

$$\frac{d}{dx} \ln (\sin^{-1} 2x) = \frac{1}{\sin^{-1} 2x} \times \frac{d}{dx} (\sin^{-1} 2x)$$

$$= \frac{1}{\sin^{-1} 2x} \times \frac{1}{\sqrt{(1 - 4x^2)}} \times \frac{d}{dx} (2x)$$

$$= \frac{2}{\sin^{-1} 2x \sqrt{(1 - 4x^2)}}.$$

Exercise 9.3

Differentiate with respect to x:

1. $\sin^{-1} 3x$.	**2.** $\cos^{-1} 4x$.	**3.** $\tan^{-1} 5x$.
4. $\sin^{-1} (\frac{1}{3}x)$.	**5.** $\cos^{-1} \frac{1}{4}x$.	**6.** $\cot^{-1} 5x$.
7. $\sin^{-1} (x - 1)$.	**8.** $\sin^{-1} (1 - x)$.	**9.** $\sin^{-1} (2x - 1)$.
10. $\tan^{-1} (\sqrt{x})$.	**11.** $\tan^{-1} (x^2)$.	**12.** $\tan^{-1} (x + 1)$.

13. $\tan^{-1}(e^x)$. **14.** $\tan^{-1}(\sin x)$. **15.** $\tan^{-1}(\cot x)$.

16. $\tan^{-1}\left(\dfrac{1}{x}\right)$. **17.** $\cot^{-1}(x)$. **18.** $\sin^{-1}(\sqrt{x})$.

19. $\sin^{-1}(x^2)$. **20.** $[\sin^{-1}x]^2$. **21.** $x\sin^{-1}x$.

22. $x\tan^{-1}x$. **23.** $x^2\tan^{-1}x$. **24.** $\tan^{-1}(\cot x)$.

25. $\tan^{-1}(x+1)+\tan^{-1}(x-1)$. **26.** $\tan^{-1}(\ln x)$.

27. $\ln(\tan^{-1}x)$. **28.** $\sin^{-1}(2-x)$. **29.** $\cos^{-1}\sqrt{(1-x)}$.

30. $x\cos^{-1}(1-x)$.

Integration

Since
$$\frac{d}{dx}\sin^{-1}\left(\frac{x}{a}\right)=\frac{1}{\sqrt{(a^2-x^2)}}$$

it follows that
$$\int\frac{dx}{\sqrt{(a^2-x^2)}}=\sin^{-1}\left(\frac{x}{a}\right)+C.$$

Similarly since
$$\frac{d}{dx}\left(\tan^{-1}\left(\frac{x}{a}\right)\right)=\frac{a}{a^2+x^2},$$

$$\int\frac{dx}{a^2+x^2}=\frac{1}{a}\tan^{-1}\left(\frac{x}{a}\right)+C.$$

Some worked examples illustrate the use of these formulae.

Example 1. *Find* $\displaystyle\int\frac{dx}{\sqrt{(4-x^2)}}$.

Comparing with
$$\int\frac{dx}{\sqrt{(a^2-x^2)}}=\sin^{-1}\left(\frac{x}{a}\right)+C,$$

$$\int\frac{dx}{\sqrt{(4-x^2)}}=\sin^{-1}\left(\frac{x}{2}\right)+C.$$

Example 2. *Find* $\displaystyle\int\frac{dx}{\sqrt{(4-9x^2)}}$.

$$\int\frac{dx}{\sqrt{(4-9x^2)}}=\int\frac{dx}{3\sqrt{(\frac{4}{9}-x^2)}}=\frac{1}{3}\sin^{-1}\frac{x}{(\frac{2}{3})}=\frac{1}{3}\sin^{-1}\frac{3x}{2}+C.$$

Example 3. *Find* $\displaystyle\int\frac{dx}{25+x^2}$.

Comparing with
$$\int\frac{dx}{a^2+x^2}=\frac{1}{a}\tan^{-1}\left(\frac{x}{a}\right)+C,$$

$$\int\frac{dx}{25+x^2}=\frac{1}{5}\tan^{-1}\left(\frac{x}{5}\right)+C.$$

Example 4. *Find* $\int \dfrac{dx}{a^2x^2 + b^2}$.

$$\int \frac{dx}{a^2x^2 + b^2} = \frac{1}{a^2} \int \frac{dx}{x^2 + (b^2/a^2)} = \frac{1}{a^2} \left(\frac{a}{b}\right) \tan^{-1} \frac{x}{(b/a)}$$

$$= \frac{1}{ab} \tan^{-1} \frac{ax}{b} + C.$$

Example 5. *Find* $\int \dfrac{dx}{2x^2 + 2x + 1}$.

$$\int \frac{dx}{2x^2 + 2x + 1} = \tfrac{1}{2} \int \frac{dx}{x^2 + x + \tfrac{1}{2}}.$$

Put the denominator in the form $(x + a)^2 + b^2$.

$$x^2 + x + \tfrac{1}{2} = (x + \tfrac{1}{2})^2 + \tfrac{1}{4}.$$

$$\therefore \quad \int \frac{dx}{2x^2 + 2x + 1} = \tfrac{1}{2} \int \frac{dx}{(x + \tfrac{1}{2})^2 + \tfrac{1}{4}}$$

$$= \tfrac{1}{2}(2) \tan^{-1} \frac{x + \tfrac{1}{2}}{(\tfrac{1}{2})}$$

$$= \tan^{-1} (2x + 1) + C.$$

Example 6. *Find* $\int \dfrac{dx}{\sqrt{(4x - x^2)}}$.

$$\int \frac{dx}{\sqrt{(4x - x^2)}} = \int \frac{dx}{\sqrt{[4 - (x^2 - 4x + 4)]}} = \int \frac{dx}{\sqrt{[4 - (x - 2)^2]}}$$

$$= \sin^{-1} \frac{x - 2}{2} + C.$$

Example 7. *Evaluate* $\int_0^4 \dfrac{dx}{\sqrt{(4x - x^2)}}$.

$$\int_0^4 \frac{dx}{\sqrt{(4x - x^2)}} = \left[\sin^{-1} \frac{x - 2}{2} \right]_0^4 \quad \text{(see previous example)}$$

$$= \sin^{-1} \frac{2}{2} - \sin^{-1} \left(-\frac{2}{2}\right)$$

$$= \frac{\pi}{2} - \left(-\frac{\pi}{2}\right)$$

$$= \pi.$$

N.B. When inverse relations appear in an integral, their principal values must be used.

Example 8. *Find* $\int \dfrac{x^2 \, dx}{1 + x^6}$.

Method (i) $\int \dfrac{x^2 \, dx}{1 + x^6} = \tfrac{1}{3} \int \dfrac{d(x^3)}{1 + (x^3)^2} = \tfrac{1}{3} \tan^{-1} (x^3) + C.$

Method (ii)

The denominator is $1 + (x^3)^2$ and the numerator is a multiple of $d(x^3)$.

Put $y = x^3$ so that $dy = 3x^2\, dx$.

$$\int \frac{x^2\, dx}{1 + x^6} = \int \frac{\frac{1}{3}\, dy}{1 + y^2} = \frac{1}{3} \int \frac{dy}{1 + y^2} = \frac{1}{3} \tan^{-1} y$$

$$= \frac{1}{3} \tan^{-1} (x^3) + C.$$

Exercise 9.4

Integrate:

1. $\dfrac{1}{1 + 4x^2}$.

2. $\dfrac{1}{4 + x^2}$.

3. $\dfrac{1}{\sqrt{(1 - 4x^2)}}$.

4. $\dfrac{1}{\sqrt{(4 - x^2)}}$.

5. $\dfrac{1}{4 + 25x^2}$.

6. $\dfrac{1}{\sqrt{(4 - 25x^2)}}$.

7. $\dfrac{1}{9 + 16x^2}$.

8. $\dfrac{1}{\sqrt{(9 - 16x^2}}$.

9. $\dfrac{1}{\sqrt{(2x - x^2)}}$.

10. $\dfrac{1}{x^2 + 2x}$.

11. $\dfrac{1}{x^2 + 2x + 2}$.

12. $\dfrac{1}{\sqrt{(8x - x^2)}}$.

13. $\dfrac{1}{x^2 + 4x + 5}$.

14. $\dfrac{1}{x^2 + 6x + 10}$.

15. $\dfrac{1}{\sqrt{(4x - 3 - x^2)}}$.

16. $\dfrac{1}{9x^2 + 6x + 2}$.

17. $\dfrac{2x}{x^4 + 1}$.

18. $\dfrac{x}{\sqrt{(1 - x^4)}}$.

19. $\dfrac{x^2}{\sqrt{(1 - x^6)}}$.

20. $\dfrac{1}{x\{1 + (\ln x)^2\}}$.

Exercise 9.5: Miscellaneous

1. Evaluate $\displaystyle\int_0^2 \frac{dx}{\sqrt{(4 - x^2)}}$.

2. Show that $\tan^{-1} \dfrac{a - b}{1 + ab} + \tan^{-1} \dfrac{b - c}{1 + bc} = \tan^{-1} \dfrac{a - c}{1 + ac}$.

3. Find $\displaystyle\int \frac{dx}{x\sqrt{(x^2 - 1)}}$ by the substitution $x = \dfrac{1}{y}$.

4. Find $\text{Lt}_{x \to 0} \dfrac{\sin^{-1} x}{x}$.

5. Integrate with respect to x: $\dfrac{1}{\sqrt{(5 - 4x - x^2)}}$.

6. Evaluate $\sin^{-1} \dfrac{1}{\sqrt{5}} + \sin^{-1} \dfrac{1}{\sqrt{10}}$.

7. $\text{Lt}_{x \to 0} \dfrac{\tan^{-1} x - x}{x^3}$.

8. Evaluate $\displaystyle\int_0^1 \frac{\tan^{-1} x}{1 + x^2}\, dx$.

9. Find x given that $\tan^{-1}(1 + x) + \tan^{-1}(1 - x) = 32$.

10. If $y = \sin(k \sin^{-1} x)$, show that $(1 - x^2)\left(\dfrac{dy}{dx}\right)^2 = k^2(1 - y^2)$.

11. By means of the substitution $x = \dfrac{1}{t}$, evaluate $\displaystyle\int_1^2 \dfrac{dx}{x\sqrt{(x^2 - 1)}}$.

12. If $y = \sin^{-1} x$, show that $(1 - x^2)\dfrac{d^2 y}{dx^2} = x\,\dfrac{dy}{dx}$.

13. Show that $2 \sin^{-1} \frac{3}{5} = \sin^{-1} \frac{24}{25}$.

14. Show that $2 \sin^{-1} x = \sin^{-1} \{2x\sqrt{(1 - x^2)}\}$.

15. Sketch the graph of $y = \dfrac{1}{1 + x^2}$. Find the area of the region bounded by the curve, the axes and the ordinate $x = 1$.

16. Sketch the graph of $y = \dfrac{1}{\sqrt{(1 - x^2)}}$. Find the area of the region bounded by the curve, the axes and the ordinate $x = \frac{1}{2}$.

17. Evaluate $\displaystyle\int_1^{\sqrt{3}} \dfrac{dx}{1 + x^2}$.

18. If $x > 1$, show that $\dfrac{d}{dx}(\sec^{-1} x) = \dfrac{1}{x\sqrt{(x^2 - 1)}}$.

19. Find the area of the region bounded by the curve $y^2(a^2 - x^2) = a^4$ and the ordinates at $x = \pm\dfrac{a}{2}$.

20. Show that the differential coefficient of $\tan^{-1} x - x + \dfrac{x^3}{3}$ is positive for all values of x. Hence show that $\tan^{-1} x > x - \dfrac{x^3}{3}$ if $x > 0$.

21. Differentiate $\sin^{-1}\sqrt{(1 - x^2)}$ with respect to x.

22. Evaluate $\displaystyle\int_{1/2}^{3/2} \dfrac{dx}{3 + 4x^2}$.

23. Show that $\operatorname{cosec}^{-1} x + \sec^{-1} x = \dfrac{\pi}{2}$ $(x > 1)$.

24. Differentiate $\sin^{-1}\dfrac{x}{\sqrt{(1 + x^2)}} - \tan^{-1} x$. Explain your result.

25. Evaluate $\cos^{-1}\dfrac{4}{\sqrt{17}} + \cos^{-1}\dfrac{5}{\sqrt{34}}$.

26. Find the differential coefficient of $\cot^{-1} x$.

27. Show that $\sin^{-1} x + \sin^{-1} y = \sin^{-1}\{x\sqrt{(1 - y^2)} + y\sqrt{(1 - x^2)}\}$.

28. Differentiate $x^2 \tan^{-1} x - x + \tan^{-1} x$ with respect to x. Hence find $\displaystyle\int x \tan^{-1} x\, dx$.

29. Differentiate $x \tan^{-1} x - \frac{1}{2} \log(1 + x^2)$ with respect to x. Hence find $\int \tan^{-1} x \, dx$.

30. Differentiate $x \sin^{-1} x + \sqrt{(1 - x^2)}$ with respect to x. Hence find $\int \sin^{-1} x \, dx$.

10 Infinite Series and Expansions

Convergent and divergent series

We are already familiar with the sum of the first n terms of the geometric series,

$$S_n = a + ar + ar^2 + \ldots ar^{n-1}$$

where
$$S_n = a\frac{1 - r^n}{1 - r}.$$

Considering the term r^{n-1}, if $0 < r < 1$, we see that r^{n-1} becomes as small as we wish if n is sufficiently large, i.e. $r^{n-1} \to 0$, so that the sum S_n becomes as close as we wish to $a\dfrac{1}{1-r}$. This expression $a\dfrac{1}{1-r}$ is called the sum to infinity S of the geometric series, e.g.

if
$$S_n = 1 + \tfrac{1}{2} + (\tfrac{1}{2})^2 + (\tfrac{1}{2})^3 \ldots (\tfrac{1}{2})^{n-1}$$
$$S_n = 1\frac{1 - (\tfrac{1}{2})^n}{1 - \tfrac{1}{2}}.$$

As $n \to \infty$, $(\tfrac{1}{2})^n \to 0$, so $S_n \to S$, where $S = \dfrac{1}{1 - \tfrac{1}{2}}$

i.e.,
$$S = 2.$$

We can check by adding successive terms that the sum of the series becomes as close as we wish to 2.

Similarly, if $-1 < r < 0$, $r^{n-1} \to 0$ as $n \to \infty$, and $S_n \to a\dfrac{1}{1-r}$, so that we say that if $-1 < r < 1$, the 'sum to infinity' of the geometric series $a + ar + ar^2 \ldots$ is $a\dfrac{1}{1-r}$.

If however $r > 1$, then successive terms in the series become larger and larger, and it is clear that the sum S does not tend to any one finite value. We may say $S_n \to \infty$ as $n \to \infty$, e.g. $1 + 10 + 10^2 + 10^3 \ldots$ clearly exceeds any previously chosen number if we take enough terms of the series.

If $r = 1$, the series is

$$a + a + a + \ldots$$

and the sum of n terms is na. As n becomes large, na becomes large, and the series diverges.

If $r = -1$ the series is

$$a - a + a - a \ldots$$

and the sum of the n terms of the series is 0 if n is even, a if n is odd. The series neither converges nor diverges.

The geometric series

We have seen that if $-1 < r < 1$, the sum of n terms of this series approaches $a\dfrac{1}{1-r}$, as n becomes sufficiently large.

The binomial series

We have proved by induction (Chapter 3) that if n is a positive integer,

$$(a + x)^n = a^n + na^{n-1}x + \frac{n(n-1)}{1 \times 2} a^{n-2}x^2 \ldots x^n$$

for all values of a and x. It can also be proved, though the proof is not required at this stage, that if $-1 < x < 1$, for *all* values of n,

$$(1 + x)^n = 1 + nx + \frac{n(n-1)}{1 \times 2} x^2 + \frac{n(n-1)(n-2)}{1 \times 2 \times 3} x^3 \ldots$$

It is also true when $x = 1$ if $n > -1$ and if $x = -1$ when $n > 0$.

Example. *Find the expansion in ascending powers of x of (i) $(1 + x)^{\frac{1}{2}}$, (ii) $(1 - x)^{-2}$, (iii) $(1 - x)^{-3}$ and (iv) $(1 + 2x)^{-\frac{1}{2}}$, assuming the value of x to be such that the expansions are valid.*

Using the binomial expansion, we have

(i) $\qquad (1 + x)^{\frac{1}{2}} = 1 + \tfrac{1}{2}x + \dfrac{(\frac{1}{2})(-\frac{1}{2})}{1 \times 2} x^2 + \dfrac{(\frac{1}{2})(-\frac{1}{2})(-\frac{3}{2})}{1 \times 2 \times 3} x^3 \ldots$

$\qquad\qquad\qquad = 1 + \tfrac{1}{2}x - \tfrac{1}{8}x^3 + \tfrac{1}{16}x^3 \ldots$

(ii) $\qquad (1 - x)^{-2} = 1 + (-2)(-x) + \dfrac{(-2)(-3)}{1 \times 2} (-x)^2$

$\qquad\qquad\qquad = 1 + 2x + 3x^2 + 4x^3 \ldots$

(iii) $\qquad (1 - x)^{-3} = 1 + (-3)(-x) + \dfrac{(-3)(-4)}{1 \times 2} (-x)^2$

$\qquad\qquad\qquad + \dfrac{(-3)(-4)(-5)}{1 \times 2 \times 3} x^3$

$\qquad\qquad\qquad = 1 + 3x + 6x^2 + 10x^3 + \ldots$

(iv) $\qquad (1 + 2x)^{-\frac{1}{2}} = 1 + (-\tfrac{1}{2})(2x) + \dfrac{(-\frac{1}{2})(-\frac{3}{2})}{1 \times 2} (2x)^2$

$\qquad\qquad\qquad + \dfrac{(-\frac{1}{2})(-\frac{3}{2})(-\frac{5}{2})}{1 \times 2 \times 3} (2x)^3$

$\qquad\qquad\qquad = 1 - x + \tfrac{3}{2}x^2 - \tfrac{5}{2}x^3 \ldots$

Expansion (i) is valid if $-1 < x < 1$, and also if $x = -1$ or $+1$, since the index n is >0, whereas expansions (ii) and (iii) are only valid when

$-1 < x < 1$. Expansion (iv) is valid when $-1 < 2x < 1$, i.e. $-\frac{1}{2} < x < \frac{1}{2}$ (and also when $x = +\frac{1}{2}$, since $-1 < n < 0$), thus all four expansions are valid only if $-\frac{1}{2} < x \leqslant \frac{1}{2}$.

Pascal's triangle

We are familiar with Pascal's triangle, and know that the coefficients in the expansion of $(1 + x)^n$, where n is a positive integer, can be seen in the rows of Pascal's triangle. Expansions (ii) and (iii) show that the coefficients in the expansions of $(1 - x)^{-2}$ and $(1 - x)^{-3}$ can be found in the diagonals of Pascal's triangle. Many other sequences of numbers can be spotted in Pascal's triangle, even the Fibonacci sequence, by totalling along certain diagonals.

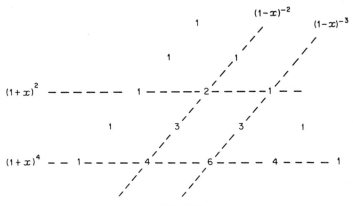

Fig. 10.1

General term

In the expansion of $(1 + x)^{-1}$, we have
$$(1 + x)^{-1} = 1 - x + x^2 - x^3 + x^4 \ldots$$
and so we see that the coefficient term containing x^r, sometimes called the general term, is $(-1)^r$. Likewise
$$(1 + x)^{-2} = 1 - 2x + 3x^2 - 4x^3 \ldots$$
and the term containing x^r is $(-1)^r (r + 1) x^r$.

Example. *Find the general term in the expansion of* $(1 + 2x)^{-4}$.
  Proceeding as before, we have
$$(1 + 2x)^{-4} = 1 + (-4)(2x) + \frac{(-4)(-5)}{1 \times 2} (2x)^2$$
$$+ \frac{(-4)(-5)(-6)}{1 \times 2 \times 3} (2x)^3.$$

Looking at the term containing x^r, we see that it is

$$\frac{(-4)(-5)(-6)\ldots(r+3)}{1\times2\times3\ldots r}(2x)^r.$$

Many of the factors cancel, and the term reduces to

$$(-1)^r\frac{1}{6}(r+1)(r+2)(r+3)2^rx^r.$$

Expansion in ascending powers of $\dfrac{1}{x}$

The expansions in ascending powers of x are only valid when x is 'small'; if x is 'large', we may find it convenient to expand in powers of $\dfrac{1}{x}$, which will then be 'small'.

Example. *Expand* $(1+2x)^{-2}$ *in powers of* $\dfrac{1}{x}$, *and give the range of values of* x *for which the expansion is valid.*

$$(1+2x)^{-2}=\frac{1}{(1+2x)^2}=\frac{1}{4x^2\left(1+\dfrac{1}{2x}\right)^2}$$

$$=\frac{1}{4x^2}\left(1+(-2)\left(\frac{1}{2x}\right)+\frac{(-2)(-3)}{1\times2}\left(\frac{1}{2x}\right)^2\ldots\right)$$

$$=\frac{1}{4x^2}-\frac{1}{4x^3}+\frac{3}{16x^4}\ldots$$

This expansion is valid if $-1<\dfrac{1}{2x}<1$, i.e. $x<-\frac{1}{2}$ or $x>\frac{1}{2}$.

Exercise 10.1

1. Find the sum of the first n terms of each of the following geometric series, and the limiting sum that each approaches as n becomes larger and larger:

   (i) $1+\frac{1}{3}+\frac{1}{9}+\frac{1}{27}\ldots$
   (ii) $1+\frac{1}{5}+\frac{1}{25}\ldots$
   (iii) $1-\frac{1}{4}+\frac{1}{16}\ldots$
   (iv) $1-\frac{1}{10}+\frac{1}{100}\ldots$
   (v) $1+0.1+0.01+0.001\ldots$
   (vi) $2+\frac{1}{2}+\frac{1}{8}\ldots$
   (vii) $10+0.1+0.001\ldots$
   (viii) $10^6+10^3+1+\ldots$
   (ix) $1-\frac{2}{3}+\frac{4}{9}+\ldots$
   (x) $1+\frac{9}{10}+\left(\frac{9}{10}\right)^2+\ldots$

2. Find which of the following geometric series has a 'sum to infinity' and find that sum to infinity where it exists:

(i) $1 + \frac{3}{4} + \frac{9}{16} \ldots$

(ii) $1 - \frac{4}{3} + \frac{16}{9} \ldots$

(iii) $1 - \frac{4}{5} + \frac{16}{25} \ldots$

(iv) $10 - 9 + 8.1 \ldots$

(v) $1 + 1.1 + 1.21 \ldots$

3. Assuming the value of x to be such that the expansions are valid, find the first four terms in the expansions in ascending powers of x of each of the following:

(i) $(1 + x)^{-4}$; (ii) $(1 - 2x)^{-2}$; (iii) $(1 + 3x)^{-2}$;

(iv) $(1 - x)^{\frac{1}{3}}$; (v) $(1 - 2x)^{-\frac{1}{2}}$; (vi) $(1 + 2x)^{\frac{3}{2}}$;

(vii) $(1 + \frac{1}{2}x)^{-2}$; (viii) $(1 - 3x)^{\frac{1}{3}}$; (ix) $(1 - 4x)^{-\frac{1}{4}}$;

(x) $\dfrac{1}{1 + 2x}$; (xi) $\dfrac{1}{\sqrt{(4 + x^2)}}$; (xii) $\dfrac{1}{3 + x^2}$;

(xiii) $(4 + x)^{\frac{1}{2}}$; (xiv) $(4 + 9x)^{\frac{1}{2}}$; (xv) $(8 + x)^{\frac{1}{3}}$;

(xvi) $x(1 + x^2)^{\frac{1}{2}}$; (xvii) $\dfrac{x}{(1 - 2x)}$; (xviii) $\dfrac{x^2}{(1 + 3x)}$;

(xix) $(1 - x)^{-n}$; (xx) $(1 - x^2)^{-n}$.

4. State the range of values of x for which each of the expansions in Q. 3 (i)–(x) is valid.

5. Find the coefficient of x^r in each of the expansions in Q. 3 (i)–(vi), (x), (xii), (xix) and (xx).

6. Find the first negative coefficient in the expansion of $(1 + x)^{\frac{3}{2}}$ in ascending powers of x.

7. How many terms have positive coefficients in the expansion of $(1 - x)^{\frac{1}{2}}$ in ascending powers of x?

8. Assuming the value of x to be such that each expansion is valid, find the first three terms in the expansion of each of the following in ascending powers of $\dfrac{1}{x}$:

(i) $(1 + x)^{-1}$; (ii) $(1 - 2x)^{-3}$; (iii) $(1 + 3x)^{-2}$;

(iv) $(1 + 4x^2)^{-1}$; (v) $(4 + x^2)^{-1}$.

9. By considering the identity $(1 - x^3) \equiv (1 - x)(1 + x + x^2)$ find the first four terms in the expansion in ascending powers of x of $\dfrac{1}{1 + x + x^2}$.

10. Find the first four terms in the expansion in ascending powers of x of $\dfrac{1}{1 - x + x^2}$.

Find also the general term in this expansion.

11. Use the identity $[x - (1 + x^2)^{\frac{1}{2}}][x + (1 + x^2)^{\frac{1}{2}}] \equiv -1$ to find the first three terms in the expansion in ascending powers of x of $\dfrac{1}{x - (1 + x^2)^{\frac{1}{2}}}$.

12. Show that $(1 - x)^{-1} - 2(1 + 2x)^{\frac{1}{2}} + (1 + 3x) \equiv x^2$, if terms containing x^3 and higher powers of x can be neglected.

The expansion of e^x

Let us suppose that it is possible to expand e^x as an infinite series in ascending powers of x and that

$$e^x = a_0 + a_1 x + a_2 x^2 + a_3 x^3 + \ldots$$

Putting $x = 0$ gives

$$e^0 = a_0. \quad \therefore \quad a_0 = 1.$$

Differentiating,

$$e^x = a_1 + 2a_2 x + 3a_3 x^2 + \ldots na_n x^{n-1} + \ldots$$

Putting $x = 0$ gives

$$1 = a_1.$$

Differentiating again gives

$$e^x = 2a_2 + 3(2)a_3 x + \ldots + n(n-1)a_n x^{n-2} + \ldots$$

Putting $x = 0$ gives

$$1 = 2a_2. \quad \therefore \quad a_2 = \tfrac{1}{2}.$$

Differentiating again and putting $x = 0$ gives

$$1 = 3(2)a_3. \quad \therefore \quad a_3 = \frac{1}{3!}.$$

Proceeding in this way we have

$$e^x = 1 + x + \frac{x^2}{2!} + \frac{x^3}{3!} + \ldots + \frac{x^n}{n!} + \ldots$$

It may be proved that this expansion is convergent for all values of x but the proof is outside the scope of this book.

The value of e

Putting $x = 1$ gives

$$e = 1 + \frac{1}{1!} + \frac{1}{2!} + \frac{1}{3!} + \ldots$$

Tabulating the values:

$$1 = 1.000\,000$$

$$\frac{1}{1!} = 1.000\,000$$

$$\frac{1}{2!} = 0.500\,000$$

$$\frac{1}{3!} = 0.166\,667 \quad \left(\frac{1}{3} \text{ of } \frac{1}{2!}\right)$$

$$\frac{1}{4!} = 0.041\,667 \quad \left(\frac{1}{4} \text{ of } \frac{1}{3!}\right)$$

$$\frac{1}{5!} = 0.008\,333 \quad \left(\frac{1}{5} \text{ of } \frac{1}{4!}\right)$$

$$\frac{1}{6!} = 0.001\,389 \quad \left(\frac{1}{6} \text{ of } \frac{1}{5!}\right)$$

$$\frac{1}{7!} = 0.000\,198 \quad \left(\frac{1}{7} \text{ of } \frac{1}{6!}\right)$$

$$\frac{1}{8!} = 0.000\,025 \quad \left(\frac{1}{8} \text{ of } \frac{1}{7!}\right)$$

$$\frac{1}{9!} = 0.000\,003 \quad \left(\frac{1}{9} \text{ of } \frac{1}{8!}\right)$$

$$\overline{2.718\,282}$$

Subsequent terms will have a zero in the sixth decimal place. The value of e correct to 6 significant figures is $2.718\,28$ which agrees with the figure previously found.

Other exponential expansions

If in the expansion

$$e^x = 1 + x + \frac{x^2}{2!} + \frac{x^3}{3!} + \ldots + \frac{x^n}{n!} + \ldots$$

x is replaced by kx, we have

$$e^{kx} = 1 + kx + \frac{k^2 x^2}{2!} + \frac{k^3 x^3}{3!} + \ldots + \frac{k^n x^n}{n!} + \ldots$$

Suppose now we put $k = \ln a$. Then

$$e^{kx} = e^{x \ln a} = e^{\ln ax} = a^x.$$

$$\therefore \quad a^x = 1 + x \ln a + \frac{x^2 (\ln a)^2}{2!} + \ldots + \frac{x^n (\ln a)^n}{n!} + \ldots$$

Example 1. *Express (i) $\frac{1}{e}$, (ii) $e^x + \frac{1}{e^x}$ as infinite series.*

(i)
$$\frac{1}{e} = e^{-1} = 1 - 1 + \frac{1}{2!} - \frac{1}{3!} + \frac{1}{4!} - \frac{1}{5!} - \ldots$$

$$= \frac{1}{2!} - \frac{1}{3!} + \frac{1}{4!} - \frac{1}{5!} + \ldots$$

(ii)
$$e^x = 1 + x + \frac{x^2}{2!} + \frac{x^3}{3!} + \ldots$$

$$\frac{1}{e^x} = e^{-x} = 1 - x + \frac{x^2}{2!} - \frac{x^3}{3!} + \ldots$$

$$\therefore \quad e^x + e^{-x} = 2\left(1 + \frac{x^2}{2!} + \frac{x^4}{4!} + \ldots + \frac{x^{2n}}{(2n)!} + \ldots\right).$$

Example 2. *Find the coefficient of* x^n *in the expansion of* e^{2-x}.

$$e^{2-x} = e^2 \cdot e^{-x} = e^2 \left(1 - x + \frac{x^2}{2!} - \ldots + (-1)^n \frac{x^n}{n!} - \ldots \right).$$

The coefficient of x^n is $(-1)^n \dfrac{e^2}{n!}$.

Exercise 10.2

1. Write down the first four non-zero terms in series equal to
   (i) e^{2x};   (ii) $e^{-\frac{1}{2}x}$;   (iii) e^{x^2};
   (iv) $e^x - e^{-x}$;   (v) 3^x;   (vi) $(\frac{1}{2})^x$;
   (vii) e^{-2};   (viii) $e^{\frac{1}{2}}$;   (ix) $\frac{1}{2}(e + e^{-1})$;
   (x) $2^{\frac{1}{2}}$.

2. Calculate the value of $\dfrac{1}{e}$ to 4 decimal places.

3. Find the first four terms in the expansion of $(x^2 + 1)e^{-x}$.

4. Find the coefficient of x^3 in the expansion of $(1 + x)e^x$.

5. Find the coefficient of x^3 in the expansion of e^{1+2x}.

6. Find the first three terms on the expansion of e^{3-x}.

7. Write down the coefficient of x^3 in the expansion of 10^x.

8. Find $\mathrm{Lt}_{x \to 0} \dfrac{e^x - 1}{x}$.

9. Find $\mathrm{Lt}_{x \to 0} \dfrac{e^{2x} - 1 - 2x}{x^2}$.

10. Find the coefficient of x^n in the expansion of $(1 + x + x^2)e^x$.

11. Find the sum to infinity of the series $1 + \frac{1}{3} + \frac{1}{9} + \frac{1}{27} + \ldots$

12. The expansion of $(a + bx)e^x$ begins with the terms $4 + 5x$. Find the values of a and b.

13. Find the first three terms in the expansion of $\dfrac{e^x + e^{-x}}{e^{3x}}$.

14. Find the coefficient of x^n in the expansion of $\dfrac{e^{3x} + e^{2x}}{e^x}$.

15. Find the sum to infinity of the series $1 + e^{-x} + e^{-2x} + \ldots$

16. Find the first three terms in the expansion of $e^{-x} - (1 - x)^{-1/2}$.

17. Find the first three terms in the expansion of $e^{2x} - (1 - 3x)^{-1/3}$.

18. Show that $\left(\dfrac{e^x + e^{-x}}{2}\right)^2 - \left(\dfrac{e^x - e^{-x}}{2}\right)^2 = 1$.

19. In the expansion $a^x = 1 + x \ln a + \dfrac{x^2}{2!}(\ln a)^2 + \ldots$, put $a = 1 + y$. By equating coefficients of x on the two sides of the equation, find an expansion for $\ln (1 + y)$. For what values of y is the expansion valid?

20. Find the coefficient of x^r in the expansion of $(1 - 2x)e^{2x}$.

Maclaurin's expansion

If it is possible to expand a function of x as a series in ascending powers of x, a method similar to that used for the exponential function applies.

Suppose that $f(x)$ can be expanded as an infinite series in ascending powers of x and that

$$f(x) = A_0 + A_1x + A_2x^2 + A_3x^3 + \ldots$$

Suppose that $f_n(x)$ stands for the nth differential coefficient of $f(x)$ with respect to x and that $f_n(0)$ is its value when $x = 0$.

Putting $x = 0$ gives

$$f(0) = A_0.$$

Differentiating gives

$$f_1(x) = A_1 + 2A_2x + 3A_3x^2 + \ldots$$

Putting $x = 0$ gives

$$f_1(0) = A_1.$$

Differentiating again gives

$$f_2(x) = 2A_2 + 3(2)A_3x + \ldots$$

Putting $x = 0$ gives

$$f_2(0) = 2A_2. \quad \therefore \quad A_2 = \frac{f_2(0)}{2!}.$$

Differentiating again and putting $x = 0$ gives

$$f_3(0) = 3(2)A_3. \quad \therefore \quad A_3 = \frac{f_3(0)}{3!}.$$

$$\therefore \quad f(x) = f(0) + xf_1(0) + \frac{x^2}{2!}f_2(0) + \frac{x^3}{3!}f_3(0) + \ldots$$

$$+ \frac{x^n}{n!}f_n(0) + \ldots$$

The expansion is valid provided that the infinite series is convergent.

Example 1. $\ln(1 + x)$.

N.B. $\ln x$ cannot be expanded as an infinite series because the value of $\ln x$ when $x = 0$ is not finite.

$$f(x) = \ln(1 + x) \qquad f(0) = 0.$$

$$f_1(x) = \frac{1}{1 + x} \qquad f_1(0) = 1.$$

$$f_2(x) = -\frac{1}{(1 + x)^2} \qquad f_2(0) = -1.$$

$$f_3(x) = \frac{2}{(1 + x)^3} \qquad f_3(0) = 2.$$

$$f_4(x) = -\frac{2 \times 3}{(1 + x)^4} \qquad f_4(0) = -6.$$

$$\therefore \quad \ln(1+x) = x - \frac{x^2}{2} + \frac{x^3}{3} - \frac{x^4}{4} \cdots$$

This expansion is valid provided $-1 < x \leqslant 1$.
Replacing x by $-x$ gives

$$\ln(1-x) = -x - \frac{x^2}{2} - \frac{x^3}{3} - \frac{x^4}{4} \cdots$$

This expansion is valid provided $-1 \leqslant x < 1$.

Example 2. *sin x.*

$$
\begin{array}{ll}
f(x) = \sin x & f(0) = 0 \\
f_1(x) = \cos x & f_1(0) = 1 \\
f_2(x) = -\sin x & f_2(0) = 0 \\
f_3(x) = -\cos x & f_3(0) = -1 \\
f_4(x) = \sin x & f_4(0) = 0 \\
f_5(x) = \cos x & f_5(0) = 1.
\end{array}
$$

$$\therefore \quad \sin x = x - \frac{x^3}{3!} + \frac{x^5}{5!} \cdots$$

Example 3. *cos x.*

$$
\begin{array}{ll}
f(x) = \cos x & f(0) = 1 \\
f_1(x) = -\sin x & f_1(0) = 0 \\
f_2(x) = -\cos x & f_2(0) = -1 \\
f_3(x) = \sin x & f_3(0) = 0 \\
f_4(x) = \cos x & f_4(0) = 1.
\end{array}
$$

$$\therefore \quad \cos x = 1 - \frac{x^2}{2!} + \frac{x^4}{4!} - \cdots$$

Example 4. *tan^{-1} x.*

$$
\begin{array}{ll}
f(x) = \tan^{-1} x & f(0) = 0 \\[2mm]
f_1(x) = \dfrac{1}{1+x^2} & f_1(0) = 1 \\[3mm]
f_2(x) = -\dfrac{2x}{(1+x^2)^2} & f_2(0) = 0 \\[3mm]
f_3(x) = -\dfrac{2}{(1+x^2)^2} + \dfrac{8x^2}{(1+x^2)^3} & f_3(0) = -2.
\end{array}
$$

$$\therefore \quad \tan^{-1} x = x - \frac{x^3}{3} + \cdots$$

(This series is more easily obtained by expanding $(1 + x^2)^{-1}$ as $1 - x^2 + x^4 - x^6 \ldots$ Then, assuming it is possible to equate the integrals of the two sides of the equation,

$$\tan^{-1} x + C = x - \frac{x^3}{3} + \frac{x^5}{5} \cdots$$

and as $\tan^{-1} x = 0$ when $x = 0$, $C = 0$.)

Example 5. *Expand sec x tan x as far as the term in x^3.*

$$f(x) = \sec x \tan x. \qquad\qquad\qquad\qquad f(0) = 0.$$
$$f_1(x) = \sec^3 x + \sec x \tan^2 x. \qquad\qquad f_1(0) = 1.$$
$$f_2(x) = 3 \sec^3 \tan x + \sec x \tan^3 x + 2 \tan x \sec^3 x$$
$$\qquad = 5 \sec^3 x \tan x + \sec x \tan^3 x. \qquad f_2(0) = 0.$$
$$f_3(x) = 15 \sec^3 x \tan^2 x + 5 \sec^5 x + \sec x \tan^4 x$$
$$\qquad + 3 \tan^2 x \sec^3 x. \qquad\qquad\qquad f_3(0) = 5.$$

$$\therefore \quad \sec x \tan x = x + \frac{5x^3}{3!} + \ldots$$

Taylor's expansion

Maclaurin's expansion is a particular case of Taylor's expansion which tells us what change occurs in a function for a small variation of the independent variable. It states that

$$f(x + h) = f(x) + hf_1(x) + \frac{h^2}{2!}f_2(x) + \frac{h^3}{3!}f_3(x) + \ldots$$

This when h is small gives us an approximation for $f(x + h)$ and this approximation may be taken to as many terms as we wish.

We have already seen in Chapter 5 that $f(x) + hf_1(x)$ is an approximation for $f(x + h)$ when h is small and Taylor's expansion gives the following terms in the series.

Maclaurin's expansion is deduced from Taylor's by putting x equal to zero and h equal to x.

Brook Taylor (1685–1731) published his theorem about 1715 although he had discovered it at least three years previously. Mathematicians were slow to appreciate the power of the theorem and the proof, as given by Taylor, was worthless as it entirely ignored the principles of convergency.

Colin Maclaurin (1698–1746), after whom Maclaurin's theorem is named, was primarily a geometer and his theorem had been previously given by both Taylor and Stirling.

It was not until the time of Cauchy that any advance was made in a rigorous treatment of infinite series and his *Analyse Algébrique*, published in 1821, was the first real attempt to treat the subject without assumptions of convergency.

Example. *Find the value of tan 45° 1' to 5 places of decimals.*

If
$$f(x) = \tan x$$
$$f_1(x) = \sec^2 x$$
$$f_2(x) = 2 \sec^2 x \tan x$$
$$f_3(x) = 4 \sec^2 x \tan^2 x + 2 \sec^4 x.$$

So, by Taylor's expansion,

$$\tan (x + h) = \tan x + h \sec^2 x + \frac{h^2}{2!} (2 \sec^2 x \tan x)$$
$$+ \frac{h^3}{3!} (4 \sec^2 x \tan^2 x + 2 \sec^4 x) + \ldots$$

Putting $x = 45°$,

$$\tan(45° + h) = 1 + 2h + \frac{h^2}{2}(4) + \frac{h^3}{3!}(8 + 8) + \ldots$$

$$= 1 + 2h + 2h^2 + \frac{8}{3}h^3 + \ldots$$

Remember, since we are using differentiation, that h must be in radians.

$$\therefore \quad h = \frac{1°}{60} = \frac{\pi}{60 \times 180} \text{ radians.}$$

$$\therefore \quad \tan 45° \, 1' = 1 + \frac{2\pi}{60 \times 180} + \frac{2\pi^2}{60^2 \times 180^2} + \frac{8\pi^3}{3 \times 60^3 \times 180^3} + \ldots$$

$$\frac{\pi}{60 \times 90} = 0.000\,581\,8.$$

$$\frac{\pi}{60 \times 90} \simeq 0.000\,581\,8 \quad \text{and} \quad \frac{2\pi^2}{60^2 \times 180^2} \simeq 0.000\,000\,2$$

and so $\dfrac{2\pi^2}{60^2 \times 180^2}$ will not affect the 5th place.

So $f(x) + hf_1(x)$ was sufficient for the approximation but Taylor's theorem proves that the approximation is correct to 5 places of decimals.

$$\therefore \quad \tan 45° \, 1' = 1.000\,581\,8 \simeq 1.000\,58.$$

Exercise 10.3

1. Use Maclaurin's theorem to find the first three terms in the expansion of each of the following:

(i) e^{2x}; (ii) e^{x^2}; (iii) $\sin kx$;
(iv) $\tan ax$; (v) $\sec x$; (vi) $\sin^2 x$;
(vii) $\sin(x^2)$; (viii) $x \, e^x$; (ix) $\arcsin x$;
(x) $\arctan x$.

2. Use Maclaurin's theorem to find the first three terms in the expansion of each of the following:

(i) $\dfrac{1}{(1 + x)}$; (ii) $\dfrac{1}{(1 + 2x)}$; (iii) $\dfrac{1}{(2 + x)}$;

(iv) $\dfrac{1}{(1 + x)^{\frac{1}{2}}}$; (v) $\dfrac{1}{(1 + 3x)^2}$.

3. Expand $\sin x \sin 2x$ as far as the term in x^3.

4. Expand $e^{\sin x}$ as far as the term in x^3.

5. Prove that $x \cot x = 1 - \dfrac{x^2}{3} - \dfrac{x^4}{45} \ldots$

6. Expand $\sin(x + h)$ in terms of h as far as the term in h^3.

7. Expand e^{x+h} in terms of h as far as the term in h^3.

8. Expand $\cos(x + h)$ in terms of h as far as the term in h^3.

9. If x is sufficiently small for powers of x above the second to be neglected,

prove that $\dfrac{1}{1 + e^x} = \frac{1}{4}(2 - x)$.

10. Prove that $e^{\tan x} = 1 + x + \frac{1}{2}x^2 + \frac{1}{2}x^3 + \ldots$

11. Prove that $\ln (\sec x + \tan x) = x + \dfrac{x^3}{6} + \ldots$

12. Find $\sin 30° \, 1'$ to 4 places of decimals.

13. Find $\cos 60° \, 2'$ to 4 places of decimals.

14. Prove that $\sqrt{(1 - x^2)} \sin^{-1} x = x - \dfrac{x^3}{3} - \dfrac{2x^5}{15} \ldots$

15. Show that $\dfrac{\sin^{-1} x}{\sqrt{(1 - x^2)}} = x + \frac{2}{3}x^3 + \frac{8}{15}x^5 + \ldots$

Calculation of logarithms

We have seen that

$$\ln (1 + x) = x - \frac{x^2}{2} + \frac{x^3}{3} \ldots + (-1)^{n-1} \frac{x^n}{n} \ldots$$

provided $-1 < x \leqslant 1$, and that

$$\ln (1 - x) = -x - \frac{x^2}{2} - \frac{x^3}{3} \ldots - \frac{x^n}{n} \ldots$$

provided $-1 \leqslant x < 1$.

These series may be used to calculate logarithms but their disadvantage is that they converge slowly, i.e. a large number of terms must be taken to get four-figure accuracy. For example, putting $x = 1$,

$$\ln 2 = 1 - \tfrac{1}{2} + \tfrac{1}{3} - \tfrac{1}{4} \ldots$$

and the thousandth term of this series is numerically 0.001.

Subtracting one series from the other,

$$\ln (1 + x) - \ln (1 - x) = 2\left\{ x + \frac{x^3}{3} + \frac{x^5}{5} \ldots \right\}$$

or

$$\ln \frac{1 + x}{1 - x} = 2\left\{ x + \frac{x^3}{3} + \frac{x^5}{5} \ldots \right\}.$$

Put $\dfrac{1 + x}{1 - x} = \dfrac{m}{n}$ so that $n + nx = m - mx$ and $x = \dfrac{m - n}{m + n}$.

Then $\quad \ln \dfrac{m}{n} = 2\left\{ \dfrac{m - n}{m + n} + \dfrac{1}{3}\left(\dfrac{m - n}{m + n}\right)^3 + \dfrac{1}{5}\left(\dfrac{m - n}{m + n}\right)^5 \ldots \right\}.$

Since $\dfrac{m - n}{m + n}$ lies between ± 1 for all positive values of m and n, this series is valid for all positive values of the variables and has the advantage of rapid convergency. It is this series which is most frequently used for the calculation of logarithms. Remember that logarithms so calculated are to base e.

Example 1. *Calculate ln 2 to 4 places of decimals.*

Put $\qquad m = 2, n = 1 \quad$ so that $\quad \dfrac{m-n}{m+n} = \dfrac{1}{3}.$

Then $\qquad \ln 2 = 2\{\frac{1}{3} + \frac{1}{3}(\frac{1}{3})^3 + \frac{1}{5}(\frac{1}{3})^5 + \ldots\}.$

$\frac{1}{3} = 0.333\,333$	$\frac{1}{3} = 0.333\,333$
$(\frac{1}{3})^3 = 0.037\,037$ (dividing by 9)	$\frac{1}{3}(\frac{1}{3})^3 = 0.012\,346$
$(\frac{1}{3})^5 = 0.004\,115$	$\frac{1}{5}(\frac{1}{3})^5 = 0.000\,823$
$(\frac{1}{3})^7 = 0.000\,457$	$\frac{1}{7}(\frac{1}{3})^7 = 0.000\,065$
$(\frac{1}{3})^9 = 0.000\,051$	$\frac{1}{9}(\frac{1}{3})^9 = 0.000\,006$
$(\frac{1}{3})^{11} = 0.000\,006$	
	$\overline{0.346\,573}$

$$\therefore \quad \ln 2 = 2(0.346\,573)$$
$$= 0.693\,146$$

The value of ln 2 correct to 4 places of decimals is 0.6931.

Example 2. *Calculate ln 10 to 4 places of decimals.*

If we put

$$\frac{m}{n} = 10, \quad \frac{m-n}{m+n} = \frac{9}{11}$$

and powers of this converge slowly.

It is helpful to use the value of ln 2 already found and to calculate $\ln \frac{10}{8}$.

$$\ln \tfrac{10}{8} = 2\{\tfrac{1}{9} + \tfrac{1}{3}(\tfrac{1}{9})^3 + \tfrac{1}{5}(\tfrac{1}{9})^5 + \ldots\}$$

$\frac{1}{9} = 0.111\,111$	$\frac{1}{9} = 0.111\,111$
$(\frac{1}{9})^2 = 0.012\,346$	
$(\frac{1}{9})^3 = 0.001\,372$	$\frac{1}{3}(\frac{1}{9})^3 = 0.000\,457$
$(\frac{1}{9})^4 = 0.000\,152$	
$(\frac{1}{9})^5 = 0.000\,017$	$\frac{1}{5}(\frac{1}{9})^5 = 0.000\,003$
	$\overline{0.111\,571}$

$$\therefore \quad \ln \tfrac{10}{8} = 0.223\,142$$
$$\ln 10 = 0.223\,142 + \ln 8$$
$$= 0.223\,142 + 3 \log 2 \quad (\text{since } 8 = 2^3)$$
$$= 0.223\,142 + 2.079\,438$$
$$= 2.302\,580$$
$$\simeq 2.302\,6.$$

To calculate logarithms to the base 10 from Napierian logarithms, we must use the formula

$$\log_{10} x = \frac{\ln x}{\ln 10},$$

which means we must divide the corresponding logarithms by 2.302 6.

Applications to expansions and to summing series

The logarithmic series may be used in the expansion of more complicated expressions and may also be used in the summation of series as shown below.

Example 1. *Find the coefficient of x^n in the expansion of*
$$(1 - x - x^2) \ln (1 - x).$$
$$\ln (1 - x) = -x - \frac{x^2}{2} - \frac{x^3}{3} \ldots - \frac{x^{n-2}}{n-2} - \frac{x^{n-1}}{n-1} - \frac{x^n}{n} \ldots$$

The coefficient of x^n in the product $(1 - x - x^2) \ln (1 - x)$ is
$$-\frac{1}{n} + \frac{1}{n-1} + \frac{1}{n-2} = \frac{-(n-1)(n-2) + n(n-2) + n(n-1)}{n(n-1)(n-2)}$$
$$= \frac{n^2 - 2}{n(n-1)(n-2)}.$$

This is true provided all three terms appear in the expansion, i.e. $n \geqslant 3$.
The coefficient of x is -1.
The coefficient of x^2 is $-\frac{1}{2} + 1$ or $\frac{1}{2}$.

Example 2. *Sum to infinity the series* $\dfrac{x}{1 \times 2} + \dfrac{x^2}{2 \times 3} + \dfrac{x^3}{3 \times 4} + \ldots$

The general term is $\dfrac{x^r}{r(r+1)}$.

$$\frac{1}{r(r+1)} = \frac{1}{r} - \frac{1}{r+1} \quad \text{and so} \quad \frac{x^r}{r(r+1)} = \frac{x^r}{r} - \frac{x^r}{r+1}.$$

Putting each term in this form, we get
$$S = \left(\frac{x}{1} - \frac{x}{2} \right) + \left(\frac{x^2}{2} - \frac{x^2}{3} \right) + \left(\frac{x^3}{3} - \frac{x^3}{4} \right) + \ldots$$
$$= \left(\frac{x}{1} + \frac{x^2}{2} + \frac{x^3}{3} + \ldots \right) - \left(\frac{x}{2} + \frac{x^2}{3} + \frac{x^3}{4} + \ldots \right)$$
$$= -\ln (1 - x) - \frac{1}{x} \{ -\ln (1 - x) - x \}$$
$$\text{(provided } -1 \leqslant x < 1)$$
$$= \left(\frac{1}{x} - 1 \right) \ln (1 - x) + 1.$$

Exercise 10.4

1. Calculate $\ln 3$ to 3 decimal places.
2. Find the coefficient of x^3 in the expansion of $(1 + x) \ln (1 + x)$.
3. If $\ln y = 1 + x + x^2$, show that $y = e (1 + x + \frac{3}{2}x^2)$ as far as the term in x^2.
4. Find the sum to infinity of $\dfrac{x}{2} + \dfrac{x^2}{3} + \dfrac{x^3}{4} + \ldots$
5. Expand $\dfrac{\ln (1 + x)}{1 - x}$ as far as the term in x^3.
6. Find the coefficient of x^n in the expansion of $\ln (2 + x)$.
7. Calculate $\ln 1.02$ correct to 4 decimal places.
8. Calculate $\ln \frac{9}{11}$ to 4 decimal places.

9. Calculate $\ln \frac{4}{3}$ to 4 decimal places.

10. Expand as far as the term in x^3 the expression $\ln (1 + x)^3$.

11. Expand $\ln (1 + x)(1 + 2x)$ as far as the term in x^3.

12. Expand $\ln \dfrac{1 + x^2}{1 + x}$ as far as the term in x^3.

13. Expand $\ln (1 + x + x^2)$ as far as the term in x^4. (Use the factors of $(1 - x^3)$.)

14. Find $\mathrm{Lt}_{x \to 0} \dfrac{\ln (1 + x)}{x}$.

15. Find $\mathrm{Lt}_{x \to 0} \dfrac{\ln \{(1 + x)(1 + 2x)\}}{x}$.

Exercise 10.5: Miscellaneous

1. Find the area of the region bounded by the curve $y = e^{kx}$, the ordinates at $x = 0$ and $x = 1$ and the x-axis.

2. Find the volume generated by rotating the region in question 1 about the axis of x.

3. Find $\mathrm{Lt}_{x - 0} \dfrac{\sin x - x}{x^3}$.

4. Expand $\sin^{-1} (mx)$ as far as the term in x^3.

5. Find the first three terms and the coefficient of x^r in the expansion of $\ln (1 - 3x + 2x^2)$ in ascending powers of x. State the range of values of x for which the expansion is valid.

6. Find the first two terms in the expansion of $\sin (m \sin^{-1} x)$ in ascending powers of x.

7. Expand $\ln \dfrac{(1 - x)^2}{(1 - 2x)^3}$ as far as the term in x^3.

8. Expand $\dfrac{x}{(1 + x)(1 - x)^2}$ as far as the term in x^3.

9. Find the coefficient of x^n in the expansion of
$$\ln \{(1 - \alpha x)(1 - \beta x)(1 - \gamma x)\}.$$

10. Calculate the value of $\ln 3$ to 3 decimal places.

11. Find the first three terms in the expansion of $e^{-3x} \ln (1 + x)$ in ascending powers of x.

12. Find the first three terms in the expansion of $\sin \{\ln (1 + x)\}$ in ascending powers of x.

13. Sum to infinity the series $\dfrac{x}{1.2} - \dfrac{x^2}{2.3} + \dfrac{x^3}{3.4} - \dfrac{x^4}{4.5} \cdots$

14. Find the first three terms in the expansion of $e^{-2x} \sin 2x$ in ascending powers of x.

15. Find the first two terms in the expansion of $\ln \cos x$ in ascending powers of x.

16. Prove that the sum to infinity of the series

$$1 - \left(\frac{1}{6}\right) + \frac{1.3}{2!}\left(\frac{1}{6}\right)^2 - \frac{1.3.5}{3!}\left(\frac{1}{6}\right)^3 + \frac{1.3.5.7}{4!}\left(\frac{1}{6}\right)^4 \cdots$$

is $\frac{1}{2}\sqrt{3}$.

[*Hint*: Express the series as a binomial expansion.]

17. Sum to infinity the series

$$1 + \left(\frac{3}{8}\right) + \frac{1.3}{2!}\left(\frac{3}{8}\right)^2 + \frac{1.3.5}{3!}\left(\frac{3}{8}\right)^3 + \cdots$$

18. Prove by induction that

$$\frac{d^n}{dx^n}(e^x \cos x) = 2^{n/2} e^x \cos\left(x + \frac{n\pi}{4}\right).$$

19. Given that $y = e^{3x}(1 - x)^2$, find the first two terms in the expansion of $\ln y$ in ascending powers of x.

20. Using the result of question 18, find the coefficient of x^n in the expansion of $e^x \cos x$ in ascending powers of x.

21. Sum to infinity the series $\dfrac{1}{1.3} + \dfrac{1}{3.5} + \dfrac{1}{5.7} + \cdots$

22. Sum to infinity the series $\dfrac{1}{1.6} + \dfrac{1}{6.11} + \dfrac{1}{11.16} + \dfrac{1}{16.21} + \cdots$

23. Find the first three terms in the expansion of $\sin^2 x$.

24. Evaluate $\mathrm{Lt}_{x \to 0} \dfrac{2 \sin x - \sin 2x}{x(\cos x - \cos 2x)}$.

25. Show that $2 \ln n - \ln(n + 1) - \ln(n - 1)$

$$= 2\left\{\frac{1}{2n^2 - 1} + \frac{1}{3}\left(\frac{1}{2n^2 - 1}\right)^3 + \cdots\right\}.$$

26. Show that $\ln(n^2 + 1) - \ln(n + 1) - \ln(n - 1)$

$$= 2\left\{\frac{1}{n^2} + \frac{1}{3n^6} + \frac{1}{5n^{10}} + \cdots\right\}.$$

27. Calculate the value of $e^{\frac{1}{3}}$ correct to 4 decimal places.

28. Show that $\ln(1 - ax) + \ln(1 - bx) = \ln(1 - px + qx^2)$, where $p = a + b$ and $q = ab$.

Using the logarithmic expansion, show that
(i) $a^2 + b^2 = p^2 - 2q$,   (ii) $a^3 + b^3 = p^3 - 3pq$.

29. Show that $2 \tan^{-1}\frac{1}{3} + \tan^{-1}\frac{1}{7} = \dfrac{\pi}{4}$.

Use this identity and the formula $\tan^{-1} x = x - \dfrac{x^3}{3} + \dfrac{x^5}{5} \cdots$, to obtain a value for π.

30. Find the first three terms in the expansion of $e^x(\cos x + \sin x)$ in ascending powers of x.

11 Curve Sketching and Inequalities

When we are considering the equation of a curve it is obviously an advantage to have some idea what the curve looks like. It is not necessary to have a perfect graph, but is usually sufficient to have a general idea of the shape of the curve from a rough sketch.

Trigonometric graphs

We are already familiar with the trigonometric graphs, and the important features of these can be illustrated by considering first $y = a \sin (x + b)$.

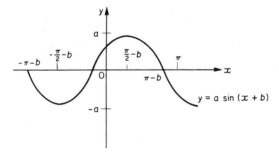

Fig. 11.1

Since $-1 \leqslant \sin x \leqslant 1$ for all values of x, $-a \leqslant y \leqslant a$ so that the curve oscillates between $-a$ and $+a$. When $x = -b$, $\sin (x + b) = 0$ and so that the graph crosses the x-axis at $x = -b$, and thereafter at intervals of π. A rough sketch showing these features is Fig. 11.1.

If instead the equation had been of the form $y = \sin 2x$, then the curve would have met the x-axis at intervals of $\pi/2$, so that $y = a \sin (2x + b)$ meets the x-axis where $x = -b$, $-b + \pi/2$, $-b + \pi$, $-b + 3\pi/2$, etc. ...

Since $\cos x = \sin (x + \pi/2)$, the cosine curve is merely the sine curve displaced by $\pi/2$ parallel to the x-axis, translated $\pi/2$ units (Fig. 11.2).

The sine and cosine curve are the trigonometric curves that occur most frequently in physical problems. The tangent curve is also sometimes met, and we should be familiar with its most important features, especially that it has asymptotes parallel to the y-axis. Figure 11.3 shows that $y = \tan kx$ has asymptotes at intervals of π/k.

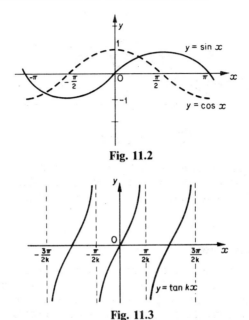

Fig. 11.2

Fig. 11.3

The exponential graph

We saw the nature of the function $y = e^x$ in Chapter 7. If x is replaced by $-x$, the curve is reflected in the y-axis, and the graph of $y = e^{-x}$ is given in Fig. 11.4(b). Remember that e^x is never negative.

If we remember that when $x = 0$, $e^x = 1$, when x is large and positive e^x is large and positive, but when x is large and negative, e^x is small but positive, then many other exponential curves can be deduced.

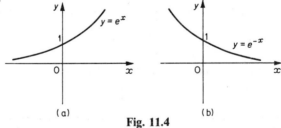

(a)   (b)

Fig. 11.4

Example. *Sketch the graph of* $y = e^{-x^2}$.

When $x = 0$, $e^{-x^2} = e^0 = 1$.

When x is large and positive, e^{-x^2} is small and positive.

When x is large but negative, e^{-x^2} is small but positive.

If we need the coordinates of the points of inflexion, they can be found using calculus, but the general features of the curve are given in Fig. 11.5.

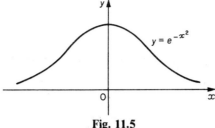

Fig. 11.5

Although these sketches are of graphs of the form $y = e^x$, whether the base is e or any other number greater than 1 does not affect the nature of the curve, and $y = a^x$ has the same shape as $y = e^x$, providing $a > 1$.

Logarithmic graph

Since $y = \ln x \Leftrightarrow x = e^y$, the graph of $y = \ln x$ can be obtained from the graph of $y = e^x$ by reflecting in the line $y = x$. Remember that there is no part of the curve for which x is negative. The nature of the curve is not affected by the base to which the logarithms are taken, and $y = \log_a x$ has the same general shape.

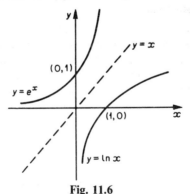

Fig. 11.6

Exercise 11.1

1. Sketch the following curves, showing the range of values of y, and the points at which each meets the x-axis:

   (i) $y = \sin 3x$;　　(ii) $y = 3 \sin x$;　　　　(iii) $y = -\sin 2x$;
   (iv) $y = \sin (2x + \pi/3)$;　　　　　(v) $y = -\sin (2x + \pi/3)$.

2. Sketch the following curves, showing the range of values of y, and the points at which each meets the y-axis:

   (i) $y = \cos 4x$;　　(ii) $y = 4 \cos x$;　　　　(iii) $y = -\cos x$;
   (iv) $y = \cos (2x + \pi/4)$;　　　　　(v) $y = \cos (\pi/4 - 2x)$.

3. Sketch the following curves, showing the range of values of y and the points of intersection of each with the y-axis:

(i) $y = 1 + \sin x$; (ii) $y = 2 - \cos x$;
(iii) $y = 1 + \cos 2x$; (iv) $y = -2 + \sin 2x$.

4. Sketch the following curves, showing the range of values of y, and the relation of each to the x-axis:

(i) $y = \sin^2 x$; (ii) $y = 1 + \cos^2 x$;
(iii) $y = 1 - 2\sin^2 x$; (iv) $y = 2\cos^2 x - 1$.

5. Sketch the following curves, showing also their asymptotes and their relation to the coordinate axes:

(i) $y = \tan 2x$; (ii) $y = \tan(x + \pi/4)$;
(iii) $y = \sec x$; (iv) $y = \operatorname{cosec} 2x$.

6. Sketch the following curves, showing where each crosses the y-axis, and the nature of the curve when x is large and negative, and when x is large and positive:

(i) $y = e^{2x}$; (ii) $y = 2e^x$;
(iii) $y = e^{-\frac{1}{2}x}$; (iv) $y = e^{1-x}$.

7. Sketch the following curves for positive values of x, showing where each crosses the y-axis, and the nature of the curve when x is large:

(i) $y = xe^x$; (ii) $y = e^x \sin x$;
(iii) $y = x \sin x$; (iv) $y = e^{-x} \sin x$.

8. Sketch the following curves, showing where each crosses the y-axis, and the nature of the curve when x is large and positive and when x is large and negative:

(i) $y = e^{1-x^2}$; (ii) $y = e^x$;
(iii) $y = \frac{1}{2}(e^x + e^{-x})$; (iv) $y = \frac{1}{2}(e^x - e^{-x})$.

9. Sketch the following terms for positive values of x, showing where each crosses the y-axis and the nature of the curve when x is large:

(i) $y = \ln 2x$; (ii) $y = \ln(x^2)$;
(iii) $y = \ln(x + 2)$; (iv) $y = (\ln x)^2$.

10. Sketch the following curves on the same pair of coordinate axes, showing the relation between the three curves:

(i) $y = 2^x$; (ii) $y = e^x$; (iii) $y = 3^x$.

Algebraic graphs

When sketching algebraic graphs there are certain questions we must ask ourselves.

(i) Where does the curve cross the coordinates axes, e.g. the curve $y = (x + 1)(x - 2)$ crosses the x-axis where $y = 0$ and $x = -1$, and at $y = 0$, $x = 2$; it crosses the y-axis where $x = 0$ and $y = -2$ (Fig. 11.7)?

(ii) Is there an axis of symmetry that can be found easily, e.g. if the curve is $y^2 = x^3$, for any given value of x, say $x = k$, there are two equal and opposite values of y, $y = +k^{\frac{3}{2}}$ and $y = -k^{\frac{3}{2}}$, so the curve is symmetrical about the x-axis (Fig. 11.8)?

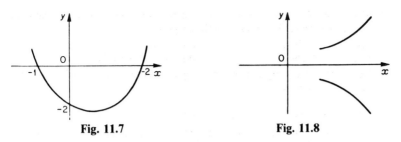

Fig. 11.7   **Fig. 11.8**

(iii) Is there a range of values of x for which there is no real value of y, e.g. if $y^2 = x(x - 1)$, where $0 < x < 1$, y^2 is negative, so there are no real values of y and the curve does not exist in that region (Fig. 11.9)?

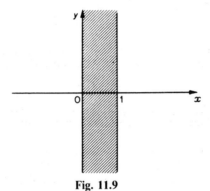

Fig. 11.9

(iv) Is there a value of x for which y is infinite, for this gives an asymptote parallel to the y-axis, e.g. if $y = \dfrac{1}{(x - 1)(x - 2)}$ y is infinite when $x = 1$ or $x = 2$, so that $x = 1$ and $x = 2$ are asymptotes to the curve (Fig. 11.10)?

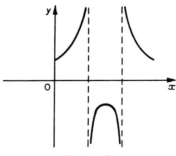

Fig. 11.10

(v) What is the nature of the curve when x becomes very large, either very large and positive, or very large and negative, e.g. if $y = 1/x^2$, as x becomes very large and positive y is very small and positive, and when x is very large and negative, y is very small but positive (Fig. 11.11)?

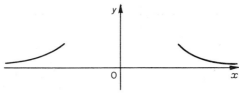

Fig. 11.11

These questions are answered in the next example.

Example. *Sketch the graph of* $y = \dfrac{(x - 1)(x - 2)}{(x + 2)(x - 3)}$.

(i) When $y = 0$, $x = 1$ or 2, so the curve crosses the x-axis at $(1, 0)$ and $(2, 0)$.

When $x = 0$, $y = -1/3$, so the curve crosses the y-axis at $(0, -1/3)$.

(ii) If a curve is symmetrical about the x-axis, x only occurs with even powers, so there is no symmetry about the x-axis in this case. Similarly the curve is not symmetrical about the y-axis. In the equation of the curve, if we interchange x and y we shall not obtain the same equation, so there does not appear to be an easily-identified axis of symmetry. (In some questions in the next exercise there is an axis of symmetry, but that will only be seen after the curve has been sketched.)

(iii) There is a value of y for every value of x, except $x = -2$ and $x = 3$ (though here we may say that 'y is infinite'), so there is no range of values of x for which the curve does not exist.

(iv) When x is just a little less than -2, say $x = -2.01$, y is very large but positive; when x is just a little greater than -2, say $x = -1.99$, y is very large but negative, so that $x = -2$ is an asymptote. Similarly, when x is just a little less than 3, say $x = 2.99$, y is very large but negative, and when x is a little more than 3, say $x = 3.01$, y is very large and positive, so that $x = 3$ is an asymptote.

(v) When x is large and positive, say $x = 10^6$, $y \simeq \dfrac{10^6 \times 10^6}{10^6 \times 10^6} = 1$, so that when x is large and positive, y is nearly equal to 1*. Similarly when y is large and negative, so that $y = 1$ is an asymptote parallel to the x-axis.

The information we have obtained from questions (i), (iv) and (v) we can display in Fig. 11.12, and we can complete the sketch as in Fig. 11.13. Remember that the graph can only cross the coordinate axes at the points we have already found.

---

* In fact, y is a little less than 1. Write $y = 1 - \dfrac{2(x - 4)}{(x + 2)(x - 3)}$ to see that $y < 1$ if x is large and positive, $y > 1$ if x is large and negative.

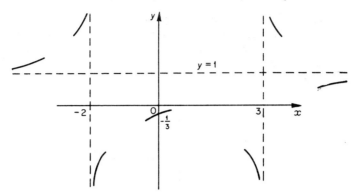

Fig. 11.12

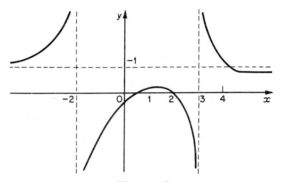

Fig. 11.13

Example 2. *Sketch the graph of* $y = \dfrac{x}{x^2 + 2}$.

Asking the same questions as before, we have

(i) When $y = 0$, $x = 0$ and when $x = 0$, $y = 0$, so that the curve only crosses the coordinate axes at the origin.

(ii) Replacing x by $-x$ and y by $-y$ we see that $y = \dfrac{-x}{x^2 + 2}$

so that the curve is symmetrical about the origin. This does not help in drawing the curve, but can be confirmed from our completed sketch.

(iii) There is a value for y for every value of x.

(iv) There is no value of x for which y is infinite, so that there are no asymptotes parallel to the y-axis.

(v) When x is large and positive, y is small and positive; when x is large and negative, y is small and negative, so that $y = 0$ is an asymptote.

These features can be put on a sketch (Fig. 11.14(a)) and completed as in Fig. 11.14(b).

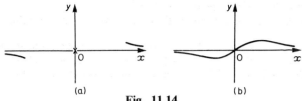

Fig. 11.14

Exercise 11.2

Sketch the following curves, showing where appropriate
  (i) where they meet the coordinate axes,
 (ii) any asymptotes parallel to the y-axis,
(iii) any asymptotes parallel to the x-axis.

1. $y = \dfrac{1}{(x-1)(x-2)}$.

2. $y = \dfrac{6}{(x+3)(x-2)}$.

3. $y = \dfrac{x}{(x+4)(x-2)}$.

4. $y = \dfrac{1}{(x+1)(x-1)}$.

5. $y = \dfrac{x}{(x+1)(x-1)}$.

6. $y = \dfrac{x^2}{(x+1)(x-1)}$.

7. $y = \dfrac{x^2}{(x+2)(x-1)}$.

8. $y = \dfrac{1}{x(x-1)}$.

9. $y = \dfrac{1}{(x-1)^2}$.

10. $y = \dfrac{x}{(x-1)^2}$.

11. $y = \dfrac{x^2}{(x-1)^2}$.

12. $y = \dfrac{x^2}{(x-1)}$.

13. $y = \dfrac{(x-1)^2}{x(x-2)}$.

14. $y = \dfrac{1}{x^2+1}$.

15. $y = \dfrac{x}{x^2+1}$.

16. $y = \dfrac{x+1}{x^2+1}$.

17. $y = \dfrac{1}{x^2+2x+2}$.

18. $y = \dfrac{x}{x^2-2x+2}$.

19. $y = \dfrac{x}{x^2+3x+2}$.

20. $y = \dfrac{x+1}{x^2+3x+2}$.

The graph of $y = |x|$

The expression $|x|$ is defined as
$$|x| = \quad x \quad \text{if} \quad x \geqslant 0,$$
$$= -x \quad \text{if} \quad x < 0$$
so that the graph of $y = |x|$ is as shown in Fig. 11.15. Graphs of other functions with modulus signs $|\ \ |$ can be deduced from this definition.

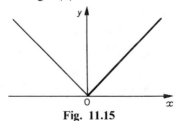

Fig. 11.15

Example 1. *Draw the graph of* $y = |2x - 3|$.

When $2x < 3$, $x < 3/2$, so that we have two ranges of values of x to consider.

When $x > 3/2$, $|2x - 3| = 2x - 3$, so we need to draw the graph of $y = 2x - 3$. But when $x < 3/2$, $|2x - 3| = -(2x - 3) = 3 - 2x$, so that we need to sketch the graph of $y = 3 - 2x$. Figure 11.16 shows the sketch of $y = |2x - 3|$.

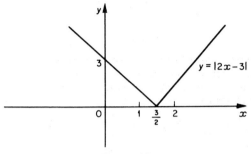

Fig. 11.16

Example 2. *Sketch the graph of* $y = |\sin x|$.

When $\sin x$ is positive, $|\sin x| = \sin x$, but when $\sin x$ is negative, $|\sin x| = -\sin x$, the reflection in the x-axis, so that for values of x for which $\sin x$ is positive the graph is merely that of $y = \sin x$, while for values of x for which $\sin x$ is negative, the graph is the reflection in the x-axis of that part of the sine curve. The sketch is shown in Fig. 11.17.

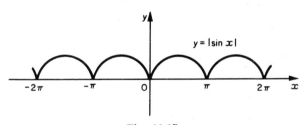

Fig. 11.17

Exercise 11.3

Sketch the following curves:

1. $y = |2x|$.

2. $y = |2x - 1|$.

3. $y = |3x - 2|$.

4. $y = x|2x|$.

5. $y = \dfrac{|x|}{x}$.

6. $y = |\cos x|$.

7. $y = |\ln x|, x > 0$.

8. $y = \dfrac{1}{|x|}$.

9. $y = \sin |x|$.

10. $y = e^{|x|}$.

Maximum and minimum points

The location of maximum and minimum points is obviously of help in sketching graphs. In the graph of $y = x(x - 1)(x - 2)$ shown in Fig. 11.18, a check on the maximum and minimum values is essential if the relative positions of the points are to be correct.

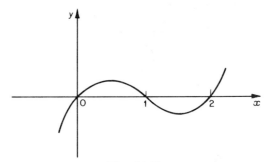

Fig. 11.18

If
$$y = x(x - 1)(x - 2) = x^3 - 3x^2 + 2x,$$
$$\frac{dy}{dx} = 3x^2 - 6x + 2.$$

For a stationary point, $\dfrac{dy}{dx} = 0$.

$$\therefore \quad 3x^2 - 6x + 2 = 0$$
$$\therefore \quad x = \frac{6 \pm \sqrt{12}}{6} = 1 \pm \sqrt{\tfrac{1}{3}}.$$

How are we to determine which is a maximum and which a minimum? A method using the sign of the gradient was discussed in *Additional Pure Mathematics*. Another method considering the sign of $\dfrac{d^2y}{dx^2}$ is now given.

At a maximum, $\dfrac{dy}{dx}$ is first $+$ve, then zero and finally $-$ve. $\dfrac{dy}{dx}$ is therefore decreasing and so its differential coefficient must be negative.

$$\therefore \quad \text{at a maximum,} \frac{d^2y}{dx^2} \text{ is } -\text{ve.}$$

At a minimum, $\dfrac{dy}{dx}$ is first $-$ve, then zero and finally $+$ve. $\dfrac{dy}{dx}$ is increasing and so its differential coefficient must be positive.

$$\therefore \quad \text{at a minimum,} \frac{d^2y}{dx^2} \text{ is } +\text{ve.}$$

In the example above $\dfrac{dy}{dx} = 3x^2 - 6x + 2$.

$$\therefore \quad \dfrac{d^2y}{dx^2} = 6x - 6.$$

When $\qquad x = 1 + \sqrt{\tfrac{1}{3}}, \dfrac{d^2y}{dx^2} = 6 + \dfrac{6}{\sqrt{3}} - 6 = \dfrac{6}{\sqrt{3}} - 6$

Since this is positive, the point must give a minimum.

When $\qquad x = 1 - \sqrt{\tfrac{1}{3}}, \dfrac{d^2y}{dx^2} = 6 - \dfrac{6}{\sqrt{3}} - 6$

which is negative. This point gives a maximum.

Point of inflexion

If the value of $\dfrac{d^2y}{dx^2}$ is zero, the point may be a maximum, a minimum or a point of inflexion. A point of inflexion is shown in Fig. 11.19. At such a point, the tangent to the curve has the parts of the curve immediately before and after the point on opposite sides of it.

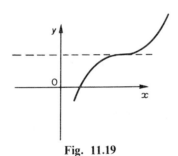

Fig. 11.19

When $\dfrac{d^2y}{dx^2} = 0$, the sign of the gradient should be considered to determine whether the point is a point of inflexion. If the gradient does not change sign, the point is in fact a point of inflexion; otherwise it is a maximum or a minimum.

A point of inflexion need not have $\dfrac{dy}{dx} = 0$ (see Fig. 11.20). At any point of inflexion, $\dfrac{d^2y}{dx^2}$ must be zero but $\dfrac{d^2y}{dx^2} = 0$ does not necessarily imply a point of inflexion.

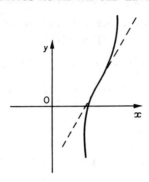

Fig. 11.20

Example 1. *Find the maximum value of* $x\,e^{-x}$.

If
$$y = x e^{-x}$$

$$\frac{dy}{dx} = e^{-x} - x e^{-x} = e^{-x}(1 - x)$$

and
$$\frac{d^2y}{dx^2} = -e^{-x}(1 - x) - e^{-x} = e^{-x}(x - 2).$$

When $\dfrac{dy}{dx} = 0, x = 1.$

For this value of x,

$$\frac{d^2y}{dx^2} = e^{-1}(-1) \quad \text{which is negative.}$$

The value $x = 1$ gives a maximum and the maximum value of y is $\dfrac{1}{e}$.

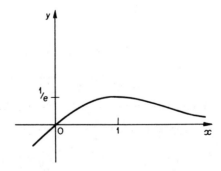

Fig. 11.21

Example 2. *Find the maximum and minimum values of* $(x - 1)^3(x - 2)$.

If
$$y = (x - 1)^3(x - 2)$$

$$\frac{dy}{dx} = (x - 1)^3 + 3(x - 1)^2(x - 2)$$

$$= (x - 1)^2(x - 1 + 3x - 6)$$

$$= (x - 1)^2(4x - 7).$$

$\dfrac{dy}{dx} = 0$ when $x = 1$ or $x = \frac{7}{4}$.

$$\frac{d^2y}{dx^2} = 2(x - 1)(4x - 7) + 4(x - 1)^2.$$

When $x = 1, \dfrac{d^2y}{dx^2} = 0.$

We must consider the sign of $\dfrac{dy}{dx}$.

If x is just less than 1, $\dfrac{dy}{dx}$ is $-$ ve.

If x is just greater than 1, $\dfrac{dy}{dx}$ is $-$ve.

$$\therefore \quad x = 1 \text{ gives a point of inflexion.}$$

When $x = \frac{7}{4}, \dfrac{d^2y}{dx^2} = 4(\frac{3}{4})^2$ which is $+$ve.

$\therefore \quad x = \frac{7}{4}$ gives a minimum. The minimum value is $(\frac{3}{4})^3(-\frac{1}{4})$ or $-\frac{27}{256}$.
A sketch of the graph is given in Fig. 11.22.

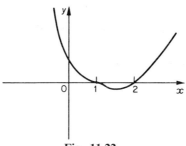

Fig. 11.22

Exercise 11.4

Distinguish between the stationary points of the following functions:

1. $x + \dfrac{1}{x}$.

2. $\dfrac{\sqrt{x}}{2} + \dfrac{2}{x}$.

3. $x^4 - 4x$.

4. $(x - 1)^2(x - 3)$.

5. $(x - 1)^3(x - 3)$.

6. $x^2 e^x$.

7. $\cos x + \sin x$.

8. $x^3(x - 1)$.

9. $x^4(x - 1)$.

10. $\sin x\, e^x$.

Symmetry of the curve

For many curves, the symmetry of the curve reveals interesting properties, and also helps in sketching the curve.

If the equation of the curve is of the form $y = f(x)$, and if $f(x) = f(-x)$, then the curve is symmetrical about the y-axis, e.g. the graph of $y = x^2 - x^4$ is shown in Fig. 11.23. If the equation of the curve is written in the form $f(x, y) = 0$, then the curve will still be symmetrical about the y-axis if $f(x, y) = f(-x, y)$.

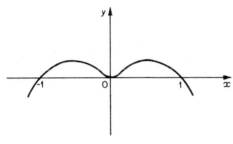

Fig. 11.23

Similarly, the curve will be symmetrical about the x-axis if the equation is $x = f(y)$ and $f(y) = f(-y)$, or if the equation is written $f(x, y) = 0$ and $f(x, y) = f(x, -y)$. (See Example 1 below.)

If x and y can be interchanged without altering the equation of the curve, the curve is symmetrical about the line $y = x$. This can be written

$$f(x, y) = f(y, x),$$

where $f(x, y) = 0$ is the equation of the curve. If x and $-y$ can be interchanged, the curve is symmetrical about $y = -x$. This can be written

$$f(x, y) = f(-y, -x),$$

where $f(x, y) = 0$ is the equation of the curve.

Example 1. *The curve $y = x^2$ is symmetrical about the y-axis but not about the x-axis.*

Example 2. *The curve $y^2 = x^2 - x^4$ is symmetrical about the x-axis and the y-axis; it is not symmetrical about the line $y = x$ or the line $y = -x$.*

Example 3. *The curve $x^2 + y^2 = 1$ is symmetrical about the x-axis and the y-axis, and also about both $y = x$ and $y = -x$.*

Example 4. *The curve $x^3 - y^3 = 3axy$ is symmetrical about the line $y = -x$ but not about $y = x$.*

Tangents to the curve at the origin

In a more detailed sketch than those we have made so far we may wish to investigate the nature of the curve at the origin. If a curve passes through the origin, then near the origin the terms of higher degree will be smaller than those of lower degree, e.g. $y = x + x^2$ will be close to $y = x$ when x is nearly 0. To find the tangents at the origin we equate to zero the terms of lowest degree.

Example 1. *The tangent at the origin to the curve* $y = x^2 + x^3$ *is* $y = 0$, *the x-axis.*

Example 2. *Find the tangents at the origin to the curve* $y^2 = 4x^2 - x3$.

Here we have two terms both of lowest degree, y^2 and x^2, so the tangents at the origin are $y^2 = x^2$, i.e. $y = x$ and $y = -x$. When x becomes large, by contrast, x^3 is much larger than x^2, so that the curve is like $y^2 = x^3$.

Example 3. *Sketch the curve* $y^2 = 4x^2 - x^3$.

First we see that when $y = 0$, $x = 0$ or 4, and when $x = 0$, $y = 0$, so that the curve only crosses the coordinate axes at $(0, 0)$ and $(4, 0)$.

Secondly we see that when we replace y by $-y$ the equation of the curve is unaltered, so that the curve is symmetrical about the x-axis.

Next we see that when $x > 4$ there are no real values of y, since y^2 is negative, so that the curve does not exist in the region $x > 4$.

There are no straight-line asymptotes parallel to the coordinate axes, so we next consider the shape near the origin. The terms of lowest degree are $y^2 = 4x^2$, and the tangents at the origin are $y = 2x$ and $y = -2x$. We notice that since the other term is $-x^3$, the curve itself will be on the side of the tangent nearer to the y-axis when x is positive. We can now sketch the curve (Fig. 11.24), and if we needed to do so, go on to find the maximum and minimum values of y when $0 < x < 4$.

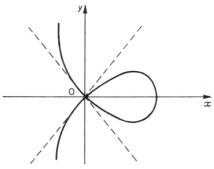

Fig. 11.24

Example 4. *Sketch the curve* $y^2 = x(x - 1)(x - 2)$.

When $y = 0$, $x = 0$ or 1 or 2; when $x = 0$, $y = 0$, so that the curve crosses the coordinate axes at $(0, 0)$, $(1, 0)$ and $(2, 0)$.

When y is replaced by $-y$, the equation of the curve is unaltered, so that the curve is symmetrical about the x-axis.

y^2 is negative when $x < 0$ or when $1 < x < 2$, so that the curve does not exist in those intervals.

The term of lowest degree is on the R.H.S., $2x$, so that the tangent at the origin is $2x = 0$, the y-axis.

The curve can now be sketched as in Fig. 11.25.

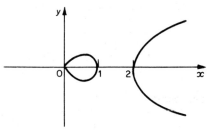

Fig. 11.25

Exercise 11.5

1. Write down the equation of the tangent at the origin to the following curves:

   (i) $y = 4x - x^2$ (ii) $y^2 - y = x^2 - 3x$
   (iii) $x = y^3 + 2y^2$ (iv) $y + x = x^5$.

2. Write down the equation of the tangents at the origin to the following curves:

   (i) $y^2 = 4x^2 + x^3$ (ii) $x^4 + x^2 = 2y^4$
   (iii) $16y^2 = x^3 + 9x^2$ (iv) $x^2 + y^2 = x^4$.

   What can you deduce from your result in (iv)?

3. Make rough sketches of the following curves:

   (i) $x^2y^2 - x^2 + y^2 = 0$ (ii) $y^2(x - 3) = x^2(x - 1)$
   (iii) $y^2(a + x) = x^2(3a - x)$ (iv) $y^2x = (2a - x)(x - a)^2$
   (v) $ay^2 = x(a - x)^2$ (vi) $y = (x - 1)(x - 2)^2(x - 3)$
   (vii) $y^4 = a^2x(a - x)$ (viii) $xy^2 = a^2(a - x)$.

The next example uses an algebraic method to find the maximum and minimum points.

Example. *Sketch the graph of* $y = \dfrac{(x - 3)^2}{(x - 1)(x - 9)}$.

From the equation $\qquad y = \dfrac{(x - 3)^2}{(x - 1)(x - 9)}$,

we have $\qquad x^2(y - 1) + x(6 - 10y) + 9(y - 1) = 0$.

For real values of x,   '$b^2 \geqslant 4ac$',

and so $\qquad (6 - 10y)^2 \geqslant 36(y - 1)^2$,

or $\qquad (3 - 5y)^2 \geqslant 9(y - 1)^2$.

$\therefore \quad 9 - 30y + 25y^2 \geqslant 9y^2 - 18y + 9$

or
$$16y^2 - 12y \geqslant 0$$
$$\therefore \quad y(4y - 3) \geqslant 0.$$
$$\therefore \quad y \text{ cannot lie between } \tfrac{3}{4} \text{ and } 0.$$

When $x \to \infty$, $y \to 1$.
When $x > 9$, $y > 0$;   as $x \to 9$, $y \to \infty$.
When $3 < x < 9$, $y < 0$;   when $x = 3$, $y = 0$.
When $1 < x < 3$, $y < 0$;   when $x \to 1$, $y \to \infty$.
When $x < 1$, $y > 0$;   when $x \to -\infty$, $y \to 1$.

When $y = \tfrac{3}{4}$, $\dfrac{(x - 3)^2}{(x - 1)(x - 9)} = \dfrac{3}{4}$

$$\therefore \quad 4x^2 - 24x + 36 = 3x^2 - 30x + 27$$
$$\therefore \quad x^2 + 6x + 9 = 0$$
$$\therefore \quad (x + 3)^2 = 0 \quad \text{or} \quad x = -3.$$

The minimum value occurs at $(-3, \tfrac{3}{4})$.
The sketch in Fig. 11.26 shows that y cannot lie between 0 and $\tfrac{3}{4}$.
The lines $x = 1$ and $x = 9$ which the curve approaches at infinity are called asymptotes. The line $y = 1$ is also an asymptote (see Fig. 11.26).

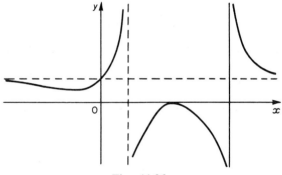

Fig. 11.26

Exercise 11.6

1. If $y = \dfrac{x(x + 1)}{x - 1}$, show that y cannot lie between $3 \pm 2\sqrt{2}$.

2. Show that $\dfrac{x(x - 2)}{x - 1}$ can take any value.

3. If $y = \dfrac{x^2}{x - 1}$, show that y cannot lie between 0 and 4.

4. If $(x - \alpha)(x - \beta)(x - \gamma) > 0$ where $\alpha > \beta > \gamma$, show that x is either larger than α or lies between β and γ.

5. If $(x - \alpha)^2(x - \beta) > 0$, show that $x > \beta$.

6. Show that $\dfrac{x}{x^2 - 1}$ can take all values.

Inequalities

If $ax = b$, and $a \neq 0$, then $x = b/a$, but if $ax < b$, $x < b/a$ *only if a is positive.*

Care must always be taken when multiplying or dividing an inequality by a number that the number is positive; if the number is negative, the inequality is altered, e.g.

$$-3x < 6 \Leftrightarrow x > -2$$

Quadratic inequalities

If $(x - a)(x - b) = 0$, $x = a$ or b, but if $(x - a)(x - b) < 0$, then $a < x < b$ and if $(x - a)(x - b) > 0$, then $x < a$ or $x > b$.

It is often helpful to sketch the graph to find the range of values that satisfy an inequality. Figure 11.27 shows that

$$(x + 1)(x - 2) > 0 \quad \text{if}$$
$$x < -1 \quad \text{or} \quad x > 2.$$

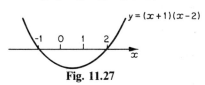

Fig. 11.27

The following examples illustrate the methods used in solving inequalities and the advantages of being able to sketch the curves easily.

Example 1. *Find the range of values of x for which* $\dfrac{1}{x - 2} > \dfrac{2}{x}$.

Method 1

When $x > 2$ both $x - 2$ and x are positive, so

$$\frac{1}{x - 2} > \frac{2}{x} \Leftrightarrow x > 2(x - 2)$$
$$\Leftrightarrow x < 4$$
$$\therefore \quad 2 < x < 4$$

is one acceptable range.

When $0 < x < 2$, $x - 2$ is negative but x is positive, so

$$\frac{1}{x - 2} > \frac{2}{x} \Leftrightarrow x < 2(x - 2)$$
$$\Leftrightarrow x > 4,$$

which is not consistent with $0 < x < 2$.

When $x < 0$, both x and $x - 2$ are negative so their product is positive and

$$\frac{1}{x - 2} > \frac{2}{x} \Leftrightarrow x > 2(x - 2)$$
$$\Leftrightarrow x < 4,$$

which is true already as $x < 0$,

$$\therefore \quad x < 0 \quad \text{or} \quad 2 < x < 4$$

satisfy the original inequality.

Method 2

Sketching the curves $y = \dfrac{1}{x-2}$ and $y = \dfrac{2}{x}$ can either be used as a check, or as an alternative method of solving the inequality.

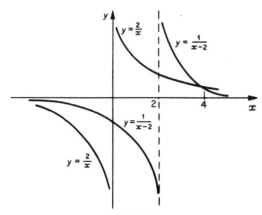

Fig. 11.28

From the graphs we see that $\dfrac{1}{x-2}$ is always greater than $\dfrac{2}{x}$ when x is negative, and also that it is greater than $\dfrac{2}{x}$ when $2 < x < 4$. The value $x = 4$ has to be found by solving the equation $\dfrac{1}{x-2} = \dfrac{2}{x}$

i.e. $x = 2(x-2), \quad x = 4$

Example 2. *Find the range of values of x for which* $|x| < |x - 2|$.

We could solve this in three stages, considering the ranges $x < 0$, $0 < x < 2$ and $x > 2$, but it is easier to draw the graphs of $y = |x|$ and $y = |x - 2|$. We can see from Fig. 11.29 that $|x| < |x - 2|$ if $x < 1$, where the value $x = 1$ was found by solving $x = 2 - x$.

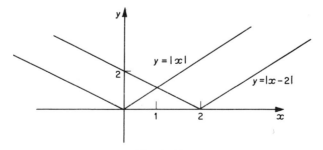

Fig. 11.29

Example 3. *Find the range of values for which* $|x| < |2x - 3|$.

The graphs of $y = |x|$ and $y = |2x - 3|$ are shown in Fig. 11.30. To find the x coordinate of P, solve $y = x$ with $y = 3 - 2x$, giving $x = 1$. To find the x coordinate of Q, solve $y = x$ with $y = 2x - 3$ giving $x = 3$. From the graphs we see that $|x| < |2x - 3|$ if $x < 1$ or $x > 3$.

Check:

when $x = 0$, $|x| = 0$, $|2x - 3| = 3$ and $0 < 3$;

when $x = 2$, $|x| = 2$, $|2x - 3| = 1$ and $2 \not< 1$;

when $x = 4$, $|x| = 4$, $|2x - 3| = 5$ and $4 < 5$.

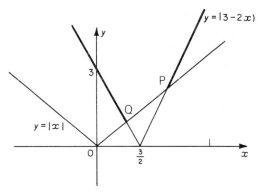

Fig. 11.30

Exercise 11.7

Solve the following inequalities:

1. $4x + 8 > 0$.

2. $10 + 5x < 0$.

3. $x^2 - 4 > 0$.

4. $x^2 + 16 < 25$.

5. $(x - 1)(x - 5) > 0$.

6. $(x + 1)(x - 2) < 0$.

7. $x^2 - 4x + 3 < 0$.

8. $x^2 - 4x - 4 > 1$.

9. $(x - 1)^2(x - 3) < 0$.

10. $\dfrac{(x - 1)^2}{(x - 3)} > 0$.

11. $\dfrac{2x}{x - 1} > 3$.

12. $\dfrac{x - 1}{x} < 2$.

13. $\dfrac{6}{x} \geqslant 5 - x$.

14. $\dfrac{6}{x} \leqslant 5 - x$.

15. $x + 3 \geqslant \dfrac{10}{x}$.

16. $x \leqslant \dfrac{1}{3 - 2x}$.

17. $|x| < |3x - 2|$.

18. $|x| > |3x - 2|$.

19. $|x - 2| > |2x - 7|$.

20. $|2x - 1| < |3x - 4|$.

Exercise 11.8: Miscellaneous

1. Sketch the graph of $y = (x - 1)(x + 5)$ without making a table of values.

2. Sketch a graph which passes through the origin, has negative gradient when $x < 1$ and positive gradient when $x > 1$.

3. Show that the gradient of $x^3 - 3x^2 + 3x + 3$ is positive for all values of x. Hence show that $x^3 - 3x^2 + 3x + 3 > 3$ when $x > 0$.

4. Find the values of λ for which $x^2 + x + 1 + \lambda(x^2 - x + 1)$ is a perfect square.

5. Sketch the graph of $y = x^3 + 3x - 4$.

6. For what values of x is $\dfrac{(x - 1)(x - 2)}{(x - 3)(x - 4)} > 0$?

7. For what values of x is $\dfrac{x}{x - 1} > 1$?

8. For what values of x is $\dfrac{x}{x - 1} > 2$?

9. For what values of x is $\dfrac{x - 1}{x - 3} > 1$?

10. For what values of x is $\dfrac{x - 1}{x - 3} > 2$?

11. Show that $\dfrac{(x - a)^2}{x}$ can take any positive value.

12. By putting $y = tx$, obtain a parametric representation of the curve $x^3 + y^3 = 3xy$ and sketch the curve.

13. Find the maximum and minimum values of $(1 + t^2) e^{-\frac{1}{4}t^2}$.

14. Show that the equation $\cos^2 \theta + 2h \cos \theta \sin \theta - \sin^2 \theta = 2$ has real solutions if and only if $h^2 \geqslant 3$.

15. Show that the differential coefficient of $2x \sin x \sin^2 x$ is positive when $0 < x < \dfrac{\pi}{2}$.

16. Sketch the graph of $y = \dfrac{2x + 1}{x^2 + 2}$.

17. Show that $-\dfrac{1}{2} \leqslant \dfrac{x}{x^2 + 1} \leqslant \dfrac{1}{2}$.

18. Sketch the graph of $y = e^{-x} \sin x$.

19. Sketch the graph of $y = \dfrac{(x + 1)(x - 2)}{x - 4}$.

20. If $x^2 + y^2 + 4x + 2y + 1 = 0$ and x and y are real, show that $-3 \leqslant y \leqslant 1$.

21. If $x^2 + y^2 - 4x - 4y + 4 = 0$ and x and y are real, show that $0 \leqslant x \leqslant 4$ and $0 \leqslant y \leqslant 4$.

22. Sketch the graph of $y = \dfrac{(4 - x)(1 - x)}{4 - 3x}$.

23. Find the maximum and minimum values of the function $\dfrac{\cos x}{2 - \sin x}$ between the values 0 and 2π for x.

24. By expressing the equation $a \cos \theta + b \sin \theta + c = 0$, in terms of $\tan \dfrac{\theta}{2}$, show that the equation has real solutions if $a^2 + b^2 \geqslant c^2$.

25. Sketch the graph of $y = \dfrac{x^2(4 - x)}{2 - x}$.

26. The gradient at any point (x, y) of a curve is given by $\dfrac{dy}{dx} = 1 - x^2$ and the curve passes through the point $(0, 1)$. Sketch its graph.

27. Sketch the graph of the curve given parametrically by $x = 2(t^3 - 1)$, $y = 3t^2$.

28. Sketch the graph of $y = \dfrac{x^2 - 4x + 3}{x^2 + 1}$.

29. Sketch the graph of $y = \dfrac{x - 8}{(x + 1)(x - 2)}$.

30. Sketch the curve $y^2 = \dfrac{x^2(1 - x)}{1 + x}$.

12 Solution of Equations

Linear interpolation

If $f(x) = x^3 - 3x + 1$, $f(1) = -1$ and $f(2) = 3$, so that the curve $y = x^3 - 3x + 1$ crosses the x-axis between $x = 1$ and $x = 2$, and there is a root of $x^3 - 3x + 1 = 0$ between $x = 1$ and $x = 2$. To find a first approximation to this root, join PQ by a straight line, to cross the x-axis at X. Using similar triangles, PX:XQ = 1:3, so the x coordinate

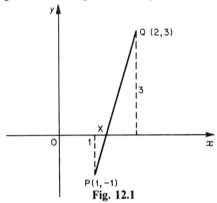

Fig. 12.1

of X is 1.25. This *may* be a good approximation to the root of the equation, and indeed will be if the curve between $x = 1$ and $x = 2$ is close to a straight line. However, we see $f(1.25) \eqsim -0.8$, so this is not much of an improvement on $x = 1$. Wondering why, we see that $f'(1) = 0$, and there is a minimum at $(1, -1)$, so that the nature of the curve between $x = 1$ and $x = 2$ is shown in Fig. 12.2, where we see that $x = 1.25$ is not a close approximation to the root of the equation.

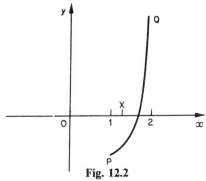

Fig. 12.2

Successive approximations: Newton-Raphson method

If $x = x_0$ is a good approximation to a root of the equation $f(x) = 0$, the exact value of the root will be $x_0 + h$, where h is small, i.e. $f(x_0 + h) = 0$. By Taylor's Theorem,

$$f(x_0 + h) = f(x_0) + hf'(x_0) + \tfrac{1}{2}h^2 f''(x_0) \ldots$$

so that, unless $f''(x_0)$ is very large, providing h is small we have

$$f(x_0 + h) \simeq f(x_0) + hf'(x_0).$$

Since $f(x_0 + h) = 0$,

$$f(x_0) + hf'(x_0) \simeq 0,$$

i.e.

$$h \simeq \frac{-f(x_0)}{f'(x_0)}$$

and a better approximation x_1 to the root is given by

$$x_1 = x_0 - \frac{f(x_0)}{f'(x_0)}.$$

The relation between successive approximations can be described by

$$x_{r+1} = x_r - \frac{f(x_r)}{f'(x_r)}$$

where x_r is any one of a sequence of approximations and x_{r+1} is the next. This is called the Newton-Raphson method of finding approximations to the roots of an equation.

Geometrical illustration

If $f'(x)$ is positive in the neighbourhood of the root and the root itself is positive, Fig. 12.3 illustrates the relation between these successive

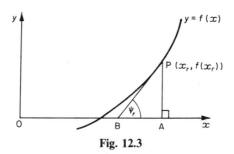

Fig. 12.3

approximations. If $x = x_r$ is a good approximation to the root of the equation and P is the point on the curve $(x_r, f(x_r))$, we can draw the tangent at P to meet the x-axis at B and B gives a better approximation to the root. Now

$$AB = \frac{AP}{\tan \psi_r}$$

$$= \frac{f(x_r)}{f'(x_r)}$$

so that the x coordinate of B is $x_r - AB$

i.e.
$$x_r - \frac{f(x_r)}{f'(x_r)}.$$

Exceptions

Sketching possible graphs we see that we may not get a better approximation if $f'(x_r) \simeq 0$, (Fig. 12.4a), or if $f'(x)$ is changing very rapidly (Fig. 12.4b). This second condition makes $f''(x)$ very large, which we have already excluded.

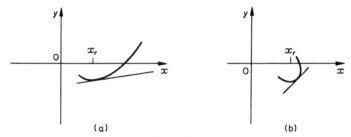

Fig. 12.4

Degree of accuracy

If we require the roots to any specified degree of accuracy, say 4 sf, we continue our iterative process until $x_{r+1} = x_r$ to 4 sf. It can be shown that the difference at each stage between the approximation and the exact value of the root is proportional to the square of the previous difference. If we start with a close approximation, then the differences soon become very small.

Example. *Find, correct to 4 sf, a root of the equation $x^3 + x = 2.2$.*

Here, write $\qquad\qquad f(x) = x^3 + x - 2.2$
and $\qquad\qquad\qquad f'(x) = 3x^2 + 1.$
Now $\qquad\qquad\qquad f(1) = -0.2$
and $\qquad\qquad\qquad f(2) = 7.8$
so that there is a root between 1 and 2. Further, since $f(1)$ is much smaller than $f(2)$, it is very likely to be much closer to 1 than to 2.

Now
$$f(1) = -0.2 \quad \text{and} \quad f'(1) = 4,$$

so
$$x_1 = 1 - \frac{-0.2}{4}, \quad \text{taking} \quad x_0 = 1,$$

$$= 1.05.$$

Repeating the process,
$$f(1.05) = 0.007\,625$$
$$f'(1.05) = 4.3075$$

so
$$x_2 = 1.05 - \frac{0.007\,625}{4.3075}$$

$$\simeq 1.048\,23.$$

Again, $f(1.048\,23) \simeq 1.06 \times 10^{-5}, f'(1.048\,23) \simeq 4.296\,36$ so that $\dfrac{f(x_2)}{f'(x_2)}$ is so small that $x_3 = x_2$, to 4 sf, and the root is 1.048, correct to 4 sf.

Notice that in this example $f'(x) = 3x^2 + 1$, so is always positive. Since the curve is continuous there cannot be any more roots. If we need to find all the roots of an equation, we have first to find a good approximation to each root.

Exercise 12.1

In Q.1–8, find better approximations to the following roots by applying the Newton-Raphson method once only:

1. $x^3 - x = 5$, near $x = 2$.
2. $x^3 + x^2 + x = 3.2$, near $x = 1$.
3. $3x^3 - 2x = 76$, near $x = 3$.
4. $x^4 + x^2 = 18$, near $x = 2$.
5. $x^5 = 35$, near $x = 2$.
6. $x^5 + 3x^2 = 3$, near $x = 1$.
7. $3 \sin x + \cos x = 3$, near $x = \pi/3$.
8. $\tan x + \sin x = 1.75$, near $x = \pi/4$.

Find solutions, correct to 4 sf, to the following:

9. $x^3 - 2 = 0$.
10. $x^3 + 2x - 5 = 0$.
11. $x^3 - 2x - 5 = 0$.
12. $\sin x - x + 0.4 = 0$.
13. $e^x - x - 2 = 0$.
14. $x \sin x = 1$ (roots between 0 and 2π only).
15. $\ln x - x + 3 = 0$.

Other iterative methods

Newton's method is the most useful iterative method for finding approximations to the roots of equations, and is often the one that converges most rapidly. Other iterative methods depend on re-writing

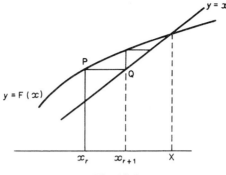

Fig. 12.5

an equation given in the form $f(x) = 0$ as $x = F(x)$, e.g. re-writing $x^3 - x - 1 = 0$ as $x = (1 + x)^{\frac{1}{3}}$. We then solve the equation using the iteration $x_{r+1} = F(x_r)$. Figure 12.5 shows that we solve $y = x$ with $y = F(x)$. We can see that if x_r is a good approximation to the root X, the coordinates of P are $(x_r, F(x_r))$ the y coordinate of Q is $F(x_r)$, and the x coordinate is also $F(x_r)$, since Q lies on $y = x$. Thus our next approximation x_{r+1} is given by

$$x_{r+1} = F(x_r).$$

This equation is called an *algorithm*.

By forming various equations like $x = F(x)$, we soon obtain iterations that do not converge, and it can be proved that if the iteration is to converge, $|F'(x_0)| < 1$. Although we do not prove this result here, Fig. 12.5 shows a curve for which $|F'(x_0)| < 1$, and we can easily sketch curves for which $|F'(x_0)| > 1$ to show that they do not converge. We can also see that the smaller $|F'(x_0)|$, the more rapid the convergence. Successive approximations may converge to a root from above or from below, or may oscillate about the exact root.

Example. *Solve by an iterative method $x^2 - 15x - 1 = 0$.*

The equation can be re-written $x = 15 + \dfrac{1}{x}$, and we can see that $x = 15$ is clearly a good approximation to a root. $F'(15) = \dfrac{-1}{225}$, so that we can use the algorithm

$$x_{r+1} = 15 + \frac{1}{x_r}$$

which we know will converge rapidly, since $|F'(15)|$ is very small.

Taking $x_0 = 15$,

$$x_1 = 15 + \frac{1}{15} \simeq 15.0667$$

$$x_2 = 15 + \frac{1}{15.0667} \simeq 15.066$$

$$x_3 = 15 + \frac{1}{15.066\,372} \simeq 15.066$$

so that, correct to 5 sf, a root is 15.066. As this equation is a quadratic, the sum of the roots is 15, and we can write down the other root as -0.066, though we notice that this is correct to only 2 sf.

If we try to use the same algorithm to find the root near to $x = 0$, we have

$$F'(0) = \frac{-1}{0}, \text{ so that this algorithm will not converge to the required root.}$$

However we can rearrange the equation as

$$x = \frac{1}{15}(x^2 - 1)$$

and use
$$x_{r+1} = \frac{1}{15}(x_r^2 - 1), \text{ since now } F'(0) = 0.$$

Taking $x_0 = 0$, we have $x_1 = -0.066\,7$
$$x_2 = -0.066\,370\,3$$
$$x_3 = -0.066\,372\,9$$
and $\qquad\qquad x_4 = -0.066\,372\,9$

so that the other root is $x = -0.066\,373$, to 5 sf. Notice that until we had obtained the roots to a good degree of accuracy, there was little point in writing down seven decimal places for x_1.

Example 2. *Solve by an iterative method* $x^3 + 3x - 7 = 0$.

We can rearrange this equation as
$$x = \tfrac{1}{3}(7 - x^3)$$
or
$$x = \sqrt[3]{(7 - 3x)}$$
or
$$x = \frac{7 - 3x}{x^2}$$

or in other ways. We can see that $x = 1$ will be a fair approximation to a root, but that $x = 1.4$ will be a very good approximation.

When $\qquad F(x) = \tfrac{1}{3}(7 - x^3), \quad F'(x) = -x^2,$

so $|F'(1.4)| \not< 1$ and this iteration will not converge.

When $\qquad F(x) = \sqrt[3]{(7 - 3x)}, \quad F'(x) = -(7 - 3x)^{-\frac{2}{3}}$

so $F'(1.4) \simeq -0.5$ and this is a possible algorithm, though convergence will be slow.

The third iteration is $F(x) = -\dfrac{3x - 7}{x^2}, \quad F'(x) = \dfrac{3}{x^2} - \dfrac{14}{x^3}, \quad F'(1.4) \simeq -3.6$

so $|F'(1.4)| \not< 1$ and this also will not converge.

There are other iterations, but we shall use
$$x_{r+1} = \sqrt[3]{(7 - 3x_r)}.$$
Taking $\qquad\qquad x_0 = 1.4,$
$$x_1 = \sqrt[3]{2.8} \simeq 1.4095$$
$$x_2 = 1.4047\ldots$$

$$x_3 = 1.4071 \ldots$$
$$x_4 = 1.4059 \ldots$$
$$x_5 = 1.406\,495 \ldots$$

Since these approximations oscillate we can see that the exact root is between 1.4059 and 1.4064, so that correct to 4 sf, the root is 1.406.

Exercise 12.2

1. The equation $x^3 - 2x - 5 = 0$ can be rearranged as

$$x = \tfrac{1}{2}(x^3 - 5),$$
$$x = \sqrt[3]{(2x + 5)},$$
$$x = \frac{2x + 5}{x^2}$$

or
$$x = \frac{5}{x^2 - 2}.$$

Given that there is a root near to $x = 2$, find $F'(2)$ in each case. Hence find an algorithm and obtain the root correct to 3 sf.

2. Find algorithms to obtain the roots of $x^3 - 8x - 1 = 0$, given that the roots are near to 3, near to 0 and near to -3. Use these algorithms to obtain each root correct to 3 sf.

   Find a check for your values, by considering the coefficients of some of the terms in the original equation.

3. An algorithm to obtain $\sqrt{5}$ is $x_{r+1} = \tfrac{1}{2}\!\left(x_r + \dfrac{5}{x_r}\right)$. Rearrange the equation $x^2 = 5$ to obtain this algorithm, and use the algorithm to find $\sqrt{5}$, correct to 3 sf.

4. Given that $x^4 = 12x - 7$ has roots near to 2 and to 0.5, find each of those roots correct to 3 sf. Investigate whether there are any other roots of this equation.

5. The equation $x\,e^x = 1$ has a root close to 0.5. Show that $x_{r+1} = e^{-x_r}$ is a suitable algorithm, and obtain the root correct to 3 sf.

6. The equation $x\,e^x = 10$ has a root close to 1.8. Show that $x_{r+1} = 10\,e^{-x_r}$ is not a suitable algorithm, and find one that can given this root. Obtain the value of this root to 3 sf.

7. Given that $3 \ln x - x = 8$ has a root near to $x = 4$, find this root correct to 3 sf.

8. Given that $3 \sin x = 2x$ has a root near to $x = 1.5$, obtain this root to 3 sf.

9. Find, correct to 3 sf, the root near to $x = -2$ of the equation $x^5 - 6x + 6 = 0$.

10. Find, correct to 3 sf, the root of $\cos x = 4x$.

Two simultaneous linear equations

When we consider the solution of two simultaneous linear equations in two unknowns, we see that either, as in

$$2x + y = 5$$
and $$x - 2y = 0 \quad \text{(A)}$$

we have one solution $x = 2$, $y = 1$; or as in

$$2x + y = 5$$
and $$2x + y = 0 \quad \text{(B)}$$

we have no solution, or as in

$$2x + y = = 5$$
and $$4x + 2y = 10 \quad \text{(C)}$$

we have an infinite number of solutions, so that for all values of λ, $x = \lambda$, $y = 5 - 2\lambda$ is a solution. Of these equations, (A) represent a pair of straight lines meeting in a point, (B) a pair of parallel straight lines that do not meet, and (C) a pair of coincident straight lines, satisfied by an infinite number of points. Writing the equations

$$ax + by = p$$
and $$cx + dy = q$$
as $$A.x = b$$

these have a unique solution $x = A^{-1}.b$ if and only if A^{-1} exists, i.e., det $A \neq 0$, where

$$\det A = \begin{vmatrix} a & b \\ c & d \end{vmatrix} = ad - bc.$$

Thus a pair of simultaneous linear equations can have

a unique solution
no solution
or an infinite number of solutions.

When det $A \neq 0$, we have a unique solution and can solve the equations as they stand; when det $A = 0$ we should inspect the equations carefully.

Example. *Find values of a and b if the equations*

$$2x + 3y = 1$$
and $$4x + ay = b$$

have (i) *a unique solution,*
   (ii) *an infinite number of solutions,*
   (iii) *no solutions.*

(i) First, det $A = \begin{vmatrix} 2 & 3 \\ 4 & a \end{vmatrix} = 2a - 12$

$\therefore$ det $A = 0$ if and only if $a = 6$.

The equations have a unique solution for all values of b, and all values of a except $a = 6$.

(ii) If $a = 6$, the equations are

$$2x + 3y = 1$$
and $$4x + 6y = b.$$

If $b = 2$ these become $\qquad 2x + 3y = 1$

and $\qquad\qquad\qquad\qquad 4x + 6y = 2$

which represent coincident straight lines, with an infinite number of solutions of the form $x = \lambda$, $y = \frac{1}{3}(1 - 2\lambda)$, so that there is an infinite number of solutions if $a = 6$ and $b = 2$.

(iii) If $a = 6$ and $b \neq 2$, the equations become

$$2x + 3y = 1$$

and $\qquad\qquad\qquad\qquad 4x + 6y = b$

which are a pair of parallel straight lines, so that there are no solutions if $a = 6$, $b \neq 2$.

Three simultaneous equations

The equations

$$a_1x + b_1y + c_1z = p_1,$$
$$a_2x + b_2y + c_2z = p_2,$$
$$a_3x + b_3y + c_3z = p_3$$

represent planes, and we can see that three planes can either

  (i) all three meet in one point,

 (ii) all three meet in one line (Fig. 12.6a),

(iii) meet, in pairs, in three straight lines (Fig. 12.6b),

(iv) form a pair of parallel planes with a transversal (Fig. 12.6c),

 (v) form three parallel planes,

(vi) form two coincident planes cut by a third distinct plane,*

(vii) form three coincident planes.

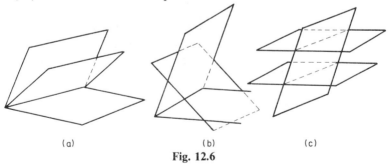

    (a)   (b)   (c)

Fig. 12.6

In case (i) we have one unique solution, in cases (ii), (vi) and (vii) we have an infinite number of solutions, and in all the other cases we have no solution. Again, writing the equations as $A \cdot x = b$, we have a unique solution $x = A^{-1} \cdot b$ if and only if A^{-1} exists, i.e. det $A \neq 0$. If det $A \neq 0$, we can find a unique solution, and usually successive elimination is the best method. If det $A = 0$, we have again to inspect the equations carefully.

---

* The third plane parallel to the two coincident planes can be included in (v).

Example 1. *Solve the equations:*

$$x + y + z = 2 \tag{1}$$
$$x + 2y + 3z = 1 \tag{2}$$
$$3x + y - 4z = 5 \tag{3}$$

First det $A = -3 \neq 0$. (See page 330.)
Subtracting (1) from (2) we have

$$y + 2z = -1 \tag{4}$$

and subtracting three times (1) from (3) we have

$$-2y - 7z = -1 \tag{5}.$$

Multiplying (4) by two and adding to (5), $-3z = -3$, i.e. $z = 1$.
Substituting in (4), $y = -3$.
Substituting in (1), $x = 4$.
Checking in (3), $3 \times 4 + (-3) - 4(1) = 5$

Example 2. *Solve the equations:*

$$x + y + z = 2 \tag{1}$$
$$x + 2y + 3z = 1 \tag{2}$$
$$3x + 4y + 5z = 5 \tag{3}$$

Now det $A = 0$, so we proceed with caution.
Subtracting (1) from (2), $y + 2z = -1$.
Subtracting three times (1) from (3),
$$y + 2z = -1.$$
These two equations are identical, so that if $z = \lambda$, $y = -1 - 2\lambda$ and $x = 3 + \lambda$, i.e., there is an infinite number of solutions of the form $x = 3 + \lambda$, $y = -1 - 2\lambda$ and $z = \lambda$.
   We notice that the three planes meet in the straight line

$$x - 3 = \frac{y + 1}{-2} = z \quad \text{(Fig. 12.6a)}.$$

Example 3. *Solve the equations:*

$$x + y + z = 2 \tag{1}$$
$$2x + 2y + 2z = 3 \tag{2}$$
$$x + 2y + 3z = 1 \tag{3}.$$

Again, det $A = 0$, so that we are not surprised to see that subtracting (1) from (3) we have $y + 2z = -1$, and subtracting (2) from twice (3) we have $2y + 4z = -1$. Indeed, we can see without any calculation that (1) and (2) are inconsistent. Thus there are no solutions of these equations. (1) and (2) represent two parallel planes and (3) is a transversal (Fig. 12.6c).

Three parallel planes

The equations
$$x + 2y + 3z = -2,$$
$$x + 2y + 3z = 0,$$
and $x + 2y + 3z = 1$
represent parallel planes and clearly there are no values of x, y and z

that satisfy all three equations. However

$$x + 2y + 3z = -2,$$
$$2x + 4y + 6z = -4$$

and
$$3x + 6y + 9z = -6$$

represent the same plane, and so have an infinite number of solutions. We can choose two parameters, λ and μ, and all points whose coordinates are of the form

$$y = \lambda, z = \mu, x = -2 - 2\lambda - 3\mu$$

will satisfy all three equations. It is interesting to compare the 'number' of solutions to three equations of this form with the 'number' of solutions to three equations of the form in Example 2.

Exercise 12.3

Solve for x and y, where possible
1. $5x + 2y = 1$; $10x - 4y = 5$.
2. $5x + 2y = 1$; $10x + 4y = 2$.
3. $5x + 2y = 1$; $10x + 4y = 3$.
4. Show that there are only two values of λ for which
$$5x + 2y = 2\lambda \quad \text{and} \quad 10x + 4y = \lambda^2$$
have solutions, and find these solutions in a suitable form.
5. Show that
$$\lambda x + 8y = 1 \quad \text{and} \quad 2x + \lambda y = 5$$
have solutions for all values of λ except for two, and find those solutions in terms of λ.

Solve for x, y and z where possible, and interpret each set of equations geometrically.

6.
$$3x - y - 2z = 0,$$
$$x + y + z = 2,$$
$$2x + y + 3z = 7.$$

7.
$$3x - y - 2z = 0,$$
$$x + y + z = 0,$$
$$2x - 2y - 3z = -2.$$

8.
$$x + y + z = 1,$$
$$2x - y - 2z = 5,$$
$$4x + y = 7.$$

9.
$$x + y + z = 1,$$
$$x + y + z = 3,$$
$$2x + 3y + z = 1.$$

10.
$$x + y + 3z = 1,$$
$$2x + 2y + 6z = 2,$$
$$3x + 3y + 9z = 3.$$

11.
$$x + y + 3z = 1,$$
$$2x + 2y + 6z = 4,$$
$$x - y - z = 0.$$

12.
$$x + y + 3z = 1,$$
$$-x - y - 3z = -1,$$
$$x + y + z = 1.$$

13. Show that there are two values of a for which the equations
$$x + 2y + z = 2,$$
$$x - 3y + 3z = a,$$
$$2x - 11y + 8z = a^2,$$
have solutions for x, y and z.

Find these solutions in a suitable form and give a geometrical interpretation.

14. Find where possible the solutions of the equations
$$3x + 2y - 2z = 1,$$
$$4x + y - z = 1,$$
$$5x - y + az = b,$$
when (i) $a = -1, b = 0$,
  (ii) $a = 1, b = \frac{4}{5}$,
  (iii) $a = 1, b = 0$.

Give a geometrical interpretation of each.

15. Find the values for a for which the equations
$$4x - 6y - z = ax,$$
$$x - 4y - z = ay,$$
$$2x + 3y + z = az,$$
have a solution other than $x = y = z = 0$. Find the ratios $x : y : z$ for each of these values of a.

Exercise 12.4: Miscellaneous

1. By linear interpolation estimate the cube root of 3, given
  (i) $1^3 = 1, 2^3 = 8$,
  (ii) $1^3 = 1, 1.5^3 = 3.375$.

2. Use Newton's method to calculate the cube root of 3, correct to 3 sf.

3. Find an algorithm of the form $x_{r+1} = F(x_r)$ to calculate the cube root of 3, correct to 3 sf.

4. Show that the equation $x^3 + 4x - 1 = 0$ has a root between 0.2 and 0.3. Find a suitable algorithm in the form $x_{r+1} = F(x_r)$ to obtain this root.

Taking a first approximation to this root as $x = 0.2$, find this root correct to 3 sf. Illustrate by a sketch graph the successive approximations to your roots.

5. Use Newton's method to find the root near to 0.2 of the equation $x^3 + 4x - 1 = 0$, giving the root correct to 3 sf. Sketch a graph to illustrate how successive approximations to the root are obtained.

6. Show that $x - 2 \sin x = 0$ has a root between 1.8 and 2. Use the Newton-Raphson method to find this root correct to 3 sf.

7. Estimate the value of $e^{-0.25}$ by linear interpolation, given that $e^0 = 1$ and $e^{-1} = 0.3679$. Compare your value with the value obtained by putting $x = -0.25$ in the first four terms of the expansion of e^x in ascending powers of x.

8. If $f(x) = x^4 - 5x^2 + 1$, show that the equation $f(x) = 0$ has four real roots between $x = -3$ and $x = 3$. Obtain these roots correct to 3 sf
   (i) by Newton's method.
   (ii) by using suitable iterations of the form $x_{r+1} = F(x_r)$,
   (iii) by regarding the equation as a quadratic in x^2.

9. Show that the equation $\ln x = x - 2$ has a root between $x = 3.1$ and $x = 3.2$. Obtain an approximation to this root
   (i) by linear interpolation between $x = 3.1$ and $x = 3.2$,
   (ii) by using one application of Newton's method, starting with $x = 3.1$.

10. A root of the equation $2x^3 + 5 \tan^2 x = 6$ is known to be near to $\pi/4$. Obtain the value of this root, correct to 3 sf. (O. & C.)

11. Find the value of $\sqrt[3]{65}$ correct to 3 significant figures.

12. Find, to 3 sf, the root of the equation $x^3 - 4x = 100$ which is near 5.

13. Find, to 3 sf, the root of the equation $x^4 - x = 15$ which is near 2.

14. Find, to 3 sf, the root of the equation $\tan x = 2x$ which is near 1.

15. When k is small, the equation $\sin x = kx$ has a root near π. Show that a better approximation is $\pi(1 - k)$.

16. When k is small, the equation $\tan x = kx$ has a root near π. Show that a better approximation is $\pi(1 + k)$.

17. When k is small, the equation $x^5 + x = k$ has a root near zero. Show that a better approximation is k.

18. Find, to 3 significant figures, the root of the equation $x^5 + x = 250$ which is near 3.

19. Find, to 3 significant figures, the root of the equation $x^4 - x^2 = 10$ which is near 2.

20. How many real roots has the equation $x = 10 \cos x$?
    Find the smallest positive root correct to two places of decimals, and show that your solution has the required degree of accuracy. (O. & C.)

21. If x is a rational approximation to the cube root of 2, and $x' = (x^2 + x + 2)/(x^2 + x + 1)$, show, by expressing $x' - x$ in the form $(2^{\frac{1}{3}} - x)f(x)$ and verifying that $1 < f(x) < 2$, or otherwise, that x' is a better approximation than x, and that if one is below the correct value, the other is above.
    Use this method to find the cube root of 2 correct to two places of decimals. (O. & C.)

22. Establish Newton's formula for obtaining an approximation to a root of the equation $f(x) = 0$.
    Show that the equation $x^3 + 3x - 3 = 0$ has only one real root and find this root, to three significant figures, using Newton's method. (M.E.I.)

23. By considering the maximum and minimum of $x^3 - 3p^2x + q$, or otherwise, prove that the cubic equation $x^3 - 3p^2x + q = 0$ has three distinct real roots if and only if $|q| < 2|p|^3$.
    Show that $x^3 - 3x + 1 = 0$ has three distinct real roots and find the root lying between the values of x corresponding to the stationary values of $x^3 - 3x + 1$, correct to two decimal places. (O. & C.)

24. Show that if the equations

$$-x - y + 3z = 0,$$
$$4x + ay + 6z = 0,$$
$$-3x - y + 3z = 0$$

have a solution other than $x = y = z = 0$, then $a = -2$. Find the solution in this case. (C.)

25. Solve the equations:

$$-x - y + 3z = b,$$
$$4x - 2y + 6z = 1,$$
$$-3x - y + 3z = 3$$

distinguishing between the cases $b = 2$ and $b \neq 2$. (C.)

26. Solve the system of equations:

$$2x + 3y + z + 1 = 0,$$
$$x - 2y - 3z + 4 = 0,$$
$$3x + 4y + 2z - 2 = 0.$$

Find the solutions of the system when the last equation is replaced by

(i) $\qquad\qquad 8x + 5y - 3z + 11 = 0,$

or by

(ii) $\qquad\qquad 4x - y - 5z + 6 = 0.$ (O.)

27. Solve for x in terms of a, b and c:

$$x + y + z = 1,$$
$$ax + by + cz = 1,$$
$$a^2x + b^2y + c^2z = 1.$$

Deduce, from the symmetry of the equations, the solutions for y and z, and check your solutions by substituting in the first equation.

28. Find how many real roots has each of the following equations:

(i) $x^3 + 3x - 4 = 0$,
(ii) $x^3 - 6x + 2 = 0$,
(iii) $4x^3 - 3x^2 - 5 = 0$.

29. Between what integers do the roots of $x^3 - 27x - 36 = 0$ lie?

30. In the system of equations,

$$kx + 3y + 2z = 4,$$
$$2x + 2y + 2z = k,$$
$$2x + y + 2z = 0$$

is it possible to find a real number k so that each of the following statements is true?

(i) $x = -2$, $y = 4$, $z = 0$ is a solution.
(ii) $x = 1$, $y = 2$, $z = -3$ is a solution.
(iii) $x = -2$, $y = 4$, $z = 0$ is one of many solutions.
(iv) $x = 2$, $y = 2$, $z = -3$ is one of many solutions.

Revision Paper B1

1. Find the solutions in the set $\mathbb{Z}$ of integers of the inequality
$$x^2 - 4x < 2.$$

2. Write down the first four terms in the binomial expansion of $(1 + 2x)^{-3}$ in ascending powers of x. State the range of values of x for which it is valid. By putting $x = -0.01$, find a value for 7^{-6} correct to four significant figures. (A.E.B.)

3. (i) Sketch, in the same diagram, the graphs of
   (a) $y = x + |x|$
   (b) $y = 2 + x - |x|$.
   Show that they enclose a parallelogram and find its area.
   (ii) For what ranges of values of x is the expression
$$\frac{x - 2}{(x - 1)(x - 4)}$$
   positive?
   Illustrate your answer graphically by sketching the curve
$$y = \frac{x - 2}{(x - 1)(x - 4)}.$$
   (M.E.I.)

4. Explain, with the use of diagrams, the use of Newton's method for obtaining the numerical solutions of an equation. Draw a diagram to show how the method can break down.
   Obtain the real factors, with integer coefficients, of
$$x^4 - 4x^3 + 3x^2 - 4x + 12.$$
   Hence or otherwise obtain the greater real root of the equation
$$x^4 - 4x^3 + 3x^2 - 4x + 11 = 0,$$
   correct to 3 decimal places. (A.E.B.)

5. If $y = e^{-x} \ln (1 + x)$, show that
$$(1 + x)\frac{d^2y}{dx^2} + (2x + 3)\frac{dy}{dx} + (x + 2)y = 0.$$
   (J.M.B.)

6. (i) Show that $\dfrac{2}{x^4 + x^2 + 1} = \dfrac{x^2 - 1}{x^3 - 1} - \dfrac{x^2 - 1}{x^3 + 1}$.

   Hence, or otherwise, express $\dfrac{1}{x^4 + x^2 + 1}$ in partial fractions,

   (ii) Expand $\dfrac{1}{1 + x + x^2}$ in a series of ascending powers of x, and show that the sum of the series up to and including the term in x^{3n-2} is
$$\frac{1 - x^{3n}}{1 + x + x^2}.$$
   (O. & C.)

7. Differentiate with respect to x:

(a) $\sqrt{(1 - x^2)} \sin^{-1} x$,   (b) $\ln (1 - \tan^2 x)$,   (c) x^x.   (C.)

8. If $y = \dfrac{A + \ln (1 + x)}{x^2}$ where A is a constant, show that

$$x(1 + x)\left(x\frac{dy}{dx} + 2y\right) = 1.$$ (L.)

9. A particle moving in a straight line starts from a fixed point O, at the time $t = 0$. Its displacement x from O after time t is given by the equation $x = t\,e^{-kt}$ where k is a constant and positive. Prove
(i) that the initial speed is independent of k;
(ii) that the time taken from the start to reach the position of greatest displacement from O is half the time taken from the start to reach the greatest speed on the return journey towards O.   (J.M.B.)

10. Express $\dfrac{2(x + 1)}{(x - 1)(2x - 1)}$ in partial fractions, and prove that

$$\int_2^5 \frac{2(x + 1)}{(x - 1)(2x - 1)}\,dx = \ln\frac{256}{27}.$$ (C.)

Revision Paper B2

1. Differentiate with respect to x

(i) $\dfrac{x^2 - 4x + 3}{2x + 1}$,

(ii) $e^{2x}(2 \cos 3x + 3 \sin 3x)$.

(iii) $\ln \{x - \sqrt{(x^2 - a^2)}\}$. (J.M.B.)

2. Differentiate $x^x + (\ln x)^x$. (L.)

3. Calculate the coordinates of the point of intersection of the curves $y = \dfrac{4e^x + 2e^{-x}}{3}$ and $y = e^{-x}$. Calculate also the coordinates of the point on the curve $y = \dfrac{4e^x + 2e^{-x}}{3}$ for which y is a minimum. (C.)

4. For a certain kind of lamp the cost in pounds per year is $\dfrac{4}{10^8} e^{0.18x} + 10^8 e^{-0.18x} + 3.7$ where x is the voltage. Find x in order that the cost may be a minimum. (L.)

5. Find the sets of real values of x for which
(i) $2x^2 + 5x - 3$ is positive,

(ii) $\dfrac{x}{x - 1} > 2$,

(iii) $x - \dfrac{3}{x} > 2$. (A.E.B.)

6. Find the values of α for which the equations
$$x + 2y + 3z = 1$$
$$5x + y + 3z = \alpha$$
$$3x + 9y + 13z = \alpha^2$$
have solutions. Find all the solutions for each value of α. (A.E.B.)

7. Show that the equation
$$x^4 - 3x^2 - 3x + 1 = 0$$
has real roots between 0 and 1 and between 2 and 3. Find the larger of these roots correct to three significant figures and check that three figure accuracy has been achieved. (O. & C.)

8. Find the derivative with respect to x of
$$(x^2 + 2)\sqrt{(1 - x^2)} + 3x^3 \sin^{-1} x.$$ (J.M.B.)

9. Prove that the area enclosed between the line $y = 3$ and the portion of the curve $y = 6 \sin x$ for which x lies between 0 and π is $6\sqrt{3} - 2\pi$. (C.)

10. Sketch the graphs of the following functions, using a separate diagram for each function and sketching enough to show the shape and position of each curve.

(i) $y = e^{-x}$,

(ii) $y = e^{-x^2}$,

(iii) $y = 2 \cos (x - \frac{1}{4}\pi)$,

(iv) $y = \begin{cases} 0 & \text{when} \quad x = 0, \\ \dfrac{x}{|x|} & \text{when} \quad x \neq 0. \end{cases}$

(M.E.I.)

Revision Paper B3

1. (a) Find the range of values of the real number x for which the following inequalities hold:

   (i) $\dfrac{1}{x+6} < \dfrac{2}{2-3x}$;   (ii) $|5 - 3x| \leqslant |x + 1|$.

   (b) Show by shading on the xy plane, the region for which
   $$x^2 + y^2 \leqslant 1, \ y \geqslant x \quad \text{and} \quad y \leqslant x + 1.$$
   Hence find
   (i) the greatest value of y,   (ii) the least value of $x + y$
   for which these inequalities hold.   (M.E.I.)

2. A pony is tethered to the centre O of a square field $ABCD$, and the length of rope is such that the pony can graze four fifths of the field. If EF is the part of the side AB which the pony can reach and angle $EOF = \theta$, prove that
   $$5 \sin \theta - 4 \cos \theta = 5\theta + 4 - 5\pi/2.$$
   Show that this equation has a root between $\frac{1}{10}\pi$ and $\frac{1}{12}\pi$ and use Newton's method to obtain the value of this root in radians correct to three places of decimals.   (O. & C.)

3. (i) Differentiate with respect to x, $x^x + x^{1/x}$.

   (ii) If $y = e^{a \sin^{-1} x}$, prove that $(1 - x^2)\dfrac{d^2y}{dx^2} - x\dfrac{dy}{dx} = a^2 y$.   (L.)

4. Write down the first three terms and the $(n + 1)$th term of the series for e^x.
   Prove that the coefficient of x^{n+1} in the expansion of $e^x(x^2 - 4x + 6)$ is
   $$\dfrac{(n - 1)(n - 2)}{(n + 1)!} \quad \text{when } n \geqslant 1.$$ (O. & C.)

5. Express as the sum of partial fractions

   (i) $\dfrac{x - 1}{(x - 2)(x - 3)}$,   (ii) $\dfrac{x - 1}{(x - 2)(x - 3)^2}$,   (iii) $\dfrac{x - 1}{(x^2 + 1)(x - 2)}$.

   (O. & C.)

6. Solve the simultaneous equations
   $$2x - y + 3z = 3$$
   $$3x + y + 2z = 7$$
   $$x + 7y - 5z = 13.$$
   Find K if the set of equations
   $$2x - y + 3z = 0$$
   $$3x + y + 2z = 0$$
   $$x + 7y + Kz = 0$$
   has a solution other than $(0, 0, 0)$. Write down the solution for which $z = 1$ and the general form of solution.

Obtain also the solution, for which $z = 1$, of the set of equations
$$2x - y + 3z = 3$$
$$3x + y + 2z = 7$$
$$x + 7y - 6z = 9$$
and write down the most general form of solution for arbitrary z.

(A.E.B.)

7. (a) Find the sum of the first n terms of the series whose rth term is
$$2^r + 2r - 1.$$
(b) If x is so small that terms in x^n, $n \geqslant 3$, can be neglected and
$$\frac{3 + ax}{3 + bx} = (1 - x)^{\frac{1}{3}},$$
find the values of a and b.

Hence, without the use of tables, find an approximation in the form p/q, where p and q are integers, for $\sqrt[3]{0.96}$. (A.E.B.)

8. Indicate by a rough sketch the form of the curves $y = e^x$ and $y = e^{2x}$.

Prove that (i) the curves intersect at an angle of $\cot^{-1} 3$; (ii) the area bounded by the curves and the line $x = 1$ is $\frac{1}{2}(e - 1)^2$. (C.)

9. Find the coordinates of the turning points on the graph of $y = e^x \sin x$ and show that the values of y at these points form a geometric progression. State the common ratio of the progression. (J.M.B.)

10. Write down the series for e^x and $\log (1 + x)$ as far as the terms in x^4.

Given that $f(x) = (1 - x)\{(1 - x) - \log (1 - x)\}$, prove that the expansion of $f(x)$ as far as the term in x^4 is
$$f(x) = 1 - x + \frac{x^2}{2} - \frac{x^3}{6} - \frac{x^4}{12}.$$
Prove that the expansion of $e^x f(x)$ as far as the term in x^4 is
$$e^x f(x) = 1 - \tfrac{1}{8}x^4.$$
(O. & C.)

Revision Paper B4

1. If $y = (A + Bx)e^{-2x}$, prove that $\dfrac{d^2y}{dx^2} + 4\dfrac{dy}{dx} + 4y = 0$. (J.M.B.)

2. Sketch the graphs of the functions
$$y = x + 2|x| \quad \text{and} \quad y = 4 + x - |x|.$$
Hence or otherwise find all the solutions to the simultaneous equations:
$$y = x + 2|x|,$$
$$y = 4 + x - |x|. \qquad \text{(J.M.B.)}$$

3. Write down the series for $\ln(1 + x)$ in ascending powers of x and state the range of values of x for which it is valid.
   Prove that, if $n > 1$,
$$\ln\frac{n}{n-1} > \frac{1}{n} > \ln\frac{n+1}{n};$$
   and deduce that, if n is a positive integer,
$$1 + \ln n > 1 + \frac{1}{2} + \frac{1}{3} + \ldots + \frac{1}{n} > \ln(n+1). \qquad \text{(C.)}$$

4. (a) Differentiate with respect to x (i) $\dfrac{2-x}{1+2x}$, (ii) $\left(x^4 - \dfrac{1}{x^2}\right)^3$,

   (iii) $\ln(\operatorname{cosec} x + \cot x)$.

   (b) If $y = x\,e^{-x}$, prove that $\dfrac{d^2y}{dx^2} + 2\dfrac{dy}{dx} + y = 0$. (L.)

5. Express $\dfrac{7x+3}{(3x-1)(x+1)^2}$ in partial fractions, and hence find the coefficient of x^n when this expression is expanded in ascending powers of x.
   (ii) Write down the first three terms in the binomial expansion of $(1 - \tfrac{1}{1000})^{1/3}$.

   Hence evaluate $(37)^{1/3}$ to 6 decimal places. (O. & C.)

6. If $y = (3\sin 2x + 4\cos 2x)/(2x + 1)$, show that
$$(2x+1)\frac{dy}{dx} + 2y = 10\cos(2x+\alpha)$$
   where $\tan\alpha = \tfrac{4}{3}$.
   If y has a stationary value, show that x is a solution of the equation
$$\tan(2x+\alpha) = 2x + 1. \qquad \text{(L.)}$$

7. A curve has an equation of the form
$$y = ax^3 + bx^2 - 9x,$$
   where a and b are constants. It is given that the curve has a stationary point when $x = -1$ and also that the tangent to the curve at the point at

which $x = 1$ cuts the y-axis at the point $(0, 1)$. Find the values of the constants a and b.

Sketch the curve.

Hence sketch the curves

(i) $y^2 = ax^3 + bx^2 - 9x$,

(ii) $y = |ax^3 + bx^2 - 9x|$. (M.E.I.)

8. If $f(x) = 2e^{-4x} - e^{-2x}$, show that $f(x) = 0$ for just one value of x. Denoting this value by a, show that $f'(2a) = 0$. Sketch the graph of the function.

Evaluate the area bounded by the x-axis, the ordinate $x = 0$, and the arc of the curve joining the points $x = 0$ and $x = a$. (C.)

9. By applying Newton's method to the function f defined by

$$f(x) = 1 - \frac{7}{x^2},$$

develop an iterative formula for calculating $\sqrt{7}$.

Hence, using 2 as a first approximation to $\sqrt{7}$, calculate $\sqrt{7}$ correct to two places of decimals.

Show that if x_n, the nth approximation to $\sqrt{7}$, has a small error e_n, then the next approximation, x_{n+1}, has an error of magnitude about $0.6e_n^2$. (M.E.I.)

10. When $x > 0$, prove that the function $(\ln x)/x$ has a maximum at $x = e$ and find its value at this point.

Find any points of inflexion, and sketch the graph of the function. How many real roots are there to the equation

$$\ln x = kx$$

where (a) $k = \frac{1}{4}$, (b) $k = 4$?

Use your graph to find how many real positive roots there are to the equation

$$x^4 = 4\{x^2 + (\ln x)^2\}. \qquad \text{(O. \& C.)}$$

Revision Paper B5

1. Show that the equations

$$x_1 + x_2 + x_3 = 0$$
$$2x_1 - x_2 - x_3 = 3$$
$$x_1 + 2x_2 + 2x_3 = k$$

have a solution for one and only one value of k. Find k and calculate this solution. (A.E.B.)

2. (a) Solve the inequality

$$\frac{x + 5}{x - 3} > x$$

where x is a real number.

(b) Illustrate in a sketch the region of the (x, y)-plane of which the points satisfy simultaneously the inequalities $x - 3 > 0$ and $x - 2y < 0$.

Sketch the graph of

$$y = x - 3 + |x - 2y|$$

for values of x in the range $x - 3 > 0$. (M.E.I.)

3. The abscissa x of a point P moving along the x-axis is given in terms of the time t by the equation $x = e^{-\frac{1}{2}t}t(t - 3)$ where $t \geqslant 0$. Show that the ratio of the extreme distances of P from the origin is $e^{2.5}:9$ and that the accelerations towards the origin in these extreme positions are in the ratio $e^{2.5}:1$. (J.M.B.)

4. If $y = x \tan^{-1} x$, prove

$$(x + x^3)\frac{dy}{dx} = y(1 + x^2) + x^2$$

and

$$(1 + x^2)\frac{d^2y}{dx^2} + 2x\frac{dy}{dx} - 2(y + 1) = 0. \qquad \text{(O. \& C.)}$$

5. If $y = e^x \sin 3x$, prove that $\dfrac{d^2y}{dx^2} - 2\dfrac{dy}{dx} + 10y = 0$.

Show that the two curves $y = e^x$ and $y = e^x \sin 3x$ intersect at the point P for which $x = \dfrac{\pi}{6}$ and that they have the same tangent at P. (P.)

6. Write down the series for $\ln(1 + x)$ and for e^x in ascending powers of x; give, in each case, the first four terms and the general term; and state the range of values of x for which each series is valid.

Find the sum of each of the series

(i) $1 - \frac{1}{2} + \frac{1}{3} - \frac{1}{4} + \frac{1}{5} \ldots$

(ii) $1 + \dfrac{x^2}{2!} + \dfrac{x^4}{4!} + \dfrac{x^6}{6!} + \ldots$ (O. \& C.)

7. (i) Find the coefficient of x^r in the expansion of $\dfrac{1 + 3x}{(1 - x)^3}$ for which $-1 < x < 1$.

(ii) Express $\dfrac{5x - 1}{(x + 1)^2(x - 2)}$ in partial fractions.

Hence obtain the first four terms in the expansion of this expression in ascending powers of x, stating the necessary restrictions on the values of x.   (O. & C.)

8. Expand $(2x + 3)^5$ and $(2x - 3)^3$ in descending powers of x and determine the coefficient of x^7 in the product of the two expansions.

By writing $(2x + 3)^5(2x - 3)^3$ as $(2x + 3)^2(4x^2 - 9)^3$ and expanding the latter product, check the answer to the first part of the question. (C.)

9. Differentiate with respect to x, (i) $\sin \sqrt{x}$, (ii) $\sqrt{\sin x}$, (iii) 10^{2x}.   (C.)

10. An equation can be written in the form $x = F(x)$ and it is known that it has a root in the neighbourhood of $x = x_1$. Explain with the aid of a diagram how the iterative formula

$$x_{r+1} = F(x_r)$$

may give the root to whatever degree of accuracy is required and state a condition for convergence.

The cubic equation $x^3 - 2x - 5 = 0$ has one real root which is near $x = 2$. The equation can be written in any one of the forms

  (i) $x = \frac{1}{2}(x^3 - 5)$,
  (ii) $x = 5(x^2 - 2)^{-1}$,
  (iii) $x = (2x + 5)^{\frac{1}{3}}$.

Choose the form for which the previous iterative formula will converge to the real root and use the formula to find this root.   (M.E.I.)

13 The Hyperbolic Functions

The hyperbolic functions: definitions

The expression $\frac{1}{2}(e^x + e^{-x})$ is so important that it has a special name and is called cosh x.
Similarly $\qquad \sinh x = \frac{1}{2}(e^x - e^{-x})$.
These are two of the **hyperbolic functions**; the others are defined as follows:

$$\tanh x = \frac{\sinh x}{\cosh x}, \quad \operatorname{cosech} x = \frac{1}{\sinh x}, \quad \operatorname{sech} x = \frac{1}{\cosh x},$$

$$\coth x = \frac{1}{\tanh x}.$$

The name 'hyperbolic' derives from the fact that the point ($a \cosh \theta$, $b \sinh \theta$) lies on the hyperbola $\dfrac{x^2}{a^2} - \dfrac{y^2}{b^2} = 1$, because if $x = a \cosh \theta$, $y = b \sinh \theta$,

$$\frac{x^2}{a^2} - \frac{y^2}{b^2} = \cosh^2 \theta - \sinh^2 \theta$$

$$= \left(\frac{e^\theta + e^{-\theta}}{2}\right)^2 - \left(\frac{e^\theta - e^{-\theta}}{2}\right)^2$$

$$= \frac{(e^{2\theta} + 2 + e^{-2\theta}) - (e^{2\theta} - 2 + e^{-2\theta})}{4}$$

$$= 1.$$

Incidentally we have proved a very important relationship between cosh x and sinh x, namely $\cosh^2 x - \sinh^2 x = 1$.

Osborn's rule

Most trigonometrical identities connecting the circular functions have a counterpart for the hyperbolic functions. The equation $\cos^2 \theta + \sin^2 \theta = 1$, for example, becomes

$$\cosh^2 \theta - \sinh^2 \theta = 1.$$

Osborn's rule tells us how to turn an identity connecting circular functions into the corresponding identity for hyperbolic functions.
$\cos \theta$ is replaced by $\cosh \theta$; $\sin \theta$ is replaced by $\sqrt{(-1)} \sinh \theta$, which means that $\sin^2 \theta$ is replaced by $-\sinh^2 \theta$ and $\sin A \sin B$ is replaced by $-\sinh A \sinh B$.

It follows of course from the definitions that sec θ is replaced by sech θ; tan θ is replaced by $\sqrt{(-1)}$ tanh θ and cosec θ by $\sqrt{(-1)}$ cosech θ.

N.B. This rule applies only to identities and not, for example, to differential coefficients.

Example 1. *Write down the hyperbolic identity corresponding to* $\sec^2 \theta = 1 + \tan^2 \theta$ *and prove it from first principles.*

$\sec^2 \theta$ becomes $\text{sech}^2 \theta$; $\tan^2 \theta$ becomes $-\tanh^2 \theta$.

The identity becomes
$$\text{sech}^2 \theta = 1 - \tanh^2 \theta \quad \text{or} \quad \text{sech}^2 \theta + \tanh^2 \theta = 1.$$

By definition, $\text{sech}\,\theta = \dfrac{1}{\cosh \theta} = \dfrac{2}{e^\theta + e^{-\theta}};$

$$\tanh \theta = \frac{\sinh \theta}{\cosh \theta} = \frac{e^\theta - e^{-\theta}}{e^\theta + e^{-\theta}}.$$

$\therefore$ $\text{sech}^2 \theta + \tanh^2 \theta = \dfrac{4}{(e^\theta + e^{-\theta})^2} + \dfrac{(e^\theta - e^{-\theta})^2}{(e^\theta + e^{-\theta})^2}$

$$= \frac{4 + e^{2\theta} - 2 + e^{-2\theta}}{(e^\theta + e^{-\theta})^2}$$

$$= \frac{e^{2\theta} + 2 + e^{-2\theta}}{(e^\theta + e^{-\theta})^2}$$

$$= \frac{(e^\theta + e^{-\theta})^2}{(e^\theta + e^{-\theta})^2}.$$

$$= 1.$$

Example 2. *Write down the hyperbolic identity corresponding to* $\cos (A + B) = \cos A \cos B - \sin A \sin B$ *and prove it from first principles.*

$\cos (A + B)$ becomes $\cosh (A + B)$; $\cos A \cos B$ becomes $\cosh A \cosh B$; $\sin A \sin B$ becomes $-\sinh A \sinh B$.

The identity becomes
$$\cosh (A + B) = \cosh A \cosh B + \sinh A \sinh B$$

since $\cosh A \cosh B + \sinh A \sinh B$

$$= \left(\frac{e^A + e^{-A}}{2}\right)\left(\frac{e^B + e^{-B}}{2}\right) + \left(\frac{e^A - e^{-A}}{2}\right)\left(\frac{e^B - e^{-B}}{2}\right)$$

$$= \frac{e^{A+B} + e^{A-B} + e^{-A+B} + e^{-A-B} + e^{A+B} - e^{A-B} - e^{-A+B} + e^{-A-B}}{4}$$

$$= \frac{e^{A+B} + e^{-A-B}}{2}$$

$$= \cosh (A + B).$$

Example 3. *Write down the hyperbolic identity corresponding to* $\sin (A + B) = \sin A \cos B + \cos A \sin B$ *and prove it from first principles.*

$\sin (A + B)$ becomes $\sqrt{(-1)} \sinh (A + B)$.
$\sin A \cos B$ becomes $\sqrt{(-1)} \sinh A \cosh B$.
$\cos A \sin B$ becomes $\sqrt{(-1)} \cosh A \sinh B$.

The identity becomes

$$\sqrt{(-1)}\sinh(A+B) = \sqrt{(-1)}\sinh A \cosh B + \sqrt{(-1)}\cosh A \sinh B$$

or $\qquad \sinh(A+B) = \sinh A \cosh B + \cosh A \sinh B.$

$\sinh A \cosh B + \cosh A \sinh B$

$$= \left(\frac{e^A - e^{-A}}{2}\right)\left(\frac{e^B + e^{-B}}{2}\right) + \left(\frac{e^A + e^{-A}}{2}\right)\left(\frac{e^B - e^{-B}}{2}\right)$$

$$= \frac{e^{A+B} + e^{A-B} - e^{-A+B} - e^{-A-B} + e^{A+B} - e^{A-B} + e^{-A+B} + e^{-A-B}}{4}$$

$$= \frac{e^{A+B} + e^{-A-B}}{2}$$

$$= \sinh(A+B).$$

Exercise 13.1

Write down the hyperbolic identities corresponding to the following and prove them:

1. $\operatorname{cosec}^2 x = 1 + \cot^2 x.$
2. $\sin 2x = 2 \sin x \cos x.$
3. $\cos 2x = \cos^2 x - \sin^2 x.$
4. $\tan 2x = \dfrac{2 \tan x}{1 - \tan^2 x}.$
5. $\sin 2x = \dfrac{2 \tan x}{1 + \tan^2 x}.$
6. $\cos 2x = \dfrac{1 - \tan^2 x}{1 + \tan^2 x}.$
7. $\sin(A - B) = \sin A \cos B - \cos A \sin B.$
8. $1 + \cos 2x = 2 \cos^2 x.$
9. $\cos 3x = 4 \cos^3 x - 3 \cos x.$
10. $\sin 3x = 3 \sin x - 4 \sin^3 x.$

cosh x and sinh x as series

We know that

$$e^x = 1 + x + \frac{x^2}{2!} + \frac{x^3}{3!} + \frac{x^4}{4!} + \dots$$

and

$$e^{-x} = 1 - x + \frac{x^2}{2!} - \frac{x^3}{3!} + \frac{x^4}{4!} \dots$$

Therefore $\qquad \cosh x = \tfrac{1}{2}(e^x + e^{-x})$

$$= 1 + \frac{x^2}{2!} + \frac{x^4}{4!} + \dots$$

and $\qquad \sinh x = \tfrac{1}{2}(e^x - e^{-x})$

$$= x + \frac{x^3}{3!} + \frac{x^5}{5!} + \dots$$

Compare the series for $\cos x$ and $\sin x$, i.e.

$$\cos x = 1 - \frac{x^2}{2!} + \frac{x^4}{4!} \dots$$

$$\sin x = x - \frac{x^3}{3!} + \frac{x^5}{5!} \dots$$

Differential coefficients of cosh x and sinh x

$$\frac{d}{dx}(\cosh x) = \frac{d}{dx}\left(\frac{e^x + e^{-x}}{2}\right) = \frac{e^x - e^{-x}}{2} = \sinh x.$$

$$\frac{d}{dx}(\sinh x) = \frac{d}{dx}\left(\frac{e^x - e^{-x}}{2}\right) = \frac{e^x + e^{-x}}{2} = \cosh x.$$

$$\left(\text{Compare } \frac{d}{dx}\cos x = -\sin x \text{ and } \frac{d}{dx}\sin x = \cos x.\right)$$

It follows that $\int \cosh x \, dx = \sinh x + c$ and that

$$\int \sinh x \, dx = \cosh x + c.$$

Example 1. *Differentiate* $\cosh^2 3x$.

$$\frac{d}{dx}\cosh^2 3x = 2\cosh 3x \times \frac{d}{dx}(\cosh 3x)$$
$$= 2\cosh 3x \times 3\sinh 3x$$
$$= 6\cosh 3x \sinh 3x.$$

Example 2. *Evaluate* $\int_0^{1/2} \sinh 2x \, dx$.

$$\int_0^{1/2} \sinh 2x \, dx = \left[\frac{\cosh 2x}{2}\right]_0^{1/2} = \frac{\cosh 1 - \cosh 0}{2}.$$

$$\cosh 1 = \frac{e^1 + e^{-1}}{2} = \frac{e^2 + 1}{2e}; \quad \cosh 0 = \frac{e^0 + e^{-0}}{2} = 1.$$

$$\therefore \quad \int_0^{1/2} \sinh 2x \, dx = \frac{1}{2}\left(\frac{e^2 + 1}{2e} - 1\right) = \frac{(e-1)^2}{4e}.$$

Exercise 13.2

Differentiate with respect to x:

1. $\tanh x$.	**2.** $\operatorname{sech} x$.	**3.** $\operatorname{cosech} x$.
4. $\coth x$.	**5.** $\sinh 5x$.	**6.** $\cosh 4x$.
7. $\sinh^2 x$.	**8.** $x \sinh 2x$.	**9.** $\sinh x + \cosh x$.
10. $\sinh x - \cosh x$.	**11.** $\log \sinh x$.	**12.** $\log \cosh x$.
13. $\sinh^3 3x$.	**14.** $\cosh^2 2x$.	**15.** $\sinh^2 x + \cosh^2 x$.

Integrate

16. $\tanh x$.	**17.** $\coth x$.	**18.** $\sinh 3x$.
19. $\cosh 4x$.	**20.** $\tanh 2x$.	**21.** $\coth 5x$.
22. $\sinh x + \cosh x$.	**23.** $\sinh x - \cosh x$.	**24.** $\sinh x \cosh x$.
25. $\cosh^2 x$.		

Evaluate

26. $\displaystyle\int_0^1 \sinh x \, dx.$ **27.** $\displaystyle\int_0^1 \cosh x \, dx.$ **28.** $\displaystyle\int_0^1 \tanh x \, dx.$

29. $\displaystyle\int_0^{\frac{1}{2}} \tanh 2x \, dx.$ **30.** $\displaystyle\int_0^1 (\sinh x + \cosh x) \, dx.$

The inverse hyperbolic relations

The graph of $y = \cosh x$ is shown in Fig. 13.1. This is most easily drawn as the mean between e^x and e^{-x}.

If $x = \cosh y$, then $y = \cosh^{-1} x$ and this is called the inverse cosh relation.

The graph of $\cosh^{-1} x$ is the image of the graph of $\cosh x$ in the line $y = x$ and is shown in Fig. 13.2 (see $\cos x$ and $\cos^{-1} x$).

It will be seen from the graph that $\cosh^{-1} x$ is double valued, i.e. for any value of x greater than 1, there are two values of $\cosh^{-1} x$ which are in fact equal and opposite.

The graph of $\sinh x$ is shown in Fig. 13.3, and also that of $\sinh^{-1} x$ which is its reflection in the line $y = x$.

It will be seen that $\sinh^{-1} x$ is single valued and exists for all values of x.

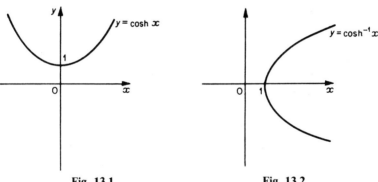

Fig. 13.1   Fig. 13.2

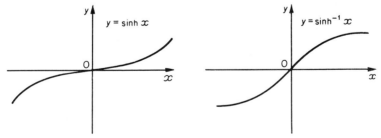

Fig. 13.3

The differential coefficients of the inverse relations

Let $\qquad y = \cosh^{-1} x \quad$ so that $\quad \cosh y = x.$

Then

$$\sinh y \frac{dy}{dx} = 1$$

and

$$\frac{dy}{dx} = \frac{1}{\sinh y}$$

$$= \frac{1}{\sqrt{(\cosh^2 y - 1)}} \, (\text{using } \cosh^2 y - \sinh^2 y = 1)$$

$$= \pm \frac{1}{\sqrt{(x^2 - 1)}}$$

Therefore

$$\frac{d}{dx} (\cosh^{-1} x) = \pm \frac{1}{\sqrt{(x^2 - 1)}}.$$

The ambiguity of the sign exists because of the double value of $\cosh^{-1} x$. We shall assume that the positive value of y is taken in which case the gradient is seen from the figure to be positive and

$$\frac{d}{dx} (\cosh^{-1} x) = \frac{1}{\sqrt{(x^2 - 1)}}.$$

Let $\qquad z = \sinh^{-1} x \quad$ so that $\quad \sinh z = x.$

Then $\qquad \cosh z \dfrac{dz}{dx} = 1$

and so

$$\frac{dz}{dx} = \frac{1}{\cosh z}$$

$$= \frac{1}{\sqrt{(1 + \sinh^2 z)}}$$

$$= \frac{1}{\sqrt{(1 + x^2)}}$$

It will be seen from the graph of $\sinh^{-1} x$ that the gradient is everywhere positive and so there is no ambiguity of sign.

Therefore

$$\frac{d}{dx} (\cosh^{-1} x) = \frac{1}{\sqrt{(x^2 - 1)}}$$

and

$$\frac{d}{dx} (\sinh^{-1} x) = \frac{1}{\sqrt{(x^2 + 1)}}.$$

It follows that

$$\int \frac{dx}{\sqrt{(x^2 - 1)}} = \cosh^{-1} x + c$$

and

$$\int \frac{dx}{\sqrt{(x^2 + 1)}} = \sinh^{-1} x + c.$$

Replacing x by $\dfrac{x}{a}$ in these integrals gives

$$\int \frac{d(x/a)}{\sqrt{[(x^2/a^2) - 1]}} = \cosh^{-1}\frac{x}{a} + c$$

and

$$\int \frac{d(x/a)}{\sqrt{[x^2/a^2 + 1)]}} = \sinh^{-1}\frac{x}{a} + c,$$

or

$$\int \frac{dx}{\sqrt{(x^2 - a^2)}} = \cosh^{-1}\frac{x}{a} + c$$

and

$$\int \frac{dx}{\sqrt{(x^2 + a^2)}} = \sinh^{-1}\frac{x}{a} + c.$$

Example 1. *Find* $\displaystyle\int \frac{dx}{\sqrt{(x^2 - 4)}}$.

By putting $a = 2$, we have

$$\int \frac{dx}{\sqrt{(x^2 - 4)}} = \cosh^{-1}\frac{x}{2}.$$

Example 2. *Find* $\displaystyle\int \frac{dx}{\sqrt{(4x^2 + 9)}}$.

$$\int \frac{dx}{\sqrt{(4x^2 + 9)}} = \frac{1}{2}\int \frac{dx}{\sqrt{(x^2 + \frac{9}{4})}}$$

$$= \tfrac{1}{2}\sinh^{-1}\frac{x}{(\frac{3}{2})} \quad \text{(putting } a = \tfrac{3}{2})$$

$$= \tfrac{1}{2}\sinh^{-1}\frac{2x}{3}.$$

Inverse relations in logarithmic form

Let $\qquad y = \cosh^{-1}x \quad$ so that $\quad \cosh y = x.$

Then $\qquad x = \dfrac{e^y + e^{-y}}{2}$ from definition.

From this equation,

$$e^{2y} - 2x\,e^y + 1 = 0$$

and $\qquad e^y = x \pm \sqrt{(x^2 - 1)} \quad$ (solving the quadratic).

$\therefore \quad y = \ln\{x + \sqrt{(x^2 - 1)}\} \quad$ or $\quad \ln\{x - \sqrt{(x^2 - 1)}\}.$

But $\{x - \sqrt{(x^2 - 1)}\}\{x + \sqrt{(x^2 - 1)}\} = x^2 - (x^2 - 1) = 1.$

$$\therefore \quad \ln\{x - \sqrt{(x^2 - 1)}\} = \ln\frac{1}{\{x + \sqrt{(x^2 - 1)}\}}$$

$$= -\ln\{x + \sqrt{(x^2 - 1)}\}.$$

$$\therefore \quad y = \pm\ln\{x + \sqrt{(x^2 - 1)}\}.$$

This shows that the relation $\cosh^{-1} x$ is double valued and that the two values are equal and opposite (provided $x > 1$).

If $\qquad\qquad z = \sinh^{-1} x, \quad$ then $\quad \sinh z = x.$

From this $\qquad\qquad x = \dfrac{e^z - e^{-z}}{2}$

and $\qquad\qquad\qquad e^{2z} - 2x\, e^z - 1 = 0.$

$$\therefore \quad e^z = x \pm \sqrt{(x^2 + 1)}.$$

$$\therefore \quad z = \ln\{x + \sqrt{(x^2 + 1)}\} \quad \text{or} \quad \ln\{x - \sqrt{(x^2 + 1)}\}.$$

The expression $x - \sqrt{(x^2 + 1)}$ is negative for all values of x and so its logarithm is not real.

$$\therefore \quad \sinh^{-1} x = \ln\{x + \sqrt{(x^2 + 1)}\},$$

which shows that $\sinh^{-1} x$ is single valued and exists for all values of x.

From these alternative forms for the inverse relations, we have

(i) $\qquad \displaystyle\int \frac{dx}{\sqrt{(x^2 - a^2)}} = \cosh^{-1} \frac{x}{a} + c'$

$$= \ln\left\{\frac{x}{a} + \sqrt{\left(\frac{x^2}{a^2} - 1\right)}\right\} + c'$$

$$= \ln\{x + \sqrt{(x^2 - a^2)}\} + c' - \ln a$$

$$= \ln\{x + \sqrt{(x^2 - a^2)}\} + c.$$

(ii) $\qquad \displaystyle\int \frac{dx}{\sqrt{(x^2 + a^2)}} = \sinh^{-1} \frac{x}{a} + c'$

$$= \ln\left\{\frac{x}{a} + \sqrt{\left(\frac{x^2}{a^2} + 1\right)}\right\} + c'$$

$$\ln\{x + \sqrt{(x^2 + a^2)}\} + c' - \ln a$$

$$= \ln\{x + \sqrt{(x^2 + a^2)}\} + c.$$

These alternative forms are often more convenient in evaluating definite integrals.

Example 1. *Evaluate* $\displaystyle\int_3^6 \frac{dx}{\sqrt{(x^2 - 9)}}.$

$$\int_3^6 \frac{dx}{\sqrt{(x^2 - 9)}} = \left[\ln\{x + \sqrt{(x^2 - 9)}\}\right]_3^6$$

$$= \ln(6 + \sqrt{27}) - \ln 3$$

$$= \ln \frac{6 + \sqrt{27}}{3}$$

$$= \ln(2 + \sqrt{3}).$$

Example 2. *Evaluate* $\displaystyle\int_0^2 \frac{dx}{\sqrt{(4x^2 + 9)}}$.

$$\int_0^2 \frac{dx}{\sqrt{(4x^2 + 9)}} = \frac{1}{2}\int_0^2 \frac{dx}{\sqrt{(x^2 + \frac{9}{4})}}$$

$$= \left[\tfrac{1}{2}\ln\{x + \sqrt{(x^2 + \tfrac{9}{4})}\} \right]_0^2$$

$$= \tfrac{1}{2}\ln(2 + \tfrac{5}{2}) - \tfrac{1}{2}\ln\tfrac{3}{2}$$

$$= \tfrac{1}{2}\ln\tfrac{9}{3}$$

$$= \tfrac{1}{2}\ln 3.$$

Example 3. *Find* $\displaystyle\int \frac{dx}{\sqrt{(x^2 + 2x + 3)}}$.

$$\int \frac{dx}{\sqrt{(x^2 + 2x + 3)}} = \int \frac{dx}{\sqrt{(x + 1)^2 + 2}} = \sinh^{-1}\frac{x + 1}{2}$$

or

$$\ln\{x + 1 + \sqrt{(x^2 + 2x + 3)}\}.$$

Exercise 13.3

Differentiate

1. $\sinh^{-1}(x + 1)$. 2. $\cosh^{-1} 2x$. 3. $\sinh^{-1} 3x$.

4. $\cosh^{-1}(x + 1)$. 5. $\sinh^{-1}(2x + 1)$. 6. $\cosh^{-1}(2x + 1)$.

7. $x\sinh^{-1} x$. 8. $x^2\cosh^{-1} x$. 9. $\sinh^{-1}\left(\dfrac{1}{x}\right)$.

10. $\cosh^{-1}\left(\dfrac{1}{x}\right)$. 11. $\sinh^{-1}\sqrt{x}$. 12. $\cosh^{-1}\sqrt{x}$.

Integrate

13. $\dfrac{1}{\sqrt{(4x^2 + 1)}}$. 14. $\dfrac{1}{\sqrt{(4x^2 - 1)}}$. 15. $\dfrac{1}{\sqrt{(x^2 + 4x + 5)}}$.

16. $\dfrac{1}{\sqrt{(x^2 + 4x + 3)}}$. 17. $\dfrac{1}{\sqrt{(x^2 + 6x + 10)}}$. 18. $\dfrac{1}{\sqrt{(x^2 + 6x + 8)}}$.

19. $\dfrac{1}{\sqrt{(x^2 + 8x + 17)}}$. 20. $\dfrac{1}{\sqrt{(x^2 + 8x + 15)}}$.

Evaluate

21. $\displaystyle\int_1^2 \frac{dx}{\sqrt{(x^2 + 1)}}$. 22. $\displaystyle\int_2^3 \frac{dx}{\sqrt{(x^2 - 1)}}$.

23. $\displaystyle\int_0^1 \frac{dx}{\sqrt{(x^2 + 2x + 2)}}$. 24. $\displaystyle\int_0^1 \frac{dx}{\sqrt{(x^2 + 2x)}}$.

25. $\displaystyle\int_0^1 \frac{dx}{\sqrt{(4x^2 + 1)}}$. 26. $\displaystyle\int_2^3 \frac{dx}{\sqrt{(4x^2 - 1)}}$.

27. $\int_0^1 \dfrac{dx}{\sqrt{(x^2 + 4x + 5)}}.$

28. $\int_0^1 \dfrac{dx}{\sqrt{(x^2 + 4x + 3)}}.$

29. $\int_0^1 \dfrac{dx}{\sqrt{\{(2x + 3)^2 + 1\}}}.$

30. $\int_0^1 \dfrac{dx}{\sqrt{(2x + 3)^2 - 1\}}}.$

Exercise 13.4: Miscellaneous

1. Differentiate $x \sinh x - \cosh x$ and hence find $\displaystyle\int x \cosh x \, dx$.

2. Find $\displaystyle\int x \sinh x \, dx$.

3. Find the first three terms in the expansion of $\sinh (e^x - 1)$ in ascending powers of x.

4. Find $\dfrac{d}{dx} \tan^{-1}(e^x)$.

5. Evaluate $\displaystyle\int_0^1 \dfrac{dx}{\sqrt{(x^2 + 9)}}$.

6. Differentiate $\sin^{-1} (\tanh x)$.

7. Find the maximum value of $\sinh x - 2 \cosh x$.

8. Express $\sinh^{-1} \frac{3}{4}$ as a logarithm.

9. Given that $y = A \sinh nx + B \cosh nx$, show that $\dfrac{d^2 y}{dx^2} = n^2 y$.

10. If $\dfrac{d^2 y}{dx^2} = n^2 y$ and $y = \dfrac{dy}{dx} = 1$ when $x = 0$, express y in terms of x.

11. If $\cosh x = \frac{5}{3}$, find the values of $\sinh x$ and $\tanh x$.

12. Find the differential coefficient of $\tanh^{-1} x$.

13. Find the differential coefficient of $\operatorname{sech}^{-1} x$.

14. If $y = \sqrt{(1 + x^2)} \sinh^{-1} x$, show that
$$\dfrac{d^2 y}{dx^2} (1 + x^2) + x \dfrac{dy}{dx} = 2x + y.$$

15. Express $\tanh^{-1} \frac{1}{2}$ as a logarithm.

16. Show that $\tanh^{-1} x = \frac{1}{2} \log \dfrac{1 + x}{1 - x}$.

17. If $\tanh x = \frac{3}{5}$, find the value of $\cosh x$.

18. Show that $\cosh nx + \sinh nx = e^{nx}$.

19. Differentiate $\frac{1}{2} x \sqrt{(1 + x^2)} + \frac{1}{2} \sinh^{-1} x$ and hence integrate $\sqrt{(1 + x^2)}$.

20. Evaluate $\displaystyle\int_2^3 \dfrac{dx}{\sqrt{(x^2 - 2x)}}$.

21. Find $\displaystyle\int \dfrac{dx}{\sqrt{(x^2 - 2x + 2)}}$.

22. Find $\displaystyle\int \dfrac{dx}{\sqrt{(x^2 - 4x)}}$.

23. Show that $\tanh 3A = \dfrac{3 \tanh A + \tanh^3 A}{1 + 3 \tanh^2 A}$.

24. If $\tanh 3x = \tanh x$, show that $x = 0$.

25. If $\cosh 2x + 2 \sinh 2x = 1$, show that $x = 0$.

26. If $x = \ln 2$, find the value of $\sinh x$.

27. If $x = \ln 3$, find the value of $\cosh x$.

28. If $x = \frac{1}{2} \ln 3$, find the value of $\tanh x$.

29. Show that $\dfrac{\cosh nx + \sinh nx}{\cosh nx - \sinh nx} = e^{2nx}$.

30. Show that $\dfrac{\sinh A + \sinh B}{\cosh A + \cosh B} = \tanh \dfrac{A + B}{2}$.

31. Show that $\dfrac{\cosh A - \cosh B}{\sinh A - \sinh B} = \tanh \dfrac{A + B}{2}$.

32. Show that
$$(\cosh A - \cosh B)^2 - (\sinh A - \sinh B)^2 = -4 \sinh^2 \dfrac{A + B}{2}.$$

33. If $y = \dfrac{\sinh^{-1} x}{\surd(1 + x^2)}$, show that $\dfrac{dy}{dx} (1 + x^2) + xy = 1$.

34. If $y = \dfrac{\cosh^{-1} x}{\surd(x^2 - 1)}$, show that $\dfrac{dy}{dx} (x^2 - 1) + xy = 1$.

35. Show that $\tanh^{-1} x + \tanh^{-1} y = \tanh^{-1} \dfrac{x + y}{1 + xy}$.

36. Show that $\tanh^{-1} x - \tanh^{-1} y = \tanh^{-1} \dfrac{x - y}{1 - xy}$.

37. Show that $2 \tanh^{-1} x = \tanh^{-1} \dfrac{2x}{1 + x^2}$.

38. Differentiate $\tanh^{-1} \dfrac{2x}{1 + x^2}$.

39. Find $\displaystyle\int \dfrac{dx}{\surd\{(2x + 1)^2 - a^2\}}$.

40. Find $\displaystyle\int \dfrac{dx}{\surd\{(3x + 1)^2 + b^2\}}$.

41. Find $\displaystyle\int \dfrac{2e^x}{e^{2x} + 1} \, dx$ by the substitution $y = e^x$. Hence integrate $\operatorname{sech} x$.

42. Find $\displaystyle\int \dfrac{2e^x}{e^{2x} - 1} \, dx$. Hence integrate $\operatorname{cosec} x$.

43. Prove that $\cosh x \geqslant 1$.

44. Prove that $\cosh x > \sinh x$.

45. A particle moves along the axis of x so that its displacement from the origin t seconds after starting is given by $x = b \ln \cosh nt$. If v is the velocity and a the acceleration of the particle, show that $v^2 = n^2 b^2 - ab$.

46. Find the minimum value of $3 \cosh x + 2 \sinh x$.

47. If $y = (\cosh^{-1} x)^2$ show that $(x^2 - 1)\dfrac{d^2y}{dx^2} + x\dfrac{dy}{dx} = 2$.

48. Integrate $\cosh x \, e^x$.

49. Integrate $\sinh x \, e^x$.

50. Integrate $\cosh^2 x$.

14 Further Integration

The integral as the limit of a sum

We have so far considered integration as the inverse of differentiation, i.e.

$$\int f(x)\,dx = F(x) \Rightarrow \frac{dF(x)}{dx} = f(x),$$

e.g.

$$\int x^2\,dx = \tfrac{1}{3}x^3 + C$$

because

$$\frac{d}{dx}(\tfrac{1}{3}x^3 + C) = x^2.$$

We now look at a different definition.

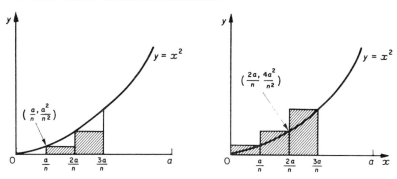

Fig. 14.1

Consider the region bounded by the curve $y = x^2$, the x-axis, and the ordinate $x = a$. Divide the interval $0 \leqslant x \leqslant a$ into n strips each of width $\dfrac{a}{n}$. The region can be bounded above and below by rectangles, as in Fig. 14.1, all of width $\dfrac{a}{n}$. The length of each rectangle is the y coordinate of a point on the curve $y = x^2$, and we can see that their lengths are $\left(\dfrac{a}{n}\right)^2, \left(\dfrac{2a}{n}\right)^2, \ldots \left(\dfrac{na}{n}\right)^2$. Considering the areas, we see from Fig. 14.1 that if A is the area of the region bounded by the curve,

$$\frac{a}{n}\left(\frac{a}{n}\right)^2 + \ldots \frac{a}{n}\left(\frac{(n-1)a}{n}\right)^2 < A < \frac{a}{n}\left\{\left(\frac{a}{n}\right)^2 + \left(\frac{2a}{n}\right)^2 + \ldots \left(\frac{na}{n}\right)^2\right\}$$

i.e. $\dfrac{a^3}{n^3}\{1^2 + 2^2 + \ldots (n-1)^2\} < A < \dfrac{a^3}{n^3}\{1^2 + 2^2 + \ldots n^2\}.$

But $\displaystyle\sum_1^k r^2 = \dfrac{k}{6}(k+1)(2k+1)$

$\therefore$ $\dfrac{a^3}{n^3}\{\tfrac{1}{6}(n-1)n(2n-1)\} < A < \dfrac{a^3}{n^3}\{\tfrac{1}{6}n(n+1)(2n+1)\}$

i.e. $\dfrac{a^3}{6}\left\{2 - \dfrac{3}{n} + \dfrac{1}{n^2}\right\} < A < \dfrac{a^3}{6}\left\{2 + \dfrac{3}{n} + \dfrac{1}{n^2}\right\}.$

As $n \to \infty$, the expressions inside each bracket tend to 2, so that $A \to \dfrac{a^3}{3}$.

Thus we can *define* $\displaystyle\int_0^a x^2\, dx$ as $\dfrac{a^3}{3}$, and then define differentiation as the inverse of integration.

Fundamental theorem of integral calculus

Although there are a few more expressions that we can integrate in the same manner, it is clear that we were fortunate in that the series that we had to sum, $\sum r^2$, was one whose sum we knew, and also that the graph was steadily increasing.* If it had been increasing for some of the interval and decreasing for the rest, then the bounding above and below by rectangles would have been much more difficult. Clearly there are not many expressions that we can integrate in this manner, but it does lead on to the fundamental theorem of integral calculus, usually written in the form

$$\dfrac{d}{dx}\int_0^x f(t)\, dt = f(x).$$

Exercise 14.1

1. Consider the region R bounded by the x-axis, the ordinate $x = a$ and the curve $y = f(x)$, for each $f(x)$ given below. Use the method on page 185 to find the area of the region R when
    (i) $f(x) = x$,   (ii) $f(x) = x^3$,
    (iii) $f(x) = x^3 + x^2$.
2. Consider the region R bounded by the x-axis, the ordinates $x = 0$ and $x = a$, and the curve $y = f(x)$, for each $f(x)$ given below. Use the method on page 185 to find the area of the region R when
    (i) $f(x) = x + 1$,   (ii) $f(x) = 3x^2 + 1$,
    (iii) $f(x) = 4x^3 + x + 1$.

* A function $f(x)$ such that $f(x_2) \geqslant f(x_1)$ for all $x_2 \geqslant x_1$ is said to be *monotonic increasing*.

3. Show that $\dfrac{1}{11^3} + \dfrac{1}{12^3} \cdots \dfrac{1}{20^3} < \displaystyle\int_{10}^{20} \dfrac{1}{x^3}\, dx < \dfrac{1}{10^3} + \dfrac{1}{11^3} \cdots \dfrac{1}{19^3}$ and

deduce an approximate value for $\displaystyle\int_{10}^{20} \dfrac{1}{x^3}\, dx$.

4. A function f of x is such that $f(x)$ is positive for all x, and $f(x)$ is monotonic increasing. Sketch a graph to illustrate that

$$f(1) + \int_1^n f(x)\, dx < f(1) + f(2) \ldots f(n) < \int_1^{n+1} f(x)\, dx.$$

5. A function f of x is such that $f(x)$ is positive for all x, and $f(x)$ steadily decreases as x increases, i.e. is monotonic decreasing. Sketch a graph to show that

$$\int_1^{n+1} f(x)\, dx < f(1) + f(2) + \ldots f(n) < \int_1^n f(x)\, dx + f(1).$$

Region with one boundary $y = 1/x$

Consider now the region bounded by the x-axis, the ordinates $x = 1$ and $x = 2$, and the curve $y = 1/x$. We can find an approximation for

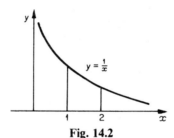

Fig. 14.2

the area of this region by bounding it above and below with rectangles, but we cannot easily find a close approximation to this area, nor can we find the limit to which it tends (though of course we know $\displaystyle\int \dfrac{1}{x}\, dx = \ln x$, so that the exact value is $\ln 2$).

More generally, if we consider the region with $x = X$ as boundary

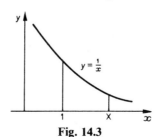

Fig. 14.3

instead of $x = 2$, it does not seem as though $\int_1^X \frac{1}{x} \, dx$ can be expressed as an algebraic function of X. Let us call $\int_1^X \frac{1}{x} \, dx$, hyp (X), since it is partly bounded by the hyperbola $y = \frac{1}{x}$.

Looking for properties of hyp (X), we see from the graph that

$$\text{hyp} (1) = \int_1^1 \frac{1}{x} \, dx = 0, \tag{1}$$

$$\text{hyp} (X) = \int_1^X \frac{1}{x} \, dx \text{ is positive if } X > 1, \tag{2}$$

$$\text{hyp} (X) \text{ is negative if } 0 < X < 1, \tag{3}$$

and $\qquad\qquad$ hyp (X) is undefined if $X < 0$. $\tag{4}$

Further $\qquad$
$$\text{hyp} (2X) = \int_1^{2X} \frac{1}{x} \, dx$$
$$= \int_1^X \frac{1}{x} \, dx + \int_X^{2X} \frac{1}{x} \, dx.$$

Now writing $x = Xz$, $\dfrac{dx}{dz} = X$,

so that $\qquad$
$$\text{hyp} (2X) = \int_1^X \frac{1}{x} \, dx + \int_1^2 \frac{1}{z} \, dz$$
$$\text{hyp} (2X) = \text{hyp} (X) + \text{hyp}(2).$$

Similarly we can generalise to show that

$$\text{hyp} (XY) = \text{hyp} (X) + \text{hyp} (Y) \tag{5}$$

Furthermore $\quad$
$$\text{hyp} (X^n) = \int_1^{X^n} \frac{1}{x} \, dx$$

Write $z^n = x$, so that

$$n z^{n-1} \frac{dz}{dx} = 1,$$

i.e. $\qquad\qquad\qquad$
$$n \frac{1}{z} \frac{dz}{dx} = \frac{1}{x}$$

$$\therefore \quad \int_1^{X^n} \frac{1}{x} \, dx = \int_1^X n \cdot \frac{1}{z} \, dz$$

$$= n \int_1^X \frac{1}{z} \, dx$$

$$\therefore \quad \text{hyp} (X^n) = n \, \text{hyp} (X). \tag{6}$$

Properties (1) and (6), especially (5) and (6), we recognise as being associated with logarithms, and we can in fact define log X as $\int \frac{1}{x} \, dx$, knowing such a function possesses the familiar properties of logarithms. It only remains to find the base of these logarithms.

The base a of a logarithm is the number a such that $\log_a = 1$, so that we require a such that $\int_1^a \frac{1}{x}\,dx = 1$. We see from Fig. 14.4 that $\int_1^2 \frac{1}{x}\,dx < 1$, so $a > 2$, that $\int_1^3 \frac{1}{x}\,dx < 2$ but is greater than 1, so that it looks as though $2 < a < 3$. It can be proved that the base is e, the base of natural logarithms, and that $\int_1^x \frac{1}{x}\,dx = \ln X$. Using this definition, it follows that $\dfrac{d}{dx}(\ln x) = \dfrac{1}{x}$.

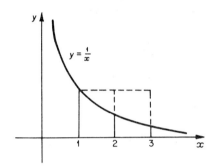

Fig. 14.4

Exercise 14.2

1. Show graphically that $\int_1^2 \frac{1}{x}\,dx \simeq 0.7$.

2. Show graphically that $\frac{1}{2} + \frac{1}{3} + \frac{1}{4} < \int_1^4 \frac{1}{x}\,dx < 1 + \frac{1}{2} + \frac{1}{3}$ and deduce $0.54 < \int_1^2 \frac{1}{x}\,dx < 0.92$.

3. Show graphically that $\frac{1}{11} + \frac{1}{12} + \ldots \frac{1}{20} < \int_{10}^{20} \frac{1}{x}\,dx < \frac{1}{10} + \frac{1}{11} + \ldots \frac{1}{19}$

   and deduce $0.67 < \int_1^2 \frac{1}{x}\,dx < 0.72$.

4. Find graphically an approximate value for hyp (3).

5. By considering $\int_1^{x+h} \frac{1}{x}\,dx - \int_1^x \frac{1}{x}\,dx$ prove $\dfrac{h}{x} < \ln(x+h) - \ln(x) < \dfrac{h}{x+h}$ and deduce $\dfrac{d}{dx}(\ln x) = \dfrac{1}{x}$.

6. By considering $\int_r^{r+1} \frac{1}{x}\,dx$ where r is a positive integer, show that $\frac{1}{r} > \frac{1}{x}$

$> \frac{1}{r+1}$, when $r < x < r + 1$ and that $\frac{1}{r} > \ln(r+1) - \ln r > \frac{1}{r+1}$.

7. Show, graphically or otherwise, that if r is an integer greater than 1, then

$$L = \tfrac{1}{2} + \tfrac{1}{3} + \tfrac{1}{4} + \ldots + \frac{1}{r} < \int_1^r \frac{1}{x}\,dx < 1 + \tfrac{1}{2} + \tfrac{1}{3} + \ldots + \frac{1}{r-1} = R.$$

Determine whether $\frac{1}{2}(L + R)$ underestimates or overestimates the value of the integral.   (C.)

8. Prove that $\sum\limits_{r=1}^{n} r^2 = \tfrac{1}{6}n(n+1)(2n+1)$.

The x-axis from $x = 1$ to $x = 2$ is divided into n equal intervals by the points $(1, 0)$, $\left(1 + \dfrac{1}{n}, 0\right)$, $\left(1 + \dfrac{2}{n}, 0\right)$, $\ldots$ $\left(1 + \dfrac{n-1}{n}, 0\right)$, $(2, 0)$.

Rectangles with sides parallel to the axes are drawn on these intervals with one vertex on the curve $y = x^2$ and the rest of each rectangle between the curve and the x-axis. Show that the sum of the areas of these rectangles is

$$1 + \left(1 - \frac{1}{n}\right)\left(\frac{4}{3} - \frac{1}{6n}\right).$$

Show further that as n increases this sum increases but remains less than $\tfrac{7}{3}$.   (O. & C.)

9. By considering the integral $\int_0^1 \frac{1}{1+x}\,dx$ as the limit of a sum prove that

$$S_n = \frac{1}{n+1} + \frac{1}{n+2} + \ldots + \frac{1}{n+n} \to \ln 2 \quad \text{as } n \to \infty.$$

By considering the value of the integral as lying between two sums prove that S_n differs from $\ln 2$ by less than

$$\frac{1}{n} - \frac{1}{2n}, \quad \text{i.e. } \frac{1}{2n}. \tag{O. & C.}$$

10. Show that, if $x > 1$,

$$\int_1^x \frac{(t-1)^2}{t^2}\,dt > 0 \quad \text{and} \quad \int_1^x \frac{t-1}{t^2}\,dt > 0.$$

From these results prove that, if $x > 1$,

$$\frac{x^2-1}{2x} > \ln x > \frac{x-1}{x}.$$

By putting $x = \dfrac{n}{n-1}$ show that

$$0 > \frac{1}{n} - \ln\frac{n}{n-1} > \frac{1}{2}\left(\frac{1}{n} - \frac{1}{n-1}\right)$$

and deduce that, if n is a positive integer greater than 1,

$$1 > 1 + \frac{1}{2} + \frac{1}{3} + \ldots + \frac{1}{n} - \ln n > \frac{1}{2} + \frac{1}{2n}. \tag{O. & C.}$$

Integration by substitution

Easy substitutions have already been employed in integration; we shall now consider other substitutions and see how they may be used. There is often no guarantee that a substitution will work; it is an experiment which must be tested. If it fails, other methods must be used.

1. $\sqrt{(a^2 - x^2)}$

When the expression $\sqrt{(a^2 - x^2)}$ occurs in an integrand, i.e. the expression to be integrated, try the substitution $x = a \sin \theta$.

Example. *Find* $\displaystyle\int \frac{dx}{(a^2 - x^2)^{\frac{3}{2}}}$.

Let
$$x = a \sin \theta; \quad \text{then} \quad dx = a \cos \theta \, d\theta$$
$$\sqrt{(a^2 - x^2)} = \sqrt{a^2(1 - \sin^2 \theta)} = a \cos \theta$$
$$\therefore \int \frac{dx}{(a^2 - x^2)^{\frac{3}{2}}} = \int \frac{a \cos \theta \, d\theta}{a^3 \cos^3 \theta} = \frac{1}{a^2} \int \sec^2 \theta \, d\theta = \frac{1}{a^2} \tan \theta + c.$$

But $\sin \theta = \dfrac{x}{a}$

$$\therefore \quad \cos \theta = \sqrt{\left(1 - \frac{x^2}{a^2}\right)} \quad \text{and} \quad \tan \theta = \frac{x}{\sqrt{(a^2 - x^2)}}.$$

$$\therefore \int \frac{dx}{(a^2 - x^2)^{\frac{3}{2}}} = \frac{x}{a^2 \sqrt{(a^2 - x^2)}} + c.$$

2. $\sqrt{(x^2 - a^2)}$

When the expression $\sqrt{(x^2 - a^2)}$ occurs in the integrand, try $x = a \sec \theta$ or $x = a \cosh \theta$.
Similarly with $\sqrt{(x^2 + a^2)}$, try $x = a \tan \theta$ or $x = a \sinh \theta$.

Example. *Find* $\displaystyle\int \frac{dx}{x^2 \sqrt{(x^2 + a^2)}}$.

Put $x = a \sinh \theta$; then $dx = a \cosh \theta \, d\theta$ and $\sqrt{(x^2 + a^2)} = a \cosh \theta$.

$$\therefore \int \frac{dx}{x^2 \sqrt{(x^2 + a^2)}} = \int \frac{a \cosh \theta \, d\theta}{a^3 \sinh^2 \theta \cosh \theta} = \frac{1}{a^2} \int \operatorname{cosech}^2 \theta \, d\theta$$
$$= -\frac{1}{a^2} \coth \theta + c.$$

But $\sinh \theta = \dfrac{x}{a}$

$$\therefore \quad \cosh \theta = \sqrt{\left(1 + \frac{x^2}{a^2}\right)} \quad \text{and} \quad \coth \theta = \frac{\sqrt{(a^2 + x^2)}}{x}.$$

$$\therefore \int \frac{dx}{x^2 \sqrt{(x^2 + a^2)}} = -\frac{\sqrt{(a^2 + x^2)}}{a^2 x} + c.$$

3. $\int \text{cosec } x \, dx, \int \text{sec } x \, dx$ and integrals of the type

$$\int \frac{dx}{a \cos x + b \sin x + c}.$$

A very useful substitution, successful in the above three integrals and in other trigonometrical integrals, is $t = \tan \dfrac{x}{2}$.

When $t = \tan \frac{1}{2}x$,

$$dt = \frac{1}{2} \sec^2 \tfrac{1}{2}x \, dx$$
$$= \tfrac{1}{2}(1 + t^2) \, dx.$$

$$\therefore \quad dx = \frac{2 \, dt}{1 + t^2}.$$

Also

$$\cos x = \frac{1 - \tan^2 \frac{1}{2}x}{1 + \tan^2 \frac{1}{2}x} = \frac{1 - t^2}{1 + t^2}; \quad \sin x = \frac{2 \tan \frac{1}{2}x}{1 + \tan^2 \frac{1}{2}x} = \frac{2t}{1 + t^2}.$$

(i) $\int \text{cosec } x \, dx = \int \dfrac{dx}{\sin x}$

$$= \int \frac{1 + t^2}{2t} \cdot \frac{2 \, dt}{1 + t^2} = \int \frac{dt}{t} = \ln t = \ln \tan \tfrac{1}{2}x + c.$$

An alternative form of the integral may be found as follows.

$$\int \text{cosec } x \, dx = \ln \tan \frac{x}{2} = \ln \frac{\sin \frac{1}{2}x}{\cos \frac{1}{2}x} = \ln \frac{2 \sin^2 \frac{1}{2}x}{2 \sin \frac{1}{2}x \cos \frac{1}{2}x}$$

$$= \ln \frac{1 - \cos x}{\sin x}$$

$$= \ln (\text{cosec } x - \cot x).$$

$$\therefore \quad \int \text{cosec } x \, dx = \ln \tan \tfrac{1}{2}x + c = \ln (\text{cosec } x - \cot x) + c.$$

(ii) $\qquad \int \text{sec } x \, dx = \int \dfrac{dx}{\cos x} = \int \dfrac{1 + t^2}{1 - t^2} \cdot \dfrac{2 \, dt}{1 + t^2}$

$$= \int \frac{2 \, dt}{1 - t^2}$$

$$= \int \left(\frac{1}{1 - t} + \frac{1}{1 + t} \right) dt$$

$$= -\ln (1 - t) + \ln (1 + t)$$

$$= \ln \frac{1 + \tan \frac{1}{2}x}{1 - \tan \frac{1}{2}x}$$

$$= \ln \tan \left(\frac{\pi}{4} + \frac{x}{2} \right)$$

since

$$\tan\left(\frac{\pi}{4}+\frac{x}{2}\right)=\frac{\tan\frac{1}{4}\pi+\tan\frac{1}{2}x}{1-\tan\frac{1}{4}\pi\tan\frac{1}{2}x}.$$

An alternative form may be found as follows.

$$\ln\frac{1+\tan\frac{1}{2}x}{1-\tan\frac{1}{2}x}=\ln\frac{\cos\frac{1}{2}x+\sin\frac{1}{2}x}{\cos\frac{1}{2}x-\sin\frac{1}{2}x}=\ln\frac{(\cos\frac{1}{2}x+\sin\frac{1}{2}x)^2}{\cos^2\frac{1}{2}x-\sin^2\frac{1}{2}x}$$

$$=\ln\frac{1+\sin x}{\cos x}$$

$$=\ln(\sec x+\tan x).$$

$$\therefore \int\sec x\,dx=\ln\tan\left(\frac{\pi}{4}+\frac{x}{2}\right)+c=\ln(\sec x+\tan x)+c.$$

This integral could also have been derived from that of cosec x by the substitution $x=\frac{\pi}{2}+y$.

Then $dx=dy;\quad \text{cosec } x=\sec y,\quad \cot x=-\tan y.$

$$\therefore \int\text{cosec } x\,dx=\ln\tan\frac{x}{2}=\ln(\text{cosec } x-\cot x)$$

becomes

$$\int\sec y\,dy=\ln\tan\left(\frac{\pi}{4}+\frac{y}{2}\right)=\ln(\sec y+\tan y).$$

(iii) $\int\dfrac{dx}{a\cos x+b\sin x+c}.$

This integral is best illustrated by examples.

Example 1. Find $\int\dfrac{dx}{\cos x+3}.$

Put $t=\tan\frac{1}{2}x$ so that $dx=\dfrac{2\,dt}{1+t^2}$

$$\int\frac{dx}{\cos x+3}=\int\frac{2\,dt/(1+t^2)}{(1-t^2)/(1+t^2)+3}=\int\frac{2\,dt}{4+2t^2}$$

$$=\int\frac{dt}{t^2+2}=\frac{1}{\sqrt2}\tan^{-1}\frac{t}{\sqrt2}$$

$$=\frac{1}{\sqrt2}\tan^{-1}\left(\frac{1}{\sqrt2}\tan\frac{x}{2}\right)+c.$$

Example 2. Find $\int\dfrac{dx}{2\sin x-\cos x+3}.$

Put $t=\tan\frac{1}{2}x$ so that $dx=\dfrac{2\,dt}{1+t^2}.$

$$\int \frac{dx}{2 \sin x - \cos x + 3} = \int \frac{2 \, dt/(1 + t^2)}{[4t/(1 + t^2)] - [(1 - t^2)/(1 + t^2)] + 3}$$

$$= \int \frac{2 \, dt}{4t - 1 + t^2 + 3 + 3t^2}$$

$$= \int \frac{2 \, dt}{4t^2 + 4t + 2}$$

$$= \int \frac{2 \, dt}{(2t + 1)^2 + 1}$$

$$= \frac{2}{2} \tan^{-1} (2t + 1)$$

$$= \tan^{-1} \left(2 \tan \frac{x}{2} + 1 \right) + c.$$

4. $\int \dfrac{dx}{x \sqrt{(ax^2 + bx + c)}}.$

This integral may be reduced to a standard form by the substitution $x = \dfrac{1}{y}.$

Example. *Find* $\int \dfrac{dx}{x \sqrt{(x^2 - 1)}}.$

Put $x = \dfrac{1}{y}$ so that $dx = -\dfrac{1}{y^2} \, dy$

$$\int \frac{dx}{x \sqrt{(x^2 - 1)}} = -\int \frac{(1/y^2) \, dy}{(1/y) \sqrt{[(1/y^2) - 1]}} = -\int \frac{dy}{\sqrt{(1 - y^2)}}$$

$$= -\sin^{-1} y$$

$$= -\sin^{-1} \left(\frac{1}{x} \right) + c.$$

Definite integrals by substitution

When evaluating a definite integral by substitution, it is generally easier to change the limits than to change the variable back as shown in the following examples.

Example 1. *Evaluate* $\displaystyle\int_0^a \sqrt{(a^2 - x^2)} \, dx.$

Put $x = a \sin \theta$ so that $dx = a \cos \theta \, d\theta$ and $\sqrt{(a^2 - x^2)} = a \cos \theta.$

When $x = a$, $\sin \theta = 1$ and $\theta = \dfrac{\pi}{2}$; when $x = 0$, $\sin \theta = 0$ and $\theta = 0.$

$$\int_0^a \sqrt{(a^2 - x^2)} \, dx = \int_0^{\pi/2} a^2 \cos^2 \theta \, d\theta = a^2 \int_0^{\pi/2} \cos^2 \theta \, d\theta.$$

The integral of $\cos^2 \theta$ is performed by expressing $\cos^2 \theta$ in terms of the double angle.

$$\int_0^{\pi/2} \cos^2 \theta \, d\theta = \tfrac{1}{2} \int_0^{\pi/2} (1 + \cos 2\theta) \, d\theta = \tfrac{1}{2} \left[\theta + \frac{\sin 2\theta}{2} \right]_0^{\pi/2}$$

$$= \tfrac{1}{2} \left(\frac{\pi}{2} \right)$$

$$= \frac{\pi}{4}$$

$$\therefore \quad \int_0^a \sqrt{(a^2 - x^2)} \, dx = \frac{\pi a^2}{4}.$$

Example 2. *Evaluate* $\displaystyle \int_{1/2}^1 \frac{dx}{x \sqrt{(4x^2 - 1)}}$.

Put $x = \dfrac{1}{y}$ so that $dx = -\dfrac{1}{y^2} \, dy$.

When $x = 1$, $y = 1$; when $x = \tfrac{1}{2}$, $y = 2$.

$$\therefore \quad \int_{1/2}^1 \frac{dx}{x \sqrt{(4x^2 - 1)}} = -\int_2^1 \frac{(1/y^2) \, dy}{(1/y) \sqrt{[(4/y^2) - 1]}}$$

$$= -\int_2^1 \frac{dy}{\sqrt{(4 - y^2)}}$$

$$\int_1^2 \frac{dy}{\sqrt{(4 - y^2)}} \qquad \begin{array}{l} \text{[Interchanging the limits changes} \\ \text{the sign of the integral]} \end{array}$$

$$= \left[\sin^{-1} \frac{y}{2} \right]_1^2$$

$$= \sin^{-1} 1 - \sin^{-1} \tfrac{1}{2}$$

$$= \frac{\pi}{2} - \frac{\pi}{6}$$

$$= \frac{\pi}{3}.$$

Exercise 14.3

Integrate

1. $\sin^2 \theta$.

2. $\sqrt{(a^2 - x^2)}$.

3. $\sec 2\theta$.

4. $\operatorname{cosec} 2\theta$.

5. $\sec \dfrac{x}{2}$.

6. $\operatorname{cosec} \dfrac{x}{2}$.

7. $\sec nx$.

8. $\operatorname{cosec} nx$.

9. $\sqrt{(x^2 - a^2)}$.

10. $\dfrac{\cosh x}{\sinh x + 1}$.

11. $\dfrac{1}{1 + \cos x}$.

12. $\dfrac{1}{1 - \cos x}$.

13. $\dfrac{1}{4 - \cos x}$.

14. $\dfrac{1}{\cos x + \sin x}$ (use the auxiliary angle).

15. $\dfrac{1}{x\sqrt{(1-x^2)}}$. **16.** $\dfrac{1}{x\sqrt{(1+x^2)}}$. **17.** $\dfrac{1}{x\sqrt{(x^2+2x)}}$.

18. $\dfrac{1}{x\sqrt{(x^2-2x)}}$. **19.** $\dfrac{1}{8-\sin x}$. **20.** $\dfrac{1}{\cos x+\sin x+1}$.

Evaluate

21. $\displaystyle\int_0^{\pi/2}\sin^2\theta\,d\theta$. **22.** $\displaystyle\int_0^{\pi/2}\cos^2\theta\,d\theta$. **23.** $\displaystyle\int_0^{\pi/4}\sin^2 2\theta\,d\theta$.

24. $\displaystyle\int_0^{\pi/4}\cos^2 2\theta\,d\theta$. **25.** $\displaystyle\int_{\pi/3}^{\pi/2}\operatorname{cosec}\theta\,d\theta$. **26.** $\displaystyle\int_0^{\pi/3}\sec\theta\,d\theta$.

27. $\displaystyle\int_0^a x\sqrt{(a^2-x^2)}\,dx$. **28.** $\displaystyle\int_1^{5/3}\dfrac{dx}{x\sqrt{(x^2-1)}}$. **29.** $\displaystyle\int_1^2\dfrac{dx}{x\sqrt{(x^2-x)}}$.

30. $\displaystyle\int_2^3\dfrac{dx}{x\sqrt{(x^2+x)}}$. **31.** $\displaystyle\int_0^{\pi}\dfrac{dx}{5-3\cos x}$. **32.** $\displaystyle\int_0^{\pi/2}\dfrac{dx}{5-4\cos x}$.

33. $\displaystyle\int_0^1\dfrac{x^2\,dx}{x^3-1}$. **34.** $\displaystyle\int_{-1}^1\dfrac{dx}{\sqrt{(4-x^2)}}$. **35.** $\displaystyle\int_0^5\dfrac{dx}{25+x^2}$.

36. $\displaystyle\int_0^1 x\sqrt{(1-x^2)}\,dx$. **37.** $\displaystyle\int_0^1\dfrac{dx}{(1+x^2)^{\frac{3}{2}}}$. **38.** $\displaystyle\int_0^1\dfrac{x+1}{\sqrt{(1-x^2)}}\,dx$.

39. $\displaystyle\int_0^1\dfrac{x^3\,dx}{1+x^4}$. **40.** Show that $\displaystyle\int_0^{\pi/2}\sin^n x\,dx=\int_0^{\pi/2}\cos^n x\,dx$.

Integration by parts

Integration by parts is a device useful for integrating some products. For example,

$$\frac{d}{dx}(x\sin x)=\sin x+x\cos x.$$

$$\therefore\quad x\cos x=\frac{d}{dx}(x\sin x)-\sin x$$

and $\displaystyle\int x\cos x\,dx=x\sin x-\int\sin x\,dx$

$$=x\sin x+\cos x+c.$$

Following the same procedure with u and v, two general functions of x,

$$\frac{d}{dx}(uv)=u\frac{dv}{dx}+v\frac{du}{dx}.$$

$$\therefore\quad u\frac{dv}{dx}=\frac{d}{dx}(uv)-v\frac{du}{dx}$$

and $\displaystyle\int u\frac{dv}{dx}\,dx=uv-\int v\frac{du}{dx}\,dx$

or $$\int u \, dv = uv - \int v \, du.$$

So $\int u \, dv$ can be found provided that $\int v \, du$ can be integrated.

In dealing with $\int x \cos x \, dx$ as in our example, we first express $\cos x \, dx$ as $d(\sin x)$.

Then $$\int x \cos x \, dx = \int x \, d(\sin x)$$

$$= x \sin x - \int \sin x \, dx.$$

[The first term is the product of the terms in the integral without the integral and differential signs; for the second term we interchange the x and $\sin x$.]

$$\therefore \quad \int x \cos x \, dx = x \sin x + \cos x + c.$$

The functions $x^n \, e^{ax}$, $x^n \sin ax$ and $x^n \cos ax$

These may be integrated by first integrating the e^{ax}, $\sin ax$ or $\cos ax$ factor of the product.

Example 1. $\int x \, e^{3x} \, dx.$

$$\int x \, e^{3x} \, dx = \int x \, d\left(\frac{e^{3x}}{3}\right) = \frac{x \, e^{3x}}{3} - \int \frac{e^{3x}}{3} \, dx$$

$$= \frac{x \, e^{3x}}{3} - \frac{e^{3x}}{9}.$$

Example 2. $\int x^2 \sin 2x \, dx.$

This needs a double application of the 'by parts' rule.

$$\int x^2 \sin 2x \, dx = \int x^2 \, d\left(-\frac{\cos 2x}{2}\right)$$

$$= -\frac{x^2 \cos 2x}{2} + \int \frac{\cos 2x}{2} \, d(x^2)$$

$$= -\frac{x^2 \cos 2x}{2} + \int x \cos 2x \, dx$$

$$= -\frac{x^2 \cos 2x}{2} + \int x \, d\left(\frac{\sin 2x}{2}\right)$$

$$= -\frac{x^2 \cos 2x}{2} + \frac{x \sin 2x}{2} - \int \frac{\sin 2x}{2} \, dx$$

$$= -\frac{x^2 \cos 2x}{2} + \frac{x \sin 2x}{2} + \frac{\cos 2x}{4} + c.$$

The functions $x^n \sin^{-1} x$, $x^n \tan^{-1} x$, $x^n (\ln x)^m$

These functions are integrated by first integrating the x^n factor.

Example 1. $\int x \tan^{-1} x \, dx.$

$$\int x \tan^{-1} x \, dx = \int \tan^{-1} x \, d\left(\frac{x^2}{2}\right)$$

$$= \frac{x^2}{2} \tan^{-1} x - \int \frac{x^2}{2} \, d(\tan^{-1} x)$$

$$= \frac{x^2}{2} \tan^{-1} x - \frac{1}{2} \int \frac{x^2}{1 + x^2} \, dx$$

$$= \frac{x^2}{2} \tan^{-1} x - \frac{1}{2} \int \left(1 - \frac{1}{1 + x^2}\right) dx$$

$$= \frac{x^2}{2} \tan^{-1} x - \frac{1}{2} x + \frac{1}{2} \tan^{-1} x + c.$$

Example 2. $\int x^2 (\ln x)^2 \, dx.$

$$\int x^2 (\ln x)^2 \, dx = \int (\ln x)^2 \, d\left(\frac{x^3}{3}\right)$$

$$= \frac{x^2}{3} (\ln x)^2 - \int \frac{x^3}{3} \, d(\ln x)^2$$

$$= \frac{x^3}{3} (\ln x)^2 - \frac{2}{3} \int x^3 (\ln x)\left(\frac{1}{x}\right) dx$$

$$= \frac{x^3}{3} (\ln x)^2 - \frac{2}{3} \int x^2 \ln x \, dx$$

$$= \frac{x^3}{3} (\ln x)^2 - \frac{2}{3} \int \ln x \, d\left(\frac{x^2}{3}\right)$$

$$= \frac{x^3}{3} (\ln x)^2 - \frac{2}{3} \cdot \frac{x^2}{3} \ln x + \frac{2}{3} \int \frac{x^3}{3} \, d(\ln x)$$

$$= \frac{x^3}{3} (\ln x)^2 - \frac{2}{9} x^3 \ln x + \frac{2}{9} \int x^3 \left(\frac{1}{x} \, dx\right)$$

$$= \frac{x^3}{3} (\ln x)^2 - \frac{2}{9} x^3 \ln x + \frac{2}{27} x^3 + c.$$

The functions $\sin^{-1} x$, $\tan^{-1} x$, $\ln x$

These are integrated by taking v in $\int u \, dv$ to be x.

Example 1. $\int \sin^{-1} x \, dx$.

$$\int \sin^{-1} x \, d(x) = x \sin^{-1} x - \int x \, d(\sin^{-1} x)$$

$$= x \sin^{-1} x - \int \frac{x}{\sqrt{(1 - x^2)}} \, dx$$

Putting $\qquad 1 - x^2 = y^2 \quad$ in $\quad \int \frac{x \, dx}{\sqrt{(1 - x^2)}} \quad$ gives

$$\int \frac{x \, dx}{\sqrt{(1 - x^2)}} = -\int \frac{y \, dy}{y} = -\int dy$$

$$= -y = -\sqrt{(1 - x^2)}$$

$$\therefore \quad \int \sin^{-1} x \, dx = x \sin^{-1} x + \sqrt{(1 - x^2)} + c.$$

Example 2. $\int \ln x \, dx$.

$$\int \ln x \, d(x) = x \ln x - \int x \, d(\ln x)$$

$$= x \ln x - \int x \left(\frac{1}{x} \, dx \right)$$

$$= x \ln x - x + c.$$

The functions $\sec^3 x$, $\mathrm{cosec}^3 x$, $e^{ax} \sin bx$, $\sqrt{(a^2 + x^2)}$

These may be integrated by forming an equation in the integral.

Example 1. $\int \sec^3 x \, dx$.

$$\int \sec^3 x \, dx = \int \sec x (\sec^2 x \, dx) = \int \sec x \, d(\tan x)$$

$$= \sec x \tan x - \int \tan x \, d(\sec x)$$

$$= \sec x \tan x - \int \tan^2 x \sec x \, dx$$

$$= \sec x \tan x - \int (\sec^2 x - 1) \sec x \, dx$$

$$= \sec x \tan x - \int \sec^3 x \, dx + \int \sec x \, dx$$

$$\therefore \quad 2 \int \sec^3 x \, dx = \sec x \tan x + \int \sec x \, dx$$

and $\qquad \int \sec^3 x \, dx = \tfrac{1}{2} \sec x \tan x + \tfrac{1}{2} \ln (\sec x + \tan x) + c.$

Example 2. $\int \sqrt{(a^2 + x^2)} \, dx.$

$$\int \sqrt{(a^2 + x^2)} \, dx$$

$$= x \sqrt{(a^2 + x^2)} - \int x \, d\{ \sqrt{(a^2 + x^2)} \}$$

$$= x \sqrt{(a^2 + x^2)} - \int \frac{x^2}{\sqrt{(a^2 + x^2)}} \, dx$$

$$= x \sqrt{(a^2 + x^2)} - \int \frac{a^2 + x^2}{\sqrt{(a^2 + x^2)}} \, dx + \int \frac{a^2}{\sqrt{(a^2 + x^2)}} \, dx$$

$$= x \sqrt{(a^2 + x^2)} - \int \sqrt{(a^2 + x^2)} \, dx + a^2 \ln \{ x + \sqrt{(a^2 + x^2)} \}$$

$$\therefore \quad \int \sqrt{(a^2 + x^2)} \, dx = \tfrac{1}{2} x \sqrt{(a^2 + x^2)} + \tfrac{1}{2} a^2 \ln \{ x + \sqrt{(a^2 + x^2)} \} + c.$$

Example 3. $\int e^{ax} \sin bx \, dx.$

$$\int e^{ax} \sin bx \, dx = \int \sin bx \, d\left(\frac{e^{ax}}{a} \right)$$

$$= \frac{e^{ax} \sin bx}{a} - \int \frac{e^{ax}}{a} \, d(\sin bx)$$

$$= \frac{e^{ax} \sin bx}{a} - \frac{b}{a} \int e^{ax} \cos bx \, dx$$

$$= \frac{e^{ax} \sin bx}{a} - \frac{b}{a} \int \cos bx \, d\left(\frac{e^{ax}}{a} \right)$$

$$= \frac{e^{ax} \sin bx}{a} - \frac{b}{a^2} \cos bx \, e^{ax} + \frac{b}{a^2} \int e^{ax} \, d(\cos bx)$$

$$= \frac{e^{ax} \sin bx}{a} - \frac{b}{a^2} \cos bx \, e^{ax} - \frac{b^2}{a^2} \int e^{ax} \sin bx \, dx$$

$$\therefore \quad \left(1 + \frac{b^2}{a^2} \right) \int e^{ax} \sin bx \, dx = \frac{e^{ax} \sin bx}{a} - \frac{b}{a^2} \cos bx \, e^{ax}$$

and $\qquad \int e^{ax} \sin bx \, dx = \dfrac{e^{ax} (a \sin bx - b \cos bx)}{a^2 + b^2} + c.$

Exercise 14.4

Integrate

1. $x \sin x$.	2. $x^2 e^x$.	3. $x \ln x$.
4. $x^2 \cos x$.	5. $x^2 \sin x$.	6. $(\ln x)^2$.
7. $\tan^{-1} x$.	8. $x e^{-x}$.	9. $x^2 e^{-x}$.
10. $e^x \sin x$.	11. $e^{-x} \sin x$.	12. $e^x \cos x$.
13. $e^{-x} \cos x$.	14. $e^{ax} \cos bx$.	15. $\sqrt{(x^2 - 1)}$.
16. $\sqrt{(x^2 + 4)}$.	17. $\operatorname{cosec}^3 x$.	18. $x^2 \ln x$.
19. $x^n \ln x$.	20. $x^3 \sin x$.	

Reduction formulae

Suppose that $I_n = \displaystyle\int \sin^n \theta \, d\theta$. This notation means that

$$I_1 = \int \sin \theta \, d\theta, \quad I_2 = \int \sin^2 \theta \, d\theta \text{ and so on.}$$

$$I_n = \int \sin^n \theta \, d\theta = \int \sin^{n-1} \theta (\sin \theta \, d\theta) = - \int \sin^{n-1} \theta \, d(\cos \theta)$$

$$= - \cos \theta \sin^{n-1} \theta + (n - 1) \int \sin^{n-2} \theta \cos \theta (\cos \theta) \, d\theta$$

$$\text{(by parts)}$$

$$= - \cos \theta \sin^{n-1} \theta + (n - 1) \int \sin^{n-2} \theta \cos^2 \theta \, d\theta$$

$$= - \cos \theta \sin^{n-1} \theta + (n - 1) \int \sin^{n-2} \theta (1 - \sin^2 \theta) \, d\theta$$

$$= - \cos \theta \sin^{n-1} \theta + (n - 1)I_{n-2} - (n - 1)I_n$$

$$\therefore \quad nI_n = - \cos \theta \sin^{n-1} \theta + (n - 1)I_{n-2}.$$

Such a formula which connects the values of an integral for two or more different values of the variable n is called a **reduction formula**:

We know that
$$I_0 = \int d\theta = \theta.$$

From the reduction formula, putting $n = 2$,
$$2I_2 = I_0 - \sin \theta \cos \theta$$

$$\therefore \quad \int \sin^2 \theta \, d\theta = \tfrac{1}{2}(\theta - \sin \theta \cos \theta).$$

In a similar way I_4 may be found and hence I_n for all even values of n.

Also
$$I_1 = \int \sin \theta \, d\theta = - \cos \theta.$$

$$\therefore \quad I_3 = \tfrac{1}{3}\{2I_1 - \cos \theta \sin^2 \theta\}$$
$$= - \tfrac{2}{3} \cos \theta - \tfrac{1}{3} \cos \theta \sin^2 \theta.$$

The integrals $\int_0^{\pi/2} \sin^n \theta \, d\theta$ and $\int_0^{\pi/2} \cos^n \theta \, d\theta$

The reduction formula proved in the last paragraph is especially useful when the limits are $\dfrac{\pi}{2}$ and θ.

If $I_n = \int_0^{\pi/2} \sin^n \theta \, d\theta$, the reduction formula for $\int \sin^n \theta \, d\theta$ becomes

$$nI_n = (n-1)I_{n-2}$$

since $\sin^{n-1}\theta \cos \theta$ disappears at both limits.

Now $\qquad I_0 = \int_0^{\pi/2} d\theta = \dfrac{\pi}{2}.$

$$\therefore \quad I_2 = \frac{1}{2} \times \frac{\pi}{2} \quad \text{and} \quad I_4 = \frac{3}{4}I_2 = \frac{3}{4} \times \frac{1}{2} \times \frac{\pi}{2}.$$

$$\therefore \quad I_n = \frac{(n-1)(n-3)\ldots 3 \times 1}{n(n-2)\ldots 4 \times 2} \times \frac{\pi}{2} \quad \text{if } n \text{ is even.}$$

Also $\qquad I_1 = \int_0^{\pi/2} \sin \theta \, d\theta = \Big[-\cos \theta \Big]_0^{\pi/2} = 1.$

$$\therefore \quad I_3 = \tfrac{2}{3} \quad \text{and} \quad I_5 = \tfrac{4}{5}I_3 = \frac{4 \times 2}{5 \times 3}.$$

$$\therefore \quad I_n = \frac{(n-1)(n-3)\ldots \times 4 \times 2}{n(n-2)\ldots \times 3 \times 1} \quad \text{if } n \text{ is odd.}$$

Let us now put $\theta = \dfrac{\pi}{2} - \varphi$ in $\int_0^{\pi/2} \sin^n \theta \, d\theta$.

The integral becomes $\int_{\pi/2}^0 \cos^n \varphi(-d\varphi)$ or $\int_0^{\pi/2} \cos^n \varphi \, d\varphi$.

Since the integral is definite, the variable is immaterial.

$$\therefore \quad \int_0^{\pi/2} \sin^n \theta \, d\theta = \int_0^{\pi/2} \cos^n \theta \, d\theta.$$

To write down the value of the integral of either $\cos^n \theta$ or $\sin^n \theta$ between 0 and $\dfrac{\pi}{2}$, form a fraction by putting n in the denominator and writing the integers from n down to 1 alternately in the denominator and numerator of the fraction. This is the value of the integral if n is odd; if n is even, multiply by the additional factor $\dfrac{\pi}{2}$.

Example 1. $\int_0^{\pi/2} \cos^3 \theta \, d\theta = \dfrac{2}{3}.$

Example 2. $\displaystyle\int_0^{\pi/2} \sin^4 \theta \, d\theta = \dfrac{3 \times 1}{4 \times 2} \times \dfrac{\pi}{2}.$

Example 3. $\displaystyle\int_0^{\pi/2} \cos^6 \theta \, d\theta = \dfrac{5 \times 3 \times 1}{6 \times 4 \times 2} \times \dfrac{\pi}{2}.$

Example 4. *Evaluate* $\displaystyle\int_0^a \sqrt{(a^2 - x^2)} \, dx.$

Put $x = a \sin \theta$ so that $dx = a \cos \theta \, d\theta$ and $\sqrt{(a^2 - x^2)} = a \cos \theta.$

When $x = a$, $\theta = \dfrac{\pi}{2}$; when $x = 0$, $\theta = 0.$

$$\therefore \quad \int_0^a \sqrt{(a^2 - x^2)} \, dx = \int_0^{\pi/2} a \cos \theta (a \cos \theta \, d\theta)$$

$$= a^2 \int_0^{\pi/2} \cos^2 \theta \, d\theta$$

$$= a^2 \times \frac{1}{2} \times \frac{\pi}{2}$$

$$= \frac{\pi a^2}{4}.$$

The integrals $\displaystyle\int_0^\pi \sin^n \theta \, d\theta$ and $\displaystyle\int_0^\pi \cos^n \theta \, d\theta$

$$\int_0^\pi \sin^n \theta \, d\theta = \int_{\pi/2}^\pi \sin^n \theta \, d\theta + \int_0^{\pi/2} \sin^n \theta \, d\theta.$$

In the first of these integrals put $\theta = \pi - \varphi$ so that

$$\sin \theta = \sin \varphi \quad \text{and} \quad d\theta = -d\varphi.$$

When $\qquad \theta = \pi, \varphi = 0; \quad \text{when } \theta = \dfrac{\pi}{2}, \varphi = \dfrac{\pi}{2}.$

$$\int_{\pi/2}^\pi \sin^n \theta \, d\theta = -\int_{\pi/2}^0 \sin^n \varphi \, d\varphi$$

$$= \int_0^{\pi/2} \sin^n \varphi \, d\varphi$$

$$= \int_0^{\pi/2} \sin^n \theta \, d\theta$$

$$\therefore \quad \int_0^\pi \sin^n \theta \, d\theta = 2 \int_0^{\pi/2} \sin^n \theta \, d\theta.$$

Example. $\int_0^\pi \sin\theta\, d\theta = 2 \int_0^{\pi/2} \sin^4\theta\, d\theta = 2 \times \dfrac{3 \times 1}{4 \times 2} \times \dfrac{\pi}{2} = \dfrac{3\pi}{8}.$

Similarly $\int_0^\pi \cos^n\theta\, d\theta = \int_{\pi/2}^\pi \cos^n\theta\, d\theta + \int_0^{\pi/2} \cos^n\theta\, d\theta.$

Putting $\theta = \pi - \varphi$ in the first of these integrals, gives

$$\cos\theta = -\cos\varphi \quad \text{and} \quad d\theta = -d\varphi.$$

$$\therefore \quad \int_{\pi/2}^\pi \cos^n\theta\, d\theta = (-1)^n \int_{\pi/2}^0 \cos^n\varphi(-d\varphi)$$

$$= (-1)^n \int_0^{\pi/2} \cos^n\varphi\, d\varphi = (-1)^n \int_0^{\pi/2} \cos^n\theta\, d\theta.$$

If n is odd,

$$\int_0^\pi \cos^n\theta\, d\theta = -\int_0^{\pi/2} \cos^n\theta\, d\theta + \int_0^{\pi/2} \cos^n\theta\, d\theta = 0.$$

If n is even,

$$\int_0^\pi \cos^n\theta\, d\theta = \int_0^{\pi/2} \cos^n\theta\, d\theta + \int_0^{\pi/2} \cos^n\theta\, d\theta = 2\int_0^{\pi/2} \cos^n\theta\, d\theta.$$

Example 1. $\int_0^\pi \cos^5\theta\, d\theta = 0.$

Example 2. $\int_0^\pi \cos^6\theta\, d\theta = 2 \int_0^{\pi/2} \cos^6\theta\, d\theta$

$$= 2 \times \dfrac{5 \times 3 \times 1}{6 \times 4 \times 2}\dfrac{\pi}{2} = \dfrac{5\pi}{16}.$$

These results could have been deduced by considering the sign of the integrand. In the second quadrant, $\sin^n\theta$ is positive and takes the same values as $\sin^n\theta$ in the first quadrant.

$$\therefore \quad \int_0^\pi \sin^n\theta\, dh = 2\int_0^{\pi/2} \sin^n\theta\, d\theta.$$

Similarly if n is even, $\cos^n\theta$ is positive in the second quadrant.

$$\therefore \quad \int_0^\pi \cos^n\theta\, d\theta = 2\int_0^{\pi/2} \cos^n d\theta \quad \text{when } n \text{ is even.}$$

If n is odd, $\cos^n\theta$ is negative in the second quadrant.

$$\therefore \quad \int_0^\pi \cos^n\theta\, d\theta = 0 \quad \text{when } n \text{ is odd.}$$

The integrals of $\cos^n\theta$ and $\sin^n\theta$ between multiples of $\dfrac{\pi}{2}$ may be connected with the corresponding integrals between $\dfrac{\pi}{2}$ and 0 in a similar way.

Example 3. $\displaystyle\int_0^{3\pi/2} \sin^3 \theta \, d\theta.$

In the first quadrant, $\sin^3 \theta$ is positive.
In the second quadrant, $\sin^3 \theta$ is positive.
In the third quadrant, $\sin^3 \theta$ is negative.

$$\therefore \int_0^{3\pi/2} \sin^3 \theta = \int_0^{\pi/2} \sin^3 \theta \, d\theta = \tfrac{2}{3}.$$

Example 4. $\displaystyle\int_{\pi/2}^{3\pi/2} \cos^5 \theta \, d\theta.$

In the second quadrant, $\cos^5 \theta$ is negative.
In this third quadrant, $\cos^5 \theta$ is negative.

$$\therefore \int_{\pi/2}^{3\pi/2} \cos^5 \theta \, d\theta = -2 \int_0^{\pi/2} \cos^5 \theta \, d\theta$$

$$= -2 \times \frac{4 \times 2}{5 \times 3} = -\frac{16}{15}.$$

Example 5. *Evaluate* $\displaystyle\int_0^{\pi/2} \cos^2 \theta \sin^4 \theta \, d\theta$ *and deduce the value of* $\displaystyle\int_0^{3\pi/2} \cos^2 \theta \sin^4 \theta \, d\theta.$

$$\int_0^{\pi/2} \cos^2 \theta \sin^4 \theta \, d\theta = \int_0^{\pi/2} (1 - \sin^2 \theta) \sin^4 \theta \, d\theta$$

$$= \int_0^{\pi/2} \sin^4 \theta \, d\theta - \int_0^{\pi/2} \sin^6 \theta \, d\theta$$

$$= \frac{3 \times 1 \times \pi}{4 \times 2 \times 2} - \frac{5 \times 3 \times 1 \times \pi}{6 \times 4 \times 2 \times 2}$$

$$= \frac{3\pi}{16} \left(1 - \frac{5}{6}\right) = \frac{3\pi}{16} \times \frac{1}{6} = \frac{\pi}{32}.$$

In the first three quadrants $\cos^2 \theta \sin^4 \theta$ is positive.

$$\therefore \int_0^{3\pi/2} \cos^2 \theta \sin^4 \theta \, d\theta = 3 \int_0^{\pi/2} \cos^2 \theta \sin^4 \theta \, d\theta = \frac{3\pi}{32}.$$

Exercise 14.5

Evaluate the following integrals:

1. $\displaystyle\int_0^{\pi/2} \cos^5 \theta \, d\theta.$ **2.** $\displaystyle\int_0^{\pi/2} \sin^4 \theta \, d\theta.$ **3.** $\displaystyle\int_0^{\pi/2} \sin \theta \, d\theta.$

4. $\displaystyle\int_0^{\pi/2} \cos^6 \theta \, d\theta.$ **5.** $\displaystyle\int_0^{\pi/2} \sin^5 \theta \, d\theta.$ **6.** $\displaystyle\int_0^{\pi/2} \cos^2 \theta \, d\theta.$

7. $\displaystyle\int_0^{\pi/2} \cos^8 \theta \, d\theta.$ **8.** $\displaystyle\int_0^{\pi/2} \sin^8 \theta \, d\theta.$ **9.** $\displaystyle\int_0^{\pi} \cos^5 \theta \, d\theta.$

10. $\displaystyle\int_0^{\pi} \sin^4 \theta \, d\theta.$ **11.** $\displaystyle\int_0^{\pi} \sin^7 \theta \, d\theta.$ **12.** $\displaystyle\int_0^{\pi} \cos^6 \theta \, d\theta.$

13. $\displaystyle\int_0^{\pi} \sin^5 \theta \, d\theta.$ **14.** $\displaystyle\int_0^{3\pi/2} \cos^5 \theta \, d\theta.$ **15.** $\displaystyle\int_0^{3\pi/2} \sin^4 \theta \, d\theta.$

16. $\displaystyle\int_{-\pi/2}^{\pi/2} \cos^5 \theta \, d\theta.$ **17.** $\displaystyle\int_{-\pi/2}^{\pi/2} \sin^4 \theta \, d\theta.$ **18.** $\displaystyle\int_0^{\pi/2} \sin^2 \theta \cos^4 \theta \, d\theta.$

19. $\displaystyle\int_{\pi}^{2\pi} \cos^2 \theta \sin^2 \theta \, d\theta.$ **20.** $\displaystyle\int_{\pi/2}^{2\pi} \cos^2 \theta \sin^4 \theta \, d\theta.$

Exercise 14.6: Miscellaneous

1. Find $\displaystyle\int \sin^3 x \cos^3 x \, dx.$

2. Integrate $\cos^3 x$.

3. Integrate $\sin^5 x$.

4. Prove
$$\frac{d}{dx}\left(\sin^{m+1} x \cos^{n-1} x\right) = (m+n)\sin^m x \cos^n x - (n-1)\sin^m x \cos^{n-2} x$$
and deduce a formula connecting
$$\int_0^{\pi/2} \sin^m x \cos^n x \, dx \quad \text{and} \quad \int_0^{\pi/2} \sin^m x \cos^{n-2} x \, dx.$$

5. Using the result of question 4, evaluate $\displaystyle\int_0^{\pi/2} \sin^3 x \cos^5 x \, dx.$

6. Find the area of the region under the curve $y = x \sin x$ between the ordinates $x = 0$ and $x = \dfrac{\pi}{2}$.

7. Find the coordinates of the centre of gravity of the region defined in question 6.

8. Find the area of the region under the curve $y = x \cos x$ between the ordinates at $x = 0$ and $x = \dfrac{\pi}{2}$.

9. Find $\displaystyle\int_0^{\pi/2} x \sin^2 x \, dx.$

10. Use the substitution $x = \pi - y$ to show that
$$\int_0^{\pi} x \sin x \, dx = \int_0^{\pi} (\pi - x) \sin x \, dx.$$

11. Using the result of question 10, show that
$$\int_0^{\pi} x \sin x \, dx = \frac{\pi}{2} \int_0^{\pi} \sin x \, dx.$$
Hence evaluate $\displaystyle\int_0^{\pi} x \sin x \, dx.$

12. Using the substitution $x = \dfrac{\pi}{2} - y$, show that

$$\int_0^{\pi/2} \cos^2 x \sin^4 x \, dx = \int_0^{\pi/2} \sin^2 x \cos^4 x \, dx.$$

13. Using the result of question 12, show that

$$\int_0^{\pi/2} \cos^2 x \sin^4 x \, dx = \tfrac{1}{2} \int_0^{\pi/2} \cos^2 x \sin^2 x \, dx.$$

Hence evaluate the integral.

14. Evaluate $\displaystyle\int_0^{\pi/4} \dfrac{d\theta}{1 + \cos 2\theta}$.

15. Evaluate $\displaystyle\int_0^{\pi/2} \dfrac{d\theta}{1 + \sin 2\theta}$.

16. Evaluate $\displaystyle\int_0^1 x^2 (1 - x)^6 \, dx$.

17. Evaluate $\displaystyle\int_1^2 \dfrac{dx}{x \sqrt{(x^2 - 1)}}$.

18. Integrate $e^x \sin 2x$.

19. Integrate $\sqrt{(4 + x^2)}$.

20. Integrate $e^x \cosh x$.

21. Find a reduction formula for $I_n = \displaystyle\int \tan^n x \, dx$.

Hence find $\displaystyle\int \tan^3 x \, dx$.

22. By differentiating $x^{m+1}(\ln x)^n$, deduce that, if

$$I_{m,n} = \int x^m (\ln x)^n \, dx,$$

$$(m + 1)I_{m,n} = x^{m+1}(\ln x)^n - n I_{m,n-1}.$$

23. Using the result of question 22, integrate $x^3 (\ln x)^2$.

24. Find a reduction formula for $I_n = \displaystyle\int x^n e^x \, dx$.

Deduce the value of $\displaystyle\int x^5 e^x \, dx$.

25. Find a reduction formula for $I_n = \displaystyle\int \cot^n x \, dx$.

Deduce the value of $\displaystyle\int \cot^4 x \, dx$.

26. Find $\displaystyle\int \dfrac{\cos (\ln x)}{x} \, dx$.

27. Show that $\displaystyle\int_a^b \dfrac{dx}{\sqrt{\{(x - a)(b - x)\}}} = \pi$.

28. Integrate $\dfrac{1}{3 - 2\cos x}$.

29. Evalute $\int_0^{\pi/2} \sin^3 x \cos^2 x \, dx$.

30. Find the value of $\int_0^1 x \sin^{-1} x \, dx$.

31. The curve $y = \sin x$ between $x = 0$ and $x = \dfrac{\pi}{2}$ is rotated about the axis of x. Find the volume generated and also the coordinates of the centre of gravity of this volume.

32. Evaluate $\int_0^\pi x^2 \sin x \, dx$.

33. Evaluate $\int_2^3 \ln x \, dx$.

34. Find the area of the region underneath the curve $y = \ln x$ between the ordinates $x = 1$ and $x = 2$. Find also the coordinates of the centre of gravity of this region.

35. Find a reduction formula for $I_n = \int_0^a (a^2 - x^2)^n \, dx$.

36. Use the substitution $t = \tan x$ to evaluate
$$\int_0^{\pi/4} \frac{dx}{\sin^2 x + 4 \cos^2 x}.$$

37. Evaluate $\int_0^\pi e^x \sin^2 x \, dx$.

38. Find $\int x^3 \tan^{-1} x \, dx$.

39. Find $\int x \sec^2 x \, dx$.

40. Given that $I_n = \int_0^1 x(1 - x)^n \, dx$, show that $2I_n = n \int_0^1 x^2 (1 - x)^{n-1} \, dx$. Hence evaluate the integral.

41. Find the area of the region under the curve $y = \sin^2 x$ between $x = 0$ and $x = \pi$.

42. Find $\int \log (x^2 - 4) \, dx$.

43. Evaluate $\int_0^1 \frac{x^4}{(1 + x^2)^2} \, dx$.

44. Find $\int x^4 (\ln x)^2 \, dx$.

45. Show that $\int_0^\pi \frac{\cos^2 x \, dx}{\cos^2 x + 4 \sin^2 x} = \frac{\pi}{3}$.

46. Find $\int \frac{(x + 1) e^x}{(x + 2)^2} \, dx$.

47. Find $\int e^{ax} \cos^2 bx \; dx.$

48. Evaluate $\int_0^{\pi/2} \sin^7 \theta \cos^2 \theta \; d\theta$ and $\int_0^{\pi} \sin^7 \theta \cos^2 \theta \; d\theta.$

49. If $I_n = \int \dfrac{e^x}{x^n} \; dx$, show that $I_n - nI_{n+1} = \dfrac{e^x}{x^n}.$

50. By considering the integral $\int_1^n x^{\frac{1}{2}} \; dx$, where n is a positive integer, prove that

$$2n \sqrt{n+1} \leqslant 3(\sqrt{1} + \sqrt{2} + \ldots + \sqrt{n}) \leqslant (2n+3)\sqrt{n} - 2.$$

(M.E.I.)

15 Systematic Integration

Standard integrals

We have now completed our standard forms for integration and a list of them is included at this stage.

y	$\int y\,dx$
x^n	$\dfrac{x^{n+1}}{n+1}$ $(n \neq -1)$
$\dfrac{1}{x}$	*$\ln x$
e^x	e^x
$\sin x$	$-\cos x$
$\cos x$	$\sin x$
$\tan x$	*$\ln \sec x$
$\operatorname{cosec} x$	*$\ln \tan \dfrac{x}{2}$ or $\ln (\operatorname{cosec} x - \cot x)$
$\sec x$	*$\ln \tan \left(\dfrac{\pi}{4} + \dfrac{x}{2} \right)$ or $\ln (\sec x + \tan x)$
$\cot x$	*$\ln \sin x$
$\dfrac{1}{a^2 + x^2}$	$\dfrac{1}{a} \tan^{-1} \dfrac{x}{a}$
$\dfrac{1}{a^2 - x^2}$	$\dfrac{1}{2a} \ln \dfrac{a + x}{a - x}$
$\dfrac{1}{\sqrt{(a^2 - x^2)}}$	$\sin^{-1} \dfrac{x}{a}$
$\dfrac{1}{\sqrt{(x^2 + a^2)}}$	$\ln [x + \sqrt{(x^2 + a^2)}]$ or $\sinh^{-1} \dfrac{x}{a}$
$\dfrac{1}{\sqrt{(x^2 - a^2)}}$	*$\ln [x + \sqrt{(x^2 - a^2)}]$ or $\cosh^{-1} \dfrac{x}{a}$
$\cosh x$	$\sinh x$
$\sinh x$	$\cosh x$
a^x	$\dfrac{a^x}{\ln a}$

* Strictly, $\ln |\ \ |$, e.g. $\ln |x|$, $\ln |\sec x|$.

If x is replaced in any one of these by $(ax + b)$, since

$$\frac{d}{dx}(ax + b) = a$$

the integral must be divided by a; e.g.

$$\int \cot (3x + 4)\, dx = \tfrac{1}{3} \ln \sin (3x + 4).$$

Algebraic integrals

There are four standard integrals which are of the utmost value in integrating algebraic expressions.

I. $\displaystyle\int \frac{dx}{a^2 + x^2} = \frac{1}{a} \tan^{-1} \frac{x}{a}.$

II. $\displaystyle\int \frac{dx}{a^2 - x^2} = \frac{1}{2a} \ln \frac{a + x}{a - x}$ (use partial fractions).

Also $\displaystyle\int \frac{dx}{x^2 - a^2} = \frac{1}{2a} \ln \frac{x - a}{x + a}.$

III. $\displaystyle\int \frac{dx}{\sqrt{(a^2 - x^2)}} = \sin^{-1} \frac{x}{a}.$

IV. $\displaystyle\int \frac{dx}{\sqrt{(x^2 \pm a^2)}} = \ln [x + \sqrt{(x^2 \pm a^2)}].$

The alternative forms for this integral are sometimes useful.

$$\int \frac{dx}{\sqrt{(x^2 + a^2)}} = \sinh^{-1} \frac{x}{a};$$

$$\int \frac{dx}{\sqrt{(x^2 - a^2)}} = \cosh^{-1} \frac{x}{a}.$$

Integrals involving more complicated expressions may be expressed in terms of these in the following ways.

TYPE A $\displaystyle\int \frac{dx}{ax^2 + bx + c}.$

If $(ax^2 + bx + c)$ factorizes, this is most easily done by partial fractions and this method of partial fractions applies to the integration of all fractions having a denominator that will factorize.

If the denominator does not factorize, the method of completing the square is used.

$$ax^2 + bx + c = a\left(x^2 + \frac{b}{a} x + \frac{c}{a} \right)$$

$$= a\left\{ \left(x + \frac{b}{2a} \right)^2 + \frac{c}{a} - \frac{b^2}{4a^2} \right\}.$$

The integral will now reduce to I or II as $4ac \gtrless b^2$.

Example 1. $\displaystyle\int \frac{dx}{x^2 + 3x + 2}$.

$$\frac{1}{x^2 + 3x + 2} = \frac{1}{(x + 1)(x + 2)} = \frac{1}{x + 1} - \frac{1}{x + 2}.$$

$$\therefore \int \frac{dx}{x^2 + 3x + 2} = \int \frac{dx}{x + 1} - \int \frac{dx}{x + 2}$$

$$= \ln(x + 1) - \ln(x + 2)$$

$$= \ln \frac{x + 1}{x + 2} + c.$$

Example 2. $\displaystyle\int \frac{dx}{9x^2 + 6x + 5}$.

$$\int \frac{dx}{9x^2 + 6x + 5} = \frac{1}{9} \int \frac{dx}{x^2 + \frac{2}{3}x + \frac{5}{9}} = \frac{1}{9} \int \frac{dx}{(x + \frac{1}{3})^2 + \frac{4}{9}}$$

$$= \frac{1}{9} \cdot \frac{3}{2} \tan^{-1} \frac{x + \frac{1}{3}}{\frac{2}{3}}$$

$$= \frac{1}{6} \tan^{-1} \frac{3x + 1}{2} + c.$$

Example 3. $\displaystyle\int \frac{dx}{9x^2 + 6x - 1}$.

$$\int \frac{dx}{9x^2 + 6x - 1} = \frac{1}{9} \int \frac{dx}{x^2 + \frac{2}{3}x - \frac{1}{9}} = \frac{1}{9} \int \frac{dx}{(x + \frac{1}{3})^2 - \frac{2}{9}}$$

$$= \frac{1}{9} \cdot \frac{1}{2\sqrt{\frac{2}{9}}} \ln \frac{x + \frac{1}{3} - \sqrt{\frac{2}{9}}}{x + \frac{1}{3} + \sqrt{\frac{2}{9}}}$$

$$= \frac{1}{6\sqrt{2}} \ln \frac{3x + 1 - \sqrt{2}}{3x + 1 + \sqrt{2}} + c.$$

TYPE B $$\int \frac{px + q}{ax^2 + bx + c} \, dx.$$

The differential coefficient of $(ax^2 + bx + c)$ is $2ax + b$ and the numerator of the fraction is expressed as a multiple of this together with a constant in the following way.

$$px + q = \frac{p}{2a}(2ax + b) + q - \frac{pb}{2a}.$$

$$\therefore \int \frac{px + q}{ax^2 + bx + c} \, dx$$

$$= \frac{p}{2a} \int \frac{2ax + b}{ax^2 + bx + c} \, dx + \left(q - \frac{bp}{2a}\right) \int \frac{dx}{ax^2 + bx + c}$$

The first integral is $\dfrac{p}{2a} \ln(ax^2 + bx + c)$ and the second integral is of TYPE A.

Example. $\int \dfrac{3x+4}{9x^2+6x+5}\, dx.$

$$\int \frac{3x+4}{9x^2+6x+5}\, dx = \tfrac{1}{6}\int \frac{18x+6}{9x^2+6x+5}\, dx + \int \frac{3}{9x^2+6x+5}\, dx$$

$$= \tfrac{1}{6}\ln(9x^2+6x+5) + \tfrac{1}{2}\tan^{-1}\frac{3x+1}{2} + c.$$

(See previous example.)

TYPE C
$$\int \frac{\text{polynomial in } x}{ax^2+bx+c}\, dx.$$

If the numerator is of degree equal to or larger than that of the denominator, DIVIDE.

By this method the integral is reduced to TYPE B.

Example. $\int \dfrac{x^3+1}{x^2+1}\, dx.$

$$x^3+1 = x(x^2+1) - x + 1.$$

$$\therefore \quad \int \frac{x^3+1}{x^2+1}\, dx = \int x\, dx - \int \frac{x-1}{x^2+1}\, dx$$

$$= \frac{x^2}{2} - \tfrac{1}{2}\int \frac{2x}{x^2+1}\, dx + \int \frac{dx}{x^2+1}$$

$$= \frac{x^2}{2} - \tfrac{1}{2}\ln(x^2+1) + \tan^{-1}x + c.$$

TYPE D
$$\int \frac{dx}{\sqrt{(ax^2+bx+c)}}.$$

If a is positive, the square is completed exactly as in TYPE A, and the integral reduces to IV.

If a is negative, $\sqrt{a}$ cannot be taken out of the square root as it is imaginary and so $\sqrt{(-a)}$ is extracted, after which the integral reduces to III.

Example 1. $\int \dfrac{dx}{\sqrt{(9x^2+6x+5)}}.$

$$\int \frac{dx}{\sqrt{(9x^2+6x+5)}} = \tfrac{1}{3}\int \frac{dx}{\sqrt{(x^2+\frac{2}{3}x+\frac{5}{9})}} = \tfrac{1}{3}\int \frac{dx}{\sqrt{\{(x+\frac{1}{3})^2+\frac{4}{9}\}}}$$

$$= \tfrac{1}{3}\ln\{(x+\tfrac{1}{3}) + \sqrt{[(x+\tfrac{1}{3})^2+\tfrac{4}{9}]}\}$$

$$= \tfrac{1}{3}\ln\{x+\tfrac{1}{3} + \sqrt{(x^2+\tfrac{2}{3}x+\tfrac{5}{9})}\} + c.$$

The alternative form of the answer is $\tfrac{1}{3}\sinh^{-1}\dfrac{x+\frac{1}{3}}{\frac{2}{3}}$ or

$$\tfrac{1}{3}\sinh^{-1}\frac{3x+1}{2}.$$

Example 2. $\int \dfrac{dx}{\sqrt{(8 - 6x - 9x^2)}}$.

$$\int \frac{dx}{\sqrt{(8 - 6x - 9x)^2}} = \tfrac{1}{3}\int \frac{dx}{\sqrt{(\frac{8}{9} - \frac{2}{3}x - x^2)}} = \tfrac{1}{3}\int \frac{dx}{\sqrt{[1 - (x + \frac{1}{3})^2]}}$$
$$= \tfrac{1}{3}\sin^{-1}(x + \tfrac{1}{3}) + c.$$

TYPE E
$$\int \frac{px + q}{\sqrt{(ax^2 + bx + c)}}\,dx.$$

$$px + q = \frac{p}{2a}(2ax + b) + q - \frac{pb}{2a} \quad \text{exactly as in TYPE B.}$$

$$\therefore \quad \int \frac{px + q}{\sqrt{(ax^2 + bx + c)}}\,dx$$
$$= \frac{p}{2a}\int \frac{2ax + b}{\sqrt{(ax^2 + bx + c)}}\,dx + \left(q - \frac{pb}{2a}\right)\int \frac{dx}{\sqrt{(ax^2 + bx + c)}}.$$

The first integral is $\dfrac{p}{2a} \times 2\sqrt{(ax^2 + bx + c)}$ from the previously

deduced result that $\displaystyle\int \frac{f'(x)}{\sqrt{f(x)}}\,dx = 2\sqrt{f(x)}$. The second integral is of

TYPE D.

Example 1. $\int \dfrac{3x + 4}{\sqrt{(9x^2 + 6x + 5)}}\,dx.$

$$\int \frac{3x + 4}{\sqrt{(9x^2 + 6x + 5)}}\,dx$$
$$= \tfrac{1}{6}\int \frac{18x + 6}{\sqrt{(9x^2 + 6x + 5)}}\,dx + \int \frac{3}{\sqrt{(9x^2 + 6x + 5)}}\,dx$$
$$= \tfrac{1}{3}\sqrt{(9x^2 + 6x + 5)} + \sinh^{-1}\frac{3x + 1}{2} + c \quad \text{(see previous integral).}$$

Example 2. $\int \dfrac{3x + 4}{\sqrt{(8 - 6x - 9x^2)}}\,dx.$

$$\int \frac{3x + 4}{\sqrt{(8 - 6x - 9x^2)}}\,dx$$
$$= -\tfrac{1}{6}\int \frac{-6 - 18x}{\sqrt{(8 - 6x - 9x^2)}}\,dx + \int \frac{3}{\sqrt{(8 - 6x - 9x^2)}}\,dx$$
$$= -\tfrac{1}{3}\sqrt{(8 - 6x - 9x^2)} + \sin^{-1}(x + \tfrac{1}{3}) + c \quad \text{(see previous integral).}$$

Exercise 15.1

Integrate the following:

1. $\dfrac{1}{2 + x}$.

2. $\dfrac{1}{1 + 2x}$.

3. $\dfrac{x}{2 + x}$.

4. $\dfrac{x^2}{2 + x}$.

5. $\dfrac{x^2}{x - 1}$.

6. $\dfrac{1}{1 + 4x^2}$.

7. $\dfrac{x}{4 + x^2}$.

8. $\dfrac{x^2}{4 + x^2}$.

9. $\dfrac{x}{4 - x^2}$.

10. $\dfrac{1 - x}{9 + x^2}$.

11. $\dfrac{x}{1 + 4x^2}$.

12. $\dfrac{1}{1 - 4x^2}$.

13. $\dfrac{x}{1 - 4x^2}$.

14. $\dfrac{x^2}{4 - x^2}$.

15. $\dfrac{1}{\sqrt{(4 - x^2)}}$.

16. $\dfrac{1}{\sqrt{(1 - 4x^2)}}$.

17. $\dfrac{1}{\sqrt{(9 - 4x^2)}}$.

18. $\dfrac{x}{\sqrt{(4 - x^2)}}$.

19. $\sqrt{(1 - x^2)}$.

20. $x\sqrt{(1 - x^2)}$.

21. $\dfrac{e^x}{1 + e^{2x}}$.

22. $\dfrac{e^x}{1 - e^{2x}}$.

23. $\dfrac{e^x}{1 + e^x}$.

24. $\dfrac{1}{1 + e^x}$.

25. $\dfrac{x}{1 + x^4}$.

26. $\dfrac{x}{1 - x^4}$.

27. $\dfrac{x^3}{x + 1}$.

28. $\dfrac{1}{\sqrt{(4 + x^2)}}$.

29. $\dfrac{1}{\sqrt{(x^2 - 4)}}$.

30. $\dfrac{x}{\sqrt{(x^2 - 4)}}$.

31. $\dfrac{1 + x}{2 + x}$.

32. $\dfrac{x^2 + 1}{x + 3}$.

33. $\dfrac{1}{x^2 - 3x + 2}$.

34. $\dfrac{x}{x^2 - 3x + 2}$.

35. $\dfrac{x^3}{x^2 - 3x + 2}$.

36. $\dfrac{1}{x^2 - 3x + 1}$.

37. $\dfrac{x}{x^2 - 3x + 1}$.

38. $\dfrac{x^2}{x^2 - 3x + 1}$.

39. $\dfrac{1}{\sqrt{(x^2 - 3x + 1)}}$.

40. $\dfrac{x}{\sqrt{(x^2 - 3x + 1)}}$.

41. $\dfrac{1}{\sqrt{(4x - x^2)}}$.

42. $\dfrac{1}{4x - x^2}$.

43. $\dfrac{1}{\sqrt{(4x^2 + 6x)}}$.

44. $\dfrac{x}{\sqrt{(4x^2 + 6x)}}$.

45. $\dfrac{1}{\sqrt{(1 - x - 4x^2)}}$.

46. $\dfrac{x + 1}{\sqrt{(1 - x - 4x^2)}}$.

47. $\dfrac{1}{x\sqrt{(x^2 + 1)}}$.

48. $\dfrac{1}{x\sqrt{(1 - x^2)}}$.

49. $\dfrac{1}{x\sqrt{(x^2 - 4x)}}$.

50. $\sqrt{\dfrac{x - 1}{x + 1}}$ $\left(Hint: \dfrac{x - 1}{\sqrt{(x^2 - 1)}}\right)$.

Trigonometric integrals

$\sin^m \theta \cos^n \theta$

This integral is easily performed if one (or both) of m, n is odd. If m, for example, is odd, $\sin^{m-1} \theta$ is an even power of $\sin \theta$ and, by the relationship $\sin^2 \theta = 1 - \cos^2 \theta$, can be expressed as a polynomial in $\cos \theta$. The remaining factor $\sin \theta$ is taken with the $d\theta$ to make $-d(\cos \theta)$ and the integral is expressed as a sum of powers of $\cos \theta$.

Example 1. $\int \cos^3 \theta \sin^2 \theta \, d\theta.$

$$\int \cos^3 \theta \sin^2 \theta \, d\theta = \int \cos^2 \theta \sin^2 \theta \, d(\sin \theta)$$

$$= \int \sin^2 \theta (1 - \sin^2 \theta) \, d(\sin \theta)$$

$$= \int (\sin^2 \theta - \sin^4 \theta) \, d(\sin \theta)$$

$$= \frac{\sin^3 \theta}{3} - \frac{\sin^5 \theta}{5} + C.$$

Example 2. $\int \dfrac{\cos^3 \theta}{\sin^4 \theta} \, d\theta.$

$$\int \frac{\cos^3 \theta}{\sin^4 \theta} \, d\theta = \int \frac{\cos^2 \theta}{\sin^4 \theta} \, d(\sin \theta) = \int \frac{1 - \sin^2 \theta}{\sin^4 \theta} \, d(\sin \theta)$$

$$= \int \left(\frac{1}{\sin^4 \theta} - \frac{1}{\sin^2 \theta} \right) d(\sin \theta)$$

$$= -\frac{1}{3 \sin^3 \theta} + \frac{1}{\sin \theta} + C.$$

It should be noted that $\int \sin^n \theta \, d(\sin \theta)$ is far more easily integrated than $\int \sin^n \theta \, d\theta.$

The method may also be used to integrate odd powers of $\cos \theta$ or $\sin \theta.$

Example 3. $\int \sin^5 \theta \, d\theta.$

$$\int \sin^5 \theta \, d\theta = -\int \sin^4 \theta \, d(\cos \theta) = -\int (1 - \cos^2 \theta)^2 \, d(\cos \theta)$$

$$= -\int (1 - 2 \cos^2 \theta + \cos^4 \theta) \, d(\cos \theta)$$

$$= -\cos \theta + \tfrac{2}{3} \cos^3 \theta - \tfrac{1}{5} \cos^5 \theta + c.$$

Remember that $\int 1 \, d(\cos \theta) = \cos \theta.$

m and n both even

If both *m* and *n* are even, the integration is more difficult and is performed by expressing the integrand in terms of multiple angles.

Example 1. $\int \cos^2 \theta \, d\theta.$

$$\int \cos^2 \theta \, d\theta = \tfrac{1}{2} \int (1 + \cos 2\theta) \, d\theta = \frac{\theta}{2} + \frac{\sin 2\theta}{4} + c.$$

Example 2. $\int \sin^2 \theta \, d\theta.$

$$\int \sin^2 \theta \, d\theta = \frac{1}{2} \int (1 - \cos 2\theta) \, d\theta = \frac{\theta}{2} - \frac{\sin 2\theta}{4} + c.$$

Example 3. $\int \cos^2 \theta \sin^4 \theta \, d\theta.$

$$\cos^2 \theta \sin^4 \theta = (\cos^2 \theta \sin^2 \theta) \sin^2 \theta$$
$$= \tfrac{1}{4} \sin^2 2\theta \left(\frac{1 - \cos 2\theta}{2} \right)$$
$$= \tfrac{1}{8} (1 - \cos 4\theta) \left(\frac{1 - \cos 2\theta}{2} \right)$$
$$= \tfrac{1}{16} (1 - \cos 2\theta - \cos 4\theta + \cos 2\theta \cos 4\theta)$$
$$= \tfrac{1}{16} - \tfrac{1}{16} \cos 2\theta - \tfrac{1}{16} \cos 4\theta + \frac{\cos 6\theta + \cos 2\theta}{32}$$
$$= \tfrac{1}{16} - \tfrac{1}{32} \cos 2\theta - \tfrac{1}{16} \cos 4\theta + \tfrac{1}{32} \cos 6\theta + c.$$

$$\therefore \quad \int \cos^2 \theta \sin^4 \theta \, d\theta = \tfrac{1}{16}\theta - \tfrac{1}{64} \sin 2\theta - \tfrac{1}{64} \sin 4\theta + \tfrac{1}{192} \sin 6\theta + c.$$

Exercise 15.2

Find the integrals of

1. $\cos^3 \theta.$
2. $\sin^2 \theta.$
3. $\cos \theta \sin \theta.$
4. $\cos^3 \theta \sin^2 \theta.$
5. $\cos^3 \theta \sin^3 \theta.$
6. $\dfrac{\sin \theta}{\cos^2 \theta}.$
7. $\cos^4 \theta.$
8. $\sin^4 \theta.$
9. $\cos^2 \theta \sin^2 \theta.$
10. $\cos^7 \theta \sin \theta.$

Evaluate

11. $\displaystyle\int_0^{\pi/2} \cos^3 \theta \, d\theta.$
12. $\displaystyle\int_0^{\pi} \sin^3 \theta \, d\theta.$
13. $\displaystyle\int_0^{\pi/2} \cos \theta \sin \theta \, d\theta$
14. $\displaystyle\int_0^{\pi} \cos^3 \theta \sin^2 \theta \, d\theta.$
15. $\displaystyle\int_0^{\pi} \cos^3 \theta \sin^3 \theta \, d\theta.$
16. $\displaystyle\int_0^{\pi/4} \dfrac{\sin \theta}{\cos^2 \theta} \, d\theta.$
17. $\displaystyle\int_0^{\pi/2} \cos^4 \theta \, d\theta.$
18. $\displaystyle\int_0^{\pi/4} \sin^4 \theta \, d\theta.$
19. $\displaystyle\int_0^{\pi/2} \cos^2 \theta \sin^2 \theta \, d\theta.$
20. $\displaystyle\int_0^{\pi} \cos^7 \theta \sin \theta \, d\theta.$

Exercise 15.3: Miscellaneous

1. Find $\displaystyle\int \dfrac{dx}{1 + x + x^2}.$

2. Find $\int \dfrac{dx}{x^2(x+1)}$.

3. Prove that the volume of a segment of height h of a sphere of radius r is $\frac{1}{3}\pi h^2(3r - h)$.

4. Sketch the curve $y^2 = x^2(4 - x^2)$ and find the area of one of its loops.

5. Find the coordinates of the centre of gravity of the area of the half loop of the curve $y^2 = x^2(1 - x^2)$ in the positive quadrant.

6. Find $\int \cos^7 \theta \sin^2 \theta \, d\theta$.

7. Evaluate $\displaystyle\int_0^{\pi/2} \cos^7 \theta \sin^2 \theta \, d\theta$.

8. Draw a rough sketch of the curve $y^2 x = (2 - x)(x - 1)^2$ and find the area of its loop.

9. Evaluate $\displaystyle\int_0^1 \dfrac{1 + x}{\sqrt{(1 - x)}} \, dx$.

10. Evaluate $\displaystyle\int_0^{\pi/2} \cos 2x \sin x \, dx$.

11. Find $\int \cos 2\theta \, d\theta$ and $\int (\cos^2 \theta + \sin^2 \theta) \, d\theta$. Hence find $\int \cos^2 \theta \, d\theta$ and $\int \sin^2 \theta \, d\theta$.

12. Make a rough sketch of the curve $xy^2 = 1 - x$ and find the area of the region between the curve and the axis of y.

13. Find $\int \dfrac{dx}{x\sqrt{(x^2 + 2x)}}$.

14. Integrate $\dfrac{1}{x - \sqrt{x}}$.

15. Integrate $\dfrac{1}{(x + 1)\sqrt{(1 - x^2)}}$.

16. Evaluate $\displaystyle\int_0^{\pi} \cos^3 \theta \sin^{18} \theta \, d\theta$.

17. The acceleration of a particle moving in a straight line is given in terms of the time t by the expression $2(\cos^2 t - \sin^2 t)$. If the initial velocity is zero, find the distance travelled in time t.

18. Find $\displaystyle\int_{\pi/6}^{\pi/2} \dfrac{\cos^3 x}{\sin^2 x} \, dx$.

19. Evaluate $\displaystyle\int_0^{\pi/2} \sin 2x \cos x \, dx$.

20. Find the area of the ellipse $\dfrac{x^2}{4} + \dfrac{y^2}{9} = 1$.

21. Integrate with respect to x the expression $\dfrac{x + 2}{x + 3}$.

22. Evaluate $\displaystyle\int_0^1 \frac{x^3}{x^2 + 1}\,dx$.

23. Evaluate $\displaystyle\int_0^{\pi/2} \sin 5x \cos 7x\,dx$.

24. Sketch the curve $y^2 = x^2\dfrac{a^2 - x^2}{a^2 + x^2}$ and find the area of a loop.

25. Find the area under the curve $x = a(t + \sin t)$, $y = a(1 - \cos t)$ between $t = 0$ and $t = \pi$.

26. Find the coordinates of the centre of gravity of the area included by the curve $y = \sin^2 x$ and the x-axis between $x = 0$ and $x = \pi$.

27. Find $\displaystyle\int \frac{2(x + 1)}{\surd(2x + 1)}\,dx$.

28. Sketch the curve $y^2 = \dfrac{4 - x^2}{4 + x^2}$. The part of the curve for positive values of x is rotated about the axis of x. Find the volume generated.

29. Show that $\displaystyle\int_0^1 \frac{x^5}{\surd(1 - x^2)}\,dx = \int_0^{\pi/2} \sin^5 \theta\,d\theta$. Hence evaluate the integral.

30. Show that $\displaystyle\int_0^1 x^5\surd(1 - x^2)\,dx = \int_0^{\pi/2} \sin^5 \theta \cos^2 \theta\,d\theta$. Hence evaluate the integral.

16 Mean Value; Length of Arc; Centre of Mass

Revision

We proved in *Additional Pure Mathematics* the following:

1. The area of the region bounded by the x-axis, the ordinates $x = a$ and $x = b$ and the plane curve $y = f(x)$ is

$$\int_a^b y \, dx.$$

2. The coordinates of the centre of mass (centre of gravity) of this region are given by

$$A\bar{x} = \int_a^b xy \, dx,$$

$$A\bar{y} = \tfrac{1}{2} \int_a^b y^2 \, dx.$$

3. The volume V formed by rotating this region through four right angles about the axis of x is

$$\pi \int y^2 \, dx;$$

the volume obtained by rotating similarly about the y-axis is

$$\pi \int x^2 \, dy.$$

Mean value

We are familiar with the mean $\bar{y}$ of a set of n variables $y_1, y_2, \ldots, y_n$, defined by

$$\bar{y} = \frac{1}{n}(y_1 + y_2 + y_3 + \ldots y_n).$$

If instead of n discrete variables we have a continuously varying quantity y described by $y = f(x)$, we can define the mean value y as x varies uniformly from a to b as

$$\bar{y} = \frac{1}{b - a} \int_a^b y \, dx.$$

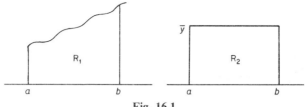

Fig. 16.1

We see from Fig. 16.1 that the area of the region R_1 bounded by the x-axis, the ordinates $x = a$, $x = b$ and the curve $y = f(x)$ is equal to the area of the rectangle R_2, bounded by the x-axis, the ordinates $x = a$, $x = b$ and the straight line $y = \bar{y}$.

Example 1. *Find the mean value of the function* $y = \sin x$ *over the interval* $0 \leqslant x \leqslant \pi$.

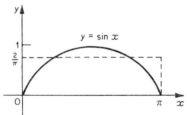

Fig. 16.2

Using the definition above, we have

$$\bar{y} = \frac{1}{\pi} \int_0^\pi \sin x \, dx$$

$$= \frac{1}{\pi} \left[-\cos x \right]_0^\pi$$

$$= \frac{2}{\pi}.$$

From Fig. 16.2 we see that the area of the rectangle - - - - is equal to the area bounded by the curve and the x-axis. Notice that the mean value of $y = \sin x$ over the interval $0 < x < 2\pi$ is zero.

Example 2. *The displacement* x *of a particle at time* t *is given by* $x = a \sin t$, *where* a *is a constant. Find the mean value of its velocity*
  (i) *with respect to time* t,
  (ii) *with respect to displacement* x,
over the interval $0 < t < \dfrac{\pi}{2}$.

Since
$$x = a \sin t,$$

$$v = \frac{dx}{dt} = a \cos t.$$

As t increases from 0 to $\dfrac{\pi}{2}$, x increases from 0 to a, so in (i), from the definition

$$\bar{v}_t = \frac{1}{\pi/2} \int_0^{\pi/2} a \cos t \, dt$$

$$= \frac{2}{\pi} [a \sin t]_0^{\pi/2} = \frac{2a}{\pi},$$

whereas in (ii),
$$\bar{v}_x = \frac{1}{a} \int_0^a a \cos t \, dx$$

$$= \frac{1}{a} \int a \cos t \, \frac{dx}{dt} \, dt,$$

$$= \frac{1}{a} \int a^2 \cos^2 t \, dt,$$

$$= \frac{1}{a} \left[a^2 \cdot \frac{1}{2} \cdot \frac{\pi}{2} \right]$$

$$= \frac{\pi}{4} a.$$

Notice that these two mean values are not the same , as the variation of velocity with time is not the same as the variation of velocity with displacement.

Exercise 16.1

Find the mean value of each of the following over the given interval, illustrating each with a sketch showing the relation of the mean to the curve.

1. $x, 0 \leqslant x \leqslant 1$.   **2.** $x^2, 0 \leqslant x \leqslant 1$.

3. $3x^2, 0 \leqslant x \leqslant 1$.   **4.** $x^2, 0 \leqslant x \leqslant 2$.

5. $x, -1 \leqslant x \leqslant 1$.   **6.** $|x|, -1 \leqslant x \leqslant 1$.

7. $\sin x, -\pi \leqslant x \leqslant \pi$.   **8.** $\sin^2 x, -\pi \leqslant x \leqslant \pi$.

9. $\sin 2x, -\pi \leqslant x \leqslant \pi$.   **10.** $\sin 2x, 0 \leqslant x \leqslant \dfrac{\pi}{2}$.

11. $\cos^2 x, 0 \leqslant x \leqslant \dfrac{\pi}{2}$.   **12.** $\cos^2 x, 0 \leqslant x \leqslant \pi$.

13. The displacement x of a particle at time t is given by $x = t^2$. Find the mean value of its velocity

    (i) with respect to time t,
    (ii) with respect to displacement x,

over the interval $0 \leqslant t \leqslant 1$.

14. The displacement x of a particle at time t is given by $x = \sin^2 t$. Find the mean value of the acceleration

    (i) with respect to time t,
    (ii) with respect to displacement x,

over the interval $0 \leqslant t \leqslant \pi$.

15. A point P is chosen on a circle of unit radius, and a chord is drawn through P. Find the mean value of the length of the chord
   (i) with respect to the length of the chord,
   (ii) with respect to the angle subtended by the chord at the centre of the circle.

Length of arc

Suppose that P and Q are two points close together on the curve $y = f(x)$ as shown in Fig. 16.3.

Suppose the increase in x between P and Q is δx and the corresponding increase in y is δy. Let the small arc PQ be δs. From the figure, using Pythagoras' theorem,

$$\delta s^2 = \delta x^2 + \delta y^2 \quad \text{approximately}$$

or

$$\left(\frac{\delta s}{\delta x}\right)^2 = 1 + \left(\frac{\delta y}{\delta x}\right)^2.$$

In the limit,

$$\left(\frac{ds}{dx}\right)^2 = 1 + \left(\frac{dy}{dx}\right)^2.$$

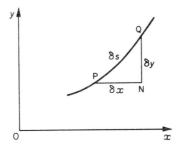

Fig. 16.3

The length of arc is therefore given by the formula

$$\int_a^b \sqrt{\left\{1 + \left(\frac{dy}{dx}\right)^2\right\}}\, dx.$$

Example. *Find the length of the curve $y = \cosh x$ between $x = 0$ and $x = 1$.*

For $y = \cosh x$,

$$\frac{dy}{dx} = \sinh x.$$

$$\therefore \left(\frac{ds}{dx}\right)^2 = 1 + \left(\frac{dy}{dx}\right)^2$$

$$= 1 + \sinh^2 x$$

$$= \cosh^2 x.$$

$$\therefore \quad \frac{ds}{dx} = \cosh x.$$

$$\therefore \quad s = \int_0^1 \cosh x \, dx = [\sinh x]_0^1$$

$$= \sinh 1$$

$$= \frac{e - 1/e}{2}$$

$$= \frac{e^2 - 1}{2\,e}.$$

Centre of mass of arc

If HK is an arc of length s, of which PQ is an element of length δs, the coordinates of the centre of mass of the arc HK are found by taking moments about the axes.

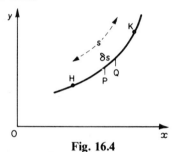

Fig. 16.4

If the coordinates of the centre of mass of the arc are $(\bar{x}, \bar{y})$, the moment of the whole arc about the axis of x is $s\bar{y}$. The moment of the element δs about the x axis is $y\,\delta s$.

$$\therefore \quad s\bar{y} = \int y \, ds.$$

Similarly

$$s\bar{x} = \int x \, ds.$$

Example. *Find the coordinates of the centre of mass of the arc of the curve* $y = \cosh x$ *between $x = 0$ and $x = 1$.*

We have already seen that the length of the arc s, is $\dfrac{e^2 - 1}{2\,e}$ and that $\dfrac{ds}{dx} = \cosh x$.

$$\therefore \quad s\bar{x} = \int x \, ds$$

$$= \int_0^1 x \cosh x \, dx = \int_0^1 x \, d(\sinh x)$$

$$= x \sinh x - \int_0^1 \sinh x \, dx \quad \text{(by parts)}$$

$$= [x \sinh x - \cosh x]_0^1$$

$$= \sinh 1 - \cosh 1 + \cosh 0$$

$$= \frac{e - 1/e}{2} - \frac{e + 1/e}{2} + 1$$

$$= 1 - \frac{1}{e} = \frac{e - 1}{e}.$$

$$\therefore \quad \bar{x} = \frac{2\,e(e - 1)}{e(e^2 - 1)} = \frac{2}{e + 1}.$$

Also $\qquad s\bar{y} = \int y \, ds$

$$= \int \cosh x(\cosh x \, dx)$$

$$= \int_0^1 \cosh^2 x \, dx = \tfrac{1}{2} \int_0^1 (1 + \cosh 2x) \, dx$$

$$= \tfrac{1}{2}\left[x + \frac{\sinh 2x}{2} \right]_0^1$$

$$= \tfrac{1}{2}\left(1 + \frac{\sinh 2}{2} \right) = \tfrac{1}{2}\left(1 + \frac{e^2 - e^{-2}}{4} \right)$$

$$= \frac{e^4 + 4\,e^2 - 1}{8}.$$

$$\therefore \quad \bar{y} = \frac{e(e^4 + 4\,e^2 - 1)}{4(e^2 - 1)}.$$

The coordinates of the centre of mass are

$$\left\{ \frac{2}{e + 1}, \frac{e(e^4 + 4\,e^2 - 1)}{4(e^2 - 1)} \right\}.$$

Theorems of Guldin and Pappus

The volume of a solid of revolution is given by the formula

$$V = \pi \int_a^b y^2 \, dx,$$

and the y coordinate of the centre of mass of the region rotated by

$$A\bar{y} = \tfrac{1}{2} \int_a^b y^2 \, dx.$$

Both these formula contain the integral $\displaystyle\int_a^b y^2 \, dx$ which may therefore be eliminated to give $V = 2\pi A \bar{y}$, or, in words:

'The volume obtained by rotating a region about any axis, not intersecting the region, is equal to the area of this region multiplied by the distance moved by the centre of mass of the region.'

This is the first of the theorems of Guldin and Pappus. The second deals with the surface area formed by rotating an arc about an axis.

Suppose in Fig. 16.5 the arc HK is rotated through four right angles about the axis of x.

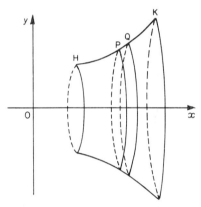

Fig. 16.5

The surface area of revolution formed by rotating the element PQ of length δs is $2\pi y\,\delta s$. Therefore, if A is the total surface area formed,

$$A = 2\pi \int y\,dx.$$

The formula

$$s\bar{y} = \int y\,ds$$

was proved in the last paragraph. Eliminating the integral $\int y\,ds$ between these formula gives

$$A = 2\pi s\bar{y}$$

which is the second of Guldin's theorems, namely:

'The area obtained by revolving an arc about an axis not intersecting the arc is equal to the length of the arc multiplied by the distance moved by the centre of mass of the arc.'

These theorems are named after the celebrated Greek geometer, Pappus, who lived at the end of the third century, and after Paul Guldin or Guldinus who later rediscovered them. They are very useful in obtaining areas or volumes when the position of the centre of mass is known and conversely in finding the position of the centre of mass when the area or volume of revolution is known.

Example 1. *The surface area of a cone.*

A cone is obtained by rotating a straight line AB about an axis AC through one end of the line. If the length of the line is l and the distance of B from AC is r, the distance moved by the C.G. of the mid-point of the line is $2\pi\left(\dfrac{r}{2}\right) = \pi r$.

The surface area of the cone is therefore $\pi r l$.

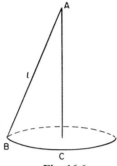

Fig. 16.6

Example 2. *The C.M. of a semicircular lamina.*

If the lamina is rotated about its diameter, we have a sphere of volume $\frac{4}{3}\pi r^3$. If the C.M. of the lamina is at a distance y from the centre along the axis of symmetry, the distance it moves in a revolution is $2\pi y$. Therefore

$$2\pi y(\tfrac{1}{2}\pi r^2) = \tfrac{4}{3}\pi r^3 \quad \text{or} \quad y = \frac{4r}{3\pi}.$$

Centre of mass of a solid of revolution

The centre of mass of a solid of revolution formed by rotating an area about the axis of x will obviously lie on the x-axis. By considering a disc of radius y and thickness δx, we see that the x coordinate of the C.M. is given by

$$V\bar{x} = \pi \int_a^b xy^2 \, dx.$$

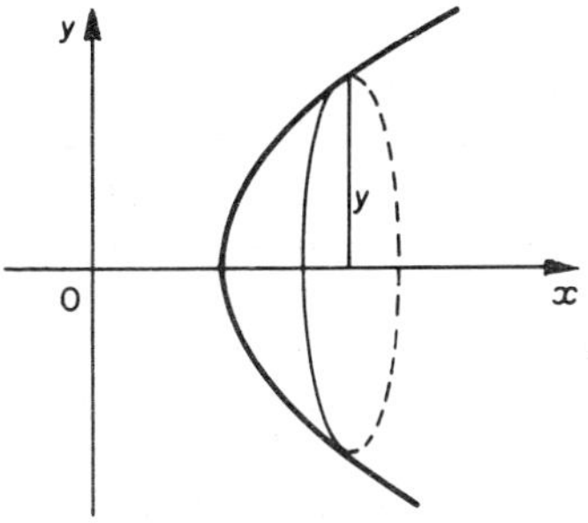

Fig. 16.7

Example. *The C.M. of a cone.*

The area of cross-section at a depth x below the vertex is $\pi x^2 \tan^2 \alpha$ where α is the semi-vertical angle.

Therefore

$$V\bar{x} = \int_0^h (\pi x^2 \tan^2 \alpha) x \, dx, \quad \text{where } h \text{ is the height.}$$

$$\therefore \quad V\bar{x} = \pi \frac{h^4}{4} \tan^2 \alpha.$$

But $\quad\quad\quad\quad V = \tfrac{1}{3}\pi r^2 h = \tfrac{1}{3}\pi h^3 \tan^2 \alpha,$

and so $\quad\quad\quad\quad \bar{x} = \tfrac{3}{4}h.$

Exercise 16.2

1. Find the centre of mass of a solid cone using Guldin's theorem.

2. Find the distance of the centre of mass of a semicircular arc from its centre.

3. Find the length of the curve $x = a \cos \theta$, $y = a \sin \theta$ between $\theta = 0$ and $\theta = \dfrac{\pi}{2}$.

4. Find the coordinates of the centre of mass of the arc defined in question 3.

5. Find the volume of a bicycle tyre of radius 1 cm if the internal diameter of the wheel is 54 cm.

6. If the parametric equations of a curve are $x = f(t)$, $y = g(t)$, show that the length of arc between $t = t_1$ and $t = t_2$ is

$$\int_{t_1}^{t_2} \sqrt{\{f'(t)^2 + g'(t)^2\}} \, dt.$$

7. Find the length of arc of the curve $x = a(\theta + \sin \theta)$, $y = a(1 + \cos \theta)$ between $\theta = 0$ and $\theta = \dfrac{\pi}{2}$.

8. Find the surface area obtained by revolving the arc defined in question 7 about the axis of x.

9. A point on a circular arc is given by $x = a \cos \theta$, $y = a \sin \theta$. Find the coordinates of the C.M. of the arc between $\theta = 0$ and $\theta = 2\alpha$.

10. The arc in question 9 is revolved about the axis of y. Find the surface area generated.

11. Using the result of question 10, show that the surface area of a zone of a sphere (i.e. the part cut off by two parallels) is $2\pi Rh$, where R is the radius of the sphere and h the distance between the parallel planes.

12. Sketch the curve $x = a \cos^3 t$, $y = a \sin^3 t$ and find its total length.

13. Find the length of arc of $x^3 = y^2$ between $x = 0$ and $x = 1$.

14. For the parabola $x = am^2$, $y = 2am$ show that $\dfrac{ds}{dm} = 2a\sqrt{(1 + m^2)}$.

15. The curve $x = a \cos^3 t$, $y = a \sin^3 t$ is rotated about the axis of x. Find the surface area generated.

16. A solid is formed by rotating that part of the parabola $y^2 = 4ax$ between $x = 0$ and $x = a$ about the axis of x. Find the coordinates of the centre of mass of the solid.

17. Find the coordinates of the centre of gravity of the arc of the circle $x^2 + y^2 = 4$ between $x = 1$ and $x = -1$ and the area obtained by revolving this arc about the axis of x.

18. Prove that the area of the curved surface of a frustrum of a cone is $\pi(r + R)l$ where r, R are the radii of the ends of the frustrum and l is the length of a slant edge.

19. Show that the volume of a frustum of a cone is $\frac{1}{3}\pi h(R^2 + Rr + r^2)$ where R, r are the radii of the ends and h is the height of the frustum.

20. Prove that the arc of the curve $y = \frac{1}{2}(e^x + e^{-x})$ measured from $x = 0$ is of length $\frac{1}{2}(e^x - e^{-x})$.

Exercise 16.3: Miscellaneous

1. Find the mass of a bar of length a, given that its density at a point distant x from one end is kx, where k is a constant.

2. Find the position of the C.M. of the bar defined in question 1.

3. Find the position of the C.M. of a hemispherical shell.

4. Find the C.M. of the area cut off from the parabola $y^2 = 4ax$ by the line $x = a$.

5. Find the position of the C.M. of the area bounded by $y^2 = x^3$ and the line $x = 1$.

6. Find the position of the C.M. of a solid formed by a cylinder of length h and radius r, capped by a hemisphere of radius r.

7. Find the length of the arc of the curve $x = a \cos^3 t$, $y = a \sin^3 t$ between $t = 0$ and $t = \dfrac{\pi}{4}$.

8. The line $x = 4a$ cuts the parabola $y^2 = 4ax$ at the points P and Q. Find the length of the arc PQ.

9. The curve $y^2 = 4ax$ is rotated about the axis of x between $x = 0$ and $x = a$. Find the position of the C.M. of the solid so formed.

10. Find the volume obtained by revolving a loop of the curve $y^2 = x^2(1 - x^2)$ about the axis of x.

11. Find the position of the C.M. of the solid defined in question 14.

12. For the curve $x = \cosh t$, $y = \cosh t + t$, show that
$$\frac{ds}{dt} = \sqrt{2} \cosh t.$$

13. The curve $\dfrac{x^2}{a^2} + \dfrac{y^2}{b^2} = 1$ is rotated about the axis of x. Find the volume generated.

14. The density at a point P of a sphere of radius a is kx where x is the distance of P from the centre. Find the mass of the sphere.

15. A rod AB of length l has a density $k(1 + x)$ where x is the distance from A. Find the mass of the rod.

16. Find the length of arc of the curve $3y = (x - 3)\sqrt{x}$ between $x = 0$ and $x = 1$.

17. Sketch the curve $9y^2 = x(x - 3)^2$ and find the volume formed by rotating its loop about the axis of x.

18. For the curve $y = a + \cosh x$, show that $\dfrac{ds}{dx} = y - a$.

19. The curve $y = \cosh x$ is rotated about the axis of x between $x = 0$ and $x = x_1$. Show that the surface area of the solid formed is $\pi\{x_1 + \frac{1}{2}\sinh 2x_1\}$.

20. A napkin ring is formed by revolving a semicircle of radius a about a straight line in its plane parallel to the bounding diameter and distant $2a$ from it, the axis of revolution being on the convex side of the semicircle. Find the area of surface of the rings.

17 Curvature

Definitions

Suppose that P and Q are two adjacent points on a curve and that the length of arc PQ is δs.

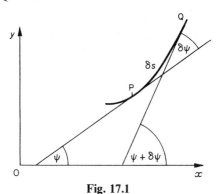

Fig. 17.1

Let the tangents at P and Q make angles ψ and $\psi + \delta\psi$ with the x-axis. Then the angle between the tangents at P and Q is $\delta\psi$.

$\dfrac{\delta\psi}{\delta s}$ is the average rate of change of the angle with respect to the arc and is called the average curvature of the arc PQ. The limit of this fraction as Q tends to P, $\dfrac{d\psi}{ds}$, is called the *curvature* at P.

The curvature is usually denoted by κ and so

$$\kappa = \frac{d\psi}{ds}.$$

If the normals at P and Q meet at C, as shown in Fig. 17.1, the angle QCP = $\delta\psi$.

The lengths of CP and CQ are approximately equal and PQ approximates to the length of arc of the circle, centre C and radius CP.

$$\therefore \quad CP(\delta\psi) = \delta s \quad \text{and} \quad CP = \frac{\delta s}{\delta\psi}.$$

The length of CP is called the *radius of curvature* of the curve at P and is denoted by ρ.

$$\therefore \quad \rho = \frac{ds}{d\psi}.$$

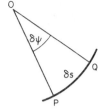

Fig. 17.2

C is called the *centre of curvature* of the curve at P and the circle, centre C and radius CP, is called the *circle of curvature* at P. This circle of course touches the original curve at P.

Cartesian formula for ρ

The gradient of the tangent is $\tan \psi$.

$$\therefore \quad \tan \psi = \frac{dy}{dx}.$$

Differentiating with respect to x,

$$\sec^2 \psi \, \frac{d\psi}{dx} = \frac{d^2 y}{dx^2}.$$

$$\therefore \quad \frac{d\psi}{dx} = \frac{d^2 y/dx^2}{\sec^2 \psi}$$

$$= \frac{d^2 y/dx^2}{1 + \tan^2 \psi}$$

$$= \frac{d^2 y/dx^2}{1 + (dy/dx)^2}.$$

But

$$\frac{d\psi}{ds} = \frac{d\psi}{dx} \times \frac{dx}{ds}$$

and from Fig. 17.3,

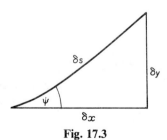

Fig. 17.3

$$\frac{dx}{ds} = \cos \psi = \frac{1}{\sec \psi}$$

$$= \frac{1}{\sqrt{(1 + \tan^2 \psi)}}$$

$$= \frac{1}{\sqrt{[1 + (dy/dx)^2]}}.$$

$$\therefore \quad \frac{d\psi}{ds} = \frac{d^2y/dx^2}{1 + (dy/dx)^2} \cdot \frac{1}{\sqrt{[1 + (dy/dx)^2]}}.$$

$$\therefore \quad \rho = \frac{\{1 + (dy/dx)^2\}^{\frac{3}{2}}}{d^2y/dx^2}.$$

It is worth noting that this formula may be obtained by expressing ψ in the form $\tan^{-1}\left(\dfrac{dy}{dx}\right)$.

Since

$$\psi = \tan^{-1}\left(\frac{dy}{dx}\right)$$

$$\frac{d\psi}{dx} = \frac{d^2y/dx^2}{1 + (dy/dx)^2}$$

and as before

$$\rho = \frac{\{1 + (dy/dx)^2\}^{\frac{3}{2}}}{d^2y/dx^2}.$$

Example. *Find the radius of curvature of the curve* $y = x^3 - x$ *at the point* $(1, 0)$.

$$y = x^3 - x$$

$$\frac{dy}{dx} = 3x^2 - 1$$

$$\frac{d^2y}{dx^2} = 6x.$$

When $x = 1$,

$$\frac{dy}{dx} = 2 \quad \text{and} \quad \frac{d^2y}{dx^2} = 6.$$

$$\rho = \frac{\{1 + (dy/dx)^2\}^{\frac{3}{2}}}{d^2y/dx^2} = \frac{(1 + 4)^{\frac{3}{2}}}{6} = \frac{5\sqrt{5}}{6}.$$

Exercise 17.1

Find the radii of curvature of the following curves at the points given.

1. $y = x^2$ at $(1, 1)$.   2. $y^2 = 4x$ at $(4, 4)$.

3. $y = x^2 + x + 1$ at $(1, 3)$.   4. $y = x^2 - 2x$ at $(2, 0)$.

5. $y = \sin x$ at $\left(\dfrac{\pi}{4}, \dfrac{1}{\sqrt{2}}\right)$.   6. $y = \tan x$ at $\left(\dfrac{\pi}{4}, 1\right)$.

7. $y = x^3$ at $(1, 1)$.

8. $y^2 = x^3$ at $(1, 1)$.

9. $y = 3x^3 + x^2 + 1$ at $(2, 29)$.

10. $y = e^x$ when $x = 1$.

11. $y = \cosh x$ when $x = c$.

12. $y^2 = 4ax$ at $(0, 0)$.

13. $2x^2 + y^2 = 9$ at $(2, 1)$.

14. $3x^2 - y^2 = 2$ at $(1, 1)$.

15. $xy = 4$ at $(2, 2)$.

16. $x^2 - y^2 = 3$ at $(2, 1)$.

17. $x^2 + y^2 = 4x$ at $(4, 0)$.

18. $y = x^2 + x^3$ at $(1, 2)$.

19. $y = \log x$ at $(1, 0)$.

20. $y = \cos x$ at $\left(\dfrac{\pi}{3}, \dfrac{1}{2} \right)$.

Parametric form for radius of curvature

Suppose that x and y are given in terms of a parameter t in the form
$x = f(t)$, $y = g(t)$.

Then
$$\frac{dx}{dt} = f'(t) \quad \text{and} \quad \frac{dy}{dt} = g'(t)$$

$$\frac{dy}{dx} = \frac{dy/dt}{dx/dt} = \frac{g'(t)}{f'(t)}.$$

Differentiating with respect to x,

$$\frac{d^2y}{dx^2} = \frac{d}{dt}\left\{ \frac{g'(t)}{f'(t)} \right\} \cdot \frac{dt}{dx}$$

$$= \frac{f'(t)g''(t) - g'(t)f''(t)}{[f'(t)]^2} \cdot \frac{1}{f'(t)}$$

$$= \frac{f'(t)g''(t) - g'(t)f''(t)}{[f'(t)]^3}.$$

$$\rho = \frac{[1 + (dy/dx)^2]^{\frac{3}{2}}}{d^2y/dx^2}$$

$$= \frac{\left\{ 1 + \left[\dfrac{g'(t)}{f'(t)} \right]^2 \right\}^{\frac{3}{2}}}{\dfrac{f'(t)g''(t) - f''(t)g'(t)}{[f'(t)]^3}}$$

$$= \frac{\{[f'(t)]^2 + [g'(t)]^2\}^{\frac{3}{2}}}{f'(t)g''(t) - f''(t)g'(t)}.$$

Example. *Find the radius of curvature of the curve $x = t^2$, $y = t^3$ at the point t.*

$$\begin{aligned} f(t) &= t^2 & g(t) &= t^3 \\ f'(t) &= 2t & g'(t) &= 3t^2 \\ f''(t) &= 2. & g''(t) &= 6t. \end{aligned}$$

$$\therefore \quad \rho = \frac{\{[f'(t)]^2 + [g'(t)]^2\}^{\frac{3}{2}}}{f'(t)g''(t) - f''(t)g'(t)}$$

$$= \frac{(4t^2 + 9t^4)^{\frac{3}{2}}}{2t(6t) - 2(3t^2)} = \frac{t^3(9t^2 + 4)^{\frac{3}{2}}}{6t^2}$$

$$= \frac{t}{6}(9t^2 + 4)^{\frac{3}{2}}.$$

The curve $x = t^2$, $y = t^3$ has a cartesian equation $x^3 = y^2$.
The radius of curvature at the point $(1, 1)$ is found by putting $t = 1$ and $\rho = \frac{1}{6}(13)^{\frac{3}{2}} = \frac{13\sqrt{13}}{6}$ (see Exercise 17.1, question 8).

Exercise 17.2

Find the radii of curvature of the following parametric curves for the value of the parameter given.

1. $x = at^2$, $y = 2at$ when $t = 0$.

2. $x = a\cos\theta$, $y = a\sin\theta$ when $\theta = \frac{\pi}{4}$.

3. $x = a\cos\theta$, $y = b\sin\theta$ when $\theta = \frac{\pi}{4}$.

4. $x = a\cosh\theta$, $y = b\sinh\theta$ when $\theta = 0$.

5. $x = ct$, $y = \frac{c}{t}$ when $t = 1$.

6. $x = \cosh\theta$, $y = 2\sinh\theta$ when $\theta = 0$.

7. $x = 4\cos\theta$, $y = \sin\theta$ when $\theta = \frac{\pi}{2}$.

8. $x = t^3$, $y = t^2$ when $t = 2$.

9. $x = a(\theta + \sin\theta)$, $y = a(1 + \cos\theta)$ at the point $\theta = 0$.

10. $x = a\cos^3 t$, $y = a\sin^3 t$ when $t = 0$.

11. $x = 1 + t$, $y = t^2$ when $t = 1$.

12. $x = \frac{1}{1+t}$, $y = \frac{t}{1+t}$ when $t = 0$.

13. $x = 1 - t^2$, $y = t(1 - t^2)$ when $t = 0$.

14. $x = \frac{t}{1+t^3}$, $y = \frac{t^2}{1+t^3}$ when $t = 0$.

15. $x = \sin t$, $y = t\sin t$ when $t = \frac{\pi}{2}$.

Curvature at origin

A good method of finding the radius of curvature at the origin is to express y as a power series in terms of x. Since the curve passes through the origin, the constant term must be zero and let us suppose that

$$y = Ax + Bx^2 + \ldots$$

Then $\quad \dfrac{dy}{dx} = A + 2Bx + \ldots \quad$ and $\quad \dfrac{d^2y}{dx^2} = 2B + \ldots$

At the origin

$$\frac{dy}{dx} = A \quad \text{and} \quad \frac{d^2y}{dx^2} = 2B.$$

$$\rho = \frac{\{1 + (dy/dx)^2\}^{\frac{3}{2}}}{d^2y/dx^2} = \frac{(1 + A^2)^{\frac{3}{2}}}{2B}.$$

Example. *Find the radius of curvature at the origin of the curve* $y = e^x - 1$.

$$y = e^x - 1 = \left(1 + x + \frac{x^2}{2!} + \ldots\right) - 1$$

$$= x + \frac{x^2}{2} + \ldots$$

$$\therefore \quad A = 1 \quad \text{and} \quad B = \tfrac{1}{2}.$$

$$\rho = \frac{(1 + A^2)^{\frac{3}{2}}}{2B} = 2\sqrt{2}.$$

Curvature in terms of dx/dy and d^2x/dy^2

We know that

$$\frac{dy}{dx} = \frac{1}{dx/dy}.$$

$$\therefore \quad \frac{d^2y}{dx^2} = \frac{d}{dx}\left(\frac{1}{dx/dy}\right)$$

$$= \frac{d}{dy}\left(\frac{1}{dx/dy}\right) \cdot \frac{dy}{dx}$$

$$= -\frac{d^2x/dy^2}{(dx/dy)^2} \cdot \frac{dy}{dx}$$

$$= -\frac{d^2x/dy}{(dx/dy)^3}.$$

$$\rho = \frac{[1 + (dy/dx)^2]^{\frac{3}{2}}}{d^2y/dx^2} = \frac{\left[1 + \left(\dfrac{1}{dx/dy}\right)^2\right]^{\frac{3}{2}}}{-\dfrac{d^2x/dy^2}{(dx/dy)^3}}$$

$$= -\frac{[1 + (dx/dy)^2]^{\frac{3}{2}}}{d^2x/dy^2}.$$

This is sometimes easier to apply than the formula in terms of $\dfrac{dy}{dx}$ and $\dfrac{d^2y}{dx^2}$. For example, in finding the curvature at the origin, it may be easier to express x in terms of y than y in terms of x.

If $$x = Cy + Dy^2 + \ldots,$$

then $$\rho = \frac{(1 + C^2)^{\frac{3}{2}}}{2D}.$$

The sign of ρ tells us which way the curve bends. Since $\rho = \dfrac{ds}{d\psi}$, when s increases with ψ, ρ is positive; when s increases as ψ decreases, ρ is negative.

The two cases are shown in Fig. 17.4.

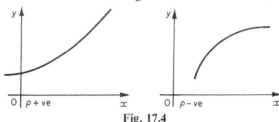

Fig. 17.4

Example. *Find the radius of curvature at the origin for the parabola* $y^2 = 4ax$.

The expansion of x in terms of y can be written down as $x = \dfrac{y^2}{4a}$.

$$\therefore \quad C = 0, \quad D = \frac{1}{4a}.$$

$$\therefore \quad \rho = -\frac{1}{1/2a} = -2a.$$

Newton's formula

If the curve considered touches the axis of x at the origin, the gradient at the origin is zero.

If $$y = Ax + Bx^2 + \ldots$$

$$\frac{dy}{dx} = A + 2Bx + \ldots$$

and the gradient at the origin is A.

$$\therefore \quad A = 0$$

and the equation of the curve is

$$y = Bx^2 + \ldots$$

So $$\rho = \frac{1}{2B}.$$

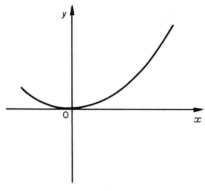

Fig. 17.5

But since $\qquad\qquad y = Bx^2 +$ higher powers of x,

$$\frac{y}{x^2} = B + \text{power of } x.$$

$$\therefore \quad \text{Lt}_{x\to 0} \frac{y}{x^2} = B \quad \text{and} \quad \text{Lt}_{x\to 0} \frac{x^2}{y} = \frac{1}{B}.$$

$$\therefore \quad \rho \, \text{Lt}_{x\to 0} \frac{x^2}{2y}.$$

This is Newton's formula for the radius of curvature at the origin when the curve touches the axis of x at the origin.

If the curve touches the axis of y at the origin,

$$\rho = \text{Lt}_{x\to 0} \frac{y^2}{2x}.$$

Example 1. *Find the radius of curvature at the origin for the curve* $y = x^2 + x^3$. The tangent at the origin is $y = 0$, i.e. the axis of x.

$$\frac{y}{x^2} = 1 + x. \qquad \text{Lt}_{x\to 0} \frac{y}{x^2} = 1. \qquad \therefore \quad \text{Lt}_{x\to 0} \frac{x^2}{y} = 1.$$

$$\rho = \text{Lt}_{x\to 0} \frac{x^2}{2y} = \frac{1}{2}.$$

Example 2. *Find the radius of curvature at the origin for the curve* $y = 1 - \cos x$.

This curve passes through the origin and since $\dfrac{dy}{dx} = \sin x$, the gradient there is zero.

$$\rho = \text{Lt}_{x \to 0} \frac{x^2}{2y} = \text{Lt}_{x \to 0} \frac{x^2}{2(1 - \cos x)} = \text{Lt}_{x \to 0} \frac{x^2}{4 \sin^2 \frac{1}{2}x}$$

$$= \text{Lt}_{x \to 0} \frac{(\frac{1}{2}x)^2}{(\sin \frac{1}{2}x)^2} = \text{Lt}_{x \to 0} \left\{ \frac{\frac{1}{2}x}{\sin \frac{1}{2}x} \right\}^2$$

$$= 1, \text{ since } \text{Lt}_{\theta \to 0} \frac{\theta}{\sin \theta} = 1.$$

Exercise 17.3

Find the radii of curvature of the following curves at the origin.

1. $y = 2x^2 + 3x^2$.   2. $x = 3y^2 + y^3$.   3. $y + 1 = \sqrt{(1 + x)}$.
4. $y = x - \sin x$.   5. $x^2 = 4y$.   6. $y^2 = x(4 - x)$.
7. $x^2 = y(2 + y)$.   8. $y^2 = x - x^3$.   9. $y = \ln(1 + x)$.
10. $y + 2 = 2 e^x$.   11. $y = \sinh x$.   12. $y = \cosh x - 1$.
13. $y^2 = x^3$.   14. $x^2 = y^3$.   15. $x^3 = 2y^4$.
16. $y = \sin^{-1} x$.   17. $y = \tan^{-1} x$.   18. $(y + 1)^2 = x + 1$.
19. $(x - 2)^2 = y + 4$.   20. $(y + 1)^3 = x + 1$.

Exercise 17.4: Miscellaneous

1. By transferring the axes to parallel axes through the point $(2, 0)$, find the radius of curvature of the curve $y = (x - 2)^2$ at the point $(2, 0)$.
2. Find the radius of curvature of the curve $y^2 = x(x - 2)$ at the point $(2, 0)$.
3. Find the radius of curvature of the curve $y^2 = x^2(x - 2)$ at the point $(2, 0)$.
4. Find the radius of curvature of the curve $y^2 = x^2(x + 1)$ at the point $(-1, 0)$.
5. Find the radius of curvature of the curve $y^2 = x^2(x - a)$ at the point $(a, 0)$.
6. Find the radius of curvature at the point θ on the cycloid $x = a(\theta + \sin \theta)$, $y = a(1 + \cos \theta)$.
7. Find the radius of curvature at the point t on the astroid $x = a \sin^3 t$, $y = a \cos^3 t$.
8. Find the radius of curvature of the curve $\sqrt{\frac{x}{a}} + \sqrt{\frac{y}{b}} = 1$ at the point (x, y).
9. Find the radius of curvature of the ellipse $\frac{x^2}{a^2} + \frac{y^2}{b^2} = 1$ at the point $(a \cos \theta, b \sin \theta)$.
10. Find the radius of curvature of the rectangular hyperbola $x^2 - y^2 = a^2$ at the point $(a \cosh \theta, a \sinh \theta)$.
11. Find the radius of curvature of the rectangular hyperbola $xy = c^2$ at the point $\left(ct, \frac{c}{t} \right)$.

12. If ρ_1 and ρ_2 are the radii of curvature at the ends of the major axis and minor axis of the ellipse $\dfrac{x^2}{a^2} + \dfrac{y^2}{b^2} = 1$, show that $\rho_1\rho_2 = ab$.

13. Prove that the equation of the cycloid $x = a(\theta + \sin\theta)$, $y = a(1 + \cos\theta)$ may be written as $s = 4a\sin\psi$. Hence find its radius of curvature.

14. Find the radius of curvature of the catenary $y = c\cosh\dfrac{x}{c}$ at the point (x, y).

15. If ρ_1 and ρ_2 are the radii of curvature of the parabola $y^2 = 4ax$ at the origin and at the end of the latus rectum $(a, 2a)$, show that $\dfrac{\rho_2}{\rho_1} = 2\sqrt{2}$.

16. Find the radius of curvature of $y^2 = x^3$ at the point (x, y).

17. Find the equation of the circle of curvature at the origin for the curve $y^2 = 4x$.

18. Find the equation of the circle of curvature at the origin for the curve $x + y = x^2$.

19. Find the equation of the circle of curvature at the origin for the curve $x + y = y^2$.

20. Prove that the coordinates of the centre of curvature of the point (x, y) on a given curve are $(x - \rho\sin\psi, y + \rho\cos\psi)$.

21. Find the centre of curvature of the parabola $y^2 = 4ax$ at the point $(am^2, 2am)$.

22. Find the radius of curvature of the curve
$$x = \frac{a(1 - t^2)}{t}, \qquad y = a(1 - t^2)$$
at the point where $t = 1$.

23. Find the radius of curvature of $x = y^2(a - y)^2$ at the origin.

24. Find the radius of curvature of $x = y^2(a - y)^2$ at the point $(0, a)$.

25. Find the greatest and least values of the radius of curvature of the ellipse $\dfrac{x^2}{a^2} + \dfrac{y^2}{b^2} = 1$.

26. Find the radius of curvature of the curve $x^{\frac{2}{3}} + y^{\frac{2}{3}}$ at the point (x, y).

27. Find the radius of curvature of the curve $xy^2 = a^2(a - x)$ at the point $(a, 0)$.

28. If ρ_1 and ρ_2 are the radii of curvature of the curve
$$y^2 = (a - x)(b - x)$$
at the points $(a, 0)$, and $(b, 0)$, find the ratio $\rho_1 : \rho_2$.

29. Find the radius of curvature of $a^2y^2 = x^2(a^2 - x^2)$ at the point $(a, 0)$.

30. Find the radius of curvature of the curve $x = \cosh t - t$, $y = \cosh t + t$ at the point t.

18 Differential Equations

Forming differential equations

Consider the equation $y = Ax + Bx^2$, where A and B are arbitrary constants.

Then
$$\frac{dy}{dx} = A + 2Bx$$

and
$$\frac{d^2y}{dx^2} = 2B.$$

$$\therefore \quad A = \frac{dy}{dx} - x\frac{d^2y}{dx^2}$$

and by substitution in $y = Ax + Bx^2$,

$$y = x\frac{dy}{dx} - x^2\frac{d^2y}{dx^2} + \tfrac{1}{2}x^2\frac{d^2y}{dx^2}$$

or
$$y = x\frac{dy}{dx} - \tfrac{1}{2}x^2\frac{d^2y}{dx^2}.$$

This equation, which connects x and y with differential coefficients, is called a *differential equation*. The highest order of the differential coefficient in the equation is $\dfrac{d^2y}{dx^2}$ or the second and so the differential equation is said to be of the *second order*.

The solution of the equation is a relation between x and y which contains no differential coefficients and so is $y = Ax + Bx^2$. This is the *general solution* or the *complete primitive* and a *particular integral* is found by giving any numerical values to A and B.

For example, $y = x - x^2$ is a particular integral.

For this function,

$$\frac{dy}{dx} = 1 - 2x \quad \text{and} \quad \frac{d^2y}{dx^2} = -2.$$

The expression $\left(x\dfrac{dy}{dx} - \tfrac{1}{2}x^2\dfrac{d^2y}{dx^2}\right)$ then equals $x - 2x^2 + x^2$ or $x - x^2$ which equals y.

Notice that in order to eliminate the two arbitrary constants A and B we need three equations and so must use the first two differential coefficients. The differential equation resulting must therefore be of the second order. The converse also applies, i.e. the solution of a differential equation of the first order contains one arbitrary constant; the solution of an equation of the second order contains two arbitrary constants and so on.

Example 1. *Form the differential equation of which* $y = Ax + x^2$ *is the general solution.*

Here
$$\frac{dy}{dx} = A + 2x \quad \text{and} \quad A = \frac{dy}{dx} - 2x.$$

$$\therefore \quad y = x\left(\frac{dy}{dx} - 2x\right) + x^2$$

or
$$y + x^2 = x\frac{dy}{dx}$$

is the differential equation.

Example 2. *Form the differential equation of which* $y = A \sin nx + B \cos nx$ *is the general solution.*

Here
$$\frac{dy}{dx} = nA \cos nx - nB \sin nx$$

and
$$\frac{d^2y}{dx^2} = -n^2A \sin nx - n^2B \cos nx$$

$$= -n^2y.$$

The differential equation is $\dfrac{d^2y}{dx^2} = -n^2y$, the equation for simple harmonic motion.

Exercise 18.1

State the orders of the following differential equations:

1. $\dfrac{dy}{dx} = y.$
2. $\left(\dfrac{dy}{dx}\right)^2 + x = y.$

3. $\dfrac{d^2y}{dx^2} + \dfrac{dy}{dx} = 4y.$
4. $\dfrac{d^2y}{dx^2} - x = \dfrac{dy}{dx}.$

5. $\dfrac{d^3y}{dx^3} = -3y.$

Eliminate the arbitrary constants from the following equations:

6. $y = Ax.$
7. $y = Ax + B.$

8. $y = Ax + \dfrac{1}{A}.$
9. $Ay + Bx = \sin x.$

10. $y = A \cosh nx + B \sinh nx.$
11. $y = A e^{nx} + B e^{-nx}.$
12. $y = A + B \ln x.$
13. $y = A \sin^{-1} x.$
14. $y = A \tan^{-1} x.$
15. $y = A + B e^x.$
16. $y = \ln x + A e^x.$
17. $y^2 = (x - A)(x - B).$
18. $y + 2 = Ax + x^2.$
19. $y = A\sqrt{(1 + x^2)}.$
20. $y = Ax + B\sqrt{(1 + x^2)}.$

The solution of a differential equation is generally not an easy operation but there are several types of equation which should be recognized. These are now considered one by one.

Variables separable

If an equation is such that all the terms containing x including dx may be collected on one side of the equation and all the terms containing y on the other, the solution may be obtained by integration.

The general type is

$$f(x)\frac{dy}{dx} = F(y).$$

Here

$$\int \frac{dx}{f(x)} = \int \frac{dy}{F(y)},$$

and the solution contains one arbitrary constant.

(There is no point in putting an arbitrary constant on each side of the equation as these may be collected to make one only.)

Example 1. *Solve* $x\frac{dy}{dx} = y.$

Here

$$\int \frac{dx}{x} = \int \frac{dy}{y}$$

and

$$\ln x = \ln y + K.$$

If K is expressed as $\ln A$,

$$\ln x = \ln y + \ln A$$
$$= \ln Ay$$

and so

$$x = Ay.$$

Example 2. *Solve* $y\frac{dy}{dx} = x.$

Here

$$\int x\, dx = \int y\, dy$$

and so

$$x^2 = y^2 + A.$$

Initial conditions

The value of the arbitrary constant in a first order equation may be calculated provided the value of y for some value of x is given. This is called the *initial condition*. In a second order equation, two initial conditions are necessary to find the two arbitrary constants.

Example 1. *A curve is such that at all points of it* $\dfrac{dy}{dx} = 1 + y$. *It is given that* $y = 0$ *when* $x = 1$. *Find the equation of the curve.*

$$\frac{dy}{dx} = 1 + y.$$

$$\therefore \quad \int dx = \int \frac{dy}{1 + y}$$

or $x + A = \ln(1 + y).$

But $x = 1$ when $y = 0$.

$$\therefore \quad 1 + A = 0 \quad \text{and} \quad A = -1.$$

The equation of the curve is $x - 1 = \ln(1 + y)$.

Example 2. *If* $\dfrac{d^2 y}{dx^2} = x$ *and* $y = 1$ *and* $\dfrac{dy}{dx} = 1$ *when* $x = 1$, *find* y *in terms of* x.

Since $\dfrac{d^2 y}{dx^2} = x,$

by integration $\dfrac{dy}{dx} = \tfrac{1}{2}x^2 + A.$

But $\dfrac{dy}{dx} = 1$ when $x = 1$.

$$\therefore \quad 1 = \tfrac{1}{2} + A \quad \text{and} \quad A = \tfrac{1}{2}.$$

So $\dfrac{dy}{dx} = \tfrac{1}{2}x^2 + \tfrac{1}{2}.$

By integration, $y = \tfrac{1}{6}x^3 + \tfrac{1}{2}x + B.$

Since $y = 1$ when $x = 1,$

$$1 = \tfrac{1}{6} + \tfrac{1}{2} + B \quad \text{and} \quad B = \tfrac{1}{3}.$$

$$\therefore \quad y = \tfrac{1}{6}x^3 + \tfrac{1}{2}x + \tfrac{1}{3}.$$

Exercise 18.2

Solve the differential equations:

1. $\dfrac{dy}{dx} = 1 + y^2.$

2. $\dfrac{dy}{dx} = \sqrt{(1 - y^2)}.$

3. $\dfrac{dy}{dx} = y^2.$

4. $\dfrac{dy}{dx} = \dfrac{y}{x^2}.$

5. $\dfrac{dy}{dx} + \dfrac{x^2}{y} = 0.$

6. $\dfrac{dy}{dx} = \dfrac{\sin x}{\sin y}.$

7. $\dfrac{dy}{dx} = \dfrac{e^x}{e^y}.$

8. $\dfrac{1}{y}\dfrac{dy}{dx} = \dfrac{2}{x}.$

9. $(x + 1)\dfrac{dy}{dx} = y.$

10. $x^2 \dfrac{dy}{dx} = y^2.$

Find the equations of the curves defined by the following:

11. $\dfrac{dy}{dx} = 1 + y^2$, given that $y = 1$ when $x = \dfrac{\pi}{4}.$

12. $\dfrac{dy}{dx} = \sqrt{(1 - y^2)}$, given that $y = \dfrac{1}{\sqrt{2}}$ when $x = 0$.

13. $\dfrac{dy}{dx} = y^2$, given that $y = 1$ when $x = 1$.

14. $\dfrac{dy}{dx} = \dfrac{y}{x^2}$, given that $y = 1$ when $x = -1$.

15. $\dfrac{dy}{dx} + \dfrac{x^2}{y} = 0$, given that $y = 1$ when $x = 2$.

16. $\dfrac{dy}{dx} = \dfrac{\sin x}{\sin y}$, given that $y = \dfrac{\pi}{2}$ when $x = 0$.

17. $\dfrac{dy}{dx} = \dfrac{e^x}{e^y}$, given that $y = 1$ when $x = 0$.

18. $\dfrac{1}{y}\dfrac{dy}{dx} = \dfrac{2}{x}$, given that $y = 4$ when $x = 1$.

19. $(x + 1)\dfrac{dy}{dx} = y$, given that $y = 4$ when $x = 1$.

20. $x^2 \dfrac{dy}{dx} = y^2$, given that $y = \tfrac{1}{3}$ when $x = \tfrac{1}{2}$.

Homogeneous equations

A homogeneous differential equation of the first order is one in which $\dfrac{dy}{dx}$ may be expressed as a function of $\dfrac{y}{x}$. It may be integrated by the substitution $y = vx$. Remember that v is a variable so that $\dfrac{dy}{dx} = v + x\dfrac{dv}{dx}$.

Example 1. *Solve the equation* $\dfrac{dy}{dx} = \dfrac{y - x}{y + x}$.

Put $y = vx$ so that

$$\frac{dy}{dx} = v + x\frac{dv}{dx}.$$

Then

$$v + x\frac{dv}{dx} = \frac{v - 1}{v + 1}.$$

$$\therefore \quad x\frac{dv}{dx} = \frac{v - 1}{v + 1} - v$$

$$= -\frac{1 + v^2}{1 + v}.$$

$$\therefore \quad \int \frac{v+1}{v^2+1}\,dv = -\int \frac{dx}{x}$$

or
$$\tfrac{1}{2}\int \frac{2v}{v^2+1}\,dv + \int \frac{dv}{v^2+1} = -\int \frac{dx}{x}.$$

$$\therefore \quad \tfrac{1}{2}\ln(v^2+1) + \tan^{-1} v = -\ln x + C.$$

$$\therefore \quad \tfrac{1}{2}\ln\!\left(\frac{y^2}{x^2}+1\right) + \tan^{-1}\frac{y}{x} + \ln x = C.$$

Since $\ln x = \tfrac{1}{2}\ln x^2$, this may be written

$$\tfrac{1}{2}\ln(x^2+y^2) + \tan^{-1}\frac{y}{x} = C.$$

Example 2. *Solve the equation* $2x^2 \dfrac{dy}{dx} = x^2 + y^2$.

Put $y = vx$ so that

$$\frac{dy}{dx} = v + x\frac{dv}{dx}.$$

Then
$$2v + 2x\frac{dv}{dx} = 1 + v^2.$$

$$\therefore \quad 2x\frac{dv}{dx} = 1 - 2v + v^2 = (v-1)^2.$$

$$\therefore \quad \int 2\frac{dv}{(v-1)^2} = \int \frac{dx}{x}$$

or
$$-\frac{2}{v-1} + C = \ln x.$$

$$\therefore \quad \frac{2x}{y-x} + \ln x = C \text{ is the solution.}$$

Exercise 18.3

Solve the following equations:

1. $x\dfrac{dy}{dx} - y = \sqrt{(x^2 - y^2)}.$ **2.** $x\dfrac{dy}{dx} - y = \sqrt{(x^2 + y^2)}.$

3. $x\dfrac{dy}{dx} - y = x.$ **4.** $x\dfrac{dy}{dx} = y + 2x.$

5. $x^2\dfrac{dy}{dx} = y^2 - xy + x^2.$ **6.** $\dfrac{dy}{dx} = \dfrac{x^2 + y^2}{xy}.$

7. $\dfrac{dy}{dx} = \dfrac{y^3}{x(x^2 + y^2)}.$ **8.** $x(x+y)\dfrac{dy}{dx} = y^2.$

9. $\dfrac{dy}{dx} = \dfrac{x^3 + y^3}{x(x^2 + y^2)}.$ **10.** $x^2\dfrac{dy}{dx} = y(x+y).$

Find the solutions of the following equations with the given initial conditions.

11. $x\dfrac{dy}{dx} - y = \sqrt{(x^2 - y^2)}$, given that $x = 1$ when $y = 1$.

12. $x\dfrac{dy}{dx} - y = (x^2 + y^2)$, given that $x = 3$ when $y = 4$.

13. $x\dfrac{dy}{dx} - y = x$, given that $y = 2$ when $x = 1$.

14. $x\dfrac{dy}{dx} = y + 2x$, given that $y = 3$ when $x = 1$.

15. $x^2\dfrac{dy}{dx} = y^2 - xy + x^2$, given that $y = 2$ when $x = 1$.

16. $\dfrac{dy}{dx} = \dfrac{x^2 + y^2}{xy}$, given that $y = 1$ when $x = 1$.

17. $\dfrac{dy}{dx} = \dfrac{y^3}{x(x^2 + y^2)}$, given that $y = 1$ when $x = \frac{1}{2}$.

18. $x(x + y)\dfrac{dy}{dx} = y^2$, given that $y = 2$ when $x = 1$.

19. $\dfrac{dy}{dx} = \dfrac{x^3 + y^3}{x(x^2 + y^2)}$, given that $y = 2$ when $x = 1$.

20. $x^2\dfrac{dy}{dx} = y(x + y)$, given that $y = \frac{1}{2}$ when $x = 1$.

Integrating factor

The equation $\dfrac{dy}{dx} + Py = Q$, where P and Q are functions of x only (i.e. do not contain y), may be integrated by multiplying throughout by the factor $e^{\int P\,dx}$. This factor, called an integrating factor, makes the left-hand side of the equation a perfect differential.

We have $\qquad e^{\int P\,dx}\cdot\dfrac{dy}{dx} + Py\,e^{\int P\,dx} = Q\,e^{\int P\,dx}$.

The left-hand side is $\qquad \dfrac{d}{dx}(y\,e^{\int P\,dx})$.

$$\therefore \quad y\,e^{\int P\,dx} = \int Q\,e^{\int P\,dx}\,dx + C.$$

Example 1. *Solve the equation* $\dfrac{dy}{dx} + \dfrac{y}{x} = 1$.

The integrating factor is $e^{\int(1/x)\,dx} = e^{\ln x}$. Since $\ln(e^{\ln x}) = \ln x$, it follows that $e^{\ln x} = x$. Similarly $e^{\ln f(x)} = f(x)$. The integrating factor is therefore x.

$$\therefore \quad x\frac{dy}{dx} + y = x$$

or

$$\frac{d}{dx}(xy) = x.$$

$$\therefore \quad xy = \tfrac{1}{2}x^2 + C.$$

N.B. This equation could also be solved by the substitution $y = vx$.

Example 2. *Solve the equation* $\dfrac{dy}{dx} + y \tan x = \cos x.$

The integrating factor is $e^{\int \tan x \, dx}$ or $e^{\ln \sec x}$. Since $e^{\ln \sec x} = \sec x$, the integrating factor is $\sec x$.

$$\therefore \quad \sec x\frac{dy}{dx} + y \sec x \tan x = 1$$

or

$$\frac{d}{dx}(y \sec x) = 1.$$

$$\therefore \quad y \sec x = x + C \text{ is the solution.}$$

Exercise 18.4

Solve the following equations:

1. $\dfrac{dy}{dx} + y = x^2.$

2. $\dfrac{dy}{dx} + y = e^{-x}.$

3. $\dfrac{dy}{dx} + \dfrac{y}{x} = x.$

4. $\dfrac{dy}{dx} + y \cot x = \operatorname{cosec} x.$

5. $\dfrac{dy}{dx} + y \cot x = x.$

6. $(1 + x^2)\dfrac{dy}{dx} + 2xy = \dfrac{1}{1 + x^2}.$

7. $\dfrac{dy}{dx} + 2y = e^{2x}.$

8. $\dfrac{dy}{dx} + \dfrac{3x^2}{1 + x^3}y = \dfrac{1}{1 + x^3}.$

9. $\dfrac{dy}{dx} + \dfrac{2y}{x} = x.$

10. $\dfrac{dy}{dx}(1 + x) - 2y = \dfrac{1}{1 + x}.$

Find the solutions of the following equations with the given initial conditions.

11. $\dfrac{dy}{dx} + y = x^2$, given that $y = 2$ when $x = 0$.

12. $\dfrac{dy}{dx} + y = e^{-x}$, given that $y = 1$ when $x = 0$.

13. $\dfrac{dy}{dx} + \dfrac{y}{x} = x$, given that $x = 1$ when $y = 0$.

14. $\dfrac{dy}{dx} + y \cot x = \operatorname{cosec} x$, given that $x = 0$ when $y = 0$.

15. $\dfrac{dy}{dx} = y \cot x = x$, given that $y = 1$ when $x = \dfrac{\pi}{2}.$

16. $(1 + x^2)\dfrac{dy}{dx} + 2xy = \dfrac{1}{1 + x^2}$, given that $y = 1$ when $x = 0$.

17. $\dfrac{dy}{dx} + 2y = e^{2x}$, given that $y = \frac{1}{4}$ when $x = 0$.

18. $\dfrac{dy}{dx} + \dfrac{3x^2}{1 + x^3}\, y = \dfrac{1}{1 + x^3}$, given that $y = 1$ when $x = 1$.

19. $\dfrac{dy}{dx} + \dfrac{2y}{x} = x$, given that $y = 1\frac{1}{2}$ when $x = 1$.

20. $\dfrac{dy}{dx}(1 + x) - 2y = \dfrac{1}{1 + x}$, given that $y = \frac{1}{3}$ when $x = 0$.

Equations of the type $d^2y/dx^2 = f(x)$

By straightforward integration,

$$\frac{dy}{dx} = \int f(x)\,dx + C.$$

By integrating this equation y may be found in terms of x.

Example. *Solve the equation* $\dfrac{d^2y}{dx^2} = \sin x.$

Here
$$\frac{dy}{dx} = -\cos x + C.$$

$$\therefore \quad y = -\sin x + Cx + D.$$

Equations of the type $d^2y/dx^2 = f(y)$

This equation may be solved by putting $\dfrac{dy}{dx} = p$.

Then
$$\frac{d^2y}{dx^2} = \frac{dp}{dx} = \frac{dp}{dy} \times \frac{dy}{dx} = p\frac{dp}{dy}.$$

$$\therefore \quad p\frac{dp}{dy} = f(y)$$

or
$$\int p\,dp = \int f(y)\,dy.$$

$$\therefore \quad \frac{p^2}{2} + C = \int f(y)\,dy.$$

This gives $\dfrac{dy}{dx}$ in terms of y and the resulting equation may be solved by separating the variables.

This type of equation often occurs in mechanics when the acceleration is given in terms of the distance. The acceleration $\dfrac{d^2x}{dt^2}$ is equal to $v\dfrac{dv}{dx}$ and when this is given in terms of x, v may be found by separating the variables. When v or $\dfrac{dx}{dt}$ has been expressed in terms of x, x may be found in terms of t by a further process of separating the variables. Simple harmonic motion, in which the acceleration is proportional to the distance from a fixed point and is directed towards it is an example.

Example 1. *A point moves along the x-axis so that its acceleration is directed towards and is proportional to its distance from the origin. Find the distance and velocity after time t.*

Suppose the acceleration is n^2x towards the origin. The acceleration of a particle moving along the x-axis is $\dfrac{d^2x}{dt^2}$ in the direction of x increasing.

$$\therefore \quad \frac{d^2x}{dt^2} = -n^2x,$$

or
$$v\frac{dv}{dx} = -n^2x.$$

$$\therefore \quad \int v\,dv = -n^2\int x\,dx$$

and
$$v^2 = C - n^2x^2.$$

Let $v = 0$ when $x = a$ so that a is the amplitude.

Then
$$C = n^2a^2 \quad \text{and} \quad v^2 = n^2(a^2 - x^2).$$

$$\therefore \quad \frac{dx}{dt} = n\sqrt{(a^2 - x^2)}$$

and
$$\int \frac{dx}{\sqrt{(a^2 - x^2)}} = n\int dt.$$

$$\therefore \quad \sin^{-1}\frac{x}{a} = nt + D$$

or
$$x = a\sin(nt + D),$$

which on expansion may be put in the form
$$x = A\sin nt + B\cos nt.$$

From this
$$\frac{dx}{dt} = nA\cos nt - nB\sin nt.$$

These are the general expressions for the distance and velocity after time t.

If t is measured from the instant the particle is at the origin, $x = 0$ when $t = 0$.

From the equation

$$nt + D = \sin^{-1}\frac{x}{a}, \quad D = 0.$$

$$\therefore \quad x = a \sin nt \quad \text{and} \quad v = na \cos nt.$$

Example 2. *Solve the equation* $\dfrac{d^2y}{dx^2} = n^2y.$

Let $\dfrac{dy}{dx} = p$ so that

$$\frac{d^2y}{dx^2} = p\frac{dp}{dy}.$$

Then $\qquad p\dfrac{dp}{dy} = n^2y$

or $\qquad \displaystyle\int p\,do = n^2\int y\,dy.$

$$\therefore \quad p^2 = n^2y^2 + C.$$

So $\qquad \dfrac{dy}{dx} = n\sqrt{(y^2 + a^2)} \quad \text{putting } C = n^2a^2.$

$$\therefore \quad \int\frac{dy}{\sqrt{(y^2 + a^2)}} = n\int dx$$

or $\qquad \sinh^{-1}\dfrac{y}{a} = nx + D.$

$$\therefore \quad y = a\sinh(nx + D).$$

This by expansion may be put in the form

$$y = A\sinh nx + B\cosh nx$$

or $\qquad y = P\,e^{nx} + Q\,e^{-nx},$

by expressing $\cosh nx$ and $\sinh nx$ in their exponential forms.

N.B. The solution of the equations $\dfrac{d^2}{dx^2} = -n^2y$ and $\dfrac{d^2y}{dx^2} = n^2y$ are important and should be memorized.

The solution of $d^2y/dx^2 + n^2y = f(x)$

We have seen that the general solution of $\dfrac{d^2y}{dx^2} + n^2y = 0$ is $y = A\cos nx + B\sin nx.$

Suppose we are able to find *any* solution, i.e. a particular integral of the equation $\dfrac{d^2y}{dx^2} + n^2y = f(x)$, and suppose that it is $y = g(x).$

Then $y = g(x)$ satisfies the equation and so

$$\frac{d^2g(x)}{dx^2} + n^2g(x) = f(x). \tag{i}$$

Now consider:

$$y = A \cos nx + B \sin nx + g(x).$$

$$\frac{dy}{dx} = -nA \sin nx + nB \cos nx + \frac{dg(x)}{dx}.$$

$$\frac{d^2y}{dx^2} = -n^2A \cos nx - n^2B \sin nx + \frac{d^2g(x)}{dx}.$$

$$\therefore \quad \frac{d^2y}{dx^2} + n^2y = \frac{d^2g(x)}{dx^2} + n^2g(x)$$

$$= f(x) \quad \text{by equation (i).}$$

$\therefore$ $A \cos nx + B \sin nx + g(x)$ is a solution of the equation $\frac{d^2y}{dx^2} + n^2y = f(x)$. Since it contains two arbitrary constants, it must be the general solution.

Similarly the general solution of $\dfrac{d^2y}{dx^2} - n^2y = f(x)$ is

$$y = A e^{nx} + B e^{-nx} + g(x)$$

where $g(x)$ is a particular solution of the equation.

In dealing with the equation $\dfrac{d^2y}{dx^2} + a\dfrac{dy}{dx} + by = f(x)$, we find first the general solution of the equation $\dfrac{d^2y}{dx^2} + a\dfrac{dy}{dx} + by = 0$ which is called the *complementary function* (C.F.). We then find any solution of the equation $\dfrac{d^2y}{dx^2} + a\dfrac{dy}{dx} + by = f(x)$, called the *particular integral* (P.I.).

The general solution of the equation $\dfrac{d^2y}{dx^2} + a\dfrac{dy}{dx} + by = f(x)$ is

$$y = \text{C.F.} + \text{P.I.}$$

Finding the particular integral

In many cases, the particular integral may be found by inspection. Examples are given to illustrate the method.

Example 1. *Find a particular integral of the equation*

$$\frac{d^2y}{dx^2} + 4y = 4.$$

When the function of x on the right-hand side of the equation is independent of x, the particular integral is found by ignoring the term $\dfrac{d^2y}{dx^2}$.

This gives $4y = 4$ or $y = 1$ and this is a particular integral since when $y = 1$,
$\dfrac{d^2y}{dx^2} = 0$.

The general solution is $y = A \cos 2x + B \sin 2x + 1$.

Check   If $y = A \cos 2x + B \sin 2x + 1$,

$$\frac{dy}{dx} = -2A \sin 2x + 2B \cos 2x,$$

$$\frac{d^2y}{dx^2} = -4A \cos 2x - 4B \sin 2x.$$

$$\therefore \quad \frac{d^2y}{dx^2} + 4y = 4.$$

Example 2. *Find a particular integral of the equation*

$$\frac{d^2y}{dx^2} - 4y = 4x + 4.$$

When the function of x on the right-hand side of the equation is linear, try $y = px + q$ where p and q are constants.

$$\frac{dy}{dx} = p \quad \text{and} \quad \frac{d^2y}{dx^2} = 0.$$

$$\therefore \quad -4px - 4q = 4x + 4 \quad \text{and} \quad p = -1, q = -1.$$

The particular integral is $y = -x - 1$ which again is found by ignoring the term $\dfrac{d^2y}{dx^2}$.

The general solution is $y = A e^{2x} + B e^{-2x} - x - 1$.

Example 3. *Find a particular integral of the equation*

$$\frac{d^2y}{dx^2} + 4y = 4x^2.$$

When the function of x is quadratic, assume that $y = ax^2 + bx + c$, where a, b and c are constants.

Then $\dfrac{dy}{dx} = 2ax + b \quad \text{and} \quad \dfrac{d^2y}{dx^2} = 2a.$

By substitution, $2a + 4ax^2 + 4bx + 4c = 4x^2.$
Equating coefficients: $4a = 4,$
$$4b = 0,$$
$$2a + 4c = 0.$$
$$\therefore \quad a = 1, \quad b = 0, \quad c = -\tfrac{1}{2}.$$

The particular integral is $x^2 - \tfrac{1}{2}$.
The general solution is $y = A \cos 2x + B \sin 2x + x^2 - \tfrac{1}{2}$.

Example 4. *Find a particular integral of the equation*

$$\frac{d^2y}{dx^2} + 4y = 3 \sin x.$$

When the function of x is linear in $\sin x$ and $\cos x$, assume that $y = a \sin x + b \cos x$, where a and b are constants.

Then
$$\frac{dy}{dx} = +a \cos x - b \sin x$$

and
$$\frac{d^2y}{dx^2} = -a \sin x - b \cos x.$$

By substitution,
$$-a \sin x - b \cos x + 4a \sin x + 4b \cos x = 3 \sin x.$$
Equating coefficients of $\sin x$ and $\cos x$,
$$3a = 3 \quad \text{and} \quad 3b = 0.$$
The particular integral is $y = \sin x$.
The general solution is $y = A \sin 2x + B \cos 2x + \sin x$.

Exercise 18.5

Find general solutions of the following:

1. $\dfrac{d^2y}{dx^2} = 9y.$

2. $\dfrac{d^2y}{dx^2} = 9x.$

3. $\dfrac{d^2y}{dx^2} = -9y.$

4. $\dfrac{d^2y}{dx^2} = -9x.$

5. $\dfrac{d^2y}{dx^2} = 9y + 9.$

6. $\dfrac{d^2y}{dx^2} = -9y + 9.$

7. $\dfrac{d^2y}{dx^2} - 9y = 9x + 18.$

8. $\dfrac{d^2y}{dx^2} + 9y = 9x + 18.$

9. $\dfrac{d^2y}{dx^2} - y = x.$

10. $\dfrac{d^2y}{dx^2} + y = x.$

11. $\dfrac{d^2y}{dx^2} - y = x^2.$

12. $\dfrac{d^2y}{dx^2} + y = x^2.$

13. $\dfrac{d^2y}{dx^2} - y = \cos 2x.$

14. $\dfrac{d^2y}{dx^2} + y = \cos 2x.$

15. $\dfrac{d^2y}{dx^2} - y = \sin 2x.$

16. $\dfrac{d^2y}{dx^2} + y = \sin 2x.$

17. $\dfrac{d^2y}{dx^2} - 4y = \sin x + \cos x.$

18. $\dfrac{d^2y}{dx^2} + 4y = \sin x + \cos x$

19. $\dfrac{d^2y}{dx^2} - 4y = x^2 + x.$

20. $\dfrac{d^2y}{dx^2} + 4y = x^2 + x.$

Find particular integrals of the following:

21. $\dfrac{d^2y}{dx^2} = 5y - 10x.$

22. $\dfrac{d^2y}{dx^2} = 5y - 10x - 5.$

23. $\dfrac{d^2y}{dx^2} = x - y.$

24. $\dfrac{d^2y}{dx^2} = x - y - 1.$

25. $\dfrac{d^2y}{dx^2} = 3y - x^2.$

26. $\dfrac{d^2y}{dx^2} = 3y - x^2 - 3x.$

27. $\dfrac{d^2y}{dx^2} = 5y - \sin x.$

28. $\dfrac{d^2y}{dx^2} = 5y - \cos x.$

29. $\dfrac{d^2y}{dx^2} = 5y - \cos x + \sin x.$

30. $\dfrac{d^2y}{dx^2} = y + 2\cos 2x - 3\sin 2x.$

Problems

The consideration of many physical and mechanical problems leads to a differential equation which must be integrated to find the solution of the problem. Examples are given below.

Example 1. *A body in a room of constant temperature 18°C starts at a temperature of 70°C and five minutes later its temperature is 57°C. Find its temperature after a further interval of five minutes.*

Newton's law of cooling states, that, if T is the temperature of a body above that of the surrounding air, the rate of decrease of T is proportional to T.

$$\therefore \quad \frac{dT}{dt} = -kT \quad \text{where } k \text{ is a constant to be determined.}$$

$$\therefore \quad \int \frac{dT}{T} = -k \int dt$$

or $\qquad \log T = C - kt.$

So $\qquad T = e^c\,e^{-kt}$

or $\qquad T = T_0\,e^{-kt}, \quad$ where T_0 is the excess temperature when $t = 0.$

$$\therefore \quad T = 52\,e^{-kt}.$$

When $\qquad t = 5,$

$$T = 57 - 18 = 39.$$

$$\therefore \quad 39 = 52\,e^{-5k} \quad \text{and} \quad e^{-5k} = \tfrac{3}{4}.$$

The excess temperature after 10 minutes is

$$52\,e^{-10k} = 52(e^{-5k})^2$$
$$= 52(\tfrac{3}{4})^2$$
$$= 29\tfrac{1}{4}.$$

The temperature of the body is $18° + 29\tfrac{1}{4}°$ or $47\tfrac{1}{4}°C.$

Example 2. *The leakage in an electric condenser is proportional to the charge. Find the charge after time t.*

If Q is the charge,

$$\frac{dQ}{dt} = -kQ.$$

$$\therefore \quad \int \frac{dQ}{Q} = k \int dt$$

and $\qquad \log Q = -kt + C.$

$$\therefore \quad Q = Q_0\,e^{-kt}, \quad \text{where } Q_0 \text{ is the initial charge.}$$

Example 3. *When a stone is thrown vertically upwards, the air resistance gives it a retardation of kv^2 g m s^{-2}, where v is the velocity in m s^{-1} and k is a constant. If the initial velocity of the stone is u, find the greatest height reached.*

The retardation due to gravity is g and so the total retardation is $g(1 + kv^2)$.

If x is the height of the stone at any time, the acceleration of the stone is $\dfrac{d^2x}{dt^2}$ in the direction of x increasing, i.e. upwards.

$$\therefore \quad \frac{d^2x}{dt^2} = -g(1 + kv^2)$$

But $\qquad \dfrac{d^2x}{dt^2} = v\dfrac{dv}{dx}$ and so $v\dfrac{dv}{dx} = -g(1 + kv^2)$.

$$\therefore \quad \int \frac{v\,dv}{1 + kv^2} = -g\int dx.$$

First method

The integral of the differential equation leads to

$$\frac{1}{2k}\ln(1 + kv^2) = -gx + C.$$

When $x = 0$, $v = u$.

$$\therefore \quad C = \frac{1}{2k}\ln(1 + ku^2).$$

$$\therefore \quad \frac{1}{2k}\ln(1 + kv^2) = \frac{1}{2k}\ln(1 + ku^2) - gx.$$

The greatest height corresponds to $v = 0$.

$$\therefore \quad gh = \frac{1}{2k}\ln(1 + ku^2)$$

and the greatest height is

$$\frac{1}{2kg}\ln(1 + ku^2) \text{ metres.}$$

Second method

When $x = 0$, $v = u$; when $v = 0$, $x = h$ (the greatest height).

Putting those corresponding values in the integral, we have

$$\int_u^0 \frac{v\,dv}{1 + kv^2} = -g\int_0^h dx.$$

$$\therefore \quad \left[\frac{1}{2k}\ln(1 + kv^2)\right]_u^0 = -g[x]_0^h.$$

$$\therefore \quad -\frac{1}{2k}\ln(1 + ku^2) = -gh$$

and the greatest height is $\dfrac{1}{2kg}\ln(1 + ku^2)$ metres.

Exercise 18.6: Miscellaneous

Solve the following equations:

1. $x\dfrac{dy}{dx} + y^2 = 1.$

2. $(x + a)\dfrac{dy}{dx} = y + b.$

3. $\tan y + x \sec^2 y \dfrac{dy}{dx} = 0.$

4. $\cos y - x \sin y \dfrac{dy}{dx} = 0.$

5. $x\dfrac{d^2 y}{dx^2} + \dfrac{dy}{dx} + 1 = 0.$

6. $\dfrac{d^2 y}{dx^2} + \left(\dfrac{dy}{dx}\right)^2 + a^2 = 0.$

7. $\dfrac{dy}{dx} = \dfrac{y + 4x}{y + x}.$

8. $(x^2 + y^2)\dfrac{dy}{dx} = xy.$

9. $x\dfrac{dy}{dx} - y = x^2.$

10. $\dfrac{dy}{dx} + y = e^{-x}.$

11. $xy + x = \dfrac{dy}{dx}.$

12. $y(x + 2)\dfrac{dy}{dx} = 1.$

13. $(ax + hy + g) + (hx + by + f)\dfrac{dy}{dx} = 0.$

14. $2y + x\dfrac{dy}{dx} = x^2.$

15. $\dfrac{d^2 y}{dx^2} = \sin 2x.$

16. $\dfrac{d^2 y}{dx^2} = 9y.$

17. $x\dfrac{d^2 y}{dx^2} = \dfrac{dy}{dx}.$

18. $\dfrac{d^2 y}{dx^2} + \dfrac{1}{x}\dfrac{dy}{dx} = 0.$

19. $\dfrac{d^2 y}{dx^2} = 3\dfrac{dy}{dx}.$

20. $\dfrac{dy}{dx} \cdot \dfrac{d^2 y}{dx^2} = 1.$

21. $\dfrac{d^2 y}{dx^2} = -4y.$

22. $x\dfrac{d^2 y}{dx^2} + \dfrac{dy}{dx} = x.$

23. $\dfrac{d^2 y}{dx^2} = 4y - 8.$

24. $\dfrac{d^2 y}{dx^2} = -4y + 8.$

25. $\dfrac{d^2 y}{dx^2} = -4y + 4x - 8.$

26. $\dfrac{d^2 y}{dx^2} = y + 10 \sin 3x.$

27. $\dfrac{d^2 y}{dx^2} + y = e^x.$

28. $\dfrac{d^2 y}{dx^2} + 4y = e^x.$

29. $\dfrac{d^2 y}{dx^2} + 16y = 16x^2.$

30. $\dfrac{d^2 y}{dx^2} - 16y = 16x^2.$

31. A particle is projected from the origin with velocity 8 m s^{-1} along the axis of x. Its acceleration is numerically equal to $4x$ m s^{-2} and is directed towards the origin. Find the amplitude of the motion.

32. With the data of question 31, find how long it is before the particle first reaches the point $x = 2$.

33. Find the periodic time of the motion defined in question 31.

34. A particle is projected from the origin with velocity 4 m s^{-1} along the axis of x. Its acceleration is $x \text{ m s}^{-2}$ away from the origin. Find the distance travelled in the first second.

35. In question 34, find the velocity of the particle after the first second.

36. In question 34, if $v \text{ m s}^{-1}$ is the velocity when the distance travelled is x m, show that $v^2 + 16$.

37. A liquid at temperature 60°C is placed in a room at 20°C. After 5 minutes its temperature is 40°C. Find the temperature after a further 5 minutes.

38. A liquid temperature 72°C is placed in a room at 25°C. After 5 minutes its temperature is 65°C. Find when its temperature is 57°C.

39. A stone is projected vertically upwards with velocity u. The retardation due to air resistance is kgv where k is a constant and v its velocity. Show that the time taken to reach the highest point is $\dfrac{1}{kg} \log (1 + ku)$.

40. In question 39, show that the velocity after time t is
$$\frac{(1 + ku) e^{-kgt} - 1}{k}.$$

41. The current C at time t in a conductor obeys the law $\dfrac{dC}{dt} + kC = 0$ where k is a constant. Initially $C = 10$ and after 1 sec, $C = 1$. Find the value of k.

42. In question 41, find the current after 2 seconds.

43. A particle moving along the axis of x satisfies the differential equation $\dfrac{d^2 x}{dt^2} + \dfrac{dx}{dt} - 2x = 0$. Show that $x = A e^t + B e^{-2t}$.

44. A particle is projected from the origin along the x-axis with velocity 3 m s^{-1}. It obeys the law $\dfrac{d^2 x}{dt^2} + \dfrac{dx}{dt} - 2x = 0$. Find the distance moved in t seconds.

45. In question 44, find the velocity after 1 second.

46. A particle under damped simple harmonic motion obeys the law $\dfrac{d^2 x}{dt^2} + 6 \dfrac{dx}{dt} + 13x = 0$. Show that $x = e^{-3t}(A \cos 2t + B \sin 2t)$.

47. A particle is projected from the origin along the x-axis with velocity 2 m s^{-1} and obeys the law $\dfrac{d^2 x}{dt^2} + 6 \dfrac{dx}{dt} + 13x = 0$. Find the distance travelled in t seconds.

48. In question 47, if the velocity after time t is zero, show that $\tan 2t = \frac{2}{3}$.

Revision Paper C1

1. A curve passes through the point $(2, 0)$ and its gradient at the point (x, y) is $x^2 - 2x$ for all values of x. Find the equation of the curve and the maximum and minimum values of y. (L.)

2. Find the maximum and minimum values (if any) of the expression $x^3 - 2x^2 + x + 7$. Sketch roughly the graph of this expression. (L.)

3. Sketch the graph of the polynomial $x^2(3x - 10)(x - 6)$ and calculate the coordinates of the turning points. (J.M.B.)

4. Write down the first four terms and the nth term in the series for e^x.
   (i) Defining $\sinh x$ and $\cosh x$ by the formulae
   $$\sinh x = \tfrac{1}{2}(e^x - e^{-x}), \quad \cosh x = \tfrac{1}{2}(e^x + e^{-x}),$$
   prove that $\cosh^2 x - \sinh^2 x = 1$, $\sinh 2x = 2 \sinh x \cosh x$.
   (ii) Find the first three terms in the expansion of $\ln (1 + e^x)$ as a series in ascending powers of x. (O. & C.)

5. Prove that $\dfrac{\sin 5\theta}{\sin \theta} - \dfrac{\cos 5\theta}{\cos \theta} = 4 \cos 2\theta$.

   By taking a particular value for θ, or otherwise, prove that $4 \cos 36° \cos 72° = 1$, and deduce that $\cos 36°$ is a root of the equation $8c^3 - 4c - 1 = 0$.

   By removing the factor $(2c + 1)$, obtain the value of $\cos 36°$ in surd form. (C.)

6. If I_n denotes $\displaystyle\int_0^a (a^2 - x^2)^n \, dx$, prove, if $n > 0$, $I_n = \dfrac{2na^2}{2n + 1} I_{n-1}$.

7. Show that, if $y = \dfrac{x^2 + 1}{x^2 - a^2}$, y takes all real values twice, except those

   for which $-\dfrac{1}{a^2} \leqslant y \leqslant 1$.

   Sketch the curve $y = \dfrac{x^2 + 1}{x^2 - 4}$, including its asymptotes. (C.)

8. If $y = (\cosh^{-1} x)^2$, show that
   $$(x^2 - 1)\frac{d^2y}{dx^2} + x\frac{dy}{dx} = 2.$$ (L.)

9. Integrate (i) $\sqrt{(4 + x^2)}$; (ii) $x^3 e^{-2x}$.

10. Solve the differential equations

    (i) $(x^2 - x)\dfrac{dy}{dx} = y$ where $y = 1$ when $x = 2$,

    (ii) $\cos x \dfrac{dy}{dx} + ny \sin x = \cos^{n+3} x$, where $y = 0$ when $x = 0$. (C.)

Revision Paper C2

1. (a) Find (i) $\int \dfrac{1+x}{\sqrt{(1-x)}}\,dx$, (ii) $\int \sin^3 x \cos^3 x\,dx$.

   (b) Find the value of a for which $\displaystyle\int_0^1 \dfrac{x-a}{(x+1)(3x+1)}\,dx = 0$. (J.M.B.)

2. Evaluate

   (a) $\displaystyle\int \dfrac{dx}{(2x-1)^3}$, (b) $\displaystyle\int \dfrac{x\,dx}{(x^2+1)^2}$, (c) $\displaystyle\int_0^{\pi/4} \cos 2x \sin x\,dx$. (L.)

3. For the curve $x = a\cos^3 t$, $y = a\sin^3 t$, prove that the length of any tangent intercepted between the two axes is constant.

   Sketch the curve and prove that the length of arc of one quadrant is $\dfrac{3a}{2}$.

   If the closed curve is rotated about either axis, prove that the area of the curved surface of the solid of revolution so formed is $\dfrac{12\pi a^2}{5}$. (L.)

4. Defining $\sinh\theta$, $\cosh\theta$, $\tanh\theta$ by the formulae $\sinh\theta = \frac{1}{2}(e^\theta - e^{-\theta})$, $\cosh\theta = \frac{1}{2}(e^\theta + e^{-\theta})$, $\tanh\theta = \dfrac{\sinh\theta}{\cosh\theta}$, prove that for any given θ, there is just one value of φ between $-\dfrac{\pi}{2}$ and $\dfrac{\pi}{2}$ such that

   $$\sin\varphi = \tanh\theta.$$

   Prove that $\tan\varphi = \sinh\theta$, $\sec\varphi = \cosh\theta$. (O. & C.)

5. Find the turning points of the curve $y = x^3 - x$.

   Sketch the curve and prove that the normals at the points A and B where the curve is again met by any line through the origin are parallel.

   If A is on the normal at the origin, find the length of AB. (L.)

6. (i) Evaluate $\displaystyle\int_0^4 \dfrac{x\,dx}{\sqrt{(2x+1)}}$.

   (ii) By means of the substitution $t = \tan x$, find

   $$\int \dfrac{dx}{\cos^2 x + 4\sin^2 x}.$$ (C.)

7. Prove that if $t = \tan\dfrac{\theta}{2}$ then $\sin\theta = \dfrac{2t}{1+t^2}$, $\cos\theta = \dfrac{1-t^2}{1+t^2}$.

   By expressing $\dfrac{3+\cos\theta}{\sin\theta}$ in terms of t, show that this expression cannot have any value between $-2\sqrt{2}$ and $+2\sqrt{2}$. (C.)

8. A sphere of radius r is cut into two portions by a plane which is distant c from the centre of the sphere. Show that the volume of the smaller of the two portions is $\frac{1}{3}\pi(r - c)^2(2r + c)$.

Show also that the distance of the centre of gravity of this portion from the centre of the sphere is $3(r + c)^2/4(2r + c)$.

Deduce the position of the centre of gravity of a uniform solid hemisphere. (C.)

9. Solve the differential equations

(i) $(1 + x)^2 \dfrac{dy}{dx} + y^2 = 1$,

(ii) $(1 + x^2) \dfrac{dy}{dx} + xy = 1 + x^2$. (C.)

10. If $p = \dfrac{dy}{dx}$, prove that $\dfrac{d^2 y}{dx^2} = p \dfrac{dp}{dy}$.

Hence solve the differential equation
$$y \frac{d^2 y}{dx^2} = 2 \frac{dy}{dx} + \left(\frac{dy}{dx}\right)^2.$$
(O. & C.)

Revision Paper C3

1. Solve the equations

   (i) $2y(x + 1)\dfrac{dy}{dx} = 4 + y^2$, given that $y = 2$ when $x = 3$,

   (ii) $y \cos^2 x \dfrac{dy}{dx} = \tan x + 2$, given that $y = 2$ when $x = \dfrac{\pi}{4}$.   (C.)

2. A uniform solid is formed by rotating the area below the curve $y = \sin x$ between the limits $x = 0$ and $x = \dfrac{\pi}{2}$ about the x-axis. Find the position of the centre of gravity of the solid.   (J.M.B.)

3. Prove that $1 + ax + a(a + 1)x^2 > 0$ for all real x provided that $a > 0$ or $a < -\frac{4}{3}$.

   Prove that $1 + ax + a(a + 1)x^2 + bx^2 > 0$ for all real x and all real a provided $b > \frac{1}{3}$.   (O. & C.)

4. Determine the coordinates of the points of maximum or minimum gradient on the curve $y = 48x^2 - 8x^4$ and calculate the area of the triangle formed by the tangents at these points and the x-axis.   (J.M.B.)

5. Investigate the stationary points of the curve $y = x^3(x - 2)$. Draw a rough sketch.

6. By means of the substitution $x = \dfrac{\pi}{2} - y$, prove that

$$\int_0^{\pi/2} \frac{\cos x}{\cos x + \sin x}\, dx = \int_0^{\pi/2} \frac{\sin x}{\cos x + \sin x}\, dx.$$

   By considering the sum of these integrals, determine their common value.   (J.M.B.)

7. Find the value of the integral $y = \displaystyle\int_0^x (x - 1)(x - 2)\, dx$.

   Find the maximum and minimum values of y, and sketch on the same diagram the graphs of y and $(x - 1)(x - 2)$ for values of x from 0 to 3.   (L.)

8. Prove by means of suitable substitutions that each of the integrals

$$\int_0^1 \frac{x^2}{(1 + x^2)^2}\, dx, \quad \int_0^{1/\sqrt{2}} \frac{x^2}{\sqrt{(1 - x^2)}}\, dx, \quad \int_{1/\sqrt{2}}^1 \sqrt{(1 - x^2)}\, dx$$

   is equal to $\displaystyle\int_0^{\pi/4} \sin^2 \theta\, d\theta$ and find the value of the integrals.   (J.M.B.)

9. By means of the substitution $x = 3 + \sin \theta$, evaluate

$$\int_2^4 \sqrt{[(4 - x)(x - 2)]}\, dx.$$

By considering the nature of the curve $y^2 = (4 - x)(x - 2)$, apply a geometric check to your result.   (C.)

10. Give a rough sketch of the curve $y^2 x = (2a - x)(x - a)^2$ and prove that the area of its loop is $\frac{1}{2}a^2(4 - \pi)$.   (O. & C.)

Revision Paper C4

1. Sketch the curve $y^2 = \dfrac{x}{2-x}$.

   Find the area bounded by the curve, the axis of y and the line $y = 1$.

   If the portion of the curve in the first quadrant between $x = 0$ and $x = 1$ perform a complete revolution about the axis of x, prove that the volume generated is $\pi(2\log 2 - 1)$. (J.M.B.)

2. A segment of a circle of radius a is revolved through four right angles about the chord by which it is bounded. Prove that the volume so formed is $2\pi a^3(\sin \alpha - \tfrac{1}{3}\sin^3 \alpha - \alpha \cos \alpha)$ where 2α is the angle subtended by the chord at the centre of the circle. (L.)

3. A particle moves along the axis of x so that its displacement from the origin t seconds after starting is given by the formula $x = a\log\cosh kt$ where a and k are constants. Find the velocity and acceleration of the particle in terms of t and prove that the acceleration can be regarded as the resultant of a constant acceleration ak^2 and a variable retardation proportional to the square of the velocity.

   Prove that the velocity of the particle never exceeds ak and that, at the instant when the velocity is $\tfrac{1}{2}ak$, the distance which the particle has travelled is $\tfrac{1}{2}a(\log 4 - \log 3)$. (O. & C.)

4. Prove that
   (i) $\cosh^{-1} x = \pm\log[x + \sqrt{(x^2 - 1)}]$;
   (ii) the area enclosed by the curve $y^2(x^2 - 2x - 3) = 1$ and the lines $x = 3\tfrac{1}{2}, x = 5$ is $2\log\dfrac{2 + \sqrt{3}}{2}$. (C.)

5. (i) Find $\displaystyle\int \frac{1 + x}{1 + \cos x}\,dx$ and $\displaystyle\int \frac{x + 1}{x^2(x^2 + 1)}\,dx$.

   (ii) Evaluate $\displaystyle\int_0^1 x^2(1 - x)^{\frac{1}{2}}\,dx$. (C.)

6. Express $\dfrac{(x - 2)(x + 1)}{(x - 3)(x + 2)}$ in the form $A + \dfrac{B}{x - 3} + \dfrac{C}{x + 2}$, where A, B, C are constants. Hence, or otherwise, show that the gradient of the graph of $y = \dfrac{(x - 2)(x + 1)}{(x - 3)(x + 2)}$ is positive when $x < \tfrac{1}{2}$ and negative when $x > \tfrac{1}{2}$.

   Find the range of values of x for which $y > 0$.

   Use these data to draw a rough sketch of the curve.

   By means of the graph, or otherwise, prove that the equation $x^2(x - 3)(x + 2) - (x - 2)(x + 1) = 0$ has four real roots. (O. & C.)

7. Prove that the expansion of $(1 + x)^2 \ln(1 + x)$ as far as the term in x^4 is $x + \tfrac{3}{2}x^2 + \tfrac{1}{3}x^3 - \tfrac{1}{12}x^4$.

8. Solve the differential equations

(i) $\dfrac{dy}{dx} - (1 + \cot x)y = 0;$ (ii) $\dfrac{d^2y}{dx^2} + 9y = 18.$ (O. & C.)

9. Sketch the curve given by $a^2y^2 = x^2(4a^2 - x^2)$ and prove that the area of one of its loops is $\frac{16}{3}a^2$.

The area bounded by the arc of this curve in the first quadrant from $x = 0$ to $x = a\sqrt{3}$ and the line $y = x$ is rotated through four right angles about the x-axis. Show that the volume generated is $\dfrac{6\sqrt{3}\pi a^3}{5}$. (J.M.B.)

10. Evaluate $\displaystyle\int_1^e \dfrac{\ln x}{x^2}\,dx.$

Revision Paper C5

1. Find $\int x^3 \tan^{-1} x \, dx$.

2. Find the coordinates of the centre of gravity of the area of the half loop of the curve $a^2 y^2 = x^2(a^2 - x^2)$ in the positive quadrant. Also find the volume obtained by rotating the whole of the loop about the x-axis.

(O. & C.)

3. Calculate the volume traced out by rotating through four right angles about the x-axis, the area bounded by

   (i) the curve $y = \tan x$ and the lines $x = 0$, $x = \dfrac{\pi}{4}$;

   (ii) the curve $y = \tan x$ and the chord $y = \dfrac{4x}{\pi}$ where $0 \leqslant x \leqslant \dfrac{\pi}{4}$.

(L.)

4. A uniform solid is formed by rotating the area below the curve $y = \sin x$ between the limits $x = 0$ and $x = \dfrac{\pi}{2}$ about the x-axis. Find the position of the centre of gravity of the solid.

(J.M.B.)

5. (a) Find $\int \dfrac{dx}{x^2(x + 1)}$.

   (b) By means of the substitution $t = \tan \dfrac{x}{2}$, find the value of

   $$\int_0^{\pi/2} \frac{dx}{3 + 5 \cos x}.$$

(C.)

6. Prove that, if a, b, c are real, the roots α, β of the equation
   $$4(a - y)(c - y) - b^2 = 0$$
   are real.

   Prove that for the quadratic equation in x
   $$ax^2 + bx + c - y(x^2 + 1) = 0$$
   to have real roots, y must have a value in the interval from α to β.

7. Use Maclaurin's series to find the first three non-zero terms in each of the expansions of $\sin x$ and $\cos x$ in ascending powers of x.
   Hence show that if x is small
   $$\frac{2x - 3 \sin x + x \cos x}{x^3(1 - \cos 2x)}$$
   is approximately equal to $\frac{1}{120}$.

(C.)

8. Evaluate the integrals

   (i) $\displaystyle\int_0^2 \frac{dx}{x^2 + 4}$, (ii) $\displaystyle\int_2^3 \frac{x \, dx}{(x + 3)(x - 1)}$, (iii) $\displaystyle\int_0^{\pi/4} \cos^3 x \, dx$,

   (iv) $\displaystyle\int_0^{\pi/4} \cos^2 2x \, dx$.

9. Find the values of the constants A, B, C, D which satisfy the identity

$$\frac{1 + 2x^3}{(1 - x)(1 + x)^2} \equiv A + \frac{B}{1 - x} + \frac{C}{(1 + x)^2} + \frac{D}{1 + x}$$

and hence evaluate $\displaystyle\int_0^{1/2} \frac{1 + 2x^3}{(1 - x)(1 + x)^2} \, dx.$ (L.)

10. (i) If $y = \sin (m \sin^{-1} x)$, prove that

$$(1 - x^2)\frac{d^2y}{dx^2} - x\frac{dy}{dx} + m^2y = 0.$$

(ii) Find $\displaystyle\int \log x \, dx$ and $\displaystyle\int e^x \sin 2x \, dx.$

(iii) Evaluate $\displaystyle\int_0^1 x^3(1 - x^2)^{\frac{1}{2}} \, dx.$ (L.)

19 Polar Coordinates

We have seen that the position of a point in a plane can be determined by reference to two axes (usually perpendicular); these are called Cartesian coordinates, after Rene Descartes, the French mathematician and philosopher (1596–1650). Another method of describing the position of a point in a plane is to refer the position of the point to a fixed point, O, the pole, and a base line passing through O. The

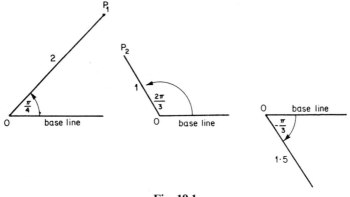

Fig. 19.1

coordinates of the point are the distance r of the point P from O, and the angle θ made by OP with the base line. Figure 19.1 illustrates the position of three points and their polar coordinates that describe those positions.

Almost invariably we measure the angle θ in radians, and we notice that although the coordinates of a point determine that point uniquely, the position of any one point P does not necessarily determine the coordinates, for P_1 in Fig. 19.1 (a) can have coordinates $(2, \pi/4)$, $(2, 9\pi/4)$, $(2, 17\pi/4)$ etc. Usually, though not always, r is positive, so it would even be possible to describe the position of P by the coordinates $(-2, 5\pi/4)$, etc.

Curves in polar coordinates

Try to *think* in polar coordinates, as we *think* in cartesian coordinates. The straight line $x = 2$ passes through all points whose x coordinate is 2; the curve $r = 2$ passes through all points whose distance from the pole is 2 units. The straight line through O making an angle θ with the base line is such that all points on that line have the property $\theta = \alpha$, so the equation of the line is $\theta = \alpha$.

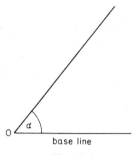

Fig. 19.2

Looking at Fig. 19.3, we see that if the perpendicular distance of the straight line from the pole O is p, all points on the line have the property that $r \sin (\alpha - \theta) = p$, and so that is one form for the equation of the line. The curve described by the equation $r = a(1 + \cos \theta)$

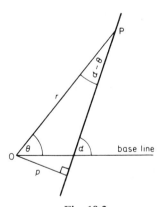

Fig. 19.3

passes through the point whose distance from O is $2a$ when $\theta = 0$, i.e. when it crosses the base line, r decreases as θ increases, becoming equal to a when $\theta = \pi/2$, then 0 when $\theta = \pi$. As θ increases from π to 2π r increases from 0 to $2a$, so that the shape of the curve is roughly that in Fig. 19.4. The curve is called a cardioid, and is sketched in greater detail on page 271.

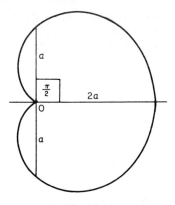

Fig. 19.4

Similarly, the curve $r = a\theta$ is such that when $\theta = 0$, $r = 0$, so that it passes through the pole, and r increases linearly with θ. When $\theta = 2\pi$, $r = 2\pi a$, and for each increase of 2π in θ, r increases by $2\pi a$, so that

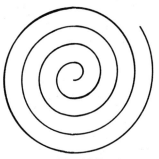

Fig. 19.5

the curve is a spiral of uniform thickness*, whereas $r = a\,e^{\theta}$ also has the property that r increases as θ increases, but as θ increases by 2π r is multiplied by the factor $e^{2\pi}$, so that this curve is a spiral** but one in which the thickness increases as θ increases.

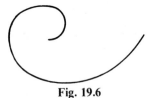

Fig. 19.6

* The spiral of Archimedes.
** An equiangular spiral, as it can be shown that the angle between OP and this tangent at P is constant.

Although with practice we should come to *sketch* curves given their polar equations, at first it may help to calculate the values of r from values of θ at convenient intervals, as in this example.

Example. *Sketch the curve* $r = 1 + \cos \theta$.

Consider θ at intervals of $\dfrac{\pi}{6}$ from 0 to 2π.

θ	0	$\dfrac{\pi}{6}$	$\dfrac{\pi}{3}$	$\dfrac{\pi}{2}$	$\dfrac{2\pi}{3}$	$\dfrac{5\pi}{6}$	π
$\cos \theta$	1	0.87	0.5	0	-0.5	-0.87	-1
$r = 1 + \cos \theta$	2	1.87	1.5	1	0.5	0.13	0

θ		$\dfrac{7\pi}{6}$	$\dfrac{4\pi}{3}$	$\dfrac{3\pi}{2}$	$\dfrac{5\pi}{3}$	$\dfrac{11\pi}{6}$	2π
$\cos \theta$		-0.87	-0.5	0	0.5	0.87	1
$r = 1 + \cos \theta$		0.13	0.5	1	1.5	1.87	2

The curve, a cardioid, is shown in Fig. 19.7.

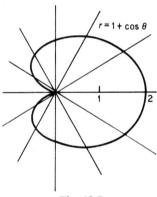

$r = 1 + \cos \theta$

Fig. 19.7

The fact that when $\theta = \pi$, $r = 0$ shows that the tangent at the origin is the line $\theta = \pi$.

Curve sketching

It is often easy to find the value of r when $\theta = 0$, and then to see whether r increases or decreases as θ increases. If r decreases, we shall usually be able to find when it is zero, or the least value of r if it never becomes zero, and the values of θ, if any, for which r is zero.

Example. *Sketch the curve* $r = a \cos 4\theta$, *for* $0 \leqslant \theta \leqslant 2\pi$.

When $\theta = 0$, $r = a$.

When $r = 0$, $\cos 4\theta = 0$, i.e. $4\theta = \dfrac{\pi}{2}, \dfrac{3\pi}{2}, \dfrac{5\pi}{2} \ldots$

i.e. $\qquad\qquad\qquad \theta = \dfrac{\pi}{8}, \quad \dfrac{3\pi}{8}, \quad \dfrac{5\pi}{8} \ldots\ldots$

When $\dfrac{\pi}{8} < \theta < \dfrac{3\pi}{8}$, $\cos 4\theta$ is negative, and the curve for $0 \leqslant \theta \leqslant \dfrac{\pi}{2}$ is shown in
Fig. 19.8(a), and the curve for $0 \leqslant \theta \leqslant 2\pi$ in Fig. 19.8(b).

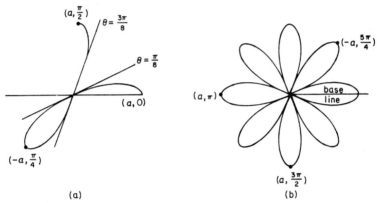

(a)   (b)

Fig. 19.8

Example. *Sketch the curve* $r = \dfrac{a}{\sqrt{\cos 2\theta}}$ *for* $0 \leqslant \theta \leqslant 2\pi$.

In this example, when $\theta = 0$, $r = a$, but as θ increases, r increases, becoming
infinite when $\theta = \dfrac{\pi}{4}$, so that $\theta = \dfrac{\pi}{4}$ is an asymptote. When $\dfrac{\pi}{4} < \theta < \dfrac{3\pi}{4}$ $\cos 2\theta$
is   negative,   so   that   there   is   no   part   of   the   curve   for
$\dfrac{\pi}{4} < \theta < \dfrac{3\pi}{4}$. When $\theta = \dfrac{3\pi}{4}$, r is again infinite so that $\theta = \dfrac{3\pi}{4}$ is an asymptote.

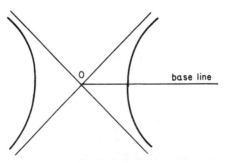

Fig. 19.9

When $\theta = \pi, r = a$, so that the curve decreases to the value a, then increases again to become infinite when $\theta = \dfrac{5\pi}{4}$. When $\dfrac{5\pi}{4} < \theta < \dfrac{7\pi}{4}$, again there is no value for r, and the shape of the curve is shown in Fig. 19.9. This is a rectangular hyperbola.

Notice that if we had had the equation $r^2 = \dfrac{a}{\cos 2\theta}$ we should have had two values for r for each value of θ, and the curve would have been completely described by taking θ in the interval $0 < \theta < \pi$.

Exercise 19.1

1. Plot the points whose polar coordinates are

   (i) $(1, 0)$,   (ii) $\left(2, \dfrac{\pi}{6}\right)$,   (iii) $\left(3, \dfrac{5\pi}{6}\right)$,

   (iv) $\left(1.5, \dfrac{5\pi}{3}\right)$,   (v) $\left(1, -\dfrac{\pi}{4}\right)$.

2. Sketch the curves whose equations are

   (i) $r = 1$,

   (ii) $\theta = \dfrac{\pi}{2}$, r being only positive,

   (iii) $\theta = \dfrac{\pi}{3}$, r being only negative,

   (iv) $r = 1, \dfrac{\pi}{4} < \theta < \dfrac{5\pi}{4}$,

   (v) $r \sin\left(\dfrac{\pi}{4} - \theta\right) = 2$.

3. Use trigonometry to show that $r = a \cos \theta$ describes a circle, centre $(\tfrac{1}{2}a, 0)$, radius $\tfrac{1}{2}a$.

4. Plot points at convenient intervals of θ, and so draw the graphs of the following:

   (i) $r = 1 + \sin \theta$,   (ii) $r = 1 + 2 \sin \theta$,

   (iii) $r = \sin 2\theta$,   (iv) $r^2 = \dfrac{1}{\sin 2\theta}$,

   (v) $r = \dfrac{1}{1 + 2 \cos \theta}$.

5. Sketch the following curves:

   (i) $r = 2 + \sin \theta$,   (ii) $r = 2 + 3 \cos \theta$,
   (iii) $r = 3 + 2 \cos \theta$,   (iv) $r = \sin 3\theta$,

   (v) $r = \dfrac{1}{2 + \cos \theta}$.

Relation between polar and cartesian coordinates

We take the base line of polar coordinates as the x-axis, and the line perpendicular to it through the pole as the y-axis, as shown in Fig. 19.10. Then we see that

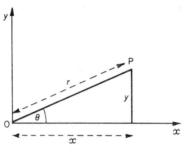

Fig. 19.10

$$x = r \cos \theta,$$
$$y = r \sin \theta,$$

and so any cartesian equation can easily be expressed in polar form.

Example. *Find the polar equation of the curve whose cartesian equation is* $x^2 - y^2 = a^2$.

Writing $x = r \cos \theta$, $y = r \sin \theta$, we have
$$r^2(\cos^2 \theta - \sin^2 \theta) = a^2,$$
i.e. $r^2 \cos 2\theta = a^2$, the rectangular hyperbola we met on page 272.

To change polar equations into cartesian, we see that
$$r^2 = x^2 + y^2$$
and
$$\theta = \tan^{-1}\left(\frac{y}{r}\right).$$

These are often more cumbersome to change, unless we can find expressions containing only $r \cos \theta$ and $r \sin \theta$.

Example 2. *Find the cartesian equation of the curve given in polar form* $r \sin (\alpha - \theta) = p$.

Since $r \sin (\alpha - \theta) = r \sin \alpha \cos \theta - r \cos \alpha \sin \theta$, the equation is
$$r \sin \alpha \cos \theta - r \cos \alpha \sin \theta = p,$$
i.e.
$$x \sin \alpha - y \cos \alpha = p,$$
a straight line.

Exercise 19.2

Express the following in polar form.

1. $x + y = 1$.
2. $xy = c^2$.

6. $x^2 + y^2 = 2x$.
7. $x^2 = y$.

3. $x = 4$.

4. $y = 2$.

5. $3x + 4y = 5$.

Express the following in cartesian form.

11. $r = 2a$.

12. $r^2 = 2r \cos \theta + 1$.

13. $r^2 = 3 - 2r \sin \theta$.

14. $r \cos \theta + 2r \sin \theta = 1$.

15. $r^2 \sin 2\theta = 1$.

8. $4x^2 + y^2 = 1$.

9. $x^2 + y^2 = 3xy$.

10. $xy = (x^2 + y^2)^2$.

16. $r^2 \cos 2\theta = 1$.

17. $r^2 = \cos 2\theta$.

18. $r^2 = a^2 \sin 2\theta$.

19. $\theta = \dfrac{\pi}{4}$.

20. $r \cos 2\theta$.

Area of sector

To find the area of a sector between the radii $\theta = \alpha$ and β consider an elemental sector as shown in Fig. 19.11.

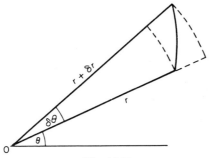

Fig. 19.11

If the area of this element is δA, it will lie in area between two isosceles triangles of sides r and $(r + \delta r)$ as indicated.

Therefore $\qquad \frac{1}{2}r^2 \sin \delta\theta < \delta A < \frac{1}{2}(r + \delta r)^2 \sin \delta\theta$

or $\qquad \frac{1}{2}r^2 \dfrac{\sin \delta\theta}{\delta\theta} < \dfrac{\delta A}{\delta\theta} < \frac{1}{2}(r + \delta r)^2 \dfrac{\sin \delta\theta}{\delta\theta}$.

Since $\dfrac{\sin \delta\theta}{\delta\theta} \to 1$ as $\delta\theta \to 0$, both upper and lower limits are equal to $\frac{1}{2}r^2$.

$$\therefore \quad \frac{dA}{d\theta} = \frac{1}{2}r^2 \quad \text{and} \quad A = \frac{1}{2} \int_\alpha^\beta r^2 \, d\theta.$$

Example 1. *The equation of a circle is $r = a$. Find its area.*

The area of the circle $= \frac{1}{2} \displaystyle\int_0^{2\pi} r^2 \, d\theta$

$$= \frac{1}{2}a^2 \int_0^{2\pi} d\theta = \pi a^2.$$

Example 2. *Find the area of the cardioid* $r = a(1 + \cos \theta)$.

$$A = \tfrac{1}{2} \int_0^{2\pi} r^2 \, d\theta = \frac{a^2}{2} \int_0^{2\pi} (1 + \cos \theta)^2 \, d\theta$$

$$= \frac{a^2}{2} \int_0^{2\pi} (1 + 2\cos \theta + \cos^2 \theta) \, d\theta.$$

But $\quad \displaystyle\int_0^{2\pi} 1 \, d\theta = [\theta]_0^{2\pi} = 2\pi; \quad \int_0^{2\pi} \cos \theta \, d\theta = [\sin \theta]_0^{2\pi} = 0;$

$$\int_0^{2\pi} \cos^2 \theta \, d\theta = 4 \int_0^{\pi/2} \cos^2 \theta \, d\theta = 4 \cdot \frac{1}{2} \cdot \frac{\pi}{2} = \pi.$$

$$\therefore \quad A = \frac{a^2}{2} (2\pi + \pi) = \frac{3\pi a^2}{2}.$$

Centre of gravity of sector and volume of revolution

The centre of gravity of an elemental sector approximately in the shape of a triangle is $\tfrac{2}{3}r$ from O and the moment of the sector about the y-axis is $\rho(\tfrac{1}{2}r^2 \, \delta\theta)\tfrac{2}{3}r \cos \theta$.

This equals the moment of the whole area about the y-axis.

$$\therefore \quad \rho A \bar{x} = \int_\alpha^\beta \tfrac{1}{3} \rho r^3 \cos \theta \, d\theta$$

or

$$A\bar{x} = \tfrac{1}{3} \int_\alpha^\beta r^3 \cos \theta \, d\theta.$$

Similarly

$$A\bar{y} = \tfrac{1}{3} \int_\alpha^\beta r^3 \sin \theta \, d\theta.$$

Using Pappus' theorem, the volume obtained by revolving this area about the axis is equal to the area multiplied by the distance moved by the C.G. of the area.

$$\therefore \quad V = A(2\pi \bar{y})$$

$$= \frac{2\pi}{3} \int_\alpha^\beta r^3 \sin \theta \, d\theta.$$

Example. *Find the coordinates of the C.G. of the upper half of the cardioid* $r = a(1 + \cos \theta)$ *and also the volume obtained by rotating this area about the axis.*

We have already shown that the area of the cardioid is $\dfrac{3\pi a^2}{2}$. If A is the area of the upper half,

$$A = \frac{3\pi a^2}{4}.$$

$$\therefore \quad \frac{3\pi a^2}{4} \bar{x} = \tfrac{1}{3} \int_0^\pi r^3 \cos \theta \, d\theta$$

$$= \tfrac{1}{3}a^3 \int_0^\pi (1 + \cos \theta)^3 \cos \theta \, d\theta$$

$$= \tfrac{1}{3}a^3 \int_0^\pi (\cos \theta + 3 \cos^2 \theta + 3 \cos^3 \theta + \cos^4 \theta) \, d\theta.$$

But $\displaystyle \int_0^\pi \cos \theta \, d\theta = \int_0^\pi \cos^3 \theta \, d\theta = 0.$ (Since $\displaystyle \int_0^\pi \cos^{2n+1} \theta \, d\theta = 0$).

$$\int_0^\pi \cos^2 \theta \, d\theta = 2 \int_0^{\pi/2} \cos^2 \theta \, d\theta = 2 \cdot \frac{1}{2} \cdot \frac{\pi}{2} = \frac{\pi}{2}.$$

$$\int_0^\pi \cos^4 \theta \, d\theta = 2 \int_0^{\pi/2} \cos^4 \theta \, d\theta = 2 \cdot \frac{3}{4} \cdot \frac{1}{2} \cdot \frac{\pi}{2} = \frac{3\pi}{8}.$$

$$\therefore \quad \frac{3\pi a^2}{4} \bar{x} = \tfrac{1}{3}a^3 \left(\frac{3\pi}{2} + \frac{3\pi}{8} \right) = \tfrac{1}{3}a^3 \cdot \frac{15\pi}{8} = \frac{5\pi a^3}{8}.$$

$$\therefore \quad \bar{x} = \frac{5a}{6}.$$

Also

$$\frac{3\pi a^2}{4} \bar{y} = \tfrac{1}{3} \int_0^\pi r^3 \sin \theta \, d\theta$$

$$= \tfrac{1}{3}a^3 \int_0^\pi (1 + \cos \theta)^3 \sin \theta \, d\theta$$

$$= -\tfrac{1}{3}a^3 \int_0^\pi (1 + \cos \theta)^3 \, d(1 + \cos \theta)$$

$$= -\tfrac{1}{3}a^3 \left[\frac{(1 + \cos \theta)^4}{4} \right]_0^\pi$$

$$= \tfrac{4}{3}a^3.$$

$$\therefore \quad \bar{y} = \frac{16a}{9\pi}.$$

The volume of rotation $= 2\pi A \bar{y} = 2\pi \cdot \dfrac{3\pi a^2}{4} \cdot \dfrac{16a}{9\pi}$

$$= \frac{8\pi a^3}{3}.$$

Length of arc

We have already shown that $(ds)^2 = (dx)^2 + (dy)^2$.

Using $\qquad\qquad x = r \cos \theta \quad$ and $\quad y = r \sin \theta,$

$$dx = dr \cos \theta - r \sin \theta \, d\theta$$

and $\qquad\qquad dy = dr \sin \theta + r \cos \theta \, d\theta.$

$$\therefore \quad (dx)^2 + (dy)^2 = dr^2 + (r \, d\theta)^2$$

and so $\qquad\qquad (ds)^2 = (dr)^2 + (r \, d\theta)^2.$

$$\therefore \quad \left(\frac{ds}{d\theta} \right)^2 = \left(\frac{dr}{d\theta} \right)^2 + r^2$$

and $\qquad\qquad s = \int \sqrt{ \left[\left(\frac{dr}{d\theta} \right)^2 + r^2 \right] } \, d\theta.$

Example. *Find the length of the arc of the cardioid* $r = a(1 + \cos \theta)$.

$$\frac{dr}{d\theta} = -a \sin \theta.$$

$$r^2 + \left(\frac{dr}{d\theta}\right)^2 = a^2(2 + 2\cos\theta) = 4a^2 \cos^2 \frac{\theta}{2}.$$

$$\therefore \quad s = 2 \int_0^\pi 2a \cos \frac{\theta}{2} \, d\theta$$

$$= \left[8a \sin \frac{\theta}{2} \right]_0^\pi$$

$$= 8a.$$

Exercise 19.3

1. Find the area of the curve $r = a\, e^\theta$ between $\theta = 0$ and $\theta = 1$.
2. Find the length of the arc of the cycloid $x = a(\theta + \sin \theta)$, $y = a(1 + \cos \theta)$ between $\theta = 0$ and $\theta = \pi$.
3. Find the length of the equiangular spiral $r = a\, e^{\theta \cot \alpha}$ between the points (r_1, θ_1) and (r_2, θ_2).
4. Prove that $r^2 \, d\theta = x \, dy - y \, dx$ and hence that the area of a sector expressed in cartesian coordinates is $\frac{1}{2} \int (x \, dy - y \, dx)$.
5. Find the area of the parabola $r(1 + \cos \theta) = 2a$ between the radii $\theta = \frac{\pi}{4}$ and $\theta = \frac{3\pi}{4}$.
6. Find the position of the centre of gravity of an arc of a circle of radius r which subtends an angle 2α at the centre of the circle.
7. Find the position of the centre of gravity of a sector of a circle of radius r and angle 2α.
8. Find the area of a loop of the curve $r^2 = a^2 \sin \theta$.
9. Find the surface area formed by rotating one arch of the cycloid $x = a(\theta + \sin \theta)$, $y = a(1 + \cos \theta)$ about the x-axis.
10. Find the area of the curve $r = 2a \cos \theta$.
11. Find the total length of the curve $r = 2a \cos \theta$.
12. Sketch the curve $r = a \sin 2\theta$ and find the area of one of its loops.
13. Find the area enclosed by the curve $r = a(1 + \cos \theta)$.
14. Find the length of arc of the curve $r = a(1 - \cos \theta)$.
15. Find the area of the sector of the curve $r\theta = a$ between $\theta = \frac{\pi}{4}$ and $\theta = \frac{\pi}{2}$.
16. Find the area of the curve $r^2 = a^2 \cos 2\theta$.
17. Find the coordinates of the C.G. of the loop of the curve $r = a \cos 2\theta$ which passes through the point $r = a$, $\theta = 0$.
18. Find the volume obtained by rotating the region of question 17 about the axis.

19. Find the length of the arc of the curve $r = a\,e^{\theta}$ between $\theta = 0$ and $\theta = \pi$.

20. Find the total length of the curve $r = \sin\theta$.

Exercise 19.4: Miscellaneous

1. Sketch the curve $r\cos\theta = a$ for values of θ between $\pm\dfrac{\pi}{2}$.

2. Sketch the curve $r\cos\theta = a + b\cos\theta$ for values of θ between $\pm\dfrac{\pi}{2}$.

3. Find the cartesian equation of the curve $r\cos\theta = a + b\cos\theta$.

4. Find the polar equation of the curve $(x^2 + y^2)^2 = x^2$. Hence sketch the curve.

5. Find the polar equation of the curve $x = 1 - m^2$, $y = m - m^3$.

6. Find the polar equation of the curve.
$$x = a(1 + \cos t), \quad y = a\sin t.$$

7. By using cartesian coordinates show that the components of velocity of a particle along and perpendicular to the radius are $\dot{r}$ and $r\dot{\theta}$.

8. Show that
$$\ddot{x} = \ddot{r}\cos\theta - 2\dot{r}\dot{\theta}\sin\theta - r\cos\theta\,\dot{\theta}^2 - r\sin\theta\,\ddot{\theta}$$
and
$$\ddot{y} = \ddot{r}\sin\theta + 2\dot{r}\dot{\theta}\cos\theta - r\sin\theta\,\dot{\theta}^2 + r\cos\theta\,\ddot{\theta}.$$

9. Using the results of question 8, show that the components of acceleration along and perpendicular to the radius are $\ddot{r} - r\dot{\theta}^2$ and $2\dot{r}\dot{\theta} + r\ddot{\theta}$.

10. If a particle is moving under the action of a force towards the pole, show that $2\dot{r}\dot{\theta} + r\ddot{\theta} = 0$.

11. Find the polar equation of the ellipse $\dfrac{x^2}{a^2} + \dfrac{y^2}{b^2} = 1$. Hence find the area of the ellipse.

12. Sketch the curve $r^2 = a^2\sin 2\theta$ and find the area of one of its loops.

13. Find the area of the sector of the hyperbola $r^2\sin 2\theta = 2c^2$ between the radii $\theta = \dfrac{\pi}{6}$ and $\theta = \dfrac{\pi}{4}$.

14. Sketch the curve $r = 1 + 2\cos\theta$ which consists of two loops, one inside the other.

15. Find the area of the inner loop in question 14.

16. Find the distance from the origin of the centre of gravity of one loop of the curve $r^2 = a^2\cos 2\theta$.

17. Show that the equation $r(a\cos\theta + b\sin\theta) = c$ represents a straight line.

18. Sketch the curve $r = a(3 + 4\cos\theta)$.

19. For the curve $r = a\sin 2\theta$, show that
$$\left(\frac{ds}{d\theta}\right)^2 = a^2(1 + 3\cos^2 2\theta).$$

20. Show that the length of arc of the curve $r = a\sec\theta$ between $\theta = \alpha$ and $\theta = \beta$ is $a(\tan\beta - \tan\alpha)$.
Give a geometrical explanation.

20 Complex Numbers

Extending a system of numbers

If we only 'know' of positive integers, we can solve the equation $2x = 6$ but not the equation $2x = -6$. We may say that the equation $2x = 6$ has a solution in the set of positive integers $\mathbb{Z}_+$. If we extend our number system by introducing negative integers we can now solve the equation $2x = -6$, so that we may say that the equation $2x = -6$ has a solution in the set of integers $\mathbb{Z}$. Similarly the equation $2x = 5$ has no solution in the set of integers, but has a solution if we extend our number system by the introduction of rationals, e.g. $\frac{5}{2}$, so that $2x = 5$ has a solution in the set of all rationals $\mathbb{Q}$. Similarly, $x^2 = 9$ has a solution in the set of integers $\mathbb{Z}$, but $x^2 = -9$ has no solution in the set of rationals, the set of irrationals, or any of the sets of numbers we have met so far.

The set $\mathbb{C}$ of complex numbers

If we extend our number system to enable us to solve equations like $x^2 = -9$, we see that equations $x^2 = -16$, $x^2 = -17$, $4x^2 = -19$ all have solutions that we can express as multiples of $\sqrt{(-1)}$, which we usually denote by i.* Thus

$$x^2 = -9 \Rightarrow x = 3i \quad \text{or} \quad -3i,$$
$$x^2 = -17 \Rightarrow x = i\sqrt{17} \quad \text{or} \quad -i\sqrt{17}$$
and $\quad x^2 + 4x + 13 = 0 \Rightarrow (x + 2)^2 = -9$
$$\Rightarrow x = -2 + 3i \quad \text{or} \quad -2 - 3i.$$

Numbers of the form $a + ib$, e.g. $2 + 3i$ are called complex numbers. a is usually called the 'real' part, b the 'imaginary' part. If $b = 0$, the number is said to be wholly real; if $a = 0$, the number is wholly 'imaginary'.

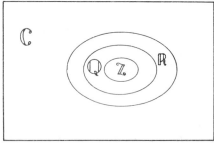

Fig. 20.1

* We use i to denote the positive square root of -1.

It was proved by Gauss (1777–1855) that all polynomials can be solved in $\mathbb{C}$, even polynomials with complex coefficients, and it can also be shown that equations like $10^x = -2$ and $\sin x = 2$ have solutions in $\mathbb{C}$.

Operations on complex numbers

Two complex numbers $a + ib$ and $c + id$ are equal only if $a = c$ and $b = d$. Addition and subtraction are defined by

$$(a + ib) + (c + id) = (a + c) + i(b + d)$$
$$(a + ib) - (c + id) = (a - c) + i(b - d),$$

and multiplication by

$$(a + ib)(c + id) = (ac - bd) + i(bc + ad).$$

We can see that 0 is the identity element under addition, and 1 is the identity element under multiplication.

Although we can divide 'by inspection',

e.g.
$$\frac{2 + 2i}{1 + i} = \frac{2(1 + i)}{1 + i} = 2$$

and
$$\frac{-2 + 2i}{1 + i} = 2i\frac{(1 + i)}{1 + i} = 2i,$$

we usually find it more convenient to use the method outlined below.

For any complex number $x + iy$, x is the 'real' part and y is the 'imaginary' part. If $z = x + iy$, this can be written $\mathbb{R}(z)$ or Re $(z) = x$, $\mathbb{I}(z)$ or Imag $(z) = y$.

Complex conjugate

Any complex number $x + iy$ we can denote by z; associated with any one number $x + iy$ we have another number $x - iy$ which we call the complex conjugate of z, written $\bar{z}$. We notice that the roots of the quadratic equation $x^2 + 4x + 13 = 0$ on page 280 are complex conjugates, $-2 + 3i$ and $-2 - 3i$, and that their sum and their product are both real. Indeed, since

$$(x + iy) + (x - iy) = 2x$$
and
$$(x + iy)(x - iy) = x^2 + y^2$$

the sum and product of any pair of complex conjugates are real. We can see that for any quadratic equation with real coefficients, if it has complex roots then those roots are complex conjugates. This can be extended to equations of higher degree.

Division by a complex number

We may have simplified expressions like $\dfrac{1}{\sqrt{2} - 1}$ by multiplying numerator and denominator by $\sqrt{2} + 1$,

i.e. $$\frac{1}{\sqrt{2} - 1} = \frac{\sqrt{2} + 1}{(\sqrt{2} - 1)(\sqrt{2} + 1)} = \sqrt{2} + 1,$$

and we can write similarly

$$\frac{1}{2 + i} = \frac{2 - i}{(2 + i)(2 - i)} = \frac{2 - i}{5} = \frac{1}{5}(2 - i)$$

and $$\frac{3 + i}{2 - i} = \frac{(3 + i)(2 + i)}{(2 - i)(2 + i)} = \frac{5(1 + i)}{5} = 1 + i.$$

Thus to divide by a complex number z we often find it simpler to multiply numerator and denominator by the complex conjugate $\bar{z}$.

Example. If $a = 2 + i$ and $b = 3 - 2i$, find (i) $a + b$, (ii) $a - 2b$, (iii) a^2, (iv) ab, (v) $\dfrac{a}{b}$.

(i) $a + b = (2 + i) + (3 - 2i) = (2 + 3) + (i - 2i) = 5 - i.$

(i) $a - 2b = (2 + i) - 2(3 - 2i) = (2 - 6) + (i + 4i) = -4 + 5i.$

(iii) $a^2 = (2 + i)(2 + i) = 4 + 2i + 2i + (i)(i) = 3 + 4i$, using $i^2 = -1$.

(iv) $ab = (2 + i)(3 - 2i) = 6 - 4i + 3i + 2 = 8 - i.$

(v) $\dfrac{a}{b} = \dfrac{(2 + i)}{(3 - 2i)} = \dfrac{(2 + i)(3 + 2i)}{(3 - 2i)(3 + 2i)} = \dfrac{4 + 7i}{13}.$

Exercise 20.1

1. If $a = 1 + i$, $b = 2 - i$, $c = 2 + 3i$, express in the form $x + iy$:

(i) $a + b$, (ii) $a + 2b - c$, (iii) ab,

(iv) $a^2 c$, (v) $(a + b)c^2$, (vi) $a^2 + b^2$,

(vii) $\dfrac{1}{a + b}$, (viii) $\dfrac{a}{b}$, (ix) $\dfrac{b}{a}$,

(x) $\dfrac{b}{c}$, (xi) $\dfrac{b}{a + c}$, (xii) $\dfrac{ab}{c^2}$.

2. Solve the following equations, giving their roots in the form $x + iy$ (where either x or y may be zero):

(i) $x^2 + 4x + 20 = 0$,

(ii) $x^2 + 4x + 7 = 0$,

(iii) $x^2 + 25 = 0$,

(iv) $x^2 + 2ix - 2 = 0$,

(v) $x^2 + 2ix + 2 = 0$.

3. Form quadratic equations with roots:

(i) $4i$, (ii) $5 \pm 4i$,

(iii) $2 \pm i\sqrt{3}$, (iv) $1 + 2i, 2 - i$.

4. If $z = 1 + i$, write down the complex conjugate $\bar{z}$ and express $\dfrac{z}{\bar{z}}$ in the form $x + iy$.

5. If $z = \dfrac{1}{2 - 3i}$, express z in the form $x + iy$, write down $\bar{z}$ and hence evaluate $z\bar{z}$.

6. If $x + iy = \dfrac{3 - i}{2 + i}$, find x and y.

7. If $x + iy = \dfrac{2 + 3i}{i}$, find x and y.

8. If $x + iy = (a + ib)(c + id)$, show that $x - iy = (a - ib)(c - id)$.

9. If $x + iy = \dfrac{a + ib}{c + id}$ show that $x - iy = \dfrac{a - ib}{c - id}$.

10. Factorize $x^3 + 1$ and hence solve the equation $x^3 + 1 = 0$.

11. Factorize $x^3 - 1$ and hence solve the equation $x^3 - 1 = 0$.

12. If $a + ib = \dfrac{1}{x + iy}$, show that $(a^2 + b^2)(x^2 + y^2) = 1$.

13. Factorize $x^3 - 27$ and hence solve the equation $x^3 = 27$.

14. Show that the line $x - 1 + i(y - 2) = 0$ passes through one real point and find it.

15. Show that the line $x - i - 3y - iy = 0$ passes through one real point and find it.

16. If $z = \cos\theta + i\sin\theta$, find the value of $\dfrac{1}{z}$.

17. If $z = \cos\theta + i\sin\theta$, find the value of $z\bar{z}$.

18. If $z = \cos\theta + i\sin\theta$, find the values of $z + \dfrac{1}{z}$ and $z - \dfrac{1}{z}$.

19. Show that $(\cos\theta + i\sin\theta)^2 = \cos 2\theta + i\sin 2\theta$.

20. Show that $(\cos\alpha + i\sin\alpha)(\cos\beta + i\sin\beta) = \cos(\alpha + \beta) + i\sin(\alpha + \beta)$.

21. Solve the equation $x^2 - 2x\cos\theta + 1 = 0$.

22. Find x and y given that $x + y + i(x - y) = 3 + i$.

23. Find a and b given that $2a + b + i(a + 2b) = 7 + 8i$.

24. Given that $\sqrt{(x + iy)} = a + ib$, show that $x = a^2 - b^2$ and $y = 2ab$. Hence find the real and imaginary parts of $\sqrt{(12i - 5)}$.

25. Find the real and imaginary parts of $\sqrt{(7 - 24i)}$.

26. Simplify $(1 + i\sqrt{3})^4 + (1 - i\sqrt{3})^4$.

27. If $z = \cos\theta + i\sin\theta$, find the value of $z^2 + \dfrac{1}{z^2}$.

28. Show that $(\cos 60° + i\sin 60°)(\cos 30° + i\sin 30°) = i$.

29. Show that $(\cos 60° + i\sin 60°)(\cos 120° + i\sin 120°) = -1$.

30. If $z = \cos\theta + i\sin\theta$, find the value of $z^2 + \bar{z}^2$.

Geometric representation of complex numbers

We are familiar with the representation of real numbers along a number-line; since complex numbers consist of two independent parts,

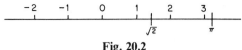

Fig. 20.2

the real and the imaginary parts, we need to represent them in a plane, using two dimensions. This is called an Argand diagram, having been used by the mathematician Jean-Robert Argand (1768–1822) in an essay written in 1806. We use the x-axis to represent the real part and the y-axis to represent the imaginary part. In Fig. 20.3, the point $(2, 3)$ represents the complex number $2 + 3i$.

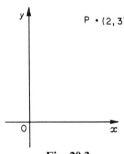

Fig. 20.3

Looking at the representation of the addition of the two complex numbers $1 + i$ and $3 + i$, in Fig. 20.4, we see the similarity with vector addition. This similarity is made closer by the definition of terms *modulus* and *argument*, similar to the magnitude and direction of a vector.

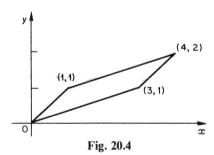

Fig. 20.4

Modulus and argument of a complex number

If the point P in an Argand diagram represents the complex number $z \equiv x + iy$, the length OP, always taken as positive, is called the modulus of z, written $|z|$ or $|x + iy|$. From Fig. 20.5, we see that $|x + iy| = \sqrt{(x^2 + y^2)}$.

The angle measured anti-clockwise, from OX to OP is called the

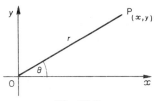

Fig. 20.5

argument (sometimes amplitude) of z, written arg (z) or amp (z). It is convenient to choose the amplitude so that it always lies between $-\pi$ and π (occasionally we use degrees, $\pm 180°$). For example, the argument of a complex number represented by a point in the second quadrant lies between $\dfrac{\pi}{2}$ and π; in the third quadrant lies between $\dfrac{-\pi}{2}$ and $-\pi$; and in the fourth quadrant between 0 and $\dfrac{-\pi}{2}$.

From Fig. 20.5 it is easily seen that
$$x = r \cos \theta \quad \text{and} \quad y = r \sin \theta$$
so that $z \equiv x + iy$ can be written in the form $z \equiv r(\cos \theta + i \sin \theta)$; this is called the modulus-argument (or modulus-amplitude) form, and is especially useful when manipulating products and quotients,

Example 1. *Find the modulus and argument of $1 - i$.*
From Fig. 20.6,
$$\text{OP}^2 = 1^2 + 1^2 = 2$$
$$\therefore \quad |1 - i| = \sqrt{2}$$
From the figure, $\qquad \arg (1 - i) = \dfrac{-\pi}{4}.$

Example 2. *Find the modulus and argument of $-3 + 4i$.*
From Fig. 20.7,
$$\text{OP}^2 = 3^3 + 4^2.$$
$$\therefore \quad \text{OP} = 5 \quad \text{and} \quad |z| = 5.$$
Also $\qquad \tan \alpha = \tfrac{4}{3} \quad \text{and so} \quad \alpha = 53.1°.$
The argument is $(180° - 53.1°)$, i.e. $126.9°$.

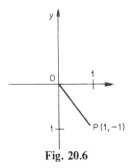

Fig. 20.6

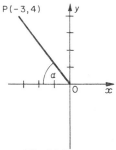

Fig. 20.7

Example 3. *Find the argument of 4(sin 108° + i cos 108°).*

To find the argument the expression needs to be put in the form $r(\cos \theta + i \sin \theta)$ where $-180° < \theta \leqslant 180°$.

$$4(\sin 108° + i \cos 108°) = 4(\cos 18° - i \sin 18°)$$
$$= 4[\cos (-18°) + i \sin (-18°)].$$

So the modulus is 4 and the argument is $-18°$.

Use of an Argand diagram

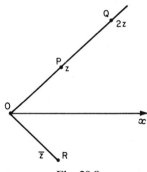

Fig. 20.8

In Fig. 20.8, if P represents any complex number z, Q, representing $2z$ lies on OP produced, as arg $(2z)$ = arg (z), and R representing $\bar{z}$, is the reflection of P in the x-axis, for if

$$z = r(\cos \theta + \sin \theta),$$
$$\bar{z} = r(\cos \theta - \sin \theta)$$
$$= r(\cos (-\theta) + \sin (-\theta)),$$

so that arg $\bar{z} = -$ arg z, and $|\bar{z}| = |z|$.

Example. *Show that for all complex numbers* $z_1, z_2, |z_1 + z_2| \leqslant |z_1| + |z_2|$.

In Fig. 20.9,

$$OQ = |z_1 + z_2|; \qquad OP_1 = |z_1| \quad \text{and} \quad OP_2 = P_1Q = |z_2|.$$

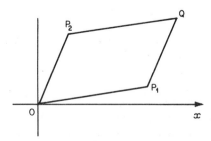

Fig. 20.9

Since $OQ \leqslant OP_1 + P_1Q$,
$$|z_1 + z_2| \leqslant |z_1| + |z_2|.$$
Equality occurs only when O, P_1 and P_2 are collinear, i.e. when arg (z_1) = arg (z_2).
This can be extended by Induction to show that
$$|z_1 + z_2 + \ldots z_n| \leqslant |z_1| + |z_2| + \ldots |z_n|.$$

Loci in an Argand diagram

Since $|z|$ is the distance of the point P representing the complex number z, when $|z| = 3$, the distance of the point P from the origin O is constant, 3 units, so that $|z| = 3$ describes the boundary of a circle, centre O, radius 3 units. Similarly $|z| < 3$ describes the interior of this circle, and $|z| > 3$ describes the region outside this circle. More loci are considered on page 291.

Exercise 20.2

1. Represent on the Argand diagram the points
   (a) $3i$, (b) $1 + 2i$, (c) $3 - 5i$, (d) $-2 - 5i$.
2. Find the modulus of (a) $1\frac{1}{2} + 2i$, (b) $5 - 12i$, (c) $8 + 15i$.
3. Find the argument of (a) $1 + i$, (b) $3 - 5i$, (c) $-2 - 3i$.
4. Find $\left|\dfrac{3 + 4i}{1 + i}\right|$.
5. Find arg $\left(\dfrac{\sqrt{3} + i}{1 + i}\right)$.
6. Show $|z_1 - z_2| \geqslant |z_1| - |z_2|$.
7. Write down the modulus and argument of $2(\sin 60° + i \cos 60°)$.
8. Write down the modulus and argument of $3(\sin 20° - i \cos 20°)$.
9. Write down the argument of $z - \bar{z}$.
10. If $z = 2\left(\cos \dfrac{\pi}{4} + i \sin \dfrac{\pi}{4}\right)$, find the argument of iz.
11. If $z = r(\cos \theta + i \sin \theta)$, and θ is acute, find the argument of iz.
12. Find the modulus of iz.
13. What complex number represents $\overrightarrow{AB}$ where $B = 2 + 3i$ and $A = 1 + 2i$? Find its argument.
14. If $z_1 = 3 + 4i$ and $z_2 = 2 + 3i$, find arg $(z_1 - z_2)$. What angle does this represent on the Argand diagram?
15. Find $|(1 + i)(\sqrt{3} + i)|$.
16. Find arg $(1 + i)(\sqrt{3} + i)$.
17. Find $|z_1 - z_2|$ where $z_1 = 7 + 5i$, $z_2 = 3 + 2i$.
18. If $|z| = 1$, describe the locus of the point (x, y).
19. If $|z| = 2$, describe the locus of the point (x, y).
20. If $|z - 1| = 1$, describe the locus of the point (x, y).

The product of two complex numbers

Suppose that
$$z_1 = r_1(\cos \theta_1 + i \sin \theta_1) \quad \text{and} \quad z_2 = r_2(\cos \theta_2 + i \sin \theta_2).$$
Then
$$
\begin{aligned}
z_1 z_2 &= r_1 r_2 (\cos \theta_1 + i \sin \theta_1)(\cos \theta_2 + i \sin \theta_2) \\
&= r_1 r_2 \{(\cos \theta_1 \cos \theta_2 + i^2 \sin \theta_1 \sin \theta_2) \\
&\qquad\qquad + i(\cos \theta_1 \sin \theta_2 + \cos \theta_2 \sin \theta_1)\} \\
&= r_1 r_2 \{(\cos \theta_1 \cos \theta_2 - \sin \theta_1 \sin \theta_2) + i \sin (\theta_1 + \theta_2)\} \\
&= r_1 r_2 \{\cos (\theta_1 + \theta_2) + i \sin (\theta_1 + \theta_2)\}.
\end{aligned}
$$
So
$$|z_1 z_2| = r_1 r_2 \quad \text{and} \quad \arg z_1 z_2 = \theta_1 + \theta_2.$$
The modulus of the product is therefore the product of the separate moduli; the argument of the product is the sum of the separate arguments.

If
$$z_3 = r_3(\cos \theta_3 + i \sin \theta_3),$$
$$
\begin{aligned}
z_1 z_2 z_3 &= r_1 r_2 r_3 \{\cos (\theta_1 + \theta_2) + i \sin (\theta_1 + \theta_2)\}(\cos \theta_3 + i \sin \theta_3) \\
&= r_1 r_2 r_3 \{\cos (\theta_1 + \theta_2 + \theta_3) + i \sin (\theta_1 + \theta_2 + \theta_3)\}.
\end{aligned}
$$

The quotient of two complex numbers

Since by the product rule
$$
\begin{aligned}
r_1(\cos \theta_1 + i \sin \theta_1) . r_2\{\cos (\theta_2 - \theta_1) + i \sin (\theta_2 - \theta_1)\} & \\
= r_1 r_2(\cos \theta_2 + i \sin \theta_2) &
\end{aligned}
$$
it follows that
$$\frac{r_1 r_2(\cos \theta_2 + i \sin \theta_2)}{r_1(\cos \theta_1 + i \sin \theta_1)} = r_2\{\cos (\theta_2 - \theta_1) + i \sin (\theta_2 - \theta_1)\}.$$
The modulus of the quotient of two complex numbers is therefore the quotient of their moduli; the argument of the quotient is the difference of their separate arguments.

de Moivre's theorem

Since
$$z_1 z_2 = r_1 r_2 \cos (\theta_1 + \theta_2) + i \sin (\theta_1 + \theta_2),$$
it follows that
$$(\cos \theta_1 + i \sin \theta_1)(\cos \theta_2 + i \sin \theta_2) = \cos (\theta_1 + \theta_2) + i \sin (\theta_1 + \theta_2),$$
whence
$$(\cos \theta + i \sin \theta)^2 = \cos 2\theta + i \sin 2\theta.$$
Similarly
$$(\cos \theta + i \sin \theta)^3 = \cos 3\theta + i \sin 3\theta,$$
suggesting that possibly
$$(\cos \theta + i \sin \theta)^n = \cos n\theta + i \sin n\theta.$$
This is a very important theorem, called de Moivre's theorem, after Abraham de Moivre (1667–1754), a friend and fellow member of the

Royal Society with Isaac Newton. This theorem is true for all values of n, positive, negative, integer or rational. The only amendment needed is to specify that when n is irrational, this gives *one* of the values of $(\cos \theta + i \sin \theta)^n$, e.g. *one* value of $(\cos \theta + i \sin \theta)^{\frac{1}{2}}$ is $\cos \frac{1}{2}\theta + i \sin \frac{1}{2}\theta$. We shall only use this theorem for n, a positive integer, when it can be easily proved by Induction.

Example 1. *Evaluate* $\left| \dfrac{4 - 3i}{8 + 15i} \right|$.

$$\left| \frac{4 - 3i}{8 + 15i} \right| = \frac{|4 - 3i|}{|8 + 15i|}, \text{ dividing the moduli,}$$

$$= \frac{\sqrt{(4^2 + 3^2)}}{\sqrt{(8^2 + 15^2)}}$$

$$= \frac{5}{17}.$$

Example 2. *Find* $arg \left(\dfrac{\sqrt{3} + i}{1 + i} \right)$.

$$\arg \left(\frac{\sqrt{3} + i}{1 + i} \right) = \arg (\sqrt{3} + i) - \arg (1 + i),$$

subtracting the arguments.

Now
$$\sqrt{3} + i = 2\left(\frac{\sqrt{3}}{2} + i \frac{1}{2} \right)$$

$$= 2\left(\cos \frac{\pi}{6} + i \sin \frac{\pi}{6} \right)$$

$$\therefore \quad \arg (\sqrt{3} + i) = \frac{\pi}{6}.$$

Similarly
$$1 + i = \sqrt{2}\left(\frac{1}{\sqrt{2}} + i \frac{1}{\sqrt{2}} \right)$$

$$= \sqrt{2}\left(\cos \frac{\pi}{4} + i \sin \frac{\pi}{4} \right)$$

$$\therefore \quad \arg (1 + i) = \frac{\pi}{4}$$

$$\therefore \quad \arg \left(\frac{\sqrt{3} + i}{1 + i} \right) = \frac{\pi}{6} - \frac{\pi}{4}$$

$$= -\frac{\pi}{12}.$$

Example 3. *Express in modulus—argument form* $a + ib$.

Draw a right-angled triangle as shown in Fig. 20.10 with the sides including the right angle of lengths a and b.

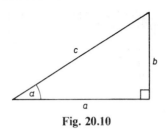

Fig. 20.10

The length of the hypotenuse is $\sqrt{(a^2 + b^2)}$

and
$$a = \sqrt{(a^2 + b^2)} \cos \alpha; \quad b = \sqrt{(a^2 + b^2)} \sin \alpha.$$
$$\therefore \quad a + ib = \sqrt{(a + b^2)}(\cos \alpha + i \sin \alpha)$$

or
$$\sqrt{(a^2 + b^2)}\{\cos (2r\pi + \alpha) + i \sin (2r\pi + \alpha)\}.$$

The modulus is $\sqrt{(a^2 + b^2)}$; the argument $(2r\pi + \alpha)$ where r is chosen so that the angle lies between $\pm \pi$.

Example 4. *Use de Moivre's theorem to expand* $\cos 3\theta$ *and* $\sin 3\theta$.

$$\cos 3\theta + i \sin 3\theta = (\cos \theta + i \sin \theta)^3$$
$$= \cos^3 \theta + 3 \cos^2 \theta(i \sin \theta) + 3 \cos \theta(i \sin \theta)^2 + (i \sin \theta)^3.$$

Equating real and imaginary parts,
$$\cos 3\theta = \cos^3 \theta - 3 \cos \theta \sin^2 \theta;$$
$$\sin 3\theta = 3 \cos^2 \theta \sin \theta - \sin^3 \theta.$$

This method may be used to expand cos and sin of any multiple angle.

Exercise 20.3

1. Evaluate $\left| \dfrac{1 - i}{7 + i} \right|$.

2. Evaluate $\left| \dfrac{3 + 4i}{3 - 4i} \right|$.

3. Evaluate $\left| \dfrac{1 + 3i}{8 + i} \right|$.

4. Evaluate $|(6 - 3i)(2 + i)|$.

5. Find arg $(2 + i)(3 + i)$.

6. Find arg $\left(\dfrac{1 + i}{\sqrt{3} + i} \right)$

   (i) by finding the arguments and subtracting,

   (ii) by first writing $\dfrac{1 + i}{\sqrt{3} + i}$ in the form $a + ib$.

7. Simplify $\left(\cos \dfrac{\pi}{3} + i \sin \dfrac{\pi}{3} \right)\left(\cos \dfrac{\pi}{6} + i \sin \dfrac{\pi}{6} \right)$.

8. Simplify $\left(\cos \dfrac{\pi}{5} + i \sin \dfrac{\pi}{5} \right)\left(\cos \dfrac{2\pi}{5} + i \sin \dfrac{2\pi}{5} \right)^2$.

9. Simplify $\left(\cos \dfrac{3\pi}{7} + i \sin \dfrac{3\pi}{7}\right)\left(\cos \dfrac{2\pi}{7} + i \sin \dfrac{2\pi}{7}\right)^2.$

10. Simplify $\left(\cos \dfrac{\pi}{6} + i \sin \dfrac{\pi}{6}\right)^3.$

11. Simplify $\dfrac{\cos 2\theta + i \sin 2\theta}{\cos \theta + i \sin \theta}.$

12. Simplify $\dfrac{\cos 3\theta + i \sin 3\theta}{\cos \theta + i \sin \theta)^2}.$

13. Simplify $\dfrac{\cos 3\theta + i \sin 3\theta}{\cos 2\theta + i \sin 2\theta}.$

14. Evaluate $\left(\dfrac{-1 + i\sqrt{3}}{2}\right)^3.$

15. Evaluate $\left(\dfrac{\sqrt{3} + i}{2}\right)^3.$

16. Evaluate $(1 + i)^6.$

17. Expand $\cos 4\theta$ and $\sin 4\theta$ by de Moivre's theorem. Use your expansion to express $\cos 4\theta$ as a polynomial in $\cos \theta$.

18. Expand $\cos 5\theta$ and $\sin 5\theta$ by de Moivre's theorem. Use your expansion to express $\sin 5\theta$ as a polynomial in $\sin \theta$.

19. If $\arg (z_3 - z_1) = \arg (z_2 - z_1)$, show that the points z_1, z_2, z_3 are collinear.

20. What are the greatest and least values of $|z|$ when $|z - 2| = 1$?

Further loci

In Fig. 20.11, let P_1 represent z_1 and P_2 represent z_2. Then $(z_2 - z_1)$ is represented by P_1P_2, and $(z_1 - z_2)$ is represented by P_2P_1, so
$$|z_1 - z_2| = P_1P_2 \quad \text{and} \quad \arg (z_1 - z_2)$$
is equal to the angle between OX and P_2P_1.

We have seen that $|z| = 3$ describes the circle centre O, radius 3; similarly $|z - a| = r$, where r is real and a is complex, describes the circle centre a radius r.

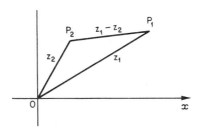

Fig. 20.11

Example 1. *Describe the locus of z given that* $|z - 1 - 2i| = 3$.

$$|z - 1 - 2i| = |z - (1 + 2i)|$$
$$\therefore \quad |z - 1 - 2i| = 3$$

is a circle centre $(1, 2)$ radius 3, since the distance of any point z from $(1, 2)$ is constant, 3.

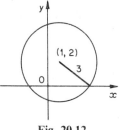

Fig. 20.12

Example 2. *Sketch the region described by* $|z| < 1$ *and* $-\dfrac{\pi}{4} < arg\ z < \dfrac{\pi}{4}$.

The region $|z| < 1$ is the interior of the unit circle, centre the origin. All points whose arguments are between $-\dfrac{\pi}{4}$ and $+\dfrac{\pi}{4}$ lie in one quadrant of this circle, as shown in Fig. 20.13, where we have shaded the outer boundary of the required region.

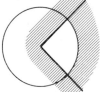

Fig. 20.13

Example 3. *Find the locus described by* $|z - 2| = |z - 1 - i|$.

$|z - 2|$ is the distance of the point P from the point $(2, 0)$; $|z - 1 - i|$ is the distance of the point P from $(1, 1)$. All points equidistant from these points lie on the perpendicular bisector of the line AB, as shown in Fig. 20.14.

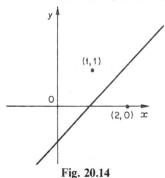

Fig. 20.14

Example 4. *Describe the locus of z if* $\left|\dfrac{z - 1 - i}{z - 1 + i}\right| = 2.$

We know that $\left|\dfrac{z - 1 - i}{z - 1 + i}\right| = \dfrac{|z - 1 - i|}{|z - 1 + i|}$ so the required locus is $|z - 1 - i|$
$= 2|z - 1 + i|$. The locus is such that the distance from $(1, 1)$ is twice the distance from $(1, -1)$, and is therefore a circle of Appollonius, centre on the line joining $(1, 1)$ and $(1, -1)$.

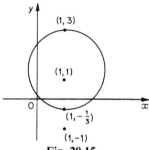

Fig. 20.15

The following loci are among the most useful at the level:
1. $|z - a| = r$ is a circle centre a, radius r.
2. $\arg z = \alpha$ is a straight line through O inclined an angle α to the base line OX.
3. $|z - a| = |z - b|$ is the perpendicular bisector of the line joining a to b.
4. $|z - a| = k|z - b|$ is a circle, as in Example 4.

Example 5. *If z_1, z_2 and z_3 are the points A, B and C on the Argand diagram, identify* $\dfrac{z_3 - z_1}{z_2 - z_1}.$

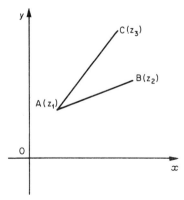

Fig. 20.16

$$\left|\frac{z_3 - z_1}{z_2 - z_1}\right| = \frac{|z_3 - z_1|}{|z_2 - z_1|} = \frac{CA}{BA}.$$

$$\arg\left(\frac{z_3 - z_1}{z_2 - z_1}\right) = \arg(z_3 - z_1) - \arg(z_2 - z_1)$$

But $\arg(z_3 - z_1)$ is the angle which AC makes with the x-axis and arg $(z_2 - z_1)$ is the angle which AB makes with the x axis.

$$\therefore \quad \arg\left(\frac{z_3 - z_1}{z_2 - z_1}\right) = C\hat{A}B.$$

So $\dfrac{z_3 - z_1}{z_2 - z_1}$ is a complex number whose modulus is $\dfrac{CA}{BA}$ and whose argument is the angle $C\hat{A}B$.

$$\therefore \quad \frac{z_3 - z_1}{z_2 - z_1} = \frac{CA}{BA}(\cos C\hat{A}B + i \sin C\hat{A}B).$$

Exercise 20.4

1. Plot a point P to represent z and on the same diagram plot points to represent the numbers

   (i) $\bar{z}$; (ii) $\dfrac{1}{z}$; (iii) $z - 1$; (iv) $z + i$; (v) $z - 1 - i$.

2. If $|z - 2| = 3$, describe the locus of z.

3. If $|z - 1 + 2i| < 3$, describe the locus of z.

4. If $|z - 1| = |z + 1|$, describe the locus of z.

5. Show the points z_1, z_2, z_3 are collinear if and only if $\arg\left(\dfrac{z_1 - z_3}{z_1 - z_2}\right)$ is zero.

6. If $\left|\dfrac{z - 1}{z + 2}\right| = 2$, describe the locus of z.

7. If $\left|\dfrac{z - i}{z + i}\right| < 2$, describe the locus of z.

8. Find the angles of the triangle formed by the points $1 + i$, $3 + 4i$, $4 + 3i$.

9. Find the centre and radius of the circle $|z - 1 - 2i| = 5$.

10. Given that $|z - a| + |z - b| = k$, show that the locus of z is an ellipse. (Use the focal distance property.)

11. Show that the lines joining z_1 and z_2 to the origin are perpendicular if $\arg\left(\dfrac{z_1}{z_2}\right) = \dfrac{\pi}{2}$.

12. If $|z_1 - z_2| = |z_1 + z_2|$, show that the arguments of z_1 and z_2 differ by $\dfrac{\pi}{2}$.

13. Describe the locus of points z given that $\arg z = \dfrac{\pi}{6}$.

14. Describe the locus of points z given that $\arg(z - 1) = \dfrac{\pi}{4}$.

15. Describe the locus of points z given that $\arg\left(\dfrac{z-1}{z+1}\right) < \dfrac{\pi}{2}$.

16. If the points z_1, z_2, z_3 and z_4 form a parallelogram with $z_1 z_3$ a diagonal, show that $z_1 + z_3 = z_2 + z_4$.

17. Find the centroid of the triangle formed by the points z_1, z_2, z_3.

18. Find the modulus and argument of $(1 + i)^2$.

19. If $|z - 2i| \leqslant 1$, find the maximum value of $|z|$.

20. If $|z - 3 - i| \leqslant 2$, find the least value of $|z|$.

Exercise 20.5: Miscellaneous

1. Given that $|z| = 1$, represent on a diagram the points z, $\bar{z}$, z^2 and $\dfrac{1}{z}$.

2. Represent on the Argand diagram the points

(a) $2 + i$; (b) $3 - 4i$; (c) $2\left(\cos\dfrac{\pi}{4} + i\sin\dfrac{\pi}{4}\right)$;

(d) $3\left(\cos\dfrac{3\pi}{4} + i\sin\dfrac{3\pi}{4}\right)$.

3. Find the modulus and argument of each of the following:

(a) $2 + 5i$; (b) $-1 - \sqrt{3}i$; (c) $4i$; (d) $\left(\sin\dfrac{\pi}{4} + i\cos\dfrac{\pi}{4}\right)$.

4. If P_1, P_2 represent the points z_1, z_2 construct the points which represent

(a) $z_1 + z_2$; (b) $z_1 - z_2$; (c) $2z_1$; (d) $2z_1 + z_3$.

5. Draw the graphs of the following:

(a) $|z| = 3$; (b) $|z - 1| = 2$; (c) $|z - 1 - 2i| = 1$.

6. Solve the equation $x^2 + 2x\cos\theta + 1 = 0$.

7. Separate into real and imaginary parts

(a) $\dfrac{1+i}{i}$; (b) $\dfrac{1}{3+i}$; (c) $\dfrac{2+i}{3+i}$; (d) $\dfrac{1}{1 + \cos\theta + i\sin\theta}$.

8. If $x + iy = 3 - 4i$, find $x^2 + y^2$.

9. Show that the roots of the equation $x^3 + 1 = 0$ are represented in the Argand diagrams as vertices of an equilateral triangle.

10. Find the equation whose roots are 2, $3 + 4i$ and $3 - 4i$.

11. Express $\cos 5\theta$ in terms of $\cos\theta$ and $\sin\theta$.

12. Simplify $\dfrac{(\cos\theta + i\sin\theta)^4}{\cos 2\theta + i\sin 2\theta}$.

13. Express in modulus argument form

(a) $\cos\theta - i\sin\theta$; (b) $[\sqrt{2}(\cos\theta + i\sin\theta)]^2$; (c) $\cos\dfrac{\pi}{3} - i\sin\dfrac{\pi}{3}$.

14. Find x and y given that $x + iy = (1 - i)^2$.

15. Show that $1 + \cos\theta + i\sin\theta = 2\cos\dfrac{\theta}{2}\left(\cos\dfrac{\theta}{2} + i\sin\dfrac{\theta}{2}\right)$.

Hence simplify $(1 + \cos\theta + i\sin\theta)^4$.

16. Find the cartesian equation of the circle $\left|\dfrac{z-1}{z+1}\right| = 2$.

17. Given that $(x + iy)(X + iY) = (a + ib)$ show that
$$(x^2 + y^2)(X^2 + Y^2) = a^2 + b^2.$$

18. If $|z - 1 + 2i| \leqslant 1$, shade the region inside which z must lie in the Argand diagram.

19. If $|z - 1| = |z - i|$, show the locus of z in an Argand diagram.

20. If A, B, C are the points $(1, 0)$, $(4, 0)$ and $(0, 2)$, find the angles ABC and ACO. Hence show that the circle through A, B and C touches the y-axis at C.

21. If A, B, C, D are the points $(3, 0)$, $(4, 0)$, $(0, 2)$ and $(0, 6)$, find the angles CBD and CAD. Hence show that ABCD is a cyclic quadrilateral.

22. By considering $\left(\cos\dfrac{2r\pi}{5} + i\sin\dfrac{2r\pi}{5}\right)^5$, find the 5 fifth roots of unity.

23. Find the seventh roots of unity.

24. By expressing i in the form $\cos\dfrac{\pi}{2} + i\sin\dfrac{\pi}{2}$, find the fourth roots of i.

25. If P_1, P_2 and P_3 are z_1, z_2 and z_3 show, that, if
$$\frac{z_1 - z_2}{z_1 - z_3} = \cos\frac{\pi}{3} + i\sin\frac{\pi}{3},$$
$P_1P_2P_3$ is an equilateral triangle.

26. Show the condition for $P_1P_2P_3$ to be equilateral is
$$z_1{}^2 + z_2{}^2 + z_3{}^2 = z_1z_2 + z_2z_3 + z_3z_1.$$

27. Given that $\arg(z_1 - z_2) = \arg(z_3 - z_4)$, show that $\dfrac{z_1 - z_2}{z_3 - z_4}$ is real.

28. Given that OP_1P_2 is an isosceles triangle with $OP_1 = OP_2$ and the angle $P_1OP_2 = 45°$, show that $z_1{}^2 + z_2{}^2 = \sqrt{2}z_1z_2$.

29. Given that OP_1P_2 is an isosceles triangle with $OP_1 = OP_2$ and the angle $P_1OP_2 = 90°$, show that $z_1{}^2 + z_2{}^2 = 0$.

30. If z_1, z_2, z_3 are the vertices of an isosceles triangle which is right-angled at z_3, show that $z_1{}^2 + z_2{}^2 + 2z_3{}^2 = 2z_3(z_1 + z_2)$.

21 Vectors

Revision

We have seen in *Additional Pure Mathematics* that it is often convenient to describe a vector by its components. A vector in two dimensions can be written $x\mathbf{i} + y\mathbf{j}$ or $\begin{pmatrix} x \\ y \end{pmatrix}$; in three dimensions $x\mathbf{i} + y\mathbf{j} + z\mathbf{k}$ or $\begin{pmatrix} x \\ y \\ z \end{pmatrix}$, where $\mathbf{i}$, $\mathbf{j}$, $\mathbf{k}$ are unit vectors and the entry in each place in the matrix gives the component in that direction. We shall find it convenient to use both the $\mathbf{i}$, $\mathbf{j}$, $\mathbf{k}$ and the matrix form. This approach can be generalised later for as many dimensions as we wish. The magnitude of a vector in two dimensions is $\sqrt{(x^2 + y^2)}$; in three dimensions is $\sqrt{(x^2 + y^2 + z^2)}$.

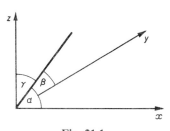

Fig. 21.1

In two dimensions, the vector $x\mathbf{i} + y\mathbf{j}$ makes with the unit vector $\mathbf{i}$ an angle arc tan (y/x). Direction is more difficult to describe in three dimensions, but we can say that the vector $x\mathbf{i} + y\mathbf{j} + z\mathbf{k}$ makes angles α, β, γ with $\mathbf{i}$, $\mathbf{j}$, $\mathbf{k}$ where

$$\cos \alpha = \frac{x}{\sqrt{(x^2 + y^2 + z^2)}}, \quad \cos \beta = \frac{y}{\sqrt{(x^2 + y^2 + z^2)}}$$

and $\quad \cos \gamma = \dfrac{z}{\sqrt{(x^2 + y^2 + k^2)}}$

or we can describe the direction by the direction-ratios, $x:y:z$.

Addition and subtraction of vectors

Addition (and subtraction) of vectors can be defined by addition (or subtraction) of corresponding components, e.g.

$$\begin{pmatrix} 2 \\ 3 \\ 1 \end{pmatrix} + \begin{pmatrix} 5 \\ 6 \\ 7 \end{pmatrix} = \begin{pmatrix} 7 \\ 9 \\ 8 \end{pmatrix}$$

which can be shown to be equivalent to addition of vectors by the parallelogram law; if vector addition is defined by the parallelogram law, then this can be shown to be equivalent to addition of the components (*Additional Pure Mathematics*, Chapter 12). Many simple problems can be solved merely by drawing a clear diagram and using geometry or trigonometry.

Example. *Vectors* **a** *and* **b** *are inclined at 60°, and* $|\mathbf{a}| = 8$, $|\mathbf{b}| = 5$. *Calculate* $|\mathbf{a} + \mathbf{b}|$ *and* $|\mathbf{a} - \mathbf{b}|$.

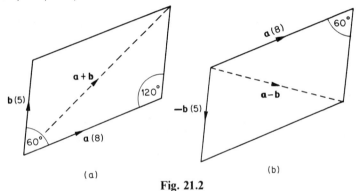

Fig. 21.2

From Fig. 21.2, using the cosine formula we have

$$(|\mathbf{a} + \mathbf{b}|)^2 = |\mathbf{a}|^2 + |\mathbf{b}|^2 - 2|\mathbf{a}||\mathbf{b}| \cos 120°$$
$$= 64 + 25 - 2 \times 8 \times 5 \times (-\tfrac{1}{2})$$
$$= 129$$
$$= \sqrt{129}, \text{ about } 11.4.$$

From Fig. 21.2(b),

$$(|\mathbf{a} - \mathbf{b}|)^2 = |\mathbf{a}|^2 + |\mathbf{b}|^2 - 2|\mathbf{a}||\mathbf{b}| \cos 60°$$
$$= 64 + 25 - 2 \times 8 \times 5 \times \tfrac{1}{2}$$
$$= 49$$

so $\qquad |\mathbf{a} - \mathbf{b}| = 7.$

Parallel vectors

If points *A*, *B*, *C*, *D*, position vectors* **a**, **b**, **c**, **d** respectively, are the

---

* Strictly, when we say 'the point *P* has position vector **p**' we mean that the position vector *P* relative to an origin *O* is **p**.

vertices of a parallelogram, AB is equal and parallel to CD,
i.e.
$$\mathbf{b} - \mathbf{a} = \mathbf{d} - \mathbf{c};$$
if they are the vertices of a trapezium in which AB is parallel to CD,
$$\mathbf{b} - \mathbf{a} = \lambda(\mathbf{d} - \mathbf{c}), \text{ for some scalar } \lambda.$$

Example. Show that the points A, B, C, D position vectors

$$\mathbf{a} = \begin{pmatrix} 1 \\ 1 \\ 0 \end{pmatrix}, \quad \mathbf{b} = \begin{pmatrix} 2 \\ 3 \\ 1 \end{pmatrix}, \quad \mathbf{c} = \begin{pmatrix} 4 \\ 4 \\ 0 \end{pmatrix}, \quad \mathbf{d} = \begin{pmatrix} 5 \\ 3 \\ -2 \end{pmatrix}$$

respectively are the vertices of a trapezium.

$$\mathbf{d} - \mathbf{a} = \begin{pmatrix} 4 \\ 2 \\ -2 \end{pmatrix} \text{ and } \mathbf{c} - \mathbf{b} = \begin{pmatrix} 2 \\ 1 \\ -1 \end{pmatrix}$$

so $\mathbf{d} - \mathbf{a} = 2(\mathbf{c} - \mathbf{b})$, and $ABCD$ is a trapezium in which AD is parallel to CB and twice the length of CB.

Section theorem

If points A, B have position vectors $\mathbf{a}$, $\mathbf{b}$ respectively, the position vector of the point P that divides AB in the ratio $\lambda : \mu$ is

$$\frac{\mu \mathbf{a} + \lambda \mathbf{b}}{\lambda + \mu}$$

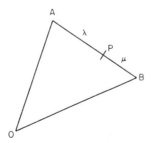

Fig. 21.3

As a special case, the position vector of the midpoint of AB is $\frac{1}{2}(\mathbf{a} + \mathbf{b})$. This is true if the point P divides AB internally or externally; in the latter case λ or μ is negative.

Example. *Points A and B have position vectors.*

$$\mathbf{a} = \begin{pmatrix} 2 \\ 3 \\ 1 \end{pmatrix} \quad \text{and} \quad \mathbf{b} = \begin{pmatrix} 5 \\ 0 \\ -2 \end{pmatrix}.$$

Find the position vectors of
(i) R, the point dividing AB internally in the ratio 1:2,
(ii) S, the point dividing AB (externally) in the ratio 2: −1.

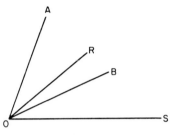

Fig. 21.4

Since R divides AB in the ratio 2:1,

$$\mathbf{r} = \frac{1}{2+1} \left[2 \begin{pmatrix} 5 \\ 0 \\ -2 \end{pmatrix} + 1 \begin{pmatrix} 2 \\ 3 \\ 1 \end{pmatrix} \right]$$

$$= \begin{pmatrix} 4 \\ 1 \\ -1 \end{pmatrix}.$$

Since S divides AB (externally) in the ratio 2: −1,

$$\mathbf{s} = \frac{1}{2-1} \left[2 \begin{pmatrix} 5 \\ 0 \\ -2 \end{pmatrix} - 1 \begin{pmatrix} 2 \\ 3 \\ 1 \end{pmatrix} \right]$$

$$= \begin{pmatrix} 8 \\ -3 \\ -5 \end{pmatrix} \Bigg]$$

Figure 21.5 shows that these position vectors are reasonable.

Some of the questions in this next exercise should be compared with those in Exercise 23.1, where the 'classical' methods of cartesian geometry are used.

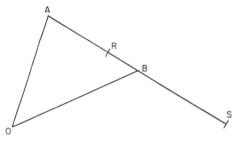

Fig. 21.5

Exercise 21.1

1. Vectors **a** and **b** are inclined at right angles, and $|\mathbf{a}| = 8$, $|\mathbf{b}| = 15$. Find $|\mathbf{a} + \mathbf{b}|$ and $|\mathbf{a} - \mathbf{b}|$.

2. Vectors **a** and **b** are inclined at 60°, and $|\mathbf{a}| = 3$, $|\mathbf{b}| = 5$. Find $|\mathbf{a} + \mathbf{b}|$ and $|\mathbf{a} - \mathbf{b}|$.

3. Vectors **a** and **b** are inclined at 45°, and $|\mathbf{a}| = 2$, $|\mathbf{b}| = 3$. Find, correct to 3sf, $|\mathbf{a} + 2\mathbf{b}|$, $|2\mathbf{a} - \mathbf{b}|$.

4. Vectors **a** and **b** are perpendicular, and $|\mathbf{a}| = 7$, $|\mathbf{a} + \mathbf{b}| = 25$. Find $|\mathbf{b}|$ and $|\mathbf{a} - \mathbf{b}|$.

5. Points A, B, C have position vectors, relative to an origin O, $(2\mathbf{i} + \mathbf{k})$, $(4\mathbf{j} + 10\mathbf{k})$ and $(6\mathbf{i} + 10\mathbf{j} + 11\mathbf{k})$ respectively. Find the magnitude of the vectors OA, OB, OC, AB, BC, CA.

6. Points A, B, C have position vectors, relative to an origin O, $(\mathbf{j} + \mathbf{k})$, $(3\mathbf{i} - \mathbf{j} + 2\mathbf{k})$ and $(5\mathbf{i} + 3\mathbf{j} + 4\mathbf{k})$ respectively. Find the magnitude of the vectors OA, OB, OC, AB, BC, CA.

7. Points A, B, C have position vectors $2\mathbf{i} + 3\mathbf{j}$, $4\mathbf{i} + 5\mathbf{j}$, $6\mathbf{i} + 9\mathbf{j}$ respectively. Find the length of the line joining A to the midpoint of BC.

8. Find the position vector of each of the two points of trisection of the line joining the points position vectors $3\mathbf{i} + \mathbf{j}$, $9\mathbf{i} - 11\mathbf{j}$.

9. Points A and B have position vectors $2\mathbf{i} + \mathbf{k}$, $6\mathbf{i} - 4\mathbf{j} - 3\mathbf{k}$ respectively. Find the position vectors of the points P and Q which divide AB internally in the ratio 3:1 and externally in the ratio 3:−1. Find also the position vectors of the points dividing AB in the ratio 1:3 and −1:3.

10. Points A and B have position vectors $-\mathbf{i} + \mathbf{j} - 2\mathbf{k}$ and $4\mathbf{i} + \mathbf{j} + 3\mathbf{k}$ respectively. Find the position vectors of points P and Q that divide AB in the ratio 2:3 and 3:2. Find also the position vectors of points dividing AB externally in the ratio 3:−2 and 2:−3.

11. Show that the points position vectors $3\mathbf{i} - 5\mathbf{j}$, $2\mathbf{i} + 5\mathbf{j}$, $6\mathbf{j}$ and $\mathbf{i} - 4\mathbf{j}$ are the vertices of a parallelogram.

12. Show that the points position vectors $\mathbf{i} + \mathbf{j} + 2\mathbf{k}$, $3\mathbf{i} + 3\mathbf{j} + 3\mathbf{k}$, $\mathbf{i} + \mathbf{j}$ and $-\mathbf{i} - \mathbf{j} - \mathbf{k}$ are the vertices of a parallelogram.

13. Find whether the points position vectors $\mathbf{i} - 4\mathbf{j}$, $\mathbf{i} + \mathbf{j}$, $5\mathbf{i} + 2\mathbf{j}$ and $4\mathbf{i} + \mathbf{j}$ are the vertices of a trapezium.

14. Find whether the points position vectors $-\mathbf{i} - \mathbf{j} - 2\mathbf{k}$, $\mathbf{j} + \mathbf{k}$, $\mathbf{i} + 5\mathbf{j} + 2\mathbf{k}$ and $-\mathbf{i} + \mathbf{j} - 4\mathbf{k}$ are the vertices of a trapezium.

15. Points A, B, C have position vectors $\mathbf{i} + \mathbf{j} + \mathbf{k}$, $2\mathbf{j} - 3\mathbf{k}$ and $3\mathbf{i} + 2\mathbf{k}$. By finding the lengths of AB, BC and CA, determine which is the largest angle in the triangle ABC, and whether this angle is less than, equal to or greater than a right angle.

Path of a particle

If $\mathbf{r}$ is the position vector of a particle and $\mathbf{r}$ is expressed in terms of a parameter t (time), the position of the particle is known at any time t, and the path of the particle can be deduced. Thus if $\mathbf{r} = b \cos t\mathbf{i} + b \sin t\mathbf{j}$, the particle moves so that the magnitude $|\mathbf{r}|$ is constant, and the particle is a constant distance b from the origin, so the particle is moving in a circle, centre O, radius b. We can also see this by deducing from

$$\mathbf{r} = b \cos t\mathbf{i} + b \sin t\mathbf{j}$$

that $x = b \cos t, \quad y = b \sin t,$

so that the path of the particle is $x^2 + y^2 = b^2$.

If the path of the particle is given by $\mathbf{r} = (\mathbf{i} + 2\mathbf{j}) + t(2\mathbf{i} + 3\mathbf{j})$, we can identify this as a straight line, being of the form $\mathbf{r} = \mathbf{a} + \lambda\mathbf{b}$, a straight line through the point position vector $\mathbf{i} + 2\mathbf{j}$, parallel to the vector $2\mathbf{i} + 3\mathbf{j}$.

Velocity and acceleration

Since velocity is defined as the rate of change of displacement, $\mathbf{v} = d\mathbf{r}/dt$; similarly, acceleration is defined as the rate of change of velocity, i.e. $\mathbf{a} = d\mathbf{v}/dt$. For the particle moving in the path $\mathbf{r} = b \cos t\mathbf{i} + b \sin t\mathbf{j}$,

$$\mathbf{v} = \frac{d\mathbf{r}}{dt} = -b \sin t\mathbf{i} + b \cos t\mathbf{j}$$

and

$$\mathbf{a} = \frac{d\mathbf{v}}{dt} = -b \cos t\mathbf{i} - b \sin t\mathbf{j}$$

We notice that $\mathbf{a} = -\mathbf{r}$, the acceleration of a particle describing a circle is always inwards along the radius (see also Ex. 21.2, Q. 4). The *speed* of a particle is the magnitude of its velocity.

Example. *The position vector of a particle is given by* $\mathbf{r} = 2t^3\mathbf{i} + 3t\mathbf{j}$. *Show that the acceleration is constant in direction but varying in magnitude.*

Since $\mathbf{r} = 2t^3\mathbf{i} + 3t\mathbf{j}$

$$\mathbf{v} = 6t^2\mathbf{i} + 3\mathbf{j}$$

and $\mathbf{a} = 12t\mathbf{i},$

which is always in the direction of $\mathbf{i}$, but with magnitude proportional to t.

Exercise 21.2

1. The position vector of a particle P is given by $\mathbf{r}$. Find the velocity and acceleration of the particle in each of the following cases:
   (i) $\mathbf{r} = t^2\mathbf{i} + 2\mathbf{j}$,   (ii) $\mathbf{r} = t^2\mathbf{i} + t^2\mathbf{j}$,
   (iii) $\mathbf{r} = \sin t\mathbf{i} + \mathbf{j}$,   (iv) $\mathbf{r} = e^t\,(\mathbf{i} + \mathbf{j})$.
2. Describe the paths of the particles whose position vectors are given in Q.1.
3. The position vector of a particle is given by $\mathbf{r} = c\cos t\mathbf{i} + c\sin t\mathbf{j} + bt\mathbf{k}$. Find the velocity and acceleration of the particle, and describe the path of the particle.
4. The position vector of a particle is given by $\mathbf{r} = c\cos 2t\mathbf{i} + c\sin 2t\mathbf{j} + \mathbf{k}$. Find the velocity and acceleration of the particle, and show that the acceleration is a scalar multiple of $(\mathbf{r} - \mathbf{k})$. Describe the path of the particle.
5. Two particles initially have position vectors $\mathbf{i} + \mathbf{j} + \mathbf{k}$ and $\mathbf{i} + 4\mathbf{j} + \mathbf{k}$. Their constant velocity vectors are $\mathbf{i} + 3\mathbf{j} - \mathbf{k}$ and $2\mathbf{i} + 2\mathbf{j} - \mathbf{k}$ respectively. Find the position vectors of these particles at time t, and hence show that the particles do not collide.

Scalar product

We have defined the scalar product of two vectors $\mathbf{a}$, $\mathbf{b}$ as
$$\mathbf{a} \cdot \mathbf{b} = ab\cos\theta,$$
where θ is the angle between $\mathbf{a}$ and $\mathbf{b}$. We see that it is commutative, i.e. $\mathbf{a} \cdot \mathbf{b} = \mathbf{b} \cdot \mathbf{a}$, and have seen (*Additional Pure Mathematics*, Chapter 15) that it is distributive over addition, i.e. $\mathbf{a} \cdot (\mathbf{b} + \mathbf{c}) = \mathbf{a} \cdot \mathbf{b} + \mathbf{a} \cdot \mathbf{c}$.

One particularly important application of the scalar product is that if $\mathbf{a}$ and $\mathbf{b}$ are two non-zero vectors,
$$\mathbf{a} \cdot \mathbf{b} = 0 \Leftrightarrow \mathbf{a} \text{ and } \mathbf{b} \text{ are perpendicular.}$$

Example 1. *If* $\mathbf{a} = 2\mathbf{i} + \mathbf{j} + 2\mathbf{k}$ *and* $\mathbf{b} = -\mathbf{i} + 7\mathbf{j} + 4\mathbf{k}$, $\mathbf{c} = 2\mathbf{i} + 2\mathbf{j} - 3\mathbf{k}$, *show that* $\mathbf{c}$ *is perpendicular to both* $\mathbf{a}$ *and* $\mathbf{b}$, *and find the cosine of the angle between* $\mathbf{a}$ *and* $\mathbf{b}$.

$$\mathbf{a} \cdot \mathbf{c} = (2\mathbf{i} + \mathbf{j} + 2\mathbf{k}) \cdot (2\mathbf{i} + 2\mathbf{j} - 3\mathbf{k})$$
$$= 4 + 2 - 6,$$
since $\mathbf{i} \cdot \mathbf{i} = \mathbf{j} \cdot \mathbf{j} = \mathbf{k} \cdot \mathbf{k} = 1$ and $\mathbf{i} \cdot \mathbf{j} = \mathbf{j} \cdot \mathbf{k} = \mathbf{k} \cdot \mathbf{i} = 0$
and
$$\mathbf{b} \cdot \mathbf{c} = (-\mathbf{i} + 7\mathbf{j} + 4\mathbf{k}) \cdot (2\mathbf{i} + 2\mathbf{j} - 3\mathbf{k})$$
$$= -2 + 14 - 12$$
$$= 0$$
so that $\mathbf{c}$ is perpendicular to $\mathbf{a}$ and to $\mathbf{b}$.
$$\mathbf{a} \cdot \mathbf{b} = (2\mathbf{i} + \mathbf{j} + 2\mathbf{k}) \cdot (-\mathbf{i} + 7\mathbf{j} + 4\mathbf{k})$$
$$= -2 + 7 + 8$$
$$= 13.$$

Now $\qquad a = |\mathbf{a}| = \sqrt{(2^2 + 1^2 + 2^2)} = 3$
and $\qquad b = \sqrt{((-1)^2 + 7^2 + 4^2)} = \sqrt{66}$,
so that from $\qquad \mathbf{a} \cdot \mathbf{b} = ab \cos \theta$,
$$13 = 3\sqrt{66} \cos \theta,$$
$$\cos \theta = \frac{13}{3\sqrt{66}}.$$

Example 2. *Points A, B, C have position vectors $\mathbf{i} + 2\mathbf{j}$, $4\mathbf{i} + 3\mathbf{j}$ and $-\mathbf{i} - 4\mathbf{j}$ respectively. Find the cosine of the angle ABC.*

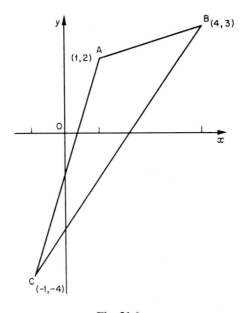

Fig. 21.6

The points A, B, C are shown in Fig. 21.6. We see $\overrightarrow{BA} = -3\mathbf{i} - \mathbf{j}$, $\overrightarrow{BC} = -5\mathbf{i} - 7\mathbf{j}$, so that $|\overrightarrow{BA}| = \sqrt{10}$, $|\overrightarrow{BC}| = \sqrt{74}$ and $\mathbf{a} \cdot \mathbf{b} = 22$, so that $\cos \theta = \dfrac{11}{\sqrt{185}}$.

Notice that $\cos \theta$ is positive, showing that θ is acute. We had to take care to measure both vectors *from* the point of intersection B, so that we were finding the angle between BA and BC, and not the angle between AB and BC, for this would be the obtuse (exterior) angle. A clear diagram helped us to avoid the possible error.

Equation of a straight line

A straight line through the point position vector **a** in the direction of the vector **b**, will be **r** = **a** + λ**b**, where λ is a parameter that determines each point on the line.

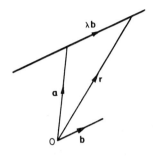

Fig. 21.7

Example. *The equation of the straight line through points A, B where* **a** = *3***i** + *4***j** + *5***k** *and* **b** = *6***i** + *5***j** + *4***k** *is* **r** = **a** + λ(**b** − **a**)

i.e. **r** = *3***i** + *4***j** + *5***k** + λ(*3***i** + **j** − **k**).

Equation of a plane

A plane Π will be determined if we know a vector perpendicular to Π, and a point through which Π passes. Suppose that **a** is the position vector of a point in Π, and **n** a vector perpendicular to Π. Then if **r** is the position vector of any point in Π, **r** − **a** lies in Π and so is perpendicular to **n**,

i.e. (**r** − **a**).**n** = 0,

i.e. **r**.**n** = **a**.**n**.

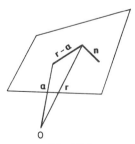

Fig. 21.8

Example. *The equation of the plane through the point position vector* $3\mathbf{i} + 4\mathbf{j} + 5\mathbf{k}$ *perpendicular to the vector* $\mathbf{i} - 2\mathbf{j} + 3\mathbf{k}$ *is* $\mathbf{r}.\mathbf{a} = \mathbf{a}.\mathbf{n}$

Therefore $\mathbf{r}.(\mathbf{i} - 2\mathbf{j} + 3\mathbf{k}) = (3\mathbf{i} + 4\mathbf{j} + 5\mathbf{k}).(\mathbf{i} - 2\mathbf{j} + 3\mathbf{k}) = 10.$

This can be written $x - 2y + 3z = 10.$

Plane through three points

A plane is determined by three points. If those points are A, B and C, then if we can find a vector perpendicular to AB and perpendicular to AC, that vector will be perpendicular to the plane ABC, and will serve as the vector $\mathbf{n}$ is the above equation of the plane. The method is illustrated in the next example.

Example. *The position vectors of points* A, B, C *are* $\mathbf{i} - \mathbf{j} - \mathbf{k}$, $3\mathbf{i} + 2\mathbf{j} - \mathbf{k}$ *and* $-\mathbf{i} + \mathbf{k}$ *respectively. Find the equation of the plane* ABC.

The vector $\overrightarrow{AB}$ is $2\mathbf{i} + 3\mathbf{j}$; the vector $\overrightarrow{BC}$ is $-4\mathbf{i} - 2\mathbf{j} + 2\mathbf{k}$. Let $\mathbf{n}$ be the vector $p\mathbf{i} + q\mathbf{j} + r\mathbf{k}$. Then since $\mathbf{n}$ is perpendicular to $\overrightarrow{AB}$,

$$(p\mathbf{i} + q\mathbf{j} + r\mathbf{k}).(2\mathbf{i} + 3\mathbf{j}) = 0,$$

i.e. $2p + 3q = 0.$

Since $\mathbf{n}$ is perpendicular to $\overrightarrow{BC}$,

$$(p\mathbf{i} + q\mathbf{j} + r\mathbf{k}).(-4\mathbf{i} - 2\mathbf{j} + 2\mathbf{k}) = 0,$$

i.e. $-4p - 2q + 2r = 0,$

$$2p + q - r = 0.$$

Since we are only interested in the direction of $\mathbf{n}$, we can give p (or q or r) any value we wish. Here, take $p = 3$, to avoid fractions in q. Then $q = -2$ and $r = 4$, so that

$$\mathbf{n} = 3\mathbf{i} - 2\mathbf{j} + 4\mathbf{k}$$

and the equation of the plane $\mathbf{r}.\mathbf{n} = \mathbf{a}.\mathbf{n}$ becomes is

$$\mathbf{r}.(3\mathbf{i} - 2\mathbf{j} + 4\mathbf{k}) = (\mathbf{i} - \mathbf{j} - \mathbf{k}).(3\mathbf{i} - 2\mathbf{j} + 4\mathbf{k})$$
$$= 1.$$

This can be written $3x - 2y + 4z = 1.$

Perpendicular distance of a point from a plane

If $\mathbf{p}$ is the perpendicular from the origin O onto the plane, $\mathbf{p}$ is parallel to $\mathbf{n}$, so that

$$\mathbf{p}.\mathbf{n} = pn.$$

But since $\mathbf{P}$ lies in the plane, $\mathbf{p}.\mathbf{n} = \mathbf{a}.\mathbf{n}$, so the perpendicular distance $\langle A \rangle$ of the origin from the plane is given by $p = \dfrac{\mathbf{a}.\mathbf{n}}{n}$. If $\mathbf{n}$ is a unit vector, this is merely $\mathbf{a}.\mathbf{n}$.

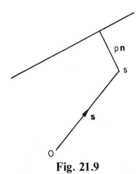

Fig. 21.9

To find the perpendicular distance of a general point S position vector $\mathbf{s}$ from the plane $\mathbf{r}.\mathbf{n} = \mathbf{a}.\mathbf{n}$, let this perpendicular distance be p, so that $\mathbf{s} + p\mathbf{n}$ lies in the plane, if $\mathbf{n}$ is a unit vector from S *towards* the plane. Since $\mathbf{s} + p\mathbf{n}$ lies in the plane,

$$(\mathbf{s} + p\mathbf{n}).\mathbf{n} = \mathbf{a}.\mathbf{n}$$
i.e. $\qquad \mathbf{s}.\mathbf{n} + p = \mathbf{a}.\mathbf{n}$
i.e. $\qquad p = \mathbf{a}.\mathbf{n} - \mathbf{s}.\mathbf{n}.$

Strictly, since p is a distance, this must be positive, so that the perpendicular distance of S from the plane is $|\mathbf{a}.\mathbf{n} - \mathbf{s}.\mathbf{n}|$.

This expression also gives us the perpendicular distance of a point S from a straight line L, if $\mathbf{n}$ is a unit vector perpendicular to L in the plane containing S.

Example. *Find the perpendicular distance of the point S $2\mathbf{i} - 3\mathbf{j} + \mathbf{k}$ from the plane* $\mathbf{r}.(2\mathbf{i} + 2\mathbf{j} - \mathbf{k}) = 5$.

First we notice that $2\mathbf{i} + 2\mathbf{j} - \mathbf{k}$ is not a unit vector, but has magnitude $\sqrt{(2^2 + 2^2 + 1^2)}$, i.e. 3 so that we write the equation of the plane in the form

$$\mathbf{r}.(\tfrac{2}{3}\mathbf{i} + \tfrac{2}{3}\mathbf{j} - \tfrac{1}{3}\mathbf{k}) = \tfrac{5}{3}$$

and see $\mathbf{a}.\mathbf{n} = \tfrac{5}{3}$.

$$\mathbf{s}.\mathbf{n} = (2\mathbf{i} - 3\mathbf{j} + \mathbf{k}).(\tfrac{2}{3}\mathbf{i} + \tfrac{2}{3}\mathbf{j} - \tfrac{1}{3}\mathbf{k})$$
$$= -1$$

so that $\qquad \mathbf{a}.\mathbf{n} - \mathbf{s}.\mathbf{n} = \tfrac{8}{3},$

the perpendicular distance of S from the plane is $\tfrac{8}{3}$.

Reflection of a point in a plane

To find the image of S when reflected in the plane in the above example, call the image T, position vector $\mathbf{t}$. Then

$$\mathbf{t} = \mathbf{s} + 2p\mathbf{n}.$$

To make sure that we have $\mathbf{n}$ in the right direction, check that $\mathbf{s} + p\mathbf{n}$ lies in the plane.

$$\mathbf{s} + p\mathbf{n} = 2\mathbf{i} - 3\mathbf{j} + \mathbf{k} + \tfrac{8}{3}(\tfrac{2}{3}\mathbf{i} + \tfrac{2}{3}\mathbf{j} - \tfrac{1}{3}\mathbf{k})$$
$$= \tfrac{34}{9}\mathbf{i} - \tfrac{11}{9}\mathbf{j} + \tfrac{1}{9}\mathbf{k}$$

and $\frac{1}{9}(34\mathbf{i} - 11\mathbf{j} + \mathbf{k}) \cdot (2\mathbf{i} + 2\mathbf{j} - \mathbf{k}) = 5$, so that $\mathbf{s} + p\mathbf{n}$ lies in the plane and $\mathbf{t} = \mathbf{s} + 2p\mathbf{n}$,

$$\therefore \quad \mathbf{t} = 2\mathbf{i} - 3\mathbf{j} + \mathbf{k} + \tfrac{16}{3}(\tfrac{2}{3}\mathbf{i} + \tfrac{2}{3}\mathbf{j} - \tfrac{1}{3}\mathbf{k})$$
$$= \tfrac{50}{9}\mathbf{i} + \tfrac{5}{9}\mathbf{j} - \tfrac{7}{9}\mathbf{k}.$$

We can check that the midpoint of ST is the point whose position vector is $\mathbf{s} + p\mathbf{n}$, which we have already found.

Exercise 21.3

1. Show that the vectors $2\mathbf{i} - 3\mathbf{j} + \mathbf{k}$ and $2\mathbf{i} + \mathbf{j} - \mathbf{k}$ are perpendicular.

2. Find the cosine of the angle between the vectors $3\mathbf{i} - \mathbf{j}$ and $2\mathbf{i} + \mathbf{j}$.

3. Show that $\tfrac{2}{3}\mathbf{i} - \tfrac{1}{3}\mathbf{j} + \tfrac{2}{3}\mathbf{k}$ is a unit vector perpendicular to $\mathbf{i} + 4\mathbf{j} + \mathbf{k}$ and $\mathbf{i} - 4\mathbf{j} - 3\mathbf{k}$.

4. Find two unit vectors perpendicular to $3\mathbf{i} - 4\mathbf{j}$.

5. Find two unit vectors perpendicular to $3\mathbf{i} + 4\mathbf{j} + 2\mathbf{k}$ and $5\mathbf{i} + 4\mathbf{j} - 2\mathbf{k}$.

6. Find unit vectors in the (x, y) plane inclined at $60°$ to the vector $\mathbf{i} + \mathbf{j}$.

7. Find the equation of the straight line through the points position vectors $3\mathbf{i} + \mathbf{j}$ and $\mathbf{i} - 4\mathbf{j}$.

8. Find the equation of the straight line through the points position vectors $\mathbf{i} + 2\mathbf{k}$ and $3\mathbf{i} - 2\mathbf{j} - \mathbf{k}$.

9. Find the equation of the plane through the points position vectors $\mathbf{i} + 3\mathbf{j} + 3\mathbf{k}$, $5\mathbf{j} + 2\mathbf{k}$, $-\mathbf{i} + \mathbf{j} - 2\mathbf{k}$.

10. Find the equation of the plane through the points position vectors $-2\mathbf{i} + \mathbf{j} - 2\mathbf{k}$, $3\mathbf{i} - \mathbf{j} - \mathbf{k}$, $4\mathbf{i} - 2\mathbf{j} + 3\mathbf{k}$.

11. Find the perpendicular distance of the point position vector $2\mathbf{i} + 3\mathbf{j} + 5\mathbf{k}$ from the plane $\mathbf{r} \cdot (\mathbf{i} + \mathbf{j} + \mathbf{k}) = 0$.

12. Find the perpendicular distance of the point position vector $3\mathbf{i} - 4\mathbf{j} - \mathbf{k}$ from the plane $\mathbf{r} \cdot (3\mathbf{i} + 4\mathbf{k}) = 1$, and the image of this point when reflected in the plane.

13. Find the perpendicular distance of the point $7\mathbf{j} - 10\mathbf{k}$ from the plane $\mathbf{r} \cdot (2\mathbf{i} + 6\mathbf{j} - 9\mathbf{k}) = 11$, and the image of the point when reflected in the plane.

14. Find the perpendicular distance of the origin from the straight line $\mathbf{r} \cdot (2\mathbf{i} + 3\mathbf{j}) = 1$.

15. Find the perpendicular distance of the point position vector $\mathbf{i} + 2\mathbf{j}$ from the line $\mathbf{r} \cdot (3\mathbf{i} - 4\mathbf{j}) = 5$, and the image of that point when reflected in the line.

16. Find the vector equations of the straight lines through the point position vector $3\mathbf{i} - 2\mathbf{j}$ parallel and perpendicular to $\mathbf{r} \cdot (3\mathbf{i} + 4\mathbf{j}) = 7$.

17. Find the area of the triangle OBC, where B and C have position vectors $3\mathbf{i} + 2\mathbf{j}$ and $5\mathbf{i} + 4\mathbf{j}$ respectively.

18. Find the equation of the straight line through the point position vector $3\mathbf{i} + \mathbf{j}$ and the midpoint of the line joining the points position vectors $2\mathbf{i} + 4\mathbf{j}$ and $7\mathbf{i} + 10\mathbf{j}$.

19. Are the points position vectors $2\mathbf{i} + \mathbf{j}$ and $5\mathbf{i} - 2\mathbf{j}$ on the same side or opposite sides of the line $\mathbf{r}.(5\mathbf{i} - 2\mathbf{j}) = 3$?

20. Find the acute angle between the straight lines $\mathbf{r}.(3\mathbf{i} - 4\mathbf{j}) = 7$ and $\mathbf{r}.(2\mathbf{i} - 3\mathbf{j}) = 5$.

21. The two straight lines $\mathbf{r}.(\mathbf{i} + m\mathbf{j}) = 2$ and $\mathbf{r}.(\mathbf{i} - m\mathbf{j}) = 3$ are perpendicular. Find the two possible values of m.

22. Find the position vector of the reflection of the point position vector $\mathbf{i} + 2\mathbf{j}$ in the line $\mathbf{r}.(\mathbf{i} - \mathbf{j}) = 0$.

23. Find the position vector of the reflection of the origin in the line $\mathbf{r}.(3\mathbf{i} + 4\mathbf{j}) = 5$.

24. Points A, B, C, D have position vectors

$$\mathbf{a} = \begin{pmatrix} 1 \\ 0 \\ 0 \end{pmatrix}, \quad \mathbf{b} = \begin{pmatrix} 4 \\ 0 \\ 0 \end{pmatrix}, \quad \mathbf{c} = \begin{pmatrix} 0 \\ 3 \\ 0 \end{pmatrix} \quad \text{and} \quad \mathbf{d} = \begin{pmatrix} 0 \\ 0 \\ 5 \end{pmatrix}.$$

Find (i) the area of the triangle ABC,
 (ii) the volume of the tetrahedron $ABCD$.

25. Points A, B, C, D have position vectors

$$\mathbf{a} = \begin{pmatrix} 1 \\ 0 \\ 0 \end{pmatrix}, \quad \mathbf{b} = \begin{pmatrix} 0 \\ 1 \\ 0 \end{pmatrix}, \quad \mathbf{c} = \begin{pmatrix} 0 \\ 0 \\ 1 \end{pmatrix} \quad \text{and} \quad \mathbf{d} = \begin{pmatrix} 2 \\ 2 \\ 2 \end{pmatrix}.$$

Find (i) the area of the triangle ABC,
 (ii) the volume of the tetrahedron.

26. Find the volume of the tetrahedron whose vertices have position vectors

$$\begin{pmatrix} 0 \\ 3 \\ -2 \end{pmatrix}, \quad \begin{pmatrix} 2 \\ 5 \\ 4 \end{pmatrix}, \quad \begin{pmatrix} 3 \\ 4 \\ 0 \end{pmatrix} \quad \text{and} \quad \begin{pmatrix} 5 \\ 2 \\ 3 \end{pmatrix}.$$

27. Find whether the straight line through the points position vectors $2\mathbf{j} + \mathbf{k}$ and $3\mathbf{i} - \mathbf{j} + 4\mathbf{k}$ meets the straight line through the points $3\mathbf{i} - \mathbf{j}$ and $-2\mathbf{i} + 4\mathbf{j} + 5\mathbf{k}$. Find also the cosine of the acute angle between these two lines.

28. Find the vector equation of the circle on points position vectors $\mathbf{i} + \mathbf{j}$ and $4\mathbf{i} - 2\mathbf{j}$ as diameter.

29. Show that the sphere on points position vectors $2\mathbf{i} + \mathbf{j} + \mathbf{k}$ and $\mathbf{i} - 4\mathbf{j} + 2\mathbf{k}$ as diameter passes through the origin.

30. Find the cosine of the angle between the planes
  $\mathbf{r}.(\mathbf{i} - \mathbf{j} + 3\mathbf{k}) = 7$ and $\mathbf{r}.(\mathbf{i} + 2\mathbf{j} + 3\mathbf{k}) = 15$.

Applications to geometry

We have seen in *Additional Pure Mathematics* many examples where vectors can be used to prove elegantly many geometrical results. We saw that we could prove that the diagonals of a parallelogram bisect each other, that the medians of a triangle concur at the centroid, and perhaps neatest of all, that using the scalar product we can prove that the altitudes of a triangle meet at a point, the orthocentre.

Many of these proofs depend on the section theorem, that if the point P divides AB in the ratio of $\lambda:\mu$, the position vector $\mathbf{p}$ of P is

$$\frac{\mu \mathbf{a} + \lambda \mathbf{b}}{\lambda + \mu} = \frac{\mu}{\lambda + \mu}\,\mathbf{a} + \frac{\lambda}{\lambda + \mu}\,\mathbf{b}.$$

Since $\dfrac{\mu}{\lambda + \mu} + \dfrac{\lambda}{\lambda + \mu} = 1$, it is often more convenient to think of this as

$$\mathbf{p} = v\mathbf{a} + (1 - v)\mathbf{b},$$

e.g. the position vector of the midpoint is $\frac{1}{2}\mathbf{a} + \frac{1}{2}\mathbf{b}$,
the position vectors of the points of trisection are $\frac{1}{3}\mathbf{a} + \frac{2}{3}\mathbf{b}$ and $\frac{2}{3}\mathbf{a} + \frac{1}{3}\mathbf{b}$.
These examples illustrate solutions to two problems.

Example 1. *In the triangle ABC, the point P divides BC in the ratio 2:1 and the point Q divides CA in the ratio 3:1. PQ produced meets BA produced in R. Find the ratio AR:RB.*

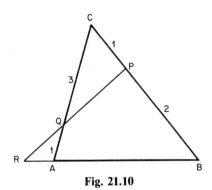

Fig. 21.10

Taking $\mathbf{a}$, $\mathbf{b}$, $\mathbf{c}$ as position vectors for A, B, C, the position vector of P is $\frac{1}{3}(\mathbf{b} + 2\mathbf{c})$ and of Q is $\frac{1}{4}(3\mathbf{a} + \mathbf{c})$. Any point on PQ has position vector

$$\lambda\tfrac{1}{3}(\mathbf{b} + 2\mathbf{c}) + (1 - \lambda)\tfrac{1}{4}(3\mathbf{a} + \mathbf{c}) = \tfrac{3}{4}(1 - \lambda)\mathbf{a} + \tfrac{1}{3}\lambda\mathbf{b} + \tfrac{1}{4}(1 + \tfrac{5}{3}\lambda)\mathbf{c}.$$

Any point on AB must be of the form $\mu\mathbf{a} + (1 - \mu)\mathbf{b}$, i.e. without any vector $\mathbf{c}$, so that $\frac{1}{4}(1 + \frac{5}{3}\lambda) = 0$, i.e. $\lambda = -\frac{3}{5}$, so

$$\mathbf{r} = \tfrac{3}{4}(1 + \tfrac{3}{5})\mathbf{a} + \tfrac{1}{3}(-\tfrac{3}{5})\mathbf{b}$$
$$= \tfrac{6}{5}\mathbf{a} - \tfrac{1}{5}\mathbf{b},$$

i.e. R divides AB externally in the ratio $-1:6$, and $AR:RB = -1:6$.

Example 2. *If O is the circumcentre of the triangle ABC, G the centroid and H the point in OG produced such that OG:GH = 1:2, prove that CH is perpendicular to AB, and that the three altitudes meet at H.*

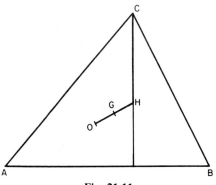

Fig. 21.11

Taking O as the origin of the position vectors, and with the usual notation, since $OA = OB = OC$,

$$|\mathbf{a}| = |\mathbf{b}| = |\mathbf{c}|.$$

The position vector of G is $\frac{1}{3}(\mathbf{a} + \mathbf{b} + \mathbf{c})$, and so the position vector of H is $(\mathbf{a} + \mathbf{b} + \mathbf{c})$.

The vector
$$\overrightarrow{CH} = (\mathbf{a} + \mathbf{b} + \mathbf{c}) - \mathbf{c}$$
$$= \mathbf{a} + \mathbf{b},$$

and this will be perpendicular to AB if $(\mathbf{a} + \mathbf{b}) \cdot (\mathbf{a} - \mathbf{b}) = 0$,

i.e. $\mathbf{a}^2 - \mathbf{b}^2 = 0$.

But $|\mathbf{a}| = |\mathbf{b}|$, so $\mathbf{a}^2 = \mathbf{b}^2$, and CH is perpendicular to AB.

Similarly BH is perpendicular to AC and AH is perpendicular to BC, so the three altitudes of the triangle concur at H.

The straight line OGH is called the Euler line of the triangle. It can be shown that the midpoint of OH is the centre of the nine-point circle, drawn through the midpoints of the sides AB, BC, CA, the midpoints of AH, BH and CH, and the feet of the altitudes drawn from each vertex A, B, C to the opposite side.

Exercise 21.4

(Throughout this exercise, where appropriate, the position vector of the point A is $\mathbf{a}$, etc.)

1. If M is the midpoint of AB, find the position vector of B in terms of $\mathbf{a}$ and $\mathbf{m}$.

2. The point P divides AB in the ratio 1:2. Find the position vector of B in terms of $\mathbf{a}$ and $\mathbf{p}$.

3. If G is the centroid of the triangle OAB, find the position vector of B in terms of $\mathbf{a}$ and $\mathbf{g}$.

4. If G is the centroid of the tetrahedron $OABC$, find the position vector of C in terms of $\mathbf{a}$, $\mathbf{b}$ and $\mathbf{g}$.

5. If $OABC$ is a parallelogram, find the position vector of C in terms of $\mathbf{a}$ and $\mathbf{b}$.

6. If $OABC$ is a trapezium with BC parallel to OA and twice the length of OA, find the position vector of C in terms of $\mathbf{a}$ and $\mathbf{b}$.

7. Find the position vector of P, the point of trisection nearer A of AB, in terms of $\mathbf{a}$ and $\mathbf{b}$, and the point vector of X, the midpoint of OP.
   AX produced meets OB at Y. Find the position vector of Y.

8. Show that three points P, Q, R are collinear if and only if there exist three scalars, λ, μ, ν, not all zero, such that
$$\lambda\mathbf{p} + \mu\mathbf{q} + \nu\mathbf{r} = 0 \quad \text{where} \quad \lambda + \mu + \nu = 0.$$

9. Four coplanar points A, B, C and D have position vectors $\mathbf{a}$, $\mathbf{b}$, $2\mathbf{a}$ and $3\mathbf{b}$ respectively. Find in terms of $\mathbf{a}$ and $\mathbf{b}$ the position vector of the point of intersection of AB and CD, both produced.

10. Points A and B have position vectors $\mathbf{a}$ and $\mathbf{b}$ as usual, and a point X is defined by
$$\mathbf{x} = \frac{b\mathbf{a} + a\mathbf{b}}{b + a + |\mathbf{b} - \mathbf{a}|}.$$
Show that
$$\frac{\mathbf{x} \cdot \mathbf{a}}{a} = \frac{\mathbf{x} \cdot \mathbf{b}}{b} \quad \text{and} \quad \frac{(\mathbf{x} - \mathbf{b}) \cdot (\mathbf{a} - \mathbf{b})}{|\mathbf{a} - \mathbf{b}|} = \frac{(\mathbf{b} - \mathbf{x}) \cdot \mathbf{b}}{b}.$$
Deduce that X is the incentre of the triangle OAB.

11. Express the scalar product $\mathbf{a} \cdot \mathbf{b}$ of two vectors in two dimensions in terms of their components a_1, a_2 and b_1, b_2 in two perpendicular directions. Use your expression to prove that, for three coplanar vectors $\mathbf{a}$, $\mathbf{b}$, $\mathbf{c}$,
$$\mathbf{a} \cdot (\mathbf{b} + \mathbf{c}) = \mathbf{a} \cdot \mathbf{b} + \mathbf{a} \cdot \mathbf{c}.$$
Show also that
$$|\mathbf{a} + \mathbf{b}|^2 + |\mathbf{a} - \mathbf{b}|^2 = 2|\mathbf{a}|^2 + 2|\mathbf{b}|^2.$$
The points P, Q, R, S are the vertices of a plane rhombus. Prove, by means of vectors, that
(i) the diagonals PR, QS are perpendicular to each other,
(ii) $PR^2 + QS^2 = PQ^2 + QR^2 + RS^2 + SP^2$. (M.E.I.)

12. In the triangle ABC, the mid-point of AB is D and the mid-point of CD is E. The position vectors, with respect to an origin O, of the points A, B and C are $\mathbf{a}$, $\mathbf{b}$ and $\mathbf{c}$ respectively. Show that the position vector of E, with respect to O, is $\frac{1}{4}\mathbf{a} + \frac{1}{4}\mathbf{b} + \frac{1}{2}\mathbf{c}$.
   The point F lies on BC, between B and C, and $BF = 2FC$. Find the position vector of F with respect to O and show that the point E lies on AF. (J.M.B.)

13. The points A, B and C have position vectors $\mathbf{a}$, $\mathbf{b}$ and $\mathbf{c}$ with respect to an origin O. The point R in the plane ABC has position vector $\mathbf{r}$ where $\mathbf{r} = \frac{1}{2}(\frac{2}{3}\mathbf{a} + \frac{1}{3}\mathbf{b}) + \frac{1}{2}\mathbf{c}$. Use the ratio theorem to obtain a geometrical description of the position of R with reference to the points A, B and C. Illustrate your answer with a diagram.

By writing $\mathbf{r}$ in the form $\lambda\mathbf{a} + \mu\,(m\mathbf{b} + n\mathbf{c})$ where $\lambda + \mu = 1$, obtain an alternative description of the position of R.

Given that the point S has position vector $\frac{2}{3}\mathbf{a} + \frac{1}{12}\mathbf{b} + \frac{1}{4}\mathbf{c}$, show that S bisects the line segment AR. (J.M.B.)

14. Points X, Y, Z have position vectors denoted by $\mathbf{x}$, $\mathbf{y}$, $\mathbf{z}$ relative to an origin O. Write the expression $\mathbf{p} = \frac{1}{2}\mathbf{x} + \frac{2}{5}\mathbf{y} + \frac{1}{10}\mathbf{z}$ in the form $a\mathbf{x} + b$ $(c\mathbf{y} + d\mathbf{z})$, where $a + b = 1$. Hence describe how the point P, with position vector $\mathbf{p}$, is related to the points X, Y, Z.

By writing $\mathbf{p}$ in terms of $\mathbf{x}$, $\mathbf{y}$, $\mathbf{z}$ in another way, give a different description of the relation of P to X, Y, Z. (S.M.P.)

15. The three vertices of a triangle ABC have position vectors $\mathbf{a}$, $\mathbf{b}$, $\mathbf{c}$ with respect to an origin O, not lying in the plane of the triangle. A point H in the plane of the triangle has position vector $\mathbf{h}$ with respect to O, where $\mathbf{h}$ satisfies the two equations:

$$(\mathbf{h} - \mathbf{a}).(\mathbf{b} - \mathbf{c}) = 0, \quad (\mathbf{h} - \mathbf{b}).(\mathbf{c} - \mathbf{a}) = 0.$$

Show that

$$(\mathbf{h} - \mathbf{c}).(\mathbf{a} - \mathbf{b}) = 0,$$

and give a geometrical interpretation of this result.

Explain why there are numbers α, β, γ such that

$$\mathbf{h} = \alpha\mathbf{a} + \beta\mathbf{b} + \gamma\mathbf{c} \quad \text{and} \quad \alpha + \beta + \gamma = 1.$$

Find α, β, γ in terms of

$$k = (\mathbf{a} - \mathbf{b}).(\mathbf{a} - \mathbf{c}), \quad l = (\mathbf{b} - \mathbf{c}).(\mathbf{b} - \mathbf{a}), \quad m = (\mathbf{c} - \mathbf{a}).(\mathbf{c} - \mathbf{b}).$$

(M.E.I.)

The vector product

Having defined the scalar (or 'dot') product of two vectors $\mathbf{a}$, $\mathbf{b}$ as $\mathbf{a}.\mathbf{b}$ $= ab\cos\theta$, we find it convenient to define a vector (or cross) product of the vectors $\mathbf{a}$, $\mathbf{b}$ by

$$\mathbf{a} \times \mathbf{b} = ab\sin\theta\mathbf{n}$$

where $\mathbf{n}$ is a unit vector at right angles to the plane containing $\mathbf{a}$ and $\mathbf{b}$, and in the direction of motion produced by rotating a right-hand screw from $\mathbf{a}$ to $\mathbf{b}$ (see Fig. 21.12).* It follows from this definition that

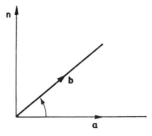

Fig. 21.12

* Sometimes the notation $\mathbf{a} \wedge \mathbf{b}$ will be found.

$\mathbf{b} \times \mathbf{a} = ab \sin \theta(-\mathbf{n})$, so that $\mathbf{a} \times \mathbf{b} = -\mathbf{b} \times \mathbf{a}$, and vector products are not commutative. On the other hand, it can be proved that the vector product is distributive over addition, i.e.

$$\mathbf{a} \times (\mathbf{b} + \mathbf{c}) = \mathbf{a} \times \mathbf{b} + \mathbf{a} \times \mathbf{c}$$

From the definition, we see that

$$\mathbf{i} \times \mathbf{i} = \mathbf{j} \times \mathbf{j} = \mathbf{k} \times \mathbf{k} = 0$$

and
$$\mathbf{i} \times \mathbf{j} = -\mathbf{j} \times \mathbf{i} = \mathbf{k}, \text{ etc.}$$

Great care must be taken in finding the vector products of two vectors given in terms of their components, as it is easy to make an error in the sign of the terms, e.g.

$$\begin{aligned}
(2\mathbf{i} + 3\mathbf{j} + 4\mathbf{k}) \times (\mathbf{i} - \mathbf{j} + 2\mathbf{k}) &= 2\mathbf{i} \times (-\mathbf{j}) + 2\mathbf{i} \times 2\mathbf{k} + 3\mathbf{j} \times \mathbf{i} \\
&\quad + 3\mathbf{j} \times 2\mathbf{k} + 4\mathbf{k} \times \mathbf{i} + 4\mathbf{k} \times (-\mathbf{j}) \\
&= 10\mathbf{i} - 5\mathbf{k}
\end{aligned}$$

and it can be seen that this product is the determinant

$$\begin{vmatrix} \mathbf{i} & \mathbf{j} & \mathbf{k} \\ 2 & 3 & 4 \\ 1 & -1 & 2 \end{vmatrix}$$

It is often found that writing the product in determinant form reduces the arithmetic errors.

Area of triangle

Since the vector product contains the sine of the angle between the vectors $\mathbf{a}$ and $\mathbf{b}$, we see that the area of the triangle OAB is $\frac{1}{2}|\mathbf{a} \times \mathbf{b}|$. More generally, the area of the triangle ABC is $\frac{1}{2}|(\mathbf{b} - \mathbf{a}) \times (\mathbf{c} - \mathbf{a})|$.

Example. *The position vectors of points A, B and C are $2\mathbf{i} + \mathbf{k}$, $3\mathbf{i} + \mathbf{j} - \mathbf{k}$ and $\mathbf{i} + 2\mathbf{j} + 3\mathbf{k}$. Find the area of the triangle ABC.*

We see that
$$(\mathbf{b} - \mathbf{a}) = \mathbf{i} + \mathbf{j} - 2\mathbf{k},$$
$$(\mathbf{c} - \mathbf{a}) = -\mathbf{i} + 2\mathbf{j} + 2\mathbf{k},$$

so
$$\begin{aligned}
\Delta ABC &= \tfrac{1}{2}|(\mathbf{b} - \mathbf{a}) \times (\mathbf{c} - \mathbf{a})| \\
&= \tfrac{1}{2}(\mathbf{i} + \mathbf{j} - 2\mathbf{k}) \times (-\mathbf{i} + 2\mathbf{j} + 2\mathbf{k}).
\end{aligned}$$

Now
$$\begin{vmatrix} \mathbf{i} & \mathbf{j} & \mathbf{k} \\ 1 & 1 & -2 \\ -1 & 2 & 2 \end{vmatrix}$$

$$= 6\mathbf{i} + 3\mathbf{k}$$
$$\therefore \quad \Delta ABC = \tfrac{1}{2}\sqrt{(6^2 + 3^2)} = \tfrac{3}{2}\sqrt{5}.$$

Perpendicular distance of a point from a straight line

If A is a point on the straight line l, equation $\mathbf{r} = \mathbf{a} + \lambda\mathbf{b}$, the perpendicular distance of the point P from l is $AP \sin \theta$. This is $|(\mathbf{p} - \mathbf{a}) \times \mathbf{b}|$ if $\mathbf{b}$ is a *unit* vector along l.

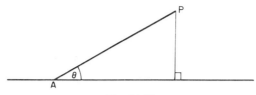

Fig. 21.13

Example. *Find the perpendicular distance of the point position vector*
$3i + 2j + k$ *from the straight line* $r = i + j + \lambda(i + 2j + 2k)$.

First notice that $i + 2j + 2k$ is not a unit vector, but has magnitude 3, so
that
$$b = \tfrac{1}{3}(i + 2j + 2k),$$
$$a = i + j$$
and
$$p - a = 2i + j + k.$$
Then
$$(p - a) \times b = (2i + j + k) \times \tfrac{1}{3}(i + 2j + 2k)$$
$$= \tfrac{1}{3}\begin{vmatrix} i & j & k \\ 2 & 1 & 1 \\ 1 & 2 & 2 \end{vmatrix}$$
$$= \tfrac{1}{3}(-3j + 3k)$$
and the perpendicular distance is
$$|(-j + k)| = \sqrt{2}.$$

Volume of a tetrahedron

The volume of a tetrahedron is $\tfrac{1}{3}$base-area × height. If O, A, B, C are
the vertices of a tetrahedron, the area of the base OAB we know is
$\tfrac{1}{2}|a \times b|$. The vector $a \times b$ is perpendicular to the base OAB, and we can
see from Fig. 21.14 that the perpendicular height of the tetrahedron is
$OC \cos \varphi$, i.e. $c.n$, where n is a unit vector along $a \times b$. Thus the

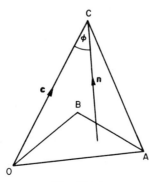

Fig. 21.14

volume of the tetrahedron is

$$\tfrac{1}{3}|\tfrac{1}{2}(\mathbf{a} \times \mathbf{b}).\mathbf{c}| = \tfrac{1}{6}|(\mathbf{a} \times \mathbf{b}).\mathbf{c}|.$$

Similarly, it can of course be shown that the volume is

$$\tfrac{1}{6}|(\mathbf{b} \times \mathbf{c}).\mathbf{a}| \quad \text{and} \quad \tfrac{1}{6}|(\mathbf{c} \times \mathbf{a}).\mathbf{b}|.$$

More generally, the volume of the tetrahedron $ABCD$ is

$$\tfrac{1}{6}|[(\mathbf{b} - \mathbf{d}) \times (\mathbf{c} - \mathbf{d})].(\mathbf{a} - \mathbf{d})|$$

or one of the equivalent forms obtained by permuting $\mathbf{a}$, $\mathbf{b}$, $\mathbf{c}$ and $\mathbf{d}$.

Example. *Find the volume of the tetrahedron $ABCD$ whose vertices have position vectors* $(\mathbf{i} + \mathbf{j})$, $(2\mathbf{i} + 2\mathbf{j} + \mathbf{k})$, $(\mathbf{i} + 3\mathbf{j} + 4\mathbf{k})$ *and* $(-\mathbf{i} - \mathbf{j} - \mathbf{k})$ *respectively.*

Since
$$\mathbf{a} = \mathbf{i} + \mathbf{j},$$
$$\mathbf{b} = 2\mathbf{i} + 2\mathbf{j} + \mathbf{k},$$
$$\mathbf{c} = \mathbf{i} + 3\mathbf{j} + 4\mathbf{k}$$
and
$$\mathbf{d} = -\mathbf{i} - \mathbf{j} - \mathbf{k}$$
$$(\mathbf{b} - \mathbf{d}) = 3\mathbf{i} + 3\mathbf{j} + 2\mathbf{k}$$
and
$$(\mathbf{c} - \mathbf{d}) = 2\mathbf{i} + 4\mathbf{j} + 5\mathbf{k}$$
and
$$(\mathbf{a} - \mathbf{d}) = 2\mathbf{i} + 2\mathbf{j} + \mathbf{k}.$$

Now
$$(\mathbf{b} - \mathbf{d}) \times (\mathbf{c} - \mathbf{d}) = \begin{vmatrix} \mathbf{i} & \mathbf{j} & \mathbf{k} \\ 3 & 3 & 2 \\ 2 & 4 & 5 \end{vmatrix}$$
$$= 7\mathbf{i} - 11\mathbf{j} + 6\mathbf{k}$$

so
$$[(\mathbf{b} - \mathbf{d}) \times (\mathbf{c} - \mathbf{d})].(\mathbf{a} - \mathbf{d}) = (7\mathbf{i} - 11\mathbf{j} + 6\mathbf{k}).(2\mathbf{i} + 2\mathbf{j} + \mathbf{k})$$
$$= -2$$

and the volume of the tetrahedron is $1/3$.

Equation of the plane through three points

If A, B and C are three points, the vector $(\mathbf{b} - \mathbf{a}) \times (\mathbf{c} - \mathbf{a})$ is perpendicular to the plane ABC, and the equation of the plane ABC is

$$(\mathbf{r} - \mathbf{a}).[(\mathbf{b} - \mathbf{a}) \times (\mathbf{c} - \mathbf{a})] = 0$$

$\mathbf{r} - \mathbf{a}$ being a vector in the plane ABC.

Example. *Find the equation of the plane through the points A, B, C position vectors* $\mathbf{i} + \mathbf{j} + 2\mathbf{k}$, $-\mathbf{i} + 2\mathbf{j} - 3\mathbf{k}$ *and* $\mathbf{j} - \mathbf{k}$ *respectively.*

Since $\mathbf{a} = \mathbf{i} + \mathbf{j} + 2\mathbf{k}$, $\mathbf{b} = -\mathbf{i} + 2\mathbf{j} - 3\mathbf{k}$ and $\mathbf{c} = \mathbf{j} - \mathbf{k}$,
$$(\mathbf{b} - \mathbf{a}) \times (\mathbf{c} - \mathbf{a}) = (-2\mathbf{i} + \mathbf{j} - 5\mathbf{k}) \times (-\mathbf{i} - 3\mathbf{k})$$
$$= -3\mathbf{i} - \mathbf{j} + \mathbf{k}$$

and the equation of the plane is
$$\mathbf{r}.(-3\mathbf{i} - \mathbf{j} + \mathbf{k}) = (\mathbf{i} + \mathbf{j} + 2\mathbf{k}).(-3\mathbf{i} - \mathbf{j} + \mathbf{k})$$
$$= -2$$

i.e.
$$\mathbf{r}.(3\mathbf{i} + \mathbf{j} - \mathbf{k}) = 2.$$

This can be written in the cartesian form $3x + y - z = 2$.

Exercise 21.5

1. If $a = 2i + j + k$, $b = 3i - j - 2k$ and $c = j + k$, find
   (i) $a \times b$,   (ii) $b \times c$,   (iii) $c \times a$.
2. Using the values of a, b and c in Q. 1, find
   (i) $(b - a) \times (c - a)$,   (ii) $(b - c) \times (a - c)$,
   (iii) $(c - b) \times (a - b)$.
3. If the position vectors of A and B are $3i + 2j - 4k$ and $2i - j + k$ respectively, find the area of the triangle OAB.
4. If the position vectors of points A, B, C are $2i + 3j + 4k$, $i - 2j - k$ and $i + 3j - k$ respectively, find the area of the triangle ABC.
5. Find the perpendicular distance of the origin from the line
   $$r = 2i + 3j + 4k + \lambda(i + j + k).$$
6. Find the perpendicular distance of the point position vector $2i - 3j + k$ from the straight line $r = i + \lambda(j + 2k)$.
7. Points A and B have position vectors $i - j - k$ and $2i + 2j + k$. Find the area of the triangle OAB.
8. Points A, B and C have position vectors $i - j - k$, $2i + 2j + k$ and $3i - j - k$. Find the area of the triangle ABC.
9. Using the points A, B, C in Q. 8, find the volume of the tetrahedron $OABC$.
10. Points A, B, C have position vectors $2i$, $3j$ and $4k$ respectively. Find the volume of the tetrahedron $OABC$.
11. Find the equation of the plane through the origin and the points position vectors $i + j + k$, $2i + 3j - k$.
12. Find the equation of the plane through the points position vectors i, $i + j + k$, $3i + 5j - 2k$.
13. Find the equation of the plane through the points position vectors $2i + 2j$, $2i + 4j + 2k$ and $-4i + 4j - 2k$.
14. Find the equation of the plane through the point position vector $i + j + k$ and containing the line
    $$r = j + 2k + \lambda(2i + 3j + 4k).$$
15. Find the equation of the plane through the origin and containing the line
    $r = i + 3j + 4k + \lambda(2i + j + 3k)$.

The reader will observe that many of these problems can be solved without the use of the vector product, but can be much more easily solved using it.

Exercise 21.6: Miscellaneous

1. Show that the four points whose position vectors are
$$\begin{pmatrix} 1 \\ 2 \\ -1 \end{pmatrix}, \begin{pmatrix} 0 \\ 3 \\ 4 \end{pmatrix}, \begin{pmatrix} 1 \\ 2 \\ 0 \end{pmatrix} \text{ and } \begin{pmatrix} 3 \\ 0 \\ -14 \end{pmatrix}$$
line in a plane.

2. The position vectors of points A, B, C and D are

$$\mathbf{a} = \begin{pmatrix} 3 \\ 4 \\ 1 \end{pmatrix} \quad \mathbf{b} = \begin{pmatrix} 5 \\ 2 \\ 3 \end{pmatrix} \quad \mathbf{c} = \begin{pmatrix} 6 \\ -1 \\ -1 \end{pmatrix} \quad \text{and } \mathbf{d} = \begin{pmatrix} 7 \\ 5 \\ -2 \end{pmatrix}.$$

   (i) Find the cosine of the angle DAB and show that the perpendicular distance of D from AB is $\sqrt{26}$.
   (ii) Show that the perpendicular distance of D from BC is $\frac{3}{2}\sqrt{14}$.

3. Three points A, B and C have position vectors $\mathbf{a}$, $\mathbf{b}$ and $\mathbf{c}$. Show that the points whose position vectors are $\mathbf{a} + 2\mathbf{b} + \mathbf{c}$, $2\mathbf{a} - \mathbf{b} - \mathbf{c}$ and $5\mathbf{a} - 10\mathbf{b} - 7\mathbf{c}$ are colinear.

4. Find the vector equation of the straight line through the origin making angles of $45°$, $60°$, $60°$ respectively with the unit vectors $\mathbf{i}$, $\mathbf{j}$ and $\mathbf{k}$.

5. Find the loci in a plane given by the following vector equations, when $\mathbf{a}$ is a constant vector and λ a variable scalar.
   (i) $|\mathbf{r}| = |\mathbf{a}|$;   (ii) $\mathbf{r} = \lambda\mathbf{a}$;   (iii) $\mathbf{r}.\mathbf{a} = \frac{1}{2}a^2$;
   (iv) $(\mathbf{r} - \mathbf{a}).\mathbf{a} = 0$;   (v) $(\mathbf{r} - \mathbf{a}).\mathbf{r} = 0$.

6. Find the loci in space of the five vector equations given in Q. 5.

7. Lines L_1 and L_2 have equations $\mathbf{r} = 2\mathbf{i} + s(2\mathbf{j} + \mathbf{k})$ and $\mathbf{r} = -\mathbf{i} - \mathbf{j} + 4\mathbf{k} + t(\mathbf{i} + \mathbf{j} - \mathbf{k})$ respectively. Show that L_1 and L_2 intersect, and find the cosine of the angle between them.

8. Points A and B have position vectors $\mathbf{i} + \mathbf{k}$ and $2\mathbf{j} - \mathbf{k}$ respectively. Find the position vector of the foot of the perpendicular from the origin O onto AB, and the area of the triangle OAB.

9. Show that the points whose position vectors are $3\mathbf{i} - 2\mathbf{j} + 4\mathbf{k}$, $7\mathbf{i} - \mathbf{j} + 5\mathbf{k}$ and $4\mathbf{i} - 4\mathbf{j} + 2\mathbf{k}$ are the vertices of a right angled triangle.

10. Points A and B have position vectors $\mathbf{a}$ and $\mathbf{b}$ respectively. Writing $|\mathbf{a}| = a$ and $|\mathbf{b}| = b$, show that the area of the triangle $OAB = \frac{1}{2}\sqrt{(a^2b^2 - (\mathbf{a}.\mathbf{b})^2)}$.

11. The position vector of a particle at time t seconds is $\mathbf{r} = t^4\mathbf{i} + 5t\mathbf{j}$. Find the velocity, speed and acceleration of the particle after 1 second.

12. The position vector of particles P_1 and P_2 are given by $\mathbf{r}_1 = t^2\mathbf{i} + 2t\mathbf{j} + t\mathbf{k}$ and $\mathbf{r}_2 = 2t\mathbf{i} - t^3\mathbf{j} + t^2\mathbf{k}$. Show that when $t = 1$, the particles are moving in perpendicular directions.

13. Find a unit vector which is perpendicular to the vector $(4\mathbf{i} + 4\mathbf{j} + 7\mathbf{k})$ and to the vector $(2\mathbf{i} + 2\mathbf{j} + \mathbf{k})$.

14. Find the unit vector perpendicular to the vectors $\mathbf{a} = 2\mathbf{i} + \mathbf{j}$ and $\mathbf{b} = 4\mathbf{i} + \mathbf{j} - \mathbf{k}$ (where $\mathbf{i}$, $\mathbf{j}$ and $\mathbf{k}$ are mutually perpendicular unit vectors) which makes an acute angle with the direction $\mathbf{j}$.   (M.E.I.)

15. Find the value of α in order that the angle between the vectors $\mathbf{i} + 2\mathbf{j} + 2\mathbf{k}$ and $\mathbf{i} + \alpha\mathbf{k}$ shall be
   (i) $\pi/2$,   (ii) $\pi/4$.   (M.E.I.)

16. (i) The position vectors of points A and B referred to the origin O are $(\mathbf{i} + 2\mathbf{j} + 2\mathbf{k})$ and $(2\mathbf{i} + 3\mathbf{j} + 6\mathbf{k})$ respectively. Prove that the line through O which bisects the acute angle AOB lies in the plane $x + 5y - 4z = 0$.
   (ii) A plane passes through the point whose position vector is $\mathbf{i} + 3\mathbf{j} - 4\mathbf{k}$. The plane is normal to the vector $(2\mathbf{i} + 2\mathbf{j} + \mathbf{k})$. Find an equation of the plane in vector form and also in cartesian form.   (L.)

17. The vertices A, B, C, D and E, F, G, H of the opposite faces of a cube have position vectors $\mathbf{0}$, $\mathbf{j}$, $\mathbf{j} + \mathbf{k}$, $\mathbf{k}$ and $\mathbf{i}$, $\mathbf{i} + \mathbf{j}$, $\mathbf{i} + \mathbf{j} + \mathbf{k}$, $\mathbf{i} + \mathbf{k}$ respectively. Prove that the mid-points of HE, EA, AB, BC are four consecutive vertices of a regular hexagon. Find a unit vector which is normal to the plane of the hexagon. (M.E.I.)

18. Define the scalar product of two 3-dimensional Euclidean vectors $\mathbf{u}$, $\mathbf{v}$. Deduce an expression for the angle between the vectors
$$\mathbf{u} = u_1\mathbf{i} + u_2\mathbf{j} + u_3\mathbf{k},$$
$$\mathbf{v} = v_1\mathbf{i} + b_2\mathbf{j} + v_3\mathbf{k},$$
in terms of u_1, u_2, u_3, v_1, v_2, v_3.

A regular tetrahedron has vertices O, A, B, C, where O is the origin, and A, B, C have position vectors with respect to O given by
$$\overrightarrow{OA} = -\mathbf{i} + \mathbf{j},$$
$$\overrightarrow{OB} = a\mathbf{i} + b\mathbf{j},$$
$$\overrightarrow{OC} = p\mathbf{i} + q\mathbf{j} + r\mathbf{k}.$$
Find numerical values of a, b, p, q, r, given that $a > 0$ and $r > 0$.

19. Points A, B, C have position vectors $5\mathbf{i} + 4\mathbf{k}$, $4\mathbf{i} - \mathbf{j} + \mathbf{k}$ and $7\mathbf{i} + 2\mathbf{j} + 3\mathbf{k}$ respectively. Find
   (i) $\cos BAC$, (ii) the area of triangle ABC.

20. Points P, Q, R have position vectors $2\mathbf{i} + 3\mathbf{j} + \mathbf{k}$, $\mathbf{i} + \mathbf{k}$ and $\mathbf{j} + 2\mathbf{k}$ respectively. Find
   (i) $\cos PRQ$, (ii) the area of the triangle PQR,
   (iii) the perpendicular distance of Q from PR.

21. A plane passes through three points A, B and C with position vectors $2\mathbf{i} - \mathbf{j} + \mathbf{k}$, $3\mathbf{i} + 2\mathbf{j} - \mathbf{k}$ and $-\mathbf{i} + 3\mathbf{j} + 2\mathbf{k}$ respectively. Show that a unit vector normal to the plane is
$$\frac{1}{3\sqrt{35}}(11\mathbf{i} + 5\mathbf{j} + 13\mathbf{k}).$$
Show that the equation of the plane is $11x + 5y + 13z = 30$. (J.M.B.)

22. The vector x satisfies
$$\mathbf{x} + \frac{\lambda}{a^2}(\mathbf{a}.\mathbf{x})\mathbf{a} = \mathbf{b},$$
where $a = |\mathbf{a}| \neq 0$. Given that $\lambda \neq -1$, show that
$$\mathbf{a}.\mathbf{x} = \frac{\mathbf{a}.\mathbf{b}}{1 + \lambda}.$$
Hence, or otherwise, find x in terms of a, $\mathbf{a}$, $\mathbf{b}$ and λ.
   In the case when $\lambda = -1$, show that either $\mathbf{b} = 0$ or $\mathbf{a}$ and $\mathbf{b}$ are perpendicular. (J.M.B.)

23. The vertices A, B and C of a triangle have position vectors $\mathbf{a}$, $\mathbf{b}$ and $\mathbf{c}$. Show that the vector $\mathbf{a} \times \mathbf{b} + \mathbf{b} \times \mathbf{c} + \mathbf{c} \times \mathbf{a}$
is perpendicular to the plane ABC and of magnitude equal to twice the area of the triangle ABC.

24. The points A, B and C have position vectors $3\mathbf{i}$, $2\mathbf{j}$ and $\mathbf{i} + 3\mathbf{j} + 8\mathbf{k}$ respectively. Find:

(i) the perpendicular distance of C from the plane OAB,

(ii) the vector equation of the plane ABC,

(iii) the position vector of D, the foot of the perpendicular from O onto the plane ABC.

25. The point O is the origin and points A, B, C, D have position vectors

$$\begin{pmatrix} 4 \\ 3 \\ 4 \end{pmatrix}, \begin{pmatrix} 6 \\ 1 \\ 2 \end{pmatrix}, \begin{pmatrix} 0 \\ 9 \\ -6 \end{pmatrix}, \begin{pmatrix} -1 \\ 1 \\ 1 \end{pmatrix},$$

respectively.

Prove that:

(i) the triangle OAB is isosceles,

(ii) D lies in the plane OAB,

(iii) CD is perpendicular to the plane OAB,

(iv) AC is inclined at an angle of $60°$ to the plane OAB. (C.)

26. The matrix $\mathbf{A} = \begin{pmatrix} \frac{1}{3} & \frac{2}{3} & \frac{2}{3} \\ \frac{2}{3} & -\frac{2}{3} & \frac{1}{3} \\ \frac{2}{3} & \frac{1}{3} & -\frac{2}{3} \end{pmatrix}$ transforms the unit vectors

$$\mathbf{i} = \begin{pmatrix} 1 \\ 0 \\ 0 \end{pmatrix}, \mathbf{j} = \begin{pmatrix} 0 \\ 1 \\ 0 \end{pmatrix}, \mathbf{k} = \begin{pmatrix} 0 \\ 0 \\ 1 \end{pmatrix}$$

into $\mathbf{A}.\mathbf{i}$, $\mathbf{A}.\mathbf{j}$ and $\mathbf{A}.\mathbf{k}$ respectively. Show that $\mathbf{A}.\mathbf{i}$, $\mathbf{A}.\mathbf{j}$ and $\mathbf{A}.\mathbf{k}$ are mutually perpendicular unit vectors.

27. (i) Define the scalar product $\mathbf{x}.\mathbf{y}$ of two three-dimensional vectors $\mathbf{x}$ and $\mathbf{y}$.

(ii) Describe the set of vectors $\mathbf{x}$ satisfying the equation

$$\mathbf{a}.\mathbf{x} = 0$$

where $\mathbf{a}$ is a given vector.

(iii) Show that if $\mathbf{x}_1$ is a solution of $\mathbf{a}.\mathbf{x} = 0$ and $\mathbf{x}_2$ is a solution of $\mathbf{a}.\mathbf{x} = k$ where k is a given real number, then $\mathbf{x}_1 + \mathbf{x}_2$ is also a solution of $\mathbf{a}.\mathbf{x} = k$.

(iv) Calculate the value of λ such that the vector $\mathbf{x} = \lambda\mathbf{a}$ is a solution of the equation $\mathbf{a}.\mathbf{x} = k$.

(v) Give a geometrical interpretation of the relationship between the set of vectors satisfying the equation $\mathbf{a}.\mathbf{x} = 0$ and the set of all vectors satisfying the equation $\mathbf{a}.\mathbf{x} = k$. (A.E.B.)

28. In three dimensions, O is the origin of position vectors and points A and B are given by $\mathbf{OA} = \mathbf{i} + \mathbf{k}$, $\mathbf{OB} = \mathbf{j} + \mathbf{k}$ respectively. The position vector of a general point P in the plane OAB is given by $\mathbf{OP} = \lambda\mathbf{OA} + \mu\mathbf{OB}$, where λ and μ are variable scalars. The position vector of the fixed point Q (which is not in the plane OAB) is given by $\mathbf{OQ} = \mathbf{i} + \mathbf{j} + \mathbf{k}$. Determine λ and μ such that QP is perpendicular to both OA and OB (i.e. such that QP is perpendicular to the plane OAB). Hence, or otherwise, find the acute angle between OQ and the plane OAB to the nearest half degree. (C.)

29. The plane π_1 is normal to the vector $\begin{pmatrix} 1 \\ -2 \\ 1 \end{pmatrix}$ and passes through the point $A(3, 1, -1)$. The plane π_2 has equation $x - y = 1$. Find the acute angle between the planes π_1 and π_2.

If π_1 and π_2 meet in the line l, verify that l passes through $(1, 0, -1)$ and is parallel to the vector $\begin{pmatrix} 1 \\ 1 \\ 1 \end{pmatrix}$. Write down a parametric equation for l, and hence find the point C on l such that AC is perpendicular to l.

If the normal through A to π_2 meets π_2 in B, show that the area of the triangle ACB is $\frac{1}{4}\sqrt{3}$ square units. (S.M.P.)

30. O is a fixed origin in a vector space of two dimensions. A given line passes through a fixed point A and is parallel to a fixed unit vector $\hat{\mathbf{u}}$. P is a variable point on the given line. $\mathbf{OA} = \mathbf{a}$, $\mathbf{OP} = \mathbf{r}$ and the length of AP is t.

Interpret the equation

$$\mathbf{r} = \mathbf{a} + t\hat{\mathbf{u}}.$$

B is another fixed point, not on the given line, and $\mathbf{OB} = \mathbf{b}$. Show that the position vector of the foot of the perpendicular from B to the given line is $\mathbf{a} + [\hat{\mathbf{u}}.(\mathbf{b} - \mathbf{a})]\hat{\mathbf{u}}$. Does this result hold also in three dimensions?

Find the perpendicular distance of the point $(3, 0, 1)$ from the line whose cartesian equation is

$$\frac{x - 1}{3} = \frac{y + 2}{4} = \frac{z}{12}. \qquad \text{(M.E.I.)}$$

31. The vectors $\mathbf{p} = 3\mathbf{i} + 4\mathbf{k}$ and $\mathbf{q} = 12\mathbf{i} + 5\mathbf{j}$ are expressed in terms of unit vectors $\mathbf{i}, \mathbf{j}, \mathbf{k}$ in the directions of the axes Ox, Oy, Oz respectively.

Find

(i) the vector $2\mathbf{p} - 3\mathbf{q}$,

(ii) unit vectors in the directions $\mathbf{p}$ and $\mathbf{q}$,

(iii) the cosine of the angle between the vectors $\mathbf{p}$ and $\mathbf{q}$,

(iv) the cosine of the angle between the vector $\mathbf{p}$ and the x-axis.

Calculate the value of α such that $(\mathbf{p} + \alpha\mathbf{q}).\mathbf{q} = 0$ and write down the cartesian equation of the plane through the origin normal to the vector $\mathbf{p} + \alpha\mathbf{q}$. (M.E.I.)

32. The position vectors of A, B, C are $\mathbf{i}$, $2\mathbf{j}$, $3\mathbf{k}$ respectively. The perpendicular from the origin O to the plane ABC meets the plane at the point D. Find

(i) the vector equation of the plane ABC,

(ii) the vector equation of the line OD,

(iii) the position vector of the point D. (A.E.B.)

33. Points A, B, C have position vectors $\mathbf{a}, \mathbf{b}, \mathbf{c}$ respectively, where $\mathbf{a} = \mathbf{i}, \mathbf{b} = \mathbf{i} + \mathbf{j}$ and $\mathbf{c} = \mathbf{i} + \mathbf{j} + \mathbf{k}$. Find the equation of the plane ABC, and which of the points D, E, F lie in that plane, D, E, F having position vectors $\mathbf{d}, \mathbf{e}, \mathbf{f}$ respectively, where $\mathbf{d} = \mathbf{k}, \mathbf{e} = 2\mathbf{i} + 2\mathbf{j} + \mathbf{k}$ and $\mathbf{f} = 2\mathbf{i} + 3\mathbf{j} + \mathbf{k}$.

34. Find the equation of the plane through the points with position vectors $-2\mathbf{i} + \mathbf{j} + 2\mathbf{k}$, $\mathbf{i} - 2\mathbf{j} + 3\mathbf{k}$, $-4\mathbf{i} + 3\mathbf{j}$. Show that the point position vector $-9\mathbf{i} + 8\mathbf{j} + 21\mathbf{k}$ lies in this plane.

35. The three points A, B and C are given by $A(0, 2, -4)$, $B(2, 0, -2)$ and $C(-8, 4, 0)$.

Find

  (i) the equation of the plane ABC,

  (ii) the coordinates of the midpoints D, E and F of the lines BC, CA and AB respectively,

  (iii) the coordinates of the point P in the plane ABC such that $\overrightarrow{PD}$ is perpendicular to $\overrightarrow{BC}$ and $\overrightarrow{PE}$ is perpendicular to $\overrightarrow{AC}$.

  (iv) Verify that $\overrightarrow{PF}$ is perpendicular to $\overrightarrow{AB}$ and show that

$$|\overrightarrow{PA}| = |\overrightarrow{PB}| = |\overrightarrow{PC}| = \sqrt{35}. \qquad \text{(M.E.I.)}$$

36. The position vectors of fixed points A and B are $\mathbf{a}$ and $\mathbf{b}$ respectively. Show on a diagram the point whose position vector is

$$\mathbf{p} = \frac{m\mathbf{a} + n\mathbf{b}}{m + n}.$$

The diagonals AC and BD of a quadrilateral $ABCD$ intersect in a point P and $\dfrac{AP}{PC} = \dfrac{m}{n}$ and $\dfrac{BP}{PD} = \dfrac{r}{s}$. Show that

$$\frac{n(r + s)\mathbf{a} - s(m + n)\mathbf{b}}{nr - sm} = \frac{r(m + n)\mathbf{d} - m(r + s)\mathbf{c}}{nr - sm}$$

where $\mathbf{a}$, $\mathbf{b}$, $\mathbf{c}$, and $\mathbf{d}$ are the position vectors of A, B, C and D respectively. Interpret this result geometrically. (A.E.B.)

37. An ellipse can be defined as the locus of a point such that the sum of the distances of that point from the foci is constant, say $2a$. Taking the position vectors of the two foci as $+\mathbf{c}$ and $-\mathbf{c}$, show that the equation of the ellipse can be written

$$a^4 - a^2(r^2 + c^2) + (\mathbf{r}.\mathbf{c})^2 = 0.$$

38. For each of the following assertions, state whether it is true or false, justifying your answer.

  (i) $(\mathbf{i} - 3\mathbf{j} + 3\mathbf{k}) \times (-\mathbf{i} - 3\mathbf{j} + 2\mathbf{k}) = 3\mathbf{i} - 5\mathbf{j} - 7\mathbf{k}$.

  (ii) If $\mathbf{a} \times \mathbf{b} = 0$ then either $\mathbf{a} = 0$ or $\mathbf{b} = 0$.

  (iii) The area of triangle ABC is $\frac{1}{2}|\mathbf{AB} \times \mathbf{AC}|$.

  (iv) If $\mathbf{a}$, $\mathbf{b}$, $\mathbf{c}$ are any vectors then $(\mathbf{a} \times \mathbf{b}) \times \mathbf{c} = \mathbf{a} \times (\mathbf{b} \times \mathbf{c})$.

  (v) The equation of the line passing through a fixed point with position vector $\mathbf{a}$, and parallel to the non-zero vector $\mathbf{u}$, can be written in the form $(\mathbf{r} - \mathbf{a}).\mathbf{u} = 0$, where $\mathbf{r}$ is the position vector of any point on the line.

(C.)

39. The position vector, relative to a fixed origin O, of a point P at time t is

$$\mathbf{r} = \mathbf{c} \cos^2 t\mathbf{i} + c \sin t \cos t\mathbf{j} + c \sin t \,\mathbf{k},$$

where c is a constant. Show that P always lies on the surface of a sphere whose centre is O and find the radius of this sphere. If $\mathbf{a}$ is the acceleration of P, show that

$$\mathbf{a}.\mathbf{r} = -c^2 \,(1 + \cos^2 t).$$

40. O is a fixed origin and A a fixed point with position-vector $\mathbf{a}$, where $|\mathbf{a}| = l$. The variable point R has position-vector $\mathbf{r}$, where $|\mathbf{r}| = l$ and $\mathbf{r} \cdot \mathbf{a} = l^2 \cos 2\alpha$ where α is a constant. Describe and sketch the locus of R in three dimensions.

B is a fixed point on the locus of R, with position-vector $\mathbf{b}$, and C is given by $\mathbf{c} = \frac{1}{2}(\mathbf{a} + \mathbf{b})$. S is a variable point such that $|\mathbf{s}| = l$ and $\mathbf{s} \cdot \mathbf{c} = l^2 \cos^2 \alpha$. Describe the locus of S and include it on the same sketch as that of R. Prove that the two loci meet at one point with a common tangent. Verify this result vectorially by considering $\mathbf{r}$ and $\mathbf{s}$ as variable with time and showing that the vectors $d\mathbf{r}/dt$, $d\mathbf{s}/dt$ are in the same direction at the common point of the loci.

[Hint: $\mathbf{r} \cdot \mathbf{r} = l^2 \Rightarrow 2\mathbf{r} \cdot d\mathbf{r}/dt = 0$.] (M.E.I.)

22 Further Matrices

Revision

In *Additional Pure Mathematics*, we defined a matrix as a rectangular array of numbers, subject to certain operations. A matrix with r rows and s columns we call an $r \times s$ matrix, and we saw that two matrices can only be added together if both are $r \times s$ matrices, i.e. of the same size. The product $\mathbf{A}.\mathbf{B}$ of two matrices is only defined if $\mathbf{A}$ is $r \times s$ and $\mathbf{B}$ is $s \times t$, i.e. if the first matrix has as many columns as the second one has rows.

Matrices can be used to describe a great variety of mathematical situations (see Ex. 22. 3, 33–40), but are often used at this level to describe geometrical transformations. The reader should be familiar with 2×2 matrices that describe rotation and reflection in the coordinate axes.

Transpose of a matrix

The transpose of a matrix $\mathbf{A}$, written $\mathbf{A}^\mathrm{T}$, is formed by interchanging the rows and columns of the matrix,

e.g. if $\mathbf{A} = \begin{pmatrix} a & b & c \\ d & e & f \end{pmatrix}$, $\mathbf{A}^\mathrm{T} = \begin{pmatrix} a & d \\ b & e \\ c & f \end{pmatrix}$

Determinant of a 2 × 2 matrix

If $\mathbf{A} = \begin{pmatrix} a & b \\ c & d \end{pmatrix}$, the expression $ad - bc$ is called the determinant of $\mathbf{A}$, written $\det \mathbf{A}$ or $|\mathbf{A}|$. This is useful when finding the inverse of a 2×2 matrix, and we have also seen that it is the factor by which the area of a plane region is multiplied under the transformation described by the matrix $\mathbf{A}$.

Singular matrix

If $\det \mathbf{A} = 0$, the matrix $\mathbf{A}$ is called a singular matrix. Clearly there cannot be an inverse of a singular matrix. We shall see that any plane region is transformed by a singular matrix into a segment of a straight line.

Inverse of a matrix

The inverse of a matrix $\mathbf{A}$, written $\mathbf{A}^{-1}$, is the matrix such that $\mathbf{A}.\mathbf{A}^{-1} = \mathbf{A}^{-1}.\mathbf{A} = \mathbf{I}$, where $\mathbf{I}$ is the unit matrix of appropriate order. If

$$\mathbf{A} = \begin{pmatrix} a & b \\ c & d \end{pmatrix}$$

$$\mathbf{A}^{-1} = \frac{1}{\det \mathbf{A}} \begin{pmatrix} d & -b \\ -c & a \end{pmatrix}$$

Geometrical transformations

We are familiar with transformations of the unit square, and we have probably investigated those transformations by finding the images under the transformation of the vertices of the unit square, or other plane rectangular figure. Let us now consider the transformation of a line, in a manner that will enable us to see the image of every point on that line.

Consider the matrix $\mathbf{A} = \begin{pmatrix} 1 & 2 \\ 2 & 4 \end{pmatrix}$, and let us find the transformation made by $\mathbf{A}$ on the x-axis. Any point on the x-axis can be written $(X, 0)$ and its position vector as $\begin{pmatrix} X \\ 0 \end{pmatrix}$. Then

$$\begin{pmatrix} 1 & 3 \\ 2 & 4 \end{pmatrix}\begin{pmatrix} X \\ 0 \end{pmatrix} = \begin{pmatrix} X \\ 2X \end{pmatrix}$$

so that the image of $(X, 0)$ will be $(X, 2X)$ for all X, i.e. the line $y = 2x$, so that $\mathbf{A}$ transforms the x-axis into the line $y = 2x$.

Consider now the transformation of another line through O, say $y = 3x$. Any point on this line can be expressed in terms of a parameter λ as $(\lambda, 3\lambda)$ and the image is given by

$$\begin{pmatrix} 1 & 3 \\ 2 & 4 \end{pmatrix}\begin{pmatrix} \lambda \\ 3\lambda \end{pmatrix} = \begin{pmatrix} 10\lambda \\ 14\lambda \end{pmatrix}$$

so that the line $y = 3x$ is transformed into the line $5y = 7x$.

Can we find a straight line L through O that is mapped into a line through O perpendicular to itself? Suppose L is $y = mx$ for some m. Then any point on L is $(\lambda, m\lambda)$, and the image is given by

$$\begin{pmatrix} 1 & 3 \\ 2 & 4 \end{pmatrix}\begin{pmatrix} \lambda \\ m\lambda \end{pmatrix} = \begin{pmatrix} (1 + 3m)\lambda \\ (2 + 4m)\lambda \end{pmatrix}$$

so that $y = mx$ maps onto $(1 + 3m)y = (2 + 4m)x$. This is perpendicular to L if

$$m\frac{(2 + 4m)}{1 + 3m} = -1$$

i.e.

$$4m^2 + 5m + 1 = 0, m = -1 \text{ or } -\tfrac{1}{4}.$$

Thus $y = -x$ and $4y = -x$ are each mapped onto straight lines perpendicular to themselves.

Check: Any point on $y = -x$ we can take as $(\lambda, -\lambda)$. Its image under **A** is given by

$$\begin{pmatrix} 1 & 3 \\ 2 & 4 \end{pmatrix}\begin{pmatrix} \lambda \\ -\lambda \end{pmatrix} = \begin{pmatrix} -2\lambda \\ -2\lambda \end{pmatrix}$$

i.e. is on the line $y = x$. Similarly, any point on $4y = -x$ can be written $(4\lambda, -\lambda)$, so its image is given by

$$\begin{pmatrix} 1 & 3 \\ 2 & 4 \end{pmatrix}\begin{pmatrix} 4\lambda \\ -\lambda \end{pmatrix} = \begin{pmatrix} \lambda \\ 4\lambda \end{pmatrix}$$

i.e. is on the line $y = 4x$.

Transformation by a singular matrix

Consider now the matrix $\mathbf{B} = \begin{pmatrix} 1 & 3 \\ 2 & 6 \end{pmatrix}$. Any point on the line $y = mx$ can be written $(\lambda, m\lambda)$ so that the image is given by

$$\begin{pmatrix} 1 & 3 \\ 2 & 6 \end{pmatrix}\begin{pmatrix} \lambda \\ m\lambda \end{pmatrix} = \begin{pmatrix} (1 + 3m)\lambda \\ (2 + 6m)\lambda \end{pmatrix}$$

and the image lies on the line $y = 2x$, whatever the value of m. Thus this matrix maps the whole of the plane onto the line $y = 2x$.

Mapping a straight line onto itself

We wish to see if we can find a straight line through O which any one given matrix **A** maps onto itself, i.e. if **x** is the position vector of any point P on that line, $\mathbf{A}.\mathbf{x}$ is the position vector of another point on that line, possibly though not necessarily, the same point as P, so that $\mathbf{A}.\mathbf{x} = \lambda\mathbf{x}$, where $\lambda\mathbf{x}$ is the position vector of Q, the image of P.

For a general matrix **A**,

$$\mathbf{A}.\mathbf{x} = \lambda\mathbf{x}$$
$$\therefore \quad (\mathbf{A} - \lambda\mathbf{I}).\mathbf{x} = 0,$$

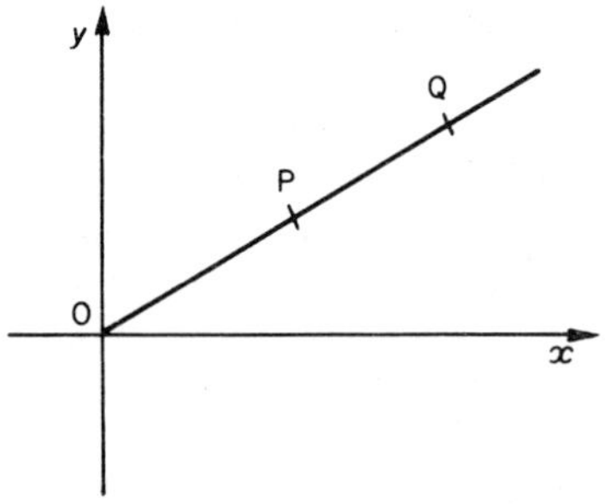

Fig. 22.1

where $\mathbf{I}$ is the 2×2 unit matrix. If this is to be true for all vectors $\mathbf{x}$, $|\mathbf{A} - \lambda \mathbf{I}| = 0$. Let us consider a particular matrix $\mathbf{A}$, say $\mathbf{A} = \begin{pmatrix} 3 & 1 \\ 3 & 5 \end{pmatrix}$.

Then
$$|\mathbf{A} - \lambda \mathbf{I}| = 0$$
$$\Rightarrow \begin{vmatrix} 3 - \lambda & 1 \\ 3 & 5 - \lambda \end{vmatrix} = 0$$

i.e.
$$(3 - \lambda)(5 - \lambda) - 3 = 0,$$
$$\lambda^2 - 8\lambda + 12 = 0, \tag{1}$$
$$(\lambda - 2)(\lambda - 6) = 0,$$

i.e.
$$\lambda = 2 \text{ or } 6.$$

When $\lambda = 2$,
$$\begin{pmatrix} 3 & 1 \\ 3 & 5 \end{pmatrix}\begin{pmatrix} x \\ y \end{pmatrix} = 2\begin{pmatrix} x \\ y \end{pmatrix}$$

i.e.
$$3x + y = 2x,$$
$$3x + 5y = 2y,$$

both of which give $y = -x$. Every point on the line $y = -x$ is mapped onto another point on that line, e.g.

$$\begin{pmatrix} 3 & 1 \\ 3 & 5 \end{pmatrix}\begin{pmatrix} 1 \\ -1 \end{pmatrix} = \begin{pmatrix} 2 \\ -2 \end{pmatrix}$$

so that $(1, -1)$ is mapped onto $(2, -2)$, and similarly $(4, -4)$ is mapped onto $(8, -8)$, etc. Notice that only in a transformation of which one value of λ is 1 is each point mapped into itself.

Looking at the other root, $\lambda = 6$,
$$\begin{pmatrix} 3 & 1 \\ 3 & 5 \end{pmatrix}\begin{pmatrix} x \\ y \end{pmatrix} = 6\begin{pmatrix} x \\ y \end{pmatrix}$$

i.e. $\qquad\qquad 3x + y = 6x$

and $\qquad\qquad 3x + 5y = 6y,$

both equations giving $y = 3x$, so that each point on $y = 3x$ is mapped onto another point on the same line, e.g.

since
$$\begin{pmatrix} 3 & 1 \\ 3 & 5 \end{pmatrix}\begin{pmatrix} 2 \\ 6 \end{pmatrix} = \begin{pmatrix} 12 \\ 36 \end{pmatrix}$$

the point $(2, 6)$ is mapped onto the point $(12, 36)$.

The equation (1) is called the *characteristic equation* of the matrix A, the roots of this equation are called the *eigen-values* (or characteristic values) of A, and any vector along each line that is mapped onto itself is called an *eigen-vector*, so that for the eigen-value $\lambda = 2$,

since
$$\begin{pmatrix} 3 & 1 \\ 3 & 5 \end{pmatrix}\begin{pmatrix} 1 \\ -1 \end{pmatrix} = 2\begin{pmatrix} 1 \\ -1 \end{pmatrix},$$

$\begin{pmatrix} 1 \\ -1 \end{pmatrix}$ is the eigen-vector corresponding to the eigen-value $\lambda = 2$.

Strictly, any scalar multiple of $\begin{pmatrix} 1 \\ -1 \end{pmatrix}$ can be the eigen-vector.

Example. *Find the image of the straight line* $2y = 3x - 1$ *under the transformation of the plane described by the matrix* $\begin{pmatrix} 3 & -2 \\ 6 & k \end{pmatrix}$ *when (i)* $k = 4$, *(ii)* $k = -4$.

(i) Any point on the line $2y = 3x - 1$ can be written in the parametric form $(2\lambda + 1, 3\lambda + 1)$; this avoids the fractions in e.g. $(\lambda, \frac{1}{2}(3\lambda + 1))$. The image is

$$\begin{pmatrix} 3 & -2 \\ 6 & 4 \end{pmatrix}\begin{pmatrix} 2\lambda + 1 \\ 3\lambda + 1 \end{pmatrix} = \begin{pmatrix} 1 \\ 24\lambda + 10 \end{pmatrix}$$

i.e. it always lies on the line $x = 1$, so that $2y = 3x - 1$ maps into the line $x = 1$.

(ii) This time the image is given by

$$\begin{pmatrix} 3 & -2 \\ 6 & -4 \end{pmatrix}\begin{pmatrix} 2\lambda + 1 \\ 3\lambda + 1 \end{pmatrix} = \begin{pmatrix} 1 \\ 2 \end{pmatrix}$$

so that all points on the line $2y - 3x - 1$ are mapped into the single point $(1, 2)$. We notice in this case that the matrix describing the transformation is singular.

Exercise 22.1

1. Find the determinant of each of the following matrices, and the inverse of each matrix where it exists.

$$A = \begin{pmatrix} 3 & 4 \\ 2 & 3 \end{pmatrix}, \quad B = \begin{pmatrix} 3 & 6 \\ 2 & 4 \end{pmatrix}, \quad C = \begin{pmatrix} 3 & 1 \\ 0 & 0 \end{pmatrix},$$

$$D = \begin{pmatrix} 3 & 0 \\ 0 & 0 \end{pmatrix}, \quad E = \begin{pmatrix} 0 & 0 \\ 0 & 0 \end{pmatrix}.$$

2. Write the vertices of the unit square $(0, 0)$, $(1, 0)$, $(1, 1)$, $(0, 1)$ in the matrix U, where

$$U = \begin{pmatrix} 0 & 1 & 1 & 0 \\ 0 & 0 & 1 & 1 \end{pmatrix}$$

Use the matrices A, B, C, D and E in Q. 1 to find the image of the unit square given by
(i) A.U; (ii) B.U; (iii) C.U; (iv) D.U; (v) E.U.

3. Find the image of the line $y = x$ under each of the transformations given by the matrices in Q. 1.

4. Find the image of the line $x + 2y = 1$ under each of the transformations given in Q. 1.

5. Find the image L' of the line $L \equiv 2x + y = 2$ under the transformation described by the matrix

$$\begin{pmatrix} 3 & 4 \\ 2 & 3 \end{pmatrix}.$$

Show that the image under this transformation of any line parallel to L is a straight line parallel to L'.

6. Find the image of the lines

(i) $x - 2y = 2$,   (ii) $x - 2y = 3$

under the transformation described by the matrix

$$\begin{pmatrix} 1 & -2 \\ 2 & -4 \end{pmatrix}.$$

7. Show that all non-singular 2×2 matrices map any family of parallel lines into another family of parallel lines.

8. Find the characteristic equation, eigen-values and eigen-vectors for each of the following matrices, illustrating each in a diagram, that the eigen-values have the property that $\mathbf{A.x} = \lambda \mathbf{x}$.

(i) $\begin{pmatrix} 1 & -2 \\ 3 & 6 \end{pmatrix}$,   (ii) $\begin{pmatrix} 1 & -2 \\ 2 & 6 \end{pmatrix}$,   (iii) $\begin{pmatrix} 1 & -2 \\ 0 & 6 \end{pmatrix}$,

(iv) $\begin{pmatrix} 1 & 0 \\ 0 & 6 \end{pmatrix}$,   (v) $\begin{pmatrix} 1 & 12 \\ 3 & 6 \end{pmatrix}$.

9. Find the determinant of each of the matrices in Q. 8, and the relationship between the determinant of each matrix and one of the terms in the characteristic equation.

10. Prove that every singular matrix has an eigen-value $\lambda = 0$, and illustrate this result geometrically.

Transformations described by 3×3 matrices

The coordinates of a point P in 3-dimensional space ($\mathbb{R}^3$) can be

displayed in the matrix $\begin{pmatrix} x \\ y \\ z \end{pmatrix}$. When this matrix is premultiplied by a

3×3 matrix $\mathbf{A}$, the point P is mapped into its image under $\mathbf{A}$. If a matrix $\mathbf{A}$ maps a point P into P', the inverse matrix $\mathbf{A}^{-1}$ maps P' back into P. These matrices may describe reflections and rotations, or more general transformations.

The determinant of a 3×3 matrix

We can define the determinant of the 3×3 matrix

$$\begin{pmatrix} a_1 & b_1 & c_1 \\ a_2 & b_2 & c_2 \\ a_3 & b_3 & c_3 \end{pmatrix} \quad \text{as} \quad a_1 \begin{vmatrix} b_2 & c_2 \\ b_3 & c_3 \end{vmatrix}$$

$$- b_1 \begin{vmatrix} a_2 & c_2 \\ a_3 & c_3 \end{vmatrix} + c_1 \begin{vmatrix} a_2 & b_2 \\ a_3 & b_3 \end{vmatrix}$$

Expanding the 2×2 determinants we see that this is equal to

$$a_1(b_3c_2 - b_3c_2) - b_1(a_3c_2 - a_2c_3) + c_1(a_2b_3 - a_3b_2)$$

which equals
$$a_1b_2c_3 + a_2b_3c_1 + a_3b_1c_2 - a_1b_3c_2 - a_2b_1c_3 - a_3b_2c_1$$
and indeed the determinant can be evaluated as above, or expanding by the diagonals, completing the diagonals where necessary with cyclic

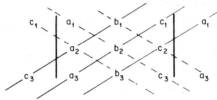

Fig. 22.2

terms, and then signing the products parallel to the leading diagonal $a_1b_2c_3$ positive, and signing the others with a negative sign. This is called the Rule of Sarrus.

Considering a 2×2 determinant, say $\begin{vmatrix} a & b \\ c & d \end{vmatrix}$ we see the above definition is an extension of the one we have always used for 2×2 determinants, if we regard it as

$$\begin{vmatrix} a & b \\ c & d \end{vmatrix} = \begin{vmatrix} a & b \\ |c| & |d| \end{vmatrix} = a|d| - b|c|$$

and $|b| = b$, $|d| = d$. We may later wish to redefine a determinant, but this is the definition appropriate to this level, and the one we shall use now.

Example. *Find the value of the determinant*

$$\begin{vmatrix} 3 & 4 & 1 \\ 2 & -1 & 2 \\ 3 & 5 & 1 \end{vmatrix}$$

Using the definition, the value is

$$3\begin{vmatrix} -1 & 2 \\ 5 & 1 \end{vmatrix} - 4\begin{vmatrix} 2 & 2 \\ 3 & 1 \end{vmatrix} + 1\begin{vmatrix} 2 & -1 \\ 3 & 5 \end{vmatrix}$$
$$= 3(-11) - 4(-4) + 1(13)$$
$$= -4.$$

Alternatively, the value may be found using

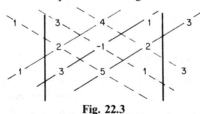

Fig. 22.3

i.e.
$$3 \times (-1) \times (1) + 4 \times (2) \times 3 + 1 \times 2 \times 5$$
$$- 3 \times 2 \times 5 - 1 \times (-1) \times 3 - 4 \times 2 \times 1$$
$$= -4.$$

Minors and cofactors

The determinant found by excluding the row and column containing a_1, i.e. $\begin{vmatrix} b_2 & c_2 \\ b_3 & c_3 \end{vmatrix}$ is called the *minor* of a_1; similarly $\begin{vmatrix} a_2 & c_2 \\ a_3 & c_3 \end{vmatrix}$ is the minor of b_1 and $\begin{vmatrix} a_2 & b_2 \\ a_3 & b_3 \end{vmatrix}$ the minor of c_1.

Rather more useful are the *cofactors* of a determinant, which are the minors when given the appropriate signs. For if A_1 is the cofactor of a_1, B_1 the cofactor of b_1 and C_1 the cofactor of c_1, then if the signs of the cofactors are chosen suitably, $\det \mathbf{A} = a_1 A_1 + b_1 B_1 + c_1 C_1$. For this expansion to be correct, the signs to be given to the cofactors must be $+ - +$,

i.e.
$$A_1 = \begin{vmatrix} b_2 & c_2 \\ b_3 & c_3 \end{vmatrix}, \quad B_1 = -\begin{vmatrix} a_2 & c_2 \\ a_3 & c_3 \end{vmatrix}, \quad C_1 = \begin{vmatrix} a_2 & b_2 \\ a_3 & b_3 \end{vmatrix}.$$

Considering the expansion of $\det \mathbf{A}$,
$$\det \mathbf{A} = a_1(b_2 c_3 - b_3 c_2) - b_1(a_2 c_3 - a_3 c_2) + c_1(a_2 b_3 - a_3 b_2)$$
$$= -a_2(b_1 c_3 - b_3 c_1) + b_2(a_1 c_3 - a_3 c_1) - c_2(a_1 b_3 - a_3 b_1),$$
expanding the brackets and then refactorising with a_2, b_2 and c_2 factors of pairs of terms,
$$= -a_2 \begin{vmatrix} b_1 & c_1 \\ b_3 & c_3 \end{vmatrix} + b_2 \begin{vmatrix} a_1 & c_1 \\ a_3 & c_3 \end{vmatrix} - c_2 \begin{vmatrix} a_1 & b_1 \\ a_3 & b_3 \end{vmatrix}$$
$$= + a_2 A_2 + b_2 B_2 + c_2 C_2,$$
the cofactors A_2, B_2 and C_2 being defined in the same way as A_1, B_1 and C_1, and signed $- + -$. We can also express $\det \mathbf{A}$ as
$$\det \mathbf{A} = a_3 A_3 + b_3 B_3 + c_3 C_3,$$
if the minors are given the signs
$$\begin{vmatrix} + & - & + \\ - & + & - \\ + & - & + \end{vmatrix}$$
according to their position in the determinant.

Expansion by alien cofactors

We have seen that $\det \mathbf{A}$ can be expanded in three ways, like $a_1 A_1 + b_1 B_1 + c_1 C_1$. Expansions without the correct suffices, e.g. $a_1 A_2 + b_1 B_2 + c_1 C_2$ are called *expansions by alien cofactors*, and we have no reason to think that an expansion like this should also be equal to the value of the determinant. Indeed,

$$a_1 A_2 + b_1 B_2 + c_1 C_2 = -a_1(b_1 c_3 - b_3 c_1) + b_1(a_1 c_3 - a_3 c_1)$$
$$-c_1(a_1 b_3 - a_3 b_1)$$
$$= 0,$$

and we can show in the same manner that all expansions by alien cofactors are equal to zero.

The adjoint matrix

Associated with any matrix $\mathbf{A}$, we find it useful to introduce a matrix called the *adjoint* matrix, written **adj A**, which is the transpose of the matrix whose entries are the cofactors of the elements in $\mathbf{A}$, i.e.

$$\mathbf{adj\ A} = \begin{pmatrix} A_1 & A_2 & A_3 \\ B_1 & B_2 & B_3 \\ C_1 & C_2 & C_3 \end{pmatrix}$$

When we consider the product of $\mathbf{A}$ and **adj A**, we notice that we have many terms like $a_1 A_1 + b_1 B_1 + c_1 C_1$, equal merely to det $\mathbf{A}$ (which here we shall write $|\mathbf{A}|$) and many other terms like $a_1 A_2 + b_1 B_2 + c_1 C_2$, which being expansions by alien cofactors, are equal to zero. In detail,

$$\mathbf{A} . (\mathbf{adj\ A}) = \begin{pmatrix} a_1 & b_1 & c_1 \\ a_2 & b_2 & c_2 \\ a_3 & b_3 & c_3 \end{pmatrix} \begin{pmatrix} A_1 & A_2 & A_3 \\ B_1 & B_2 & B_3 \\ C_1 & C_2 & C_3 \end{pmatrix}$$

$$= \begin{pmatrix} A & 0 & 0 \\ 0 & A & 0 \\ 0 & 0 & A \end{pmatrix}$$

so that we can deduce the inverse of $\mathbf{A}$,

$$\mathbf{A}^{-1} = \frac{1}{|\mathbf{A}|} \begin{pmatrix} A_1 & A_2 & A_3 \\ B_1 & B_2 & B_3 \\ C_1 & C_2 & C_3 \end{pmatrix}$$

There are many other ways of finding the inverse of a 3×3 matrix, but this method, only really applicable to 3×3 matrices, i.e. not to those of higher order, is the method often found easiest at this level.

It is interesting to compare this method with that used to find the inverse of a 2×2 matrix. For if

$$\mathbf{A} = \begin{pmatrix} a & b \\ c & d \end{pmatrix}$$

we first find the matrix consisting of the minors of each element,

$$\begin{pmatrix} d & c \\ b & a \end{pmatrix};$$

we then give the signs $\begin{matrix} + & - \\ - & + \end{matrix}$ to obtain $\begin{pmatrix} d & -c \\ -b & a \end{pmatrix}$ and transpose to

find **adj A** $= \begin{pmatrix} d & -b \\ -c & a \end{pmatrix}$ then $\mathbf{A}^{-1} = \dfrac{1}{|\mathbf{A}|} \begin{pmatrix} d & -b \\ -c & a \end{pmatrix}$, as we expect.

This example illustrates the procedure for a 3×3 matrix.

Example. *Find the inverse of the matrix*

$$\mathbf{A} = \begin{pmatrix} 4 & 1 & 3 \\ -2 & 1 & 2 \\ 5 & 2 & 1 \end{pmatrix}$$

First form the matrix consisting of the minor of each element of **A**. The minor of 4 is $1 \times 1 - 2 \times 2$, i.e. -3; of 1 is $-2 \times 1 - 5 \times 2$, i.e. -12, of 3 is $-2 \times 2 - 1 \times 5$, i.e. -9 and so on, and we have the matrix

$$\begin{pmatrix} -3 & -12 & -9 \\ -5 & -11 & 3 \\ -1 & 14 & 6 \end{pmatrix}$$

We give each term the appropriate sign from

$$\begin{matrix} + & - & + \\ - & + & - \\ + & - & + \end{matrix}$$

transpose the matrix and have

$$\mathbf{adj\ A} = \begin{pmatrix} -3 & 5 & -1 \\ 12 & -11 & -14 \\ -9 & -3 & 6 \end{pmatrix}$$

Form the product **A (adj A)**, or **adj A . A**, to check that all the terms except those in the leading diagonal are zero,

$$\mathbf{(adj\ A) . A} = \begin{pmatrix} -27 & 0 & 0 \\ 0 & -27 & 0 \\ 0 & 0 & -27 \end{pmatrix}$$

We can deduce without direct calculation that $\det \mathbf{A} = -27$,

so
$$\mathbf{A}^{-1} = \frac{1}{-27} \begin{pmatrix} -3 & 5 & -1 \\ 12 & -11 & -14 \\ -9 & -3 & 6 \end{pmatrix}$$

$$\mathbf{A}^{-1} = \frac{1}{27} \begin{pmatrix} 3 & -5 & 1 \\ -12 & 11 & 14 \\ 9 & 3 & -6 \end{pmatrix}$$

Application of the inverse matrix

As with 2×2 matrices, if a matrix $\mathbf{A}$ describes a transformation of a point P into its image P', so the inverse matrix $\mathbf{A}^{-1}$ will describe the transformation of P' back into P. The solution of sets of simultaneous equations can be made by expressing them in a matrix form $\mathbf{A}.\mathbf{x} = \mathbf{B}$ and multiplying by the inverse $\mathbf{A}^{-1}$. These are perhaps the commonest applications at this level, but there are many others to be found later on, as there are for matrices of other orders.

Exercise 22.2

1. Find which of the following matrices are singular:

(i) $\begin{pmatrix} 2 & 3 & 4 \\ -1 & 1 & -2 \\ 3 & 7 & 6 \end{pmatrix}$;

(ii) $\begin{pmatrix} 2 & 3 & 4 \\ -1 & 1 & -2 \\ 2 & -2 & 4 \end{pmatrix}$;

(iii) $\begin{pmatrix} 2 & 3 & 4 \\ -1 & 1 & -2 \\ 2 & -2 & 3 \end{pmatrix}$;

(iv) $\begin{pmatrix} 1 & 0 & 2 \\ 2 & -2 & 0 \\ 4 & -4 & 0 \end{pmatrix}$;

(v) $\begin{pmatrix} 0 & 0 & 1 \\ 0 & 2 & 0 \\ 3 & 0 & 0 \end{pmatrix}$.

2. Find the inverse of each of the following matrices:

(i) $\begin{pmatrix} 1 & 2 & 3 \\ 2 & 3 & 1 \\ 3 & 1 & 2 \end{pmatrix}$;

(ii) $\begin{pmatrix} 1 & 2 & 3 \\ 3 & 1 & 2 \\ 2 & 3 & 1 \end{pmatrix}$;

(iii) $\begin{pmatrix} 1 & 1 & 0 \\ 1 & 0 & 1 \\ 0 & 1 & 1 \end{pmatrix}$;

(iv) $\begin{pmatrix} 2 & 3 & 4 \\ -1 & 1 & 3 \\ 4 & 2 & 1 \end{pmatrix}$;

(v) $\begin{pmatrix} 2 & 1 & 5 \\ -1 & 2 & 3 \\ 4 & 1 & 7 \end{pmatrix}$.

3. By finding an inverse matrix, solve for x, y and z,

$$\begin{pmatrix} 3 & 2 & -1 \\ 4 & 0 & 2 \\ 1 & 2 & 3 \end{pmatrix} \begin{pmatrix} x \\ y \\ z \end{pmatrix} = \begin{pmatrix} -1 \\ 8 \\ 5 \end{pmatrix}.$$

4. By finding $\mathbf{A}^{-1}$, solve the equation $\mathbf{A}.\mathbf{x} = \mathbf{b}$, where

$$\mathbf{A} = \begin{pmatrix} 1 & -1 & 2 \\ 4 & 3 & 0 \\ 0 & -2 & 2 \end{pmatrix}, \mathbf{x} = \begin{pmatrix} x \\ y \\ z \end{pmatrix}, \mathbf{b} = \begin{pmatrix} -1 \\ -5 \\ 0 \end{pmatrix}.$$

5. Show that all points in the x, y plane are rotated about the z-axis through an angle α in the anti-clockwise sense by the matrix

$$\begin{pmatrix} \cos \alpha & -\sin \alpha & 0 \\ \sin \alpha & \cos \alpha & 0 \\ 0 & 0 & 1 \end{pmatrix}.$$

Deduce the matrix that rotates through an angle $-\alpha$, and verify that the product of these matrices is the 3×3 unit matrix.

6. By using a suitable parametric form for a general point on the line, show that the matrix

$$\begin{pmatrix} 1 & -1 & 2 \\ 2 & 1 & -3 \\ 4 & -3 & 2 \end{pmatrix}$$

transforms any point on the straight line

$$\frac{x-1}{2} = \frac{y}{3} = z - 1$$

into a point on the straight line

$$x - 3 = \frac{y+1}{4} = z - 6$$

and find the matrix that describes the inverse transformation.

7. Show that the matrix

$$A = \begin{pmatrix} 1 & 2 & 3 \\ 1 & 1 & 1 \\ 0 & 1 & 2 \end{pmatrix}$$

maps all points in space into the plane $x = y + z$, and that there is no inverse of A.

8. Show that the matrix

$$A = \begin{pmatrix} 0 & 3 & -3 \\ 4 & 2 & 2 \\ 2 & 1 & 1 \end{pmatrix}$$

maps all points on the line

$$\frac{x-1}{-1} = y - 3 = z - 2$$

into a single point.

9. The matrix

$$A = \begin{pmatrix} \frac{1}{2} & 0 & -\frac{1}{2} \\ 0 & 1 & 0 \\ -\frac{1}{2} & 0 & \frac{1}{2} \end{pmatrix}$$

describes a certain geometric transformation in three dimensions. What points are invariant (that is, left unaltered) by this transformation? Find the matrix A^2, and use this to deduce that there is no inverse of A.

10. Show that the matrix

$$A = \begin{pmatrix} 3 & 4 & 1 \\ 2 & 5 & 1 \\ 2 & 3 & 3 \end{pmatrix}$$

satisfies the equation

$$A^3 - 11A^2 + 26A - 16I = 0,$$

and deduce the matrix A^{-1}.

11. A matrix of the form

$$A = \begin{pmatrix} 1 & a & b \\ 0 & 1 & c \\ 0 & 0 & 1 \end{pmatrix},$$

where a, b and c can have any value, is called an echelon matrix. Find the inverse of A, and prove that for every echelon matrix A, if the matrix B is such that $B.A = I$, then B is also an echelon matrix.

12. Use the property $A.A^{-1} = A^{-1}.A = 1$ to prove that for all matrices A, B, if $C = A.B$, $C^{-1} = B^{-1}.A^{-1}$.

Exercise 22.3: Miscellaneous

1. Find the elements x and y in the matrix $A = (x \quad y)$ where $A.B = C$, given $B = \begin{pmatrix} 1 & 2 & 4 \\ 2 & 3 & 5 \end{pmatrix}$ and $C = (0 \quad 1 \quad 3)$.

2. Find the inverse of each of the following matrices, where it exists. If there is no inverse, say why there is no inverse.

(i) $\begin{pmatrix} 2 & -4 \\ 1 & 3 \end{pmatrix}$;   (ii) $\begin{pmatrix} 2 & -4 \\ 1 & -2 \end{pmatrix}$;   (iii) (4);

(iv) $\begin{pmatrix} 2 & 4 \\ 1 & 2 \\ 3 & 6 \end{pmatrix}$;   (v) $\begin{pmatrix} 1 & 2 & 0 \\ 0 & -1 & 2 \\ 0 & 0 & 3 \end{pmatrix}$;

(vi) $\begin{pmatrix} 1 & 0 & 0 \\ 0 & 2 & 0 \\ 0 & 0 & 3 \end{pmatrix}$;   (vii) $\begin{pmatrix} 0 & -1 & 0 \\ 0 & 0 & -1 \\ -1 & 0 & 0 \end{pmatrix}$;

(viii) $\begin{pmatrix} 1 & 2 & 4 \\ 2 & 4 & 8 \\ -1 & 0 & 4 \end{pmatrix}$.

3. If $\quad A = \begin{pmatrix} 2 & 9 \\ 1 & 2 \end{pmatrix}$ and $x_1 = \begin{pmatrix} 3k \\ k \end{pmatrix}$, $x_2 = \begin{pmatrix} 3k \\ -k \end{pmatrix}$

find $A.x_1$ and $A.x_2$. Interpret your result geometrically.

4. If $\quad A = \begin{pmatrix} \cos \alpha & \sin \alpha \\ -\sin \alpha & \cos \alpha \end{pmatrix}$

show that $A^{-1} = A^{T}$. Find another 2×2 matrix that has the property $A^{-1} = A^{T}$.

5. If $A = \begin{pmatrix} a & b \\ c & d \end{pmatrix}$ and $A^2 = A$, show that $a + d$ must have one of three values, and find those three values.

6. If A is a 2×2 matrix such that $A.B = B.A$ for every matrix B, show that $A = \begin{pmatrix} k & 0 \\ 0 & k \end{pmatrix}$, for some number k.

7. Show that all matrices A such that $A.B = B.A$ where B is a 3×3 diagonal matrix

$$\begin{pmatrix} a & 0 & 0 \\ 0 & b & 0 \\ 0 & 0 & c \end{pmatrix}$$

are themselves diagonal matrices.

8. If A is a 3×3 matrix such that $A.B = B.A$ for every matrix B, show that

$$A = \begin{pmatrix} k & 0 & 0 \\ 0 & k & 0 \\ 0 & 0 & k \end{pmatrix} \text{ for some } k.$$

9. Write down three different 2×2 matrices A such that $A^2 = 0$.

The matrix A is any 2×2 matrix, such that $A^2 = 0$. Show that $1 + A$ has inverse $1 - A$, where 1 is the 2×2 unit matrix.

10. For the matrix $\qquad A = \begin{pmatrix} a & b \\ c & d \end{pmatrix}$

the trace of A, written tr (A), is defined as $a + d$. If A and B are any 2×2 matrices, show that

(i) tr $(A + B) = $ tr $(A) + $ tr (B),   (ii) tr $(AB) = $ tr (BA)

Defining the trace of a 3×3 matrix similarly as the sum of the elements in its leading diagonal, prove the same results for 3×3 matrices.

11. Express in matrix form the transformation given by

$$\begin{aligned} x' &= 3x + 2y + z \\ y' &= 5x + 4y + 2z \\ z' &= 2x + 2y + \lambda z. \end{aligned}$$

When $\lambda = 3$, find the point (x', y', z') which is the image of $(2, -1, 0)$, and the point (x, y, z) of which $(2, 3, 3)$ is the image.

When $\lambda = 1$, show that all points (x, y, z) are transformed into points in the plane $x' - y' + z' = 0$.

12. If $A = \begin{pmatrix} 5 & 4 & 3 \\ -2 & -1 & 0 \\ 3 & 4 & 5 \end{pmatrix}$ and $B = \begin{pmatrix} -5 & -8 & 3 \\ 10 & 16 & -6 \\ -5 & -8 & 3 \end{pmatrix}$

find $A.B$ and $B.A$. What can you deduce about A and B?

13. If $A = \begin{pmatrix} 5 & 4 & 3 \\ -2 & -1 & 0 \\ 1 & 2 & 2 \end{pmatrix}$ and $B = \begin{pmatrix} -2 & -2 & -3 \\ 4 & 7 & 6 \\ -3 & -6 & -3 \end{pmatrix}$ find $A.B$.

Deduce A^{-1} and B^{-1}, and verify that $(A.B)^{-1} = B^{-1}.A^{-1}$.

14. If $A = \begin{pmatrix} 2 & 0 & 1 \\ 3 & -2 & -1 \\ -4 & 1 & -1 \end{pmatrix}$ find A^{-1} and hence or otherwise solve the

equations:

(i) $A \cdot x = \begin{pmatrix} 5 \\ -4 \\ -5 \end{pmatrix}$;

(ii) $A^{-1} \cdot x = \begin{pmatrix} 1 \\ 2 \\ 3 \end{pmatrix}$.

15. A transformation is defined by

$$\begin{pmatrix} x' \\ y' \\ z' \end{pmatrix} = \begin{pmatrix} -2 & 1 & 4 \\ 1 & 0 & -2 \\ 3 & 4 & -6 \end{pmatrix} \begin{pmatrix} x \\ y \\ z \end{pmatrix}.$$

Show that the set of planes perpendicular to the y-axis maps onto a set of parallel lines. What is the direction of these lines? Which of these planes is mapped onto a line through the origin?   (S.M.P.)

16. If

$$A = \begin{pmatrix} 1 & -2 & a \\ 1 & -3 & 3 \\ 1 & -4 & 5 \end{pmatrix},$$

show that the equation

$$A \begin{pmatrix} x \\ y \\ z \end{pmatrix} = \begin{pmatrix} p \\ q \\ 1 \end{pmatrix}$$

has a unique solution unless $a = 1$, but has no solution when $a = 1$ unless $p - 2q + 1 = 0$.

Find the solutions when

(i) $a = 2$, $p = q = 1$;   (ii) $a = 1$, $p = -1$ and $q = 0$.

17. Let

$$A = \begin{pmatrix} 1 & 1 & 2 \\ 0 & 1 & 2 \\ 2 & 2 & 5 \end{pmatrix}, \quad B = \begin{pmatrix} 1 & 1 & 2 \\ 0 & 1 & 2 \\ 0 & 0 & 1 \end{pmatrix}, \quad C = \begin{pmatrix} 1 & 0 & 0 \\ 0 & 1 & 2 \\ 0 & 0 & 1 \end{pmatrix}.$$

Find elementary* matrices E_1, E_2 and E_3 such that

$$E_1 A = B, \quad E_2 B = C \text{ and } E_3 C = I,$$

where I is the unit matrix. Hence, or otherwise, find the inverse matrix of A.   (S.M.P.)

* An elementary matrix is one like $\begin{pmatrix} a & 0 & 0 \\ 0 & 1 & 0 \\ 0 & 0 & 1 \end{pmatrix}$ which multiplies one row of another

matrix by a; like $\begin{pmatrix} 1 & 0 & 0 \\ 0 & 1 & b \\ 0 & 0 & 1 \end{pmatrix}$ which adds a multiple of one row to another, or

$\begin{pmatrix} 0 & 1 & 0 \\ 1 & 0 & 0 \\ 0 & 0 & 1 \end{pmatrix}$ which interchanges two rows.

18. What conditions must be applied to matrices **A** and **B** if **AB** − **BA** is to have a meaning?

If **A** is a given 2×2 matrix, write down three matrices **X** for which **AX** − **XA** = **O**.

If **A** is the matrix
$$\begin{pmatrix} 1 & 2 \\ 0 & 1 \end{pmatrix}$$

find the most general form for **X** for this equation to hold.   (S.M.P.)

19. The transformation M maps the point (a, b, c) on to the point (g, h, k) and the transformation N maps the point (g, h, k) on to the point (x, y, z), where

$$\begin{aligned} g &= a + 2b - c & x &= g \\ h &= \quad\ b - c \quad\text{and}\quad & y &= -4g - h \\ k &= \qquad\quad c & z &= 3g + 3h + 4k. \end{aligned}$$

(i) Given that $g = 1$, $h = -1$, and $k = 4$, find (a, b, c) and (x, y, z).

(ii) Write down the matrix **M** of the transformation M and the matrix **N** of the transformation N.

(iii) By solution of equations, or otherwise, find the matrix $\mathbf{M}^{-1}$ and evaluate

$$\mathbf{M}^{-1} \begin{pmatrix} 1 \\ -1 \\ 4 \end{pmatrix}.$$

(iv) Calculate the matrix **P** such that

$$\mathbf{P} \begin{pmatrix} a \\ b \\ c \end{pmatrix} = \begin{pmatrix} x \\ y \\ z \end{pmatrix}.$$ (M.E.I.)

20. A transformation matrix **M** is given by

$$\mathbf{M} = \begin{pmatrix} 1 & 0 & 4 \\ 0 & 5 & 4 \\ 4 & 4 & 3 \end{pmatrix}.$$

If O is the origin and A the point $(1, 2, 2)$, what are the co-ordinates of the image of A under the transformation **M**? If A' is the image of A, what is the ratio of the lengths of OA and OA'?

A second point B has its image B' under **M** such that

$$\mathbf{OB'} = 3\mathbf{OB}.$$

Find a set of possible coordinates of B.

A third point C, distinct from A and B, is related to its image C' under **M** by $\mathbf{OC'} = k\mathbf{OC}$, where k is a scalar. Find the value of k and a set of possible coordinates of C.   (M.E.I.)

21. Let **A** stand for the matrix

$$\begin{pmatrix} 17 & -4 & 0 \\ 23 & 49 & 3 \\ 18 & 13 & 1 \end{pmatrix}.$$

Find two matrices $\mathbf{M}_1$, $\mathbf{M}_2$ such that
(i) each has only one non-zero entry off the leading diagonal;
(ii) the product $\mathbf{M}_2\mathbf{M}_1\mathbf{A}$ has zeros above and to the right of the leading diagonal, so that its form is

$$\begin{pmatrix} * & 0 & 0 \\ * & * & 0 \\ * & * & * \end{pmatrix},$$

where the places indicated by the asterisks are occupied by numbers.
From your results deduce the value of the determinant of $\mathbf{A}$.

(S.M.P.)

22. Solve for x

$$\begin{vmatrix} x-1 & 4 & -1 \\ 1 & x+2 & 1 \\ 2x-4 & 4 & x-4 \end{vmatrix} = 0.$$

23. Solve for x

$$\begin{vmatrix} x+1 & 2 & 3 \\ 1 & x+2 & 1 \\ 2 & 2 & x+3 \end{vmatrix} = 0$$

and deduce the solutions, in the set of real numbers, of

$$\begin{vmatrix} x^2+1 & 2 & 3 \\ 1 & x^2+2 & 1 \\ 2 & 2 & x^2+3 \end{vmatrix} = 0.$$

24. Find x, y, z if

$$\begin{pmatrix} 1 & -3 & -3 \\ -8 & 6 & -3 \\ 8 & -2 & 7 \end{pmatrix}\begin{pmatrix} x \\ y \\ z \end{pmatrix} = \lambda \begin{pmatrix} x \\ y \\ z \end{pmatrix}$$

for each in turn of the values of λ, $\lambda = 1$, 4 or 9. Interpret your result geometrically.

25. If $\mathbf{a} = (a \quad b \quad c)$ write down the matrix $\mathbf{a}^\mathsf{T}$, the transpose of $\mathbf{a}$. Form the 3×3 matrix $\mathbf{A} = \mathbf{a}^\mathsf{T}.\mathbf{a}$ and show that $\det \mathbf{A} = 0$, whatever the values of a, b and c.

26. Prove that for any 2×2 non-singular matrices $\mathbf{A}$, $\mathbf{B}$
(i) $(\mathbf{A}.\mathbf{B})^{-1} = \mathbf{B}^{-1}.\mathbf{A}^{-1}$,   (ii) $(\mathbf{A}.\mathbf{B})^\mathsf{T} = \mathbf{B}^\mathsf{T}.\mathbf{A}^\mathsf{T}$.

27. Prove that for any non-singular 3×3 matrices
(i) $(\mathbf{A}.\mathbf{B})^{-1} = \mathbf{B}^{-1}.\mathbf{A}^{-1}$,   (ii) $(\mathbf{A}.\mathbf{B})^\mathsf{T} = \mathbf{B}^\mathsf{T}.\mathbf{A}^\mathsf{T}$.

28. If $\mathbf{M} = \begin{pmatrix} a_1 & b_1 \\ a_2 & b_2 \\ a_3 & b_3 \end{pmatrix}$, find the matrix $\mathbf{N}$ where $\mathbf{N} = \mathbf{M}^\mathsf{T}.\mathbf{M}$.

Show that $\mathbf{N}$ is singular if $a_1 = b_1$, $a_2 = b_2$ and $a_3 = b_3$.

29. If $\mathbf{p} = \begin{pmatrix} a \\ b \end{pmatrix}$, where a and b are any real numbers, show that the matrix

$\mathbf{M} = \mathbf{p} . \mathbf{p}^T$ is always singular but the matrix $\mathbf{N} = \mathbf{I} + \mathbf{p} . \mathbf{p}^T$, where $\mathbf{I} = \begin{pmatrix} 1 & 0 \\ 0 & 1 \end{pmatrix}$ is never singular.

30. If $\mathbf{A} = \begin{pmatrix} 2 & 1 & 3 \\ 0 & 3 & 5 \\ 0 & 0 & 4 \end{pmatrix}$, show that the equation $\det (\mathbf{A} - \lambda \mathbf{1}) = 0$ reduces to

$\lambda^3 - 9\lambda^2 + 26\lambda - 24 = 0$.

Verify by substitution that $\mathbf{A}^3 - 9\mathbf{A}^2 + 26\mathbf{A} - 24 = 0$, and use this result to calculate $\mathbf{A}^{-1}$.

(It can be proved that all matrices satisfy their characteristic equation; this is called the Cayley-Hamilton theorem.)

31. A square matrix is called an orthogonal matrix if $\mathbf{A} . \mathbf{A}^T = 1$. Prove that for all orthogonal matrices $\mathbf{A}$, $\det \mathbf{A} = \pm 1$.

32. If $\mathbf{A} = \begin{pmatrix} 1 & 1 & 1 \\ 0 & 1 & 1 \\ 0 & 0 & 1 \end{pmatrix}$ prove that $(\mathbf{A}^2)^{-1} = (\mathbf{A}^{-1})^2$.

33. List all six arrangements of the letters a, b, c. Displaying one of these arrangements in a matrix $\mathbf{p} = \begin{pmatrix} a \\ b \\ c \end{pmatrix}$ show that it is possible to find a matrix $\mathbf{M}$ such that

$$\mathbf{M} \begin{pmatrix} a \\ b \\ c \end{pmatrix} = \begin{pmatrix} b \\ c \\ a \end{pmatrix}.$$

Show that $\mathbf{M}^2 . \mathbf{p}$ is another of these arrangements, and find also $\mathbf{M}^3 . \mathbf{p}$. Show that we need three other matrices $\mathbf{N}_1, \mathbf{N}_2, \mathbf{N}_3$ to give the other three arrangements, and that in every case $\mathbf{N}_i^2 = 0$, for $i = 1, 2, 3$.

34. P and Q, who live in the same house, are on shift work, so that P is at home in the daytime and Q at night. When P comes home there is a chance of $\frac{2}{3}$ that if the cat is 'in' he will be left 'in', but if he is 'out' the chance he will be left 'out' is $\frac{1}{2}$. When Q comes home, if the cat is 'in' there is an even chance that he will be left 'in', but if he is 'out' he will certainly be brought 'in'. Express these statements as stochastic matrices $\mathbf{P}$ and $\mathbf{Q}$ respectively. By considering the product $\mathbf{PQ}$ of these matrices, find the steady state probability of the cat being 'in' after P has come home.*

(S.M.P.)

35. A businessman travels between London, Paris, Bonn and Rome. The probability of his journeys are given by the matrix

* The cat is incapable of getting in or out unaided.

$$
\begin{array}{cccc}
 & L & P & B & R \\
\begin{array}{c} L \\ P \\ B \\ R \end{array} &
\left(\begin{array}{cccc}
0.7 & 0.3 & 0 & 0 \\
0.5 & 0 & 0.4 & 0.1 \\
0 & 0.4 & 0.6 & 0 \\
0.4 & 0 & 0 & 0.6
\end{array}\right)
\end{array}
$$

so that if he is in London any one day, there is a probability of 0.7 he stays in London that night and a probability of 0.3 that he goes to Paris, whereas when he arrives one day in Bonn the probability that he goes to Paris the next day is 0.4, otherwise he stays in Bonn. If he arrives in London one Monday, find the probability

(i) that he is still in London on Friday of that week,
(ii) that he goes to Paris on Tuesday and is still there on Thursday,
(iii) that he is in Bonn on Wednesday,
(iv) that he is in Rome on Wednesday.

36. A man has two pairs of shoes A and B. On any morning if he can remember which pair he wore the previous day, he puts on the other pair, but on half of the days he forgets and then the probability is $\frac{2}{3}$ that he will put on pair A.

The probability of his wearing A on one day is p_A, and of wearing A on the next day is p'_A. The probability of his wearing B on one day is p_B, and of wearing B on the next day is p'_B. Obtain a relation of the form

$$
\begin{pmatrix} p'_A \\ p'_B \end{pmatrix} = M \begin{pmatrix} p_A \\ p_B \end{pmatrix},
$$

where M is a matrix. Write down the matrix M in detail.

Hence find the probability in the long run that on any particular day he will wear pair A—presuming that the shoes have not worn out.   (A.E.B.)

37. The coefficients of the terms in the polynomial $f(x) = ax^2 + bx + c$ can be displayed in the matrix

$$
P = \begin{pmatrix} a \\ b \\ c \end{pmatrix}
$$

Find the product $D.P$, where

$$
D = \begin{pmatrix} 0 & 0 & 0 \\ 2 & 1 & 0 \\ 1 & 0 & 0 \end{pmatrix}.
$$

Find the polynomial whose coefficients are displayed in the matrix $D.P$ and compare it with $f(x)$. Find also the polynomial given by $D^3.P$, and comment on this result.

38. The matrix M is given by

$$
M = \begin{pmatrix} 1 & 2 & -1 \\ 4 & 7 & 6 \\ 3 & 6 & 5 \end{pmatrix}
$$

Find det M and M^{-1}.

The triangle ABC is mapped onto the triangle $A'B'C'$ by the transformation $\mathbf{x}' = \mathbf{M}.\mathbf{x}$. If the coordinates of the points A', B', C' are $(0,0,0)$, $(3,1,1)$ and $(8,-1,0)$ respectively, find the coordinates of the points A, B and C. (M.E.I.)

39. Find the matrix $\mathbf{M}$ such that

$$\begin{pmatrix} 1 & R \\ 0 & 1 \end{pmatrix} \mathbf{M} = \begin{pmatrix} 2 & R \\ \dfrac{1}{R} & 1 \end{pmatrix}.$$

Hence (or otherwise) determine the circuit diagram for the 'four terminal network' described by

$$\begin{pmatrix} V_0 \\ I_0 \end{pmatrix} = \begin{pmatrix} 2 & R \\ \dfrac{1}{R} & 1 \end{pmatrix} \begin{pmatrix} V_1 \\ I_1 \end{pmatrix}.$$

[Suffices 0, 1 denote input and output respectively.]

Four such networks are joined in series and the ratio of output to input voltage is $1:55$. What is the ratio of the output and input currents? (S.M.P.)

40. The four-terminal networks of figures (a) and (b) lead respectively to voltage-current transformations represented by

(a)
$$\begin{pmatrix} V_2 \\ I_2 \end{pmatrix} = \begin{pmatrix} 1 & -R_1 \\ 0 & 1 \end{pmatrix} \begin{pmatrix} V_1 \\ I_1 \end{pmatrix},$$

and

(b)
$$\begin{pmatrix} V_2 \\ I_2 \end{pmatrix} = \begin{pmatrix} 1 & 0 \\ -1/R_2 & 1 \end{pmatrix} \begin{pmatrix} V_1 \\ I_1 \end{pmatrix}.$$

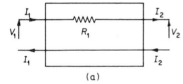 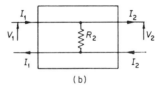

(a)　　　　　　(b)

Write down the voltage-current transformation for the four-terminal network of figure (c) and hence, or otherwise, derive the voltage-current transformation for the network of figure (d).

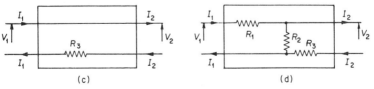

(c)　　　　　　(d)

Fig. 22.4

(S.M.P.)

Revision Paper D1

1. Plot, using values of θ at $30°$ intervals from $0°$ to $360°$, the curve whose equation in polar coordinates is $r = 5 + 4\cos\theta$.
   Show that all chords PQ drawn through the pole O are of length 10 units. Calculate the values of θ for which O trisects the chord PQ.
   (J.M.B.)

2. Find the area of a loop of the curve $r^2 = a^2 \sin\theta$.

3. If $z = 4 + 3i$, which one of the following statements is false?
   (i) $|z| = 5$,   (ii) $|\bar{z}| = 5$,   (iii) $|z\bar{z}| = 25$,
   (iv) $\cot(\arg z) = \frac{4}{3}$,   (v) $\tan(\arg \bar{z}) = \frac{3}{4}$.

4. If $z = 2(\cos\theta + i\sin\theta)$, where θ is acute, represent on an Argand diagram the points representing
   (i) z,   (ii) $\bar{z}$,   (iii) $\dfrac{1}{z}$,
   (iv) $z + 1$,   (v) $z - 1$.
   Mark also on the diagram the points for which
   (vi) $\operatorname{Re}(z - 1) = 0$,   (vii) $\operatorname{Imag}(z - i) = 0$.

5. Represent in an Argand diagram the region for which $|z - 1| < 2$ and $\operatorname{Re}(z) > 0$.

6. Show that there is a unique value of z for which $\arg(z + i) = \dfrac{\pi}{4}$ and $|z + 1| = 2$, and that this value is real.   (M.E.I.)

7. The position vectors of A, B, C are $\mathbf{i}$, $2\mathbf{j}$, $3\mathbf{k}$ respectively. The perpendicular from the origin O to the plane ABC meets the plane at the point D. Find
   (i) the vector equation of the plane ABC,
   (ii) the vector equation of the line OD,
   (iii) the position vector of the point D.   (A.E.B.)

8. A particle P moves so that its position vector $\mathbf{r}$ at time t is given by
   $$\mathbf{r} = \mathbf{a}\cos\omega t + \mathbf{b}\sin\omega t,$$
   where $\mathbf{a}, \mathbf{b}$ are constant vectors and ω is a constant. Show that
   $$\mathbf{r} \times \frac{d\mathbf{r}}{dt}$$
   is independent of t.   (L.)

9. Given that $\mathbf{A}$ and $\mathbf{B}$ are matrices such that $\mathbf{AB} = \mathbf{A}$ and $\mathbf{BA} = \mathbf{B}$, show that $(\mathbf{A} - \mathbf{B})^2 = \mathbf{0}$.   (M.E.I.)

10. Find the elements a, b, c, d in order that the transformation
    $$\begin{pmatrix} x' \\ y' \end{pmatrix} = \begin{pmatrix} a & b \\ c & d \end{pmatrix}\begin{pmatrix} x \\ y \end{pmatrix}$$
    may represent

(*a*) an anticlockwise rotation through an angle α,

(*b*) a reflection in the line $y = x \tan (\beta/2)$.

Hence prove that a reflection in the line $y = x \tan (\beta/2)$ followed by a reflection in the line $y = x \tan (\gamma/2)$ is equivalent to a rotation.   (L.)

Revision Paper D2

1. Sketch the curve whose polar equation is $r = a\cos^2\theta$, and find the area of a loop.

2. Sketch the curve whose polar equation is $r = e^\theta$, for $0 \leqslant \theta \leqslant 4$, and find the length of the arc of the curve between the points for which $\theta = 0$ and $\theta = 2\pi$.

3. Show the representation of the complex number $z = 3 + 4i$ in an Argand diagram.

    Calculate

    (i) $\arg(z)$,   (ii) $|z|$,   (iii) iz,   (iv) $\dfrac{25}{z}$.

    Indicate how each of these is represented on the diagram.   (A.E.B.)

4. Find the two complex numbers whose squares are equal to i.

    Hence, or otherwise, find the four (complex) roots of the equation $z^4 + 4 = 0$, giving the modulus and argument of each.

    Hence express $z^4 + 4$ as the product of two real quadratic polynomials.
    (O.)

5. (i) Find the complex numbers z, i.e. numbers of the form $z = x + iy$ where x and y are real, which satisfy the following equations:

    (a) $(2 - 4i)z = 4 - 3i$,
    (b) $z^2 + 2z + 1 - i = 0$.

    (ii) Find all the complex numbers z such that
    $$|z| = |z - 4| = 2.5.$$ (O. & C.)

6. Prove that, if $\mathbf{a}$ and $\mathbf{b}$ are any two non-parallel vectors lying in a plane, then any other vector $\mathbf{p}$ lying in this plane can be expressed in the form
    $$\mathbf{p} = l\mathbf{a} + m\mathbf{b},$$
    where l and m are scalars.

    Find the scalars l, m when
    $$\mathbf{a} = 2\mathbf{i} - 3\mathbf{j}, \qquad \mathbf{b} = -\mathbf{i} + 4\mathbf{j}, \qquad \mathbf{p} = 4\mathbf{i} - \mathbf{j},$$
    where $\mathbf{i}, \mathbf{j}$ are unit vectors directed along coordinate axes Ox, Oy respectively in the plane.   (M.E.I.)

7. State the geometrical relationship between the two non-zero vectors whose scalar product is zero.

    The position vector of A is $\mathbf{i} + \mathbf{k}$, and of B is $2\mathbf{j} - \mathbf{k}$. Find the position vector of C where C is the foot of the perpendicular from the origin, O, to AB. Hence find the area of the triangle OAB.   (A.E.B.)

8. (a) Prove, using a vector method, that the altitudes of a triangle are concurrent.

    (b) Given two sets of collinear points, OAA' and OBB', with $\overrightarrow{OA} = \mathbf{a}$, $\overrightarrow{OA'} = \lambda\mathbf{a}$, $\overrightarrow{OB} = \mathbf{b}$ and $\overrightarrow{OB'} = \mu\mathbf{b}$, where the vectors $\mathbf{a}$ and $\mathbf{b}$ are not parallel, show that the vector $\overrightarrow{OX}$, where X is the point of intersection of AB' and $A'B$, is given by

$$\overrightarrow{OX} = \frac{\lambda(1 - \mu)}{1 - \lambda\mu}\mathbf{a} + \frac{\mu(1 - \lambda)}{1 - \lambda\mu}\mathbf{b},$$

provided that $1 - \lambda\mu \neq 0$.
Give a geometrical interpretation of the case $1 - \lambda\mu = 0$.　　(M.E.I.)

9. The vectors $\mathbf{u}$ and $\mathbf{v}$ are given by

$$\mathbf{u} = 2\mathbf{i} - \mathbf{j} + 2\mathbf{k}$$
$$\mathbf{v} = a\mathbf{i} + b\mathbf{k}$$
and $$\mathbf{u} \times \mathbf{v} = \mathbf{i} + c\mathbf{k}.$$

Find a, b and c. Find in surd form, the cosine of the angle between $\mathbf{u}$ and $\mathbf{v}$.　　(J.M.B.)

10. A two-state Markov chain has a matrix of transition probabilities $\mathbf{P}$, where $\mathbf{P} = \begin{pmatrix} 1 - \alpha & \alpha \\ \beta & 1 - \beta \end{pmatrix}$. If there exists an equilibrium probability distribution between the states given by $\pi = (\pi_0, \pi_1)$, show that π satisfies the equation

$$\pi(\mathbf{I} - \mathbf{P}) = 0.$$

Hence evaluate π_0, π_1 in terms of α, β.
The probability of a wet day following a dry day is 0.250, and of a dry day following a wet day is 0.338. Show that the probability of a dry day occurring will be 0.575.　　(O.)

Revision Paper D3

1. The straight line whose polar equation is $r \cos \theta = 3$ meets the curve whose polar equation is $r = 5 + 2 \cos \theta$ at the points Q and R. Show that the area of the triangle OQR (where O is the origin) is $9\sqrt{3}$. Find also the areas of the two parts into which QR divides the whole of the region defined by $r \leqslant 5 + 2 \cos \theta$. (J.M.B.)

2. Solve the equations

$$z + (1 - i)w = i$$
$$(1 + i)z + iw = -1,$$

for the complex numbers z and w, giving each answer in the form $a + bi$. (S.M.P.)

3. Show, by geometrical considerations, or otherwise, that if the complex numbers z_1 and z_2 are such that $|z_1| = |z_2|$, then $\dfrac{z_1 + z_2}{z_1 - z_2}$ is pure imaginary.

Show also that, if $z_1 = i$ and $z_2 = \dfrac{1}{\sqrt{2}}(1 + i)$, then $\arg(z_1 + z_2) = \dfrac{3\pi}{8}$.

(J.M.B.)

4. Express in the form $a + ib$, where a, b are *integers*,
   (a) $(2 - i)^3$; (b) $(13 - i)/(3 - i)$; (c) $\sqrt{(-2i)}$.

   Find the roots, z_1 and z_2, of the quadratic equation

   $$z^2 - 3(1 + i)z + 5i = 0,$$

   expressing your answers in the form $c + id$, where c and d are real numbers. Explain why z_1 and z_2 are not *conjugate* complex numbers.

   Plot the positions of z_1 and z_2 on a sketch of the Argand diagram and, preferably without first solving the equation, plot in the same diagram the positions of the roots z_3, z_4 of the quadratic equation

   $$z^2 - 3(1 - i)z - 5i = 0.$$ (O. & C.)

5. (i) If $Z_1 = 1 + i$ and $Z_2 = 7 - i$, find the modulus of

   (a) $Z_1 - Z_2$, (b) $Z_1 Z_2$, (c) $\dfrac{Z_1 - Z_2}{Z_1 Z_2}$.

   (ii) Express $(1 - i\sqrt{3})^2$ in the form $r(\cos \theta + i \sin \theta)$ where r is positive and θ is between $-\pi$ and π.

   (iii) Assuming that

   $$(\cos \alpha + i \sin \alpha)^5 = \cos 5\alpha + i \sin 5\alpha,$$

   prove that
   (a) $\cos 5\alpha = \cos^5 \alpha - 10 \cos^3 \alpha \sin^2 \alpha + 5 \cos \alpha \sin^4 \alpha$,
   (b) $\sin 5\alpha = \sin^5 \alpha - 10 \sin^3 \alpha \cos^2 \alpha + 5 \sin \alpha \cos^4 \alpha$.

   Hence express $\tan 5\alpha$ as a function of $\tan \alpha$. (O. & C.)

6. Points P, Q and R have position vectors $\mathbf{p}$, $\mathbf{q}$ and $\mathbf{r}$ respectively. If $\mathbf{p} = (1 - \alpha)\mathbf{q} + \alpha\mathbf{r}$ for some number α, describe the position of P relative to Q and R.

$OABC$ are four non-coplanar points in space. A, B, C have position vectors $\mathbf{a}$, $\mathbf{b}$ and $\mathbf{c}$ relative to O. The position vector of the point V is $-\mathbf{c} + 2\mathbf{a}$, and of W is $-2\mathbf{a} + 3\mathbf{b}$. If VW meets the plane OBC in U, find the position vector of U and show that U is on BC.

Use scalar products to prove that if V is in the plane through O perpendicular to OB, and W is in the plane through O perpendicular to OC, then U is in the plane through O perpendicular to OA.   (S.M.P.)

7. Two points A and B have position vectors $\mathbf{a}$ and $\mathbf{b}$ respectively. Show that the point which divides AB internally in the ratio $m:n$ has position vector

$$\frac{n\mathbf{a} + m\mathbf{b}}{n + m}.$$

Three non-collinear points A, B and C have position vectors $\mathbf{a}$, $\mathbf{b}$ and $\mathbf{c}$ respectively. The point D divides AB internally in the ratio $2:1$. The point E divides BC internally in the ratio $2:1$. Show that DE produced meets AC produced at the point with position vector

$$\frac{4}{3}\mathbf{c} - \frac{1}{3}\mathbf{a}.$$ (L.)

8. Given that

$$\overrightarrow{OA} = 3\mathbf{i} + 4\mathbf{j} + 5\mathbf{k},$$
$$\overrightarrow{OB} = 4\mathbf{i} + 6\mathbf{j} + 7\mathbf{k},$$
$$\overrightarrow{OC} = \mathbf{i} + 5\mathbf{j} + 3\mathbf{k},$$

find

(i) the cosine of the angle BAC,
(ii) the area of the triangle ABC,
(iii) the direction cosines of the normal to the plane ABC,
(iv) the volume of the tetrahedron $OABC$.   (L.)

9. If the equations

$$a_1x + b_1y + c_1z = 0$$
$$a_2x + b_2y + c_2z = 0$$
$$a_3x + b_3y + c_3z = 0$$

have a solution other than $x = y = z = 0$, show that

$$\begin{vmatrix} a_1 & b_1 & c_1 \\ a_2 & b_2 & c_2 \\ a_3 & b_3 & c_3 \end{vmatrix} = 0.$$

Find the values of λ for which the equations

$$4x - 6y - z = \lambda x$$
$$x - 4y - x = \lambda y$$
$$2x + 3y + z = \lambda z$$

have a solution other than $x = y = z = 0$, and find the ratios $x:y:z$ for each of these values of λ.   (O. & C.)

10. What is the matrix product PQ when

$$P = \begin{pmatrix} 1 & 0 & 0 \\ -2 & 1 & 0 \\ -5 & 1 & 1 \end{pmatrix} \quad \text{and} \quad Q = \begin{pmatrix} 1 & 2 & 2 \\ 2 & 5 & 7 \\ 3 & 5 & a \end{pmatrix} ?$$

The equations

$$x + 2y + 2z = \alpha^2$$
$$2x + 5y + 7z = 2\alpha$$
$$3x + 5y + az = 3$$

are to be used to determine sets (x, y, z). Prove that, if $a = 4$, there is a unique set (x, y, z) and express the values of x, y, z in terms of α. Prove also that, if $a = 3$, there is no solution unless α has one of two values. Find these values and the corresponding sets of solutions. (O.)

Revision Paper D4

1. Plot the curve whose equation in polar coordinates is $r = 1 + \cos\theta$ and on the same diagram draw the straight line $r = \sec\theta$. Find by calculation the values of r and θ for the points where the curve and the line intersect. (J.M.B.)

2. (i) Sketch the curve whose equation in polar coordinates is $r = a(1 + \cos\theta)$. Find the areas of the two portions into which the straight line $\theta = \frac{1}{2}\pi$ divides the upper half of the figure.
   (ii) Find the volume of the solid generated by rotating the curve $r^2 = a^2 \cos\theta$ $(r > 0)$ about the line $\theta = 0$. (O. & C.)

3. (i) In modulus-argument form a complex number is $z = [r, \theta]$. By writing both z^4 and $1 + \sqrt{3}i$ in modulus-argument form and comparing the results, show that the equation

$$z^4 = 1 + \sqrt{3}i$$

   has four solutions z_0, z_1, z_2, z_3, where

$$z_n = \left[2^{\frac{1}{4}}, \frac{\pi}{12} + n\frac{\pi}{2} \right].$$

   Prove that $z_2 + z_0 = z_3 + z_1 = 0$, and mark the solutions on the complex plane.
   (ii) If k is a real number such that the equation

$$x^3 + (3 + i)x^2 + (1 - 2i)x + k = 0$$

   has a real root, find all possible values of k. (S.M.P.)

4. Mark on an Argand diagram a point P to represent a certain complex number z, and put into the same diagram points Q and R to represent the complex numbers $z - 2$ and $\dfrac{1}{z}$ respectively.

   Determine the loci of Q and R when P moves in such a way that
   (i) its modulus remains constant,
   (ii) its argument remains constant,
   (iii) its real part remains constant. (C.)

5. (i) If $2 < |z - 1 + 2i| < 3$, show that the point representing the number z in the complex plane (Argand diagram) lies in a certain region of the plane, and indicate this region.
   (ii) The equation $x^3 + px^2 + qx + 6 = 0$ (p and q being real numbers) has $1 + i$ as one root. Find p and q and solve the equation completely. (C.)

6. Express each of the complex numbers

$$a = \frac{10}{1 + 3i}, \quad b = \frac{1 + 7i}{1 - i}$$

   in the form $x + yi$, where x and y are real numbers.

The points A and B in an Argand diagram represent the complex numbers a and b respectively. The point K on the positive real axis is such that $OK = k$ units, where O is the origin. Given that angle AKB is a right angle, show that $k = 3$ and that $(a - k)/(b - k)$ is purely imaginary.

(M.E.I.)

7. A pyramid has a square base $OABC$ and vertex V. The position vectors of A, B, C, V referred to O as origin are given by $\mathbf{OA} = 2\mathbf{i}$, $\mathbf{OB} = 2\mathbf{i} + 2\mathbf{j}$, $\mathbf{OC} = 2\mathbf{j}$, $\mathbf{OV} = \mathbf{i} + \mathbf{j} + 3\mathbf{k}$.

(i) Express $\mathbf{AV}$ in terms of $\mathbf{i}$, $\mathbf{j}$ and $\mathbf{k}$.

(ii) Using scalar products, or otherwise, find a vector $\mathbf{x}$ which is perpendicular to both $\mathbf{OV}$ and $\mathbf{AV}$.

(iii) Calculate the angle between the vector $\mathbf{x}$, found in (ii), and $\mathbf{VB}$, giving your answer to the nearest degree.

(iv) Write down the acute angle between VB and the plane OVA.

(C.)

8. The vertices A, B and C of a triangle have position vectors $\mathbf{a}$, $\mathbf{b}$ and $\mathbf{c}$ respectively relative to an origin O. The point P is on BC such that $BP:PC = 3:1$; the point Q is on CA such that $CQ:QA = 2:3$; the point R is on BA produced such that $BR:AR = 2:1$. The position vectors of P, Q and R are $\mathbf{p}$, $\mathbf{q}$ and $\mathbf{r}$ respectively. Show that $\mathbf{q}$ can be expressed in terms of $\mathbf{p}$ and $\mathbf{r}$ and hence or otherwise show that P, Q and R are collinear. State the ratio of the lengths of the line segments PQ and QR. (J.M.B.)

9. (i) Given that

$$\mathbf{r} = (\cos 2t)\mathbf{a} + (\sin 2t)\mathbf{b},$$

where $\mathbf{a}$ and $\mathbf{b}$ are constant vectors, show that

(a) $\dfrac{d^2\mathbf{r}}{dt^2} + 4\mathbf{r} = 0$, (b) $\mathbf{r} + \dfrac{d\mathbf{r}}{dt} = 2\mathbf{a} \times \mathbf{b}$.

(ii) If $\dfrac{d^2\mathbf{r}}{dt^2} = \mu\mathbf{r}$, where μ is a constant scalar, verify that

(a) $\left(\dfrac{d\mathbf{r}}{dt}\right)^2 = \mu\mathbf{r}^2 + c$, where c is a constant scalar,

(b) $\mathbf{r} \times \dfrac{d\mathbf{r}}{dt}$ is a constant vector. (L.)

10. A transformation in three-dimensional space takes the point (x, y, z) to (x_1, y_1, z_1) where

$$\begin{pmatrix} x_1 \\ y_1 \\ z_1 \end{pmatrix} = \begin{pmatrix} 0 & 0 & 1 \\ 1 & 0 & 0 \\ 0 & 1 & 0 \end{pmatrix} \begin{pmatrix} x \\ y \\ z \end{pmatrix}.$$

Prove that the transformation leaves unaltered

(i) the distance between two points;

(ii) the points of the line $x = y = z$.

Assuming that the transformation is a rotation about a line, find the angle of rotation. (O.)

Revision Paper D5

1. Show that the area of the loop of the curve whose equation in polar coordinates is
$$r \cos \theta = a \cos 2\theta$$
is $a^2(2 - \tfrac{1}{2}\pi)$. (O. & C.)

2. Draw a rough sketch of the curve with the polar equation $r = a(1 + \cos \theta)$ (the cardioid).
   From a square plate of side l is cut, symmetrically, the cardioid of maximum area (the axis of the cardioid being parallel to two sides of the square). Prove that this area is $\tfrac{2}{9}\pi l^2$. (O.)

3. Obtain expressions for $\cos 7\theta$ and $\sin 7\theta$ in terms of $\cos \theta$ and $\sin \theta$ by equating the values of $(\cos \theta + i \sin \theta)^7$ given by the binomial theorem and by de Moivre's theorem.
   Hence express $\tan 7\theta$ in terms of $\tan \theta$.
   Prove that $\tan^2 \dfrac{\pi}{7} + \tan^2 \dfrac{2\pi}{7} + \tan^2 \dfrac{3\pi}{7} = 21$. (C.)

4. Prove that, if n is a positive integer,
$$(\cos \theta + i \sin \theta)^n = \cos n\theta + i \sin n\theta.$$
   By first putting n equal to 5 in this formula, or otherwise, prove that
$$\sin \frac{\pi}{10} = \frac{\sqrt{5} - 1}{4}.$$
(O. & C.)

5. Show that the equation $|z + 1| = 2|z - 1|$ represents a circle in the Argand diagram, and find its centre and radius.
   By means of a diagram drawn roughly to scale, explain how arg z varies as the point corresponding to z moves anticlockwise round the circle. (O. & C.)

6. The points P, A, B correspond in the Argand diagram to the numbers $z(= x + iy)$, a, $-a$, where a is real and positive. Find the equation in terms of x and y of the curve described by P when
   (i) $PB = kPA$,
   (ii) $PA + PB = 2b$,
   (iii) $|PA - PB| = 2c$,
   where k, b and c are positive constants with $b > a$, $c < a$. Give also, in each case, a brief geometrical description of the curve. (O.)

7. The position vectors $\overrightarrow{OA}$, $\overrightarrow{OB}$, referred to the origin O of coordinates, of two points A, B (not collinear with O) in the plane of the cartesian axes Oxy are $\mathbf{a}$, $\mathbf{b}$ respectively. Show that the position vector $\mathbf{r} = \overrightarrow{OP}$ of an arbitrary point P on the line AB is given by
$$\mathbf{r} = \mathbf{a} + t(\mathbf{b} - \mathbf{a}),$$
where t is a scalar.

Hence, or otherwise, show that, if K is the point of intersection of AB and $A'B'$ (produced if necessary), where $\overrightarrow{OA'} = 3\mathbf{a}$, $\overrightarrow{OB'} = 2\mathbf{b}$, then

$$\overrightarrow{OK} = -3\mathbf{a} + 4\mathbf{b}.$$ (O. & C.)

8. The position vectors $\mathbf{a}$, $\mathbf{b}$, $\mathbf{c}$, $\mathbf{d}$ of the points A, B, C, D respectively are given by

$$\begin{aligned}
\mathbf{a} &= 2\mathbf{i} - \mathbf{j} + 3\mathbf{k}, \\
\mathbf{b} &= \quad\;\; - \mathbf{j} + \mathbf{k}, \\
\mathbf{c} &= -\mathbf{i} - 2\mathbf{j} + 2\mathbf{k}, \\
\mathbf{d} &= 5\mathbf{i} - \mathbf{j} - 6\mathbf{k}.
\end{aligned}$$

Find

(i) a unit vector perpendicular to the plane ABC,

(ii) the length of the perpendicular from D to the plane ABC,

(iii) the position of the point D', where D' is the reflection of D in the plane ABC.   (C.)

9. $\mathbf{I}$ is the 2×2 unit matrix $\begin{pmatrix} 1 & 0 \\ 0 & 1 \end{pmatrix}$ and $\mathbf{J}$ is the matrix $\begin{pmatrix} 1 & 1 \\ 1 & 1 \end{pmatrix}$. If $\mathbf{K}$ is the matrix $\mathbf{I} + \mathbf{J}$ show that

(i) $\mathbf{K}^2 = \mathbf{I} + 4\mathbf{J}$,   (ii) $\mathbf{K}^3 = \mathbf{I} + 13\mathbf{J}$.

Prove by induction that $\mathbf{K}^n = \mathbf{I} + \frac{1}{2}(3^n - 1)\mathbf{J}$, $n \in \mathbb{Z}_+$.

The vectors $\mathbf{x} = \begin{pmatrix} x_1 \\ x_2 \end{pmatrix}$ and $\mathbf{y} = \begin{pmatrix} y_1 \\ y_2 \end{pmatrix}$ are such that $\mathbf{Kx} = \lambda\mathbf{x}$ and $\mathbf{K}^n\mathbf{y} = \mu\mathbf{y}$, where λ and μ are constants. Find the two values of λ and the two values of μ.   (C.)

10. When column vectors representing points in a plane with the usual axes are premultiplied by the matrix $\mathbf{M}$, where

$$\mathbf{M} = \begin{pmatrix} 2 & -1 \\ 1 & 0 \end{pmatrix},$$

a transformation of the plane results. Show that, under this transformation, (i) all points on the line $y = x$ are invariant points, (ii) any point on the line $y = x + c$ is transformed to another point on that line.

Prove by induction that, if $n \in \mathbb{Z}_+$, then

$$\mathbf{M}^n = \begin{pmatrix} n + 1 & -n \\ n & 1 - n \end{pmatrix}.$$

Hence show that, if the transformation represented by $\mathbf{M}$ is applied n times in succession, the line $y + x = 0$ is transformed to the line

$$y = \frac{2n - 1}{2n + 1}x.$$ (C.)

23 The Straight Line

Revision

A list of properties of the straight line proved in Chapters 22 and 23 of *Additional Pure Mathematics* is given below.

1. The distance between the points (x_1, y_1) and (x_2, y_2) is
$$\sqrt{[(x_1 - x_2)^2 + (y_1 - y_2)^2]}.$$

2. The mid-point of the straight line joining (x_1, y_1) and (x_2, y_2) is
$$\left(\frac{x_1 + x_2}{2}, \frac{y_1 + y_2}{2} \right).$$

3. The gradient of the straight line joining (x_1, y_1) and (x_2, y_2) is
$$\frac{y_2 - y_1}{x_2 - x_1}.$$

4. The coordinates of the point P dividing the join of (x_1, y_1) and (x_2, y_2) in the ratio $\lambda : \mu$ are $\left(\dfrac{\lambda x_2 + \mu x_1}{\lambda + \mu}, \dfrac{\lambda y_2 + \mu y_1}{\lambda + \mu} \right).$

5. The coordinates of the centre of gravity of the triangle formed by the points (x_1, y_1), (x_2, y_2) and (x_3, y_3) are
$$\left(\frac{x_1 + x_2 + x_3}{3}, \frac{y_1 + y_2 + y_3}{3} \right)$$

6. The area of the triangle formed by the same three points is
$$\tfrac{1}{2}(x_1 y_2 - y_1 x_2 + x_2 y_3 - x_3 y_2 + x_3 y_1 - x_1 y_3).$$
This can be written as the determinant
$$\frac{1}{2} \begin{vmatrix} x_1 & x_2 & x_3 \\ y_1 & y_2 & y_3 \\ 1 & 1 & 1 \end{vmatrix}$$

7. The equation of the straight line joining (x_1, y_1) to (x_2, y_2) is
$$\frac{y - y_1}{x - x_1} = \frac{y_2 - y_1}{x_2 - x_1}.$$

8. The equation of the straight line making intercepts a and b on the two axes is $\dfrac{x}{a} + \dfrac{y}{b} = 1.$

9. The equation of the straight line such that the perpendicular from the origin is of length p and makes an angle α with the x-axis is
$x \cos \alpha + y \sin \alpha = p.$

10. The coordinates of the point P distant r from the point A (x_1, y_1) and such that AP makes an angle θ with the x-axis are $(x_1 + r \cos \theta, y_1 + r \sin \theta)$.

11. The equation of the straight line of gradient m making an intercept c on the y-axis is $y = mx + c$.

12. The equation of the straight line through the point (x_1, y_1) of gradient m is $\dfrac{y - y_1}{x - x_1} = m$.

13. The length of the perpendicular from the point (x_1, y_1) to the line $lx + my + n = 0$ is $\dfrac{lx_1 + my_1 + n}{\sqrt{(l^2 + m^2)}}$.

14. The angle between two straight lines of gradients m and t is $\tan^{-1} \dfrac{m - t}{1 + mt}$.

15. Two straight lines are parallel if their gradients are equal.

16. Two straight lines are perpendicular if the product of their gradients is -1.

17. If $l = 0$ and $l' = 0$ are the equations of two straight lines, then $l + \lambda l' = 0$ is a family of lines all of which pass through the point of intersection of $l = 0$ and $l' = 0$.

Worked examples

The following examples illustrate some of the properties listed above.

Example 1. *Find the equations of the lines through the point $(1, 2)$ parallel and perpendicular to the line $3x + 4y = 7$.*

(i) Since the parallel line must have the same gradient, its equation is $3x + y = c$.

The value of c is found by writing down the condition that the point $(1, 2)$ satisfies the equation of the line.

$$3(1) + 4(2) = c \quad \text{and} \quad c = 11.$$

The equation of the parallel line is $3x + 4y = 11$.

(ii) Any line perpendicular to $3x + 4y = 7$ is of the form $4x - 3y = k$.

The form of the perpendicular is found by interchanging the coefficients of x and y and altering the sign between them.

The gradient of $3x + 4y = 7$ is $-\frac{3}{4}$; the gradient of $4x - 3y = k$ is $\frac{4}{3}$. Since the product of the gradients is -1, the lines are perpendicular.

To find the value of k, substitute the point $(1, 2)$ in the equation of the line.

$$4(1) - 3(2) = k \quad \text{and} \quad k = -2.$$

The equation of the perpendicular is $4x - 3y = -2$.

Example 2. *The points A, B, and C have coordinates $(2, 3)$, $(3, 4)$ and $(5, -1)$ respectively. Find the point of intersection of the line through A perpendicular to BC and the line joining B to the mid-point of AC.*

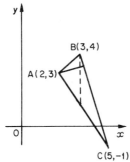

Fig. 23.1

The gradient of BC is $\dfrac{4+1}{3-5}$ or $-\frac{5}{2}$.

The gradient of the perpendicular through A is $\frac{2}{5}$.
The equation of the line through (2, 3) of gradient $\frac{2}{5}$ is

$$\frac{y-3}{x-2} = \tfrac{2}{5} \quad \text{or} \quad 5y - 2x = 11.$$

The mid-point of AC is $\left(\dfrac{2+5}{2}, \dfrac{3-1}{2}\right)$ or $(\tfrac{7}{2}, 1)$.

The equation of the line joining this point to B (3, 4) is

$$\frac{y-4}{x-3} = \frac{4-1}{3-\frac{7}{2}} = -6 \quad \text{or} \quad y + 6x = 22.$$

To find the point of intersection of $5y - 2x = 11$ and $y + 6x = 22$, solve the two equations for x and y.

$$\left.\begin{array}{r} 15y - 6x = 33 \\ y + 6x = 22 \end{array}\right\}$$

By addition $16y = 55 \quad \text{and} \quad y = \frac{55}{16}.$
By substitution, $x = \frac{99}{32}.$

The point of intersection is $(\frac{99}{32}, \frac{55}{16})$.

Exercise 23.1

1. Find the equations of the straight lines through $(3, -2)$ parallel and perpendicular to $3x + 4y = 7$.

2. Find the distance between A $(2, 3)$ and the mid-point of the straight line joining B $(4, 5)$ to C $(6, 9)$.

3. Find the gradient of the line joining the mid-point of the join of A $(1, -2)$ and B $(3, 5)$ to the mid-point of the join of C $(5, 6)$ and D $(7, 8)$.

4. Find the coordinates of the two points of trisection of the straight line joining A $(3, 1)$ to B $(9, -11)$.

5. Find the area of the triangle OBC where B is $(3, 2)$ and C is $(5, 4)$.

6. Find the equation of the straight line joining the point $(3, 1)$ to the mid-point of the join of $(2, 4)$ and $(7, 10)$.

7. Find the equations of the straight lines through $(1, -4)$ which make equal angles with the axes.

8. Find the length of the perpendicular from the point $(3, -1)$ to the line $3x + 4y + 7 = 0$.

9. Are the points $(2, 1)$ and $(5, -2)$ on the same side or on opposite sides of the line $5x - 2y - 3 = 0$?

10. The point A is $(2, 4)$. The point B is distant 5 units from A and AB makes an angle θ with the x-axis where $\tan \theta = \frac{3}{4}$. Find the coordinates of B.

11. Find the acute angle between the lines
$$3x - 4y = 7 \quad \text{and} \quad 2x - 3y = 5.$$

12. Find the equation of the straight line joining the origin to the point of intersection of $3x - 2y = 4$ and $x + y = 2$.

13. The two straight lines $x + my = 2$ and $x - my = 3$ are perpendicular. Find the possible values of m.

14. Find the coordinates of the reflection of the point $(1, 2)$ in the line $x = y$.

15. Find the coordinates of the reflection of the origin in the line $3x + 4y = 5$.

16. Find the distance between the lines $3x + 4y = 7$ and $3x + 4y = 21$.

17. The triangle OAB is such that OA = OB and the angle AOB = $90°$. Find the coordinates of B, given that A is $(2, 3)$.

18. Find the ratio in which the join of $(1, 2)$ and $(6, 5)$ is divided by the line $x = y$.

19. Find the equation of the straight line through the point of intersection of $x + y = 5$ and $3x - y = 1$ perpendicular to $2x + y = 7$.

20. Show that the points $(3, -5)$, $(2, 5)$, $(0, 6)$ and $(1, -4)$ are the vertices of a parallelogram.

Pairs of lines

The equation $(3x - y - 2)(4x - 3y - 5) = 0$ leads to $3x - y - 2 = 0$ or $4x - 3y - 5 = 0$, i.e. a pair of straight lines.

More generally if $l = 0$ and $l' = 0$ are the equations of two straight lines, $ll' = 0$ is the equation of the pair of lines. This may be stated more briefly in the form
$$ll' = 0 \Leftrightarrow l = 0 \quad \text{or} \quad l' = 0.$$

A pair of straight lines through the origin

The equation of any two straight lines through the origin are $y - mx = 0$ and $y - tx = 0$. The equation of the pair is therefore
$$(y - mx)(y - tx) = 0$$
or
$$y^2 - (m + t)yx + mtx^2 = 0 \tag{i}$$

The equation of a pair of straight lines through the origin must always be of the form
$$ax^2 + 2hxy + by^2 = 0 \tag{ii}$$

Comparing coefficients in equations (i) and (ii),

$$\frac{mt}{a} = -\frac{m+t}{2h} = \frac{1}{b}.$$

$$\therefore \quad m + t = -\frac{2h}{b} \quad \text{and} \quad mt = \frac{a}{b}.$$

So the sum and product of the gradients of a pair of straight lines through the origin may be written down from the equation. In particular, the lines are perpendicular if $mt = -1$, i.e.if

$$a + b = 0.$$

So the equation of a pair of perpendicular straight lines through the origin must be of the form

$$x^2 - y^2 = 2Hxy.$$

Example. *Find the equation of the pair of straight lines through the origin perpendicular to $x^2 + 3xy - 3y^2 = 0$.*

For the lines, $\qquad m + t = \frac{3}{3} = 1;$
$$mt = -\tfrac{1}{3}.$$

The pair perpendicular to

$$(y - mx)(y - tx) = 0$$

is $\qquad\qquad\qquad (my + x)(ty + x) = 0$

or $\qquad\qquad mty^2 + xy(m + t) + x^2 = 0.$

This becomes $\qquad -\tfrac{1}{3}y^2 + \mathbf{xy} + x^2 = 0$

or $\qquad\qquad 3x^2 + 3xy - y^2 = 0.$

The equations of the pair of angle bisectors

To find the equations of the lines bisecting the angles between $ax + bx + c = 0$ and $lx + my + n = 0$, we use the fact that, if the point (x_1, y_1) lies on either bisector, the perpendiculars from (x_1, y_1) to the two lines are equal.

This gives

$$\frac{ax_1 + by_1 + c}{\sqrt{(a^2 + b^2)}} = \pm \frac{lx_1 + my_1 + n}{\sqrt{(l^2 + m^2)}}$$

and so (x_1, y_1) must satisfy the equation

$$\frac{ax + by + c}{\sqrt{(a^2 + b^2)}} = \pm \frac{lx + my + n}{\sqrt{(l^2 + m^2)}}$$

which is the pair of angle bisectors.

Example 1. *Find the equations of the lines bisecting the angles between $3x - 4y = 1$ and $5x + 12y = 18$.*

The equations required are

$$\frac{3x - 4y - 1}{5} = \pm \frac{5x + 12y - 18}{13},$$

i.e. $39x - 52y - 13 = 25x + 60y - 90$
or $39x - 52y - 13 = -25x - 60y + 90.$

The bisectors are

$$14x - 112y + 77 = 0 \quad \text{and} \quad 64x + 8y - 103 = 0.$$

The gradients of these lines are $\frac{1}{8}$ and -8 which proves that they are perpendicular.

Example 2. *Find the incentre of the triangle formed by the points* $(3, 4)$ $(4, 3)$ *and the origin* (*see Fig. 23.2*).

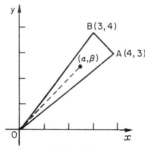

Fig. 23.2

Suppose the incentre is the point (α, β). The incentre lies on the internal bisector of the angle AOB which by symmetry is $x = y$.

$$\therefore \quad \alpha = \beta.$$

The equation of OB is

$$\frac{y}{x} = \frac{4}{3} \quad \text{or} \quad 3y - 4x = 0.$$

The length of the perpendicular from (α, β) to this line is $\dfrac{3\beta - 4\alpha}{5}$, but the sign must be carefully considered.

From the figure the point $(1, 0)$ lies on the same side of $3y - 4x = 0$ as the point (α, β). The length of the perpendicular from $(1, 0)$ is $-\frac{4}{5}$ and so the perpendicular from (α, β) must also be negative.

The positive length of the perpendicular from (α, β) to $3y - 4x = 0$ is therefore $\dfrac{4\alpha - 3\beta}{5}$.

The equation of AB is

$$\frac{y - 3}{x - 4} = -1 \quad \text{or} \quad y + x - 7 = 0.$$

The length of the perpendicular from (α, β) is $\dfrac{\alpha + \beta - 7}{\sqrt{2}}$.

This point and the origin are on the same side of the line and the length of the perpendicular from the origin is $-\dfrac{7}{\sqrt{2}}$.

So the positive length of the perpendicular from (α, β) is $\dfrac{7 - \alpha - \beta}{\sqrt{2}}$.

Since (α, β) is the incentre, the perpendiculars from it to OB and AB are equal.

$$\therefore \quad \frac{4\alpha - 3\beta}{5} = \frac{7 - \alpha - \beta}{\sqrt{2}}$$

But $\alpha = \beta$ and so

$$\frac{\alpha}{5} = \frac{7 - 2}{\sqrt{2}}$$

or

$$\sqrt{2}\alpha = 35 - 10\alpha.$$

$$\therefore \quad \alpha = \frac{35}{10 + \sqrt{2}} = \frac{35(10 - \sqrt{2})}{10^2 - 2}$$

$$= \frac{35(10 - \sqrt{2})}{98} = \frac{5(10 - \sqrt{2})}{14}.$$

The incentre is the point $\{\tfrac{5}{14}(10 - \sqrt{2}), \tfrac{5}{14}(10 - \sqrt{2})\}$.

Exercise 23.2

1. Find the equation of the angle bisectors between the lines $3x + 4y = 5$ and $5x - 12y = 8$.

2. Find the acute angle between the lines $x^2 - 5xy + 6y^2 = 0$.

3. Find the equation of the bisector of the angle between the lines $5x + 12y = 8$ and $3x - 4y = 2$ containing the origin.

4. The length of the perpendicular from a point P to the line $x + y = 2$ is double the length of the perpendicular from P to $7x + y = 8$. Find the equation of the set of points P.

5. Find the equation of the pair of lines through the origin perpendicular to $2x^2 - 2xy - y^2 = 0$.

6. Find the distance between the parallel lines $3x + y = 7$ and $3x + y = 17$.

7. Find the equation of the internal bisector of the angle between the lines $x + 7y = 8$ and $x + y = 2$.

8. The lengths of the perpendiculars from P to the lines $3x - 4y = 8$ and $3x + 4y = 12$ are in the ratio $5 : 2$. Find the equation of the locus of points P.

9. Find the equation of the pair of lines through the point $(1, 2)$ parallel to $x^2 - 5xy + 6y^2 = 0$.

10. Find the equation of the pair of lines through the point $(1, 1)$ perpendicular to $x^2 - 5xy + 6y^2 = 0$.

11. Find the equation of the pair of lines through the origin perpendicular to $3x - 4y + 1 = 0$ and $2x - y - 5 = 0$.

12. Find the tangent of the acute angle between the lines

$$2x^2 - xy - 5y^2 = 0.$$

13. Show that the line $(x - 1) + m(y - 2) = 0$ passes through the point $(1, 2)$ for all values of m.

14. Show that the line $x(m + 2) + y(m + 1) = 2m + 3$ passes through a fixed point for all values of m and find the coordinates of the point.

15. For what values of t does the line $x + y - 3 + t(7x + y - 8) = 0$ bisect an angle between $x + y = 3$ and $7x + y = 8$?

16. What are the equations of the angle bisectors between

$$x \cos \alpha + y \sin \alpha = p \quad \text{and} \quad x \cos \beta + y \sin \beta = q?$$

17. Find the equations of the angle bisectors between $x + 3y = 4$ and $3x + y = 4$.

18. Show that the lengths of the perpendiculars from $(1, 1)$ to the lines $3x + 4y = 2, 12x - 5y + 6 = 0$ and $15x - 8y + 10 = 0$ are all equal. Is $(1, 1)$ the incentre of the triangle formed by the lines?

19. Show that the lengths of the perpendiculars from $(1, 1)$ to the lines $7x - y - 1 = 0, 7x + 17y - 11 = 0$ and $x + y - 1 = 0$ are all equal. Is $(1, 1)$ the incentre of the triangle formed by the lines?

20. Find the area of the triangle formed by the points A $(1, 1)$, B $(4, 5)$ and C $(6, 13)$. Hence find the sine of the angle CAB.

Exercise 23.3: Miscellaneous

1. Find the equation of the straight line joining the origin to the point of intersection of $3x + y = 7$ and $5x - 2y = 14$.

2. The point A has coordinates $(1, 1)$ and the triangle OAP is of area 2 sq. units. Find the equation of the locus of points P.

3. Find the equation of the straight line through the intersection of $2x - y - 4 = 0$ and $3x + y = 7$ perpendicular to $x + y = 5$.

4. Find the orthocentre of the triangle formed by the lines $x = 0$, $my = m^2x + a$ and $ty = t^2x + a$.

5. Show that the area of the triangle formed by the points

$$(a + x_1, b + y_1), (a + x_2, b + y_2) \text{ and } (a + x_3, b + y_3)$$

is the same as that formed by the points (x_1, y_1), (x_2, y_2) and (x_3, y_3).

6. The coordinates of A and B are $(1, 2)$ and $(3, 7)$. Find the ratio in which the straight line AB is divided by the line $2x + y = 7$.

7. The coordinates of a point P are given in terms of a variable t by the equations $x = 3 + \cos 2t$, $y = 1 + \cos^2 t$. Show that the point P always lies on a straight line and find its equation.

8. Find the equation of the straight line which passes through the intersection of $x + y = 7$ and $3x - 4y = 2$ and makes an intercept of length 2 on the y-axis.

9. The coordinates of A and B are $(3, 4)$ and $(7, 8)$. Find the ratio in which the join of A to B is divided by the y-axis.

10. Show that the feet of the perpendiculars from the point $(5, 5)$ to the sides of the triangle formed by the point $(0, 0)$, $(1, -3)$ and $(1, 3)$ lie on a line and find the equation of this line.

11. The points A and B have coordinates $(1, 1)$ and $(3, 4)$. It is given that ABCD is a square. Find the coordinates of C and D. (Note that there are two possible answers.)

12. Are the points $(4, 3)$ and $(8, -7)$ on the same side of the line $x + y - 5 = 0$? Find the ratio of the lengths of the perpendiculars from the points to the line.

13. The points A and B have coordinates $(a, 0)$ and $(-a, 0)$. The point P moves so that $PA^2 - PB^2 = a^2$. Find the equation of the locus of points P.

14. The vertices of a quadrilateral ABCD are $(1, 1)$, $(3, 5)$, $(7, 11)$ and $(8, 14)$. Show that the joins of the mid-points of ABCD form a parallelogram.

15. One side of an equilateral triangle lies along the line $x + y = 4$ and one vertex is the point $(1, 1)$. Find the coordinates of the other vertices.

16. Find the equation of the perpendicular bisector of the joint of P $(2, 3)$ and Q $(8, 11)$. Find also the coordinates of the points on the perpendicular bisector which are distant $5\sqrt{2}$ units from either P or Q.

17. The points A and B have coordinates $(4, 3)$ and $(7, 8)$. Find the equation of the locus of points P for which $2PA = PB$.

18. The points A and B have coordinates $(1, 1)$ and $(2, 3)$. Find the equation of the locus of points P for which PA and PB are perpendicular.

19. Find the area of the triangle formed by the points $(28, 134)$, $(30, 137)$ and $(32, 139)$. (See example 5.)

20. Find the equation of the straight line through the point $(2, 3)$ perpendicular to $3x + y = 7$. Find also the coordinates of the reflection of the point in the line.

21. Find the area of the quadrilateral formed by the coordinate axes and the lines $3x + 4y = 12$ and $4x + 3y = 12$.

22. The points B and C have coordinates $(1, 2)$ and $(5, 3)$. If P and Q are the points which divide BC internally and externally in the ratio $1:2$, find the coordinates of the mid-point of PQ.

23. Find the x-coordinate of the incentre of the triangle formed by the lines $y = x$, $y + 2x = -3$ and $2y - 4x = 3$.

24. Find the coordinates of the circumcentre of the triangle formed by the points $(1, 0)$, $(2, 4)$ and $(5, 7)$.

25. Show that the points $(1, 1)$, $(3, 4)$, $(7, 11)$ and $(5, 8)$ form a parallelogram and find its area.

26. Show that the points $(a - b, a - c)$, $(a - d, a - p)$, $(a + b, a + c)$ and $(a + d, a + p)$ form a parallelogram and find its area.

27. Find the equation of the perpendicular bisector of the line joining the origin to the point (a, b) and find the length of the intercept made by the axes on this line.

28. A line is drawn through the point P $(1, 1)$ making an angle θ, where $\tan \theta = \frac{4}{3}$, with the x-axis. Find the distance from P along this line to the line $2x + 3y = 15$.

29. A line is drawn through the point P (a, b) making an angle θ with the x-axis. Find the distance from P along this line to the line $lx + my + n = 0$.

30. Find the equation of the line joining the origin to the point of intersection of $lx + my + n = 0$ and $px + qy + r = 0$.

24 The Circle

Revision

A list of properties proved in Chapter 25 of *Additional Pure Mathematics* is given below.

1. The equation of the circle, centre the origin and radius r, is
$$x^2 + y^2 = r^2.$$

2. The equation of the circle, centre (a, b) and radius r, is
$$(x - a)^2 + (y - b)^2 = r^2.$$

3. The general equation of a circle is
$$x^2 + y^2 + 2gx + 2fy + c = 0.$$
The centre of this circle is $(-g, -f)$ and its radius is
$$\sqrt{(g^2 + f^2 - c)}.$$

4. The equation of the tangent at (x_1, y_1) to
$$x^2 + y^2 + 2gx + 2fy + c = 0$$
is $\qquad xx_1 + yy_1 + g(x + x_1) + f(y + y_1) + c = 0.$

5. The equations of the tangents of gradient m to $x^2 + y^2 = r^2$ are
$y = mx \pm r\sqrt{(1 + m^2)}.$

6. The square of the length of the tangent from (x_1, y_1) to the circle
$x^2 + y^2 + 2gx + 2fy + c = 0$ is
$$x_1{}^2 + y_1{}^2 + 2gx_1 + 2fy_1 + c.$$

7. $\mathbf{S} = \mathbf{S}'$ is the equation of the common chord or the radical axis of $\mathbf{S} = 0$ and $\mathbf{S}' = 0$.

8. $\mathbf{S} + k\mathbf{S}' = 0$ is family of circles passing through the two points of intersection of $\mathbf{S} = 0$ and $\mathbf{S}' = 0$; if the circles do not intersect, it represents a family of coaxial circles of which $\mathbf{S} = 0$ and $\mathbf{S}' = 0$ are members.

The equation of a circle passing through three given points

There are two methods of finding the equation of a circle passing through three given points, and these are illustrated by the following example.

Example. *Find the equation of the circle passing through the points* A $(1, 3)$, B $(2, 2)$ *and* C $(5, 7)$.

Method (i)

Suppose the circle is $x^2 + y^2 + 2gx + 2fy + c = 0$.

Then
$$1^2 + 3^2 + 2g + 6f + c = 0,$$
$$2^2 + 2^2 + 4g + 4f + c = 0$$
and
$$5^2 + 7^2 + 10g + 14f + c = 0.$$

Simplifying these equations, we have
$$10 + 2g + 6f + c = 0,$$
$$8 + 4g + 4f + c = 0$$
and
$$74 + 10g + 14f + c = 0$$
which lead to
$$2 - 2g + 2f = 0$$
and
$$66 + 6g + 10f = 0.$$

The solution of these equations is
$$2f = -9 \quad \text{and} \quad 2g = -7.$$

By substitution,
$$10 - 7 - 27 + c = 0 \quad \text{and} \quad c = 24.$$

The equation of the circle is
$$x^2 + y^2 - 7x - 9y + 24 = 0.$$

Method (ii)

The gradient of BC is $\frac{5}{3}$.

The mid-point of BC is $(\frac{7}{2}, \frac{9}{2})$.

The equation of the perpendicular bisector of BC is
$$\frac{y - \frac{9}{2}}{x - \frac{7}{2}} = -\frac{3}{5}$$
or
$$3x + 5y = 33.$$

The gradient of AC is $\frac{4}{4}$ or 1.

The mid-point of AC is $(3, 5)$.

The equation of the perpendicular bisector of AC is
$$\frac{y - 5}{x - 3} = -1$$
or
$$x + y = 8.$$

Solving the equations $3x + 5y = 33$ and $x + y = 8$ gives
$$x = 3\tfrac{1}{2}, \quad y = 4\tfrac{1}{2},$$
which are the coordinates of the centre of the circle.

If r is the radius of the circle,
$$r^2 = (3\tfrac{1}{2} - 1)^2 + (4\tfrac{1}{2} - 3)^2$$
$$= \tfrac{25}{4} + \tfrac{9}{4}$$
$$= \tfrac{34}{4} = \tfrac{17}{2}.$$

The equation of the circle is
$$(x - \tfrac{7}{2})^2 + (y - \tfrac{9}{2})^2 = \tfrac{17}{2}$$
or
$$x^2 + y^2 - 7x - 9y + 24 = 0.$$

Condition that a circle touches a coordinate axis

A circle touches a coordinate axis, say $y = 0$, if the equation formed by solving simultaneously the equation of the circle and $y = 0$ has equal roots, i.e. taking the equation of the circle as $x^2 + y^2 + 2gx + 2fy + c = 0$ and solving with $y = 0$, $x^2 + 2gx + c = 0$ has equal roots, i.e. $g^2 = c$. Similarly if the circle touches the line $x = 0$, $f^2 = c$.

Condition that two circles touch

If two circles touch externally, that is, one is not inside the other, the distance between their centres must equal the sum of the radii; if the circles touch internally, i.e. one is inside the other, the distance between their centres is equal to the difference of their radii.

Example. *Show that the circles $x^2 + y^2 = 9$ and $x^2 + y^2 - 8x - 6y + 21 = 0$ touch.*

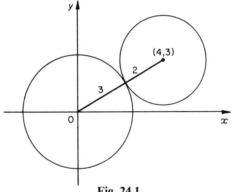

Fig. 24.1

The equation of the second circle can be written
$$(x - 4)^2 + (y - 3)^2 = 2^2$$
so we can see that its centre is $(4, 3)$ and its radius 2. The first circle has centre $(0, 0)$, radius 3, and Fig. 24.1 shows that the distance between the centres, 5, is the sum of the radii, $3 + 2$.

Orthogonal circles

Orthogonal circles cut at right angles at both points of intersection, i.e. the tangents at A and B in Fig. 24.2 to the circles are perpendicular.

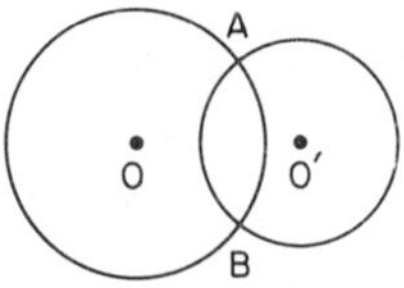

Fig. 24.2

From this it follows that the tangent at A to the circle centre O' must be the line OA.

Hence $OO'^2 = r^2 + r'^2$, where r and r' are the radii of the circles and this is the property used to discover whether two circles cut orthogonally.

Example. *Show that the circles* $x^2 + y^2 + 2x + 2y - 2 = 0$ *and* $x^2 + y^2 + 4x + 6y + 12 = 0$ *cut orthogonally.*

The first circle is $(x + 1)^2 + (y + 1)^2 = 4$.
Its centre is $(-1, -1)$ and its radius is 2.
The second circle is $(x + 2)^2 + (y + 3)^2 = 1$.
Its centre is $(-2, -3)$ and its radius is 1.
The square of the distance between the centres is
$$(2 - 1)^2 + (3 - 1)^2 \quad \text{or} \quad 5.$$
The sum of the squares of the radii is also 5 and so the circles cut orthogonally.

The condition that $x^2 + y^2 + 2gx + 2fy + c = 0$ and $x^2 + y^2 + 2Gx + 2Fy + C = 0$ should cut orthogonally

In Fig. 24.2 $\qquad OO'^2 = OA^2 + O'A^2$.

The centre of the first circle is $(-g, -f)$; that of the second circle $(-G, -F)$.

$$\therefore \quad (G - g)^2 + (F - f)^2 = g^2 + f^2 - c + G^2 + F^2 - C$$
or $\qquad\qquad 2Gg + 2Ff = C + c.$

Exercise 24.1

1. Find the equation of the circle passing through the points $(0, 0)$, $(2, 0)$ and $(0, 4)$.
2. A circle passes through the point $(5, 4)$ and touches the y-axis at $(0, 2)$. Find its equation.
3. Show that the circles
   $$x^2 + y^2 + 8x - 8y - 68 = 0 \text{ and } x^2 + y^2 - 32x + 12y - 108 = 0$$
   cut orthogonally.
4. Find the equation of the circle through the points $(2, 1)$, $(3, 2)$ and $(1, 2)$.
5. Find the equation of the circle which passes through the origin and touches the straight line $4x - 3y = 5$ at the point $(2, 1)$.
6. Show that the circles
   $$x^2 + y^2 = 25 \quad \text{and} \quad x^2 + y^2 - 10x - 4y + 25 = 0$$
   cut orthogonally.
7. Find the equation of the common chord of the circles
   $$x^2 + y^2 = 25 \quad \text{and} \quad x^2 + y^2 - 2x + 14y + 25 = 0,$$
   and find the points of intersection of the circles.

8. Find the equation of the circle through the points $(5, 3)$, $(-2, 2)$ and $(2, 4)$.

9. A circle centre C passes through the points $(3, 2)$ and $(5, -4)$. Find the equation of the locus of C.

10. Prove that the circles
$$x^2 + y^2 = 4 \text{ and } x^2 + y^2 - 6x - 8y + 16 = 0$$
touch externally.

11. Prove that the circles
$$x^2 + y^2 - 2x - 2y = 14 \text{ and } x^2 + y^2 - 14x - 18y + 94 = 0$$
touch externally.

12. Prove that the circles
$$x^2 + y^2 = 36 \quad \text{and} \quad x^2 + y^2 - 6x - 8y + 24 = 0$$
touch internally.

13. Prove that the circle $x^2 + y^2 - 4x + 5y + 4 = 0$ touches the x-axis and find the coordinates of the points in which it cuts the y-axis.

14. Find the equation of the circle orthogonal to
$$x^2 + y^2 - 2x - 4y - 2 = 0$$
which passes through the origin and the point $(2, 1)$.

15. Find the equation of the circle orthogonal to $x^2 + y^2 - 2x - 3 = 0$ which passes through the origin and the point $(1, 1)$.

16. Find the equations of the tangents to the circle
$$x^2 + y^2 - 2x - 2y = 7$$
which are parallel to $3x + 4y = 7$.

17. A circle passes through the points $(a, 0)$, $(b, 0)$ and $(0, c)$. Find its equation.

18. Find the value of k in order that the equation
$$k(x^2 + y) + (y - 2x)(y + 2x + 3) = 0$$
should represent a circle.

19. Prove that the circle on A $(6, 4)$ and B $(2, 1)$ as diameter touches the x-axis.

20. Find the length of the chord of the circle $x^2 + y^2 = 25$ intercepted by the line $3x + 4y = 5$.

Exercise 24.2: Miscellaneous

1. Find the equation of the circle passing through the origin and the points $(a, 0)$ and $(0, b)$. Show that the circle passes through the point (a, b) and find the equation of the tangent at that point.

2. Find the coordinates of the centres P and Q of the two circles each of radius 10 which pass through the points $(1, 1)$ and $(15, 3)$. Find also the equations of the circles.

3. The equations of two circles are
$$x^2 + y^2 - 2x - 2y = 4 \quad \text{and} \quad x^2 + y^2 - 3x - 3y = 8.$$
Find the equation of the locus of P from which the length of the tangent to the first circle is double that to the second.

4. Find the equation of the circle which touches the x-axis at the point $(6, 0)$ and passes through the point $(0, 4)$. Find the coordinates of the other point of intersection of the circle with the y-axis.

5. Prove that the equation of the circle on the line joining (x_1, y_1) and (x_2, y_2) as diameter is
$$(x - x_1)(x - x_2) + (y - y_1)(y - y_2) = 0.$$
Find the length of the tangent from the origin to this circle.

6. The line $x + 2y = 1$ meets the circle $x^2 + y^2 = 16$ at A and B. Find the equation of the circle on AB as diameter.

7. The line $lx + my = 1$ meets the circle $x^2 + y^2 = r^2$ at A and B. Find the equation of the circle on AB as diameter.

8. Find the equation of the circle which passes through the points of intersection of
$$x^2 + y^2 - 5x - 5y - 8 = 0 \quad \text{and} \quad x^2 + y^2 - 3x - 2y - 7 = 0$$
and also through the origin.

9. Find the equation of the circle which passes through both points of intersection of
$$x^2 + y^2 - 2x - 5y - 7 = 0 \quad \text{and} \quad x^2 + y^2 - 3x + 4y - 2 = 0$$
and also through the point $(1, 1)$.

10. Find the values of m for which the line $y + mx + 12 = 0$ is a tangent to the circle $x^2 + y^2 - 2x - 2y = 6$.

11. Find the value of k in order that
$$k(x^2 + 2y^2) + (y - 2x + 1)(y + 2x + 3) = 0$$
should be a circle.
Find the centre and radius of the circle.

12. Find the coordinates of the ends of the common chord of the circles
$$x^2 + y^2 + 6x - 6y - 2 = 0 \quad \text{and} \quad x^2 + y^2 - 4x + 4y - 2 = 0.$$

13. Find the equation of the set of points P from which the lengths of the tangents to the circles
$$x^2 + y^2 + 2gx + 2fy + c = 0 \quad \text{and} \quad x^2 + y^2 + 2Gx + 2Fy + C = 0$$
are in the ratio $3:2$.

14. The two circles
$$x^2 + y^2 - 2y - 8 = 0 \quad \text{and} \quad x^2 + y^2 - 24x + ky - 4 = 0$$
cut orthogonally. Find the value of k.

15. Find the centres of the two circles that can be drawn to touch the lines $3y = 4x$ and $3y = -4x$ and to pass through the point $(\frac{3}{5}, 1)$.

16. Find the equation of the chord of the circle
$$x^2 + y^2 - 4x - 6y - 3 = 0$$
which has $(3, 4)$ as its mid-point.

17. Find the equation of the chord of the circle
$$x^2 + y^2 - 2ax - 2by = 0$$
which has (p, q) as its mid-point.

18. A chord AB of the circle $x^2 + y^2 - 2ax - 2by = 0$ subtends an angle of $45°$ at the origin. Given that P is the mid-point of AB, find the equation of the locus of P.

19. Find the limits for the value of k if the circles $x^2 + y^2 = k^2$ and $x^2 + y^2 + 2gx + c = 0$ intersect at real points.

20. The tangents from the origin to a circle, of given radius r and variable centre C, are perpendicular. Find the equation of the locus of C.

21. A variable circle centre C cuts off intercepts of lengths $2a$ and $2b$ on the axes. Find the equation of the locus of C.

22. Find the condition that the circles

$$x^2 + y^2 + 2gx + 2fy = 0 \quad \text{and} \quad x^2 + y^2 + 2Gx + 2Fy = 0$$

should touch.

23. The foot of the perpendicular from the origin to a variable tangent of the circle $x^2 + y^2 - 2x = 0$ is N. Find the equation of the locus of N.

24. The distance of a point P from the origin is equal to the length of the tangent from P to the circle $x^2 + y^2 - 2x - 4y - 1 = 0$. Find the equation of the locus of P.

25. Show that a variable circle which passes through the origin and is orthogonal to the circle $x^2 + y^2 - 6x + 8 = 0$ also passes through another fixed point and find the coordinates of this point.

26. The points A $(3, 1)$ and B $(7, 4)$ are ends of a diameter of a circle. Show that the circle touches the x-axis and find the point of intersection of the tangent at B with the x-axis.

27. The points A (p, q) and B (r, s) are ends of a diameter of a circle which touches the y-axis. Show that

$$(q - s)^2 = 4rp.$$

28. Two circles intersect at the points $(a, 0)$ and $(-a, 0)$. Show that their equations may be taken as

$$x^2 + y^2 - 2hy = a^2 \quad \text{and} \quad x^2 + y^2 - 2ky = a^2.$$

Find the condition that the circles cut orthogonally.

29. The line $lx + my = 1$ meets the circle $x^2 + y^2 + 2x = 3$ at the points A and B. Find the equation of the circle on AB as diameter.

30. The sum of the lengths of the tangents from a point P to the circles $x^2 + y^2 = 4$ and $x^2 + y^2 = 9$ is constant and equal to 5. Find the equation of the locus of P.

25 Cartesian Equations of the Conics

The parabola

Let X be the foot of the perpendicular from the focus S to the directrix (see (Fig. 25.1).

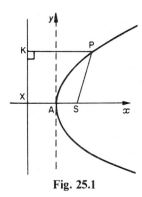

Fig. 25.1

The parabola is the locus of points P for which SP = PK, and so there is one and only one point on SX which lies on the parabola. This point is A, the mid-point of SX.

We take AS to be the x-axis and the perpendicular through A to be the y-axis and let AS = a.

The parabola is obviously symmetrical about the line AS which is called the axis of the parabola.

S = $(a, 0)$. Let P be the point (x, y).

Then $$PS^2 = (x - a)^2 + y^2$$
From the figure $$PK = x + a.$$
$$\therefore \quad (x - a)^2 + y^2 = (x + a)^2$$
or $$y^2 = 4ax,$$

which is the equation of the parabola, referred to the axis of the parabola and the tangent at the vertex (A) as axes of coordinates. The shape of the curve is shown in Fig. 25.1.

1. When $x = a$, $y = \pm 2a$ and so the length of the chord of the parabola drawn through the focus perpendicular to the axis of the parabola is $4a$. This is called the **latus rectum** of the parabola.
2. The equation of a parabola with its axis as x-axis and vertex the origin lying in the second and third quadrants is $y^2 = -4ax$.

3. The equation of a parabola with axis the y-axis and vertex the origin is $x^2 = 4ay$, where a may be negative.
4. The equation of a parabola with axis parallel to the x-axis and vertex (h, k) is $(y - k)^2 = 4a(x - h)$, where a may be negative.

Exercise 25.1

1. Find the equation of the parabola with its axis parallel to the x-axis, vertex $(2, 3)$ and latus rectum 4.
2. Find the vertex and focus of the parabola $y^2 = 8(x - 2)$.
3. Find the focus of the parabola $y^2 = 8(2 - x)$.
4. Find the vertex and focus of the parabola $x^2 = 16(y - 4)$.
5. Find the focus of the parabola $x^2 = 16(4 - y)$.
6. Find the equation of the parabola vertex $(2, 3)$ and focus $(2, 7)$.
7. Find the equation of the parabola vertex $(3, 4)$ and focus $(1, 4)$.
8. Find the latus rectum of the parabola $y^2 = 4x + 8y$.

The ellipse

If X is the foot of the perpendicular from S to the directrix, the curve is symmetrical about the line XS. We take this line to be the x-axis. The ratio SP:PK (e) is less than 1 and so there are two points on the line SX which also lie on the curve. One, A', will lie between S and X and nearer S; the other A will lie on XS produced. Let the distance AA' be $2a$ and let the mid-point of AA' be C. The point C is called the centre of the ellipse and is taken as origin.

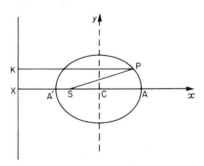

Fig. 25.2

Since A lies on the curve,
$$SA = eAX.$$
Since A' lies on the curve,
$$SA' = eA'X.$$
Adding, $$SA + SA' = e(AX + A'X).$$

But $$AX + A'X = a + CX + CX - a = 2CX.$$

$$\therefore \quad 2a = e(2CX) \quad \text{and} \quad CX = \frac{a}{e}.$$

Also $$CS = a - A'S = a - eA'X = a - e\left(\frac{a}{e} - a\right) = ae.$$

Having found the lengths of CX and CS, we can now find the equation of the curve.

Let P be (x, y). Since
$$S = (-ae, 0),$$
$$PS^2 = (x + ae)^2 + y^2,$$

and $$PK = x + CX = x + \frac{a}{e}.$$

We know that $$PS = ePK$$

and so $$(x + ae)^2 + y^2 = \left\{e\left(x + \frac{a}{e}\right)\right\}^2$$
$$= (ex + a)^2.$$
$$\therefore \quad x^2(1 - e^2) + y^2 = a^2(1 - e^2)$$

or $$\frac{x^2}{a^2} + \frac{y^2}{a^2(1 - e^2)} = 1.$$

Let $b^2 = a^2(1 - e)$ and the equation of the ellipse is
$$\frac{x^2}{a^2} + \frac{y^2}{b^2} = 1.$$

The length a is called the semi-major axis.

1. When $x = 0$, $y = \pm b$ and b is the length of the semi-minor axis. The curve, shown in Fig. 25.2, is symmetrical about both axes and so has two foci and two corresponding directrices.

   The foci are $(\pm ae, 0)$; the directrices $x = \pm\frac{a}{e}$.

2. The equation of an ellipse if the axis of length $2a$ is taken along the y-axis is $\dfrac{x^2}{b^2} + \dfrac{y^2}{a^2} = 1$.

   The major axis is still $2a$ although a^2 appears in the y^2 coefficient, i.e. the major axis is always the larger of the two axes.

3. The equation of the ellipse referred to parallel axes through the point (h, k) is $\dfrac{(x - h)^2}{a^2} + \dfrac{(y - k)^2}{b^2} = 1$.

   N.B. Remember that $CS = ae$, $CX = a/e$ and $b^2 = a^2(1 - e^2)$.

Exercise 25.2

1. Find the eccentricity of the ellipse $\dfrac{x^2}{9} + \dfrac{y^2}{4} = 1$.

2. Find the foci of the ellipse $\dfrac{x^2}{25} + \dfrac{y^2}{9} = 1$.

3. Find the foci of the ellipse $\dfrac{(x-2)^2}{25} + \dfrac{(y-3)^2}{9} = 1$.

4. Find the eccentricity of the ellipse $\dfrac{x^2}{5} + \dfrac{y^2}{9} = 1$.

5. Find the foci of the ellipse $\dfrac{(x-1)^2}{5} + \dfrac{(y-2)^2}{9} = 1$.

6. Find the centre of the ellipse $x^2 + 3y^2 - 2x - 6y = 8$.

7. Find the distances from the foci of the point P $(3, \frac{12}{5})$ on the ellipse $\dfrac{x^2}{25} + \dfrac{y^2}{9} = 1$. [*Hint*: use SP = *e*PK.]

8. An ellipse has its axes along the axes of coordinates, its eccentricity is $\frac{2}{3}$ and its semi-major axis 3. Find its equation.

9. An ellipse has its axes along the axes of coordinates, its eccentricity is $\frac{3}{4}$ and its semi-minor axis 2. Find its equation.

10. If B is an end of the minor axis of an ellipse, show that SB = a.

11. Show that the distance between the focus $(ae, 0)$ and the point $(a/e, b)$ on the directrix is b/e.

12. A point P (x', y') lies on an ellipse. Show that the sum of its focal distances is equal to the major axis of the ellipse. [*Hint*: use SP = *e*PK.]

The hyperbola

Let X be the foot of the perpendicular from the focus to the directrix. The curve is symmetrical about the line SX, which is taken as the *x*-axis.

Since e is greater than 1, there are two points on SX also on the hyperbola. One, A, lies between S and X, nearer X, and the other on SX produced (A').

Let AA' = 2a and let C be the mid-point of AA'. The point C is called the centre of the hyperbola and is taken as origin.

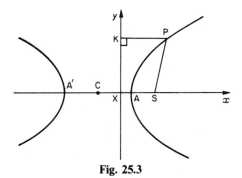

Fig. 25.3

Since A lies on the hyperbola, $SA = eAX$.

Since A' lies on the hyperbola, $SA' = eA'X$.

$$\therefore \quad SA' - SA = e(A'X - AX).$$

But $\qquad A'X - AX = (a - CX) - (a - CX) = 2CX.$

So $\qquad\qquad 2a = e(2CX) \quad \text{and} \quad CX = \dfrac{a}{e}.$

Since $SA = eAX$,

$$SA = e\left(a - \frac{a}{e}\right) = ea - a.$$

$$\therefore \quad CS = a + SA = ea.$$

Having found CS and CX, the equation of the hyperbola may be found.

The point S is $(ae, 0)$ and suppose the coordinates of any point P on the hyperbola are (x, y).

Then $PS^2 = (x - ae)^2 + y^2 \quad \text{and} \quad PK = x - CX = x - \dfrac{a}{e}.$

$$(x - ae)^2 + y^2 = \left\{e\left(x - \frac{a}{e}\right)\right\}^2$$

$$= (ex - a)^2.$$

$$x^2(e^2 - 1) - y^2 = a^2(e^2 - 1)$$

or $\qquad\qquad \dfrac{x^2}{a^2} - \dfrac{y^2}{a^2(e^2 - 1)} = 1.$

Let $b^2 = a^2(e^2 - 1)$ and the equation of the hyperbola becomes

$$\frac{x^2}{a^2} - \frac{y^2}{b^2} = 1.$$

1. When $x = 0$, $y^2 = -b^2$ and so the curve shown in Fig. 25.3 does not meet the y-axis in real points. The length of the semi-minor axis is b but this length cannot be so easily shown on the diagram as for the ellipse.

2. The curve is symmetrical about both axes. It has two foci, $(ae, 0)$ and $(-ae, 0)$ and two directrices $x = \dfrac{a}{e}$ and $x = -\dfrac{a}{e}$. The curve also has two branches as shown in the diagram.

3. If b is greater than a, the length of the major axis is $2a$ and not $2b$. The major axis is not necessarily greater than the minor axis; it always lies along the real axis.

4. The equation of the hyperbola referred to parallel axes through the point (h, k) is $\dfrac{(x - h)^2}{a^2} - \dfrac{(y - k)^2}{b^2} = 1.$

N.B. Remember that $CS = ae$, $CX = \dfrac{a}{e}$ and $b^2 = a^2(e^2 - 1)$.

The first two formulae are the same as for the ellipse, and both formulae for e are included in the equation $b^2 = a^2|1 - e^2|$.

Exercise 25.3

1. Find the eccentricity of the hyperbola $\dfrac{x^2}{16} - \dfrac{y^2}{4} = 1$.

2. Find the foci of the hyperbola $\dfrac{x^2}{16} - \dfrac{y^2}{9} = 1$.

3. Find the foci of the hyperbola $\dfrac{(x-2)^2}{16} - \dfrac{(y-3)^2}{9} = 1$.

4. Find the eccentricity of the hyperbola $\dfrac{x^2}{9} - \dfrac{y^2}{16} = 1$.

5. Find the foci of the hyperbola $\dfrac{(x-1)^2}{9} - \dfrac{(y-2)^2}{16} = 1$.

6. Find the centre of the hyperbola $x^2 - 3y^2 - 2x - 6y = 8$.

7. Find the distances from the foci of the point $P(\frac{20}{3}, 4)$ on the hyperbola $\dfrac{x^2}{16} - \dfrac{y^2}{9} = 1$.

8. If P is the point $(0, b)$ on the y-axis, show that $AP = ae$.

9. Show that the point $\frac{1}{2}a\left(t + \dfrac{1}{t}\right), \frac{1}{2}b\left(t - \dfrac{1}{t}\right)$ lies on $\dfrac{x^2}{a^2} - \dfrac{x^2}{b^2} = 1$ for all values of t.

10. Show that the length of the perpendicular from the focus to the line $\dfrac{x}{a} = \dfrac{y}{b}$ is equal to b.

11. Show that the difference between the focal distances of any point P on a hyperbola is constant and equal to the major axis of the hyperbola.

12. The two foci of a hyperbola are $(3, 0)$ and $(7, 0)$ and its eccentricity is 2. Find its equation.

The rectangular hyperbola

When b is equal to a, the equation $\dfrac{x^2}{a^2} - \dfrac{y^2}{b^2} = 1$ becomes $x^2 - y^2 = a^2$.

Let us find the equation of this hyperbola when the axes are rotated through an angle of $45°$ clockwise.

When the axes are rotated through an angle θ anticlockwise, we write $x \cos \theta - y \sin \theta$ for x and $x \sin \theta + y \cos \theta$ for y.

So for x write $x \cos(-45°) - y \sin(-45°)$ or $\dfrac{x+y}{\sqrt{2}}$.

For y write $x \sin(-45°) + y \cos(-45°)$ or $\dfrac{y-x}{\sqrt{2}}$.

The equation becomes

$$\frac{(x+y)^2}{2} - \frac{(y-x)^2}{2} = a^2$$

or

$$2xy = a^2.$$

For simplicity, write $a^2 = 2c^2$ so that the equation becomes $xy = c^2$.

This is a well-known equation; it is in fact the equation of inverse proportionality and is the relationship satisfied by the lengths of sides of a rectangle of constant area or the equation connecting pressure and volume in Boyle's law.

As x tends to zero, y tends to infinity; as y tends to zero, x tends to infinity. When x is positive, y is positive; when x is negative, y is negative. The shape of the curve is shown in Fig. 25.4. The curve is

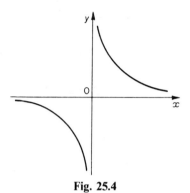

Fig. 25.4

said to approach each axis asymptotically which means that the curve gets as near each axis as we please but never actually meets the axis. The lines Ox and Oy in Fig. 25.4 are called the asymptotes. Since the asymptotes are at right angles, the curve is called the rectangular hyperbola.

1. The equation of a rectangular hyperbola referred to its axes as axes of coordinates is $x^2 - y^2 = a^2$. The asymptotes are $x = y$ and $x = -y$.
2. The equation of a rectangular hyperbola referred to its asymptotes as axes of coordinates is $xy = c^2$. The equations of the axes are $x = y$ and $x = -y$.
3. When the equation is given by the form $xy = c^2$, the length of the semi-major axis is given by $a^2 = 2c^2$.
4. The equation of a rectangular hyperbola referred to axes parallel to the asymptotes through the point (h, k) is
$$(x - h)(y - k) = c^2.$$
5. Since $b^2 = a^2$ and $b^2 = a^2(e^2 - 1)$, for any rectangular hyperbola $e = \sqrt{2}$.

Exercise 25.4

1. Find the foci of the hyperbola $xy = c^2$.
2. Find the centre of the hyperbola $xy - 2x - y + 1 = 0$.

3. Find the centre of the rectangular hyperbola $xy + 2y + 3x + 5 = 0$.
4. Find the asymptotes of the rectangular hyperbola $xy - 2x + y = 4$.
5. Show that the point $\left(ct, \dfrac{c}{t} \right)$ lies on the rectangular hyperbola $xy = c^2$ for all values of t.
6. Find the directrices of the hyperbola $xy = 2$.
7. Find the foci of the hyperbola $xy = 2$.
8. Find the equation of the rectangular hyperbola with focus $(2, 2)$ and corresponding directrix $x + y = 2$.
9. Find the lengths of the semi-axes of the hyperbola $xy = 32$.
10. Find the lengths of the semi-axes of the hyperbola $xy - x - y = 17$.
11. Show that the point $\left(2t + 1, \dfrac{1}{t} - 2 \right)$ lies on the curve $(x - 1)(y + 2) = 4$ for all values of t.
12. Express parametrically a point on the curve $xy - x + y = 17$.

The general conic

The equation of any conic must be of the form
$$ax^2 + 2hxy + by^2 + 2gx + 2fy + c = 0.$$
1. The conic is a pair of straight lines through the origin if $g = f = c = 0$.
2. The conic is a circle if $a = b$ and $h = 0$.
3. The conic is a parabola if $h^2 = ab$.
4. The conic is an ellipse if $h^2 < ab$.
5. The conic is a hyperbola if $h^2 > ab$.
6. The conic is a rectangular hyperbola if $a + b = 0$.

Some of these results have already been proved. The others should be taken for granted.

If $\qquad S = ax^2 + 2hxy + by^2 + 2gx + 2fy + c$
and $\qquad S' = a'x^2 + 2h'xy + b'y^2 + 2g'x + 2f'y + c'$,

then $S + kS' = 0$ must represent a family of conics because all terms are of the second degree or less. Any point which makes S zero and S' zero, must also make $S + kS'$ zero. So $S + kS' = 0$ is a family of conics each of which passes through all the points of intersection of $S = 0$ and $S' = 0$.

Example 1. *Find the pair of straight lines through the origin joining the points of intersection of $x^2 + 2y^2 = 4$ and $3x^2 - xy - y^2 = 2$.*

The equation of a pair of straight lines through the origin contains no constant term.

Consider the conic
$$2(3x^2 - xy - y^2 - 2) - (x^2 + 2y^2 - 4) = 0$$
chosen to make the constant term zero.

This conic must pass through all the points of intersection of the two conics and its equation is

$$5x^2 - 2xy - 4y^2 = 0,$$

which from its form is a pair of straight lines through the origin.

Example 2. *Find the equations of the parabolas passing through all the points of intersection of* $xy = 4$ *and* $x^2 + 4y^2 = x$.

Any conic passing through all the points of intersection of the two conics is

$$x^2 + 4y^2 - x + k(xy - 4) = 0.$$

The condition for this to be a parabola is

$$k^2 = 4(4), \quad \text{i.e. } k = 4 \quad \text{or} \quad -4.$$

The two parabolas are

$$x^2 - 4xy + 4y^2 - x + 16 = 0 \quad \text{and} \quad x^2 + 4xy + 4y^2 - x - 16 = 0.$$

Exercise 25.5

1. Find the equation of the conic which passes through the points of intersection of $x^2 + y^2 = 4$ and $xy = 2$ and also passes through the point $(1, 1)$. What type of conic is it?

2. Find the equation of the conic which passes through the points of intersection of $4x^2 + y^2 = 8$ and $x^2 + 2y^2 = 4$ and also through the point $(2, 1)$.

3. Find the equation of the pair of straight lines joining the origin to the points of intersection of $x^2 + y^2 = 4$ and $2x^2 - 5xy + 2y^2 = 2$.

4. Find the equation of the circle through the points of intersection of $x^2 - xy + y^2 = 2$ and $3x^2 + 5xy + 3y^2 = 14$.

5. Are the points of intersection of
$$x^2 - xy + y^2 = 2$$
and
$$x^2 + 5xy + 3y^2 = 14 \text{ concyclic}?$$

6. Find the equations of the parabola through the points of intersection of $x^2 + 2xy + y^2 = x$ and $y^2 + 2xy = y$.

7. Find the equation of the parabolas through the points of intersection of
$$4x + 2xy + y^2 - x - 3y - 3 = 0$$
and
$$y^2 + 2xy - x + y + 1 = 0.$$

8. Find the equations of the lines joining the origin to the points of intersection of $x^2 + xy + y^2 = 1$ and $3x^2 + 2y^2 = 2$.

9. Show that $ax^2 + 2hxy + by^2 = (px + qy)^2$ is the equation of the pair of straight lines joining the origin to the points of intersection of $ax^2 + 2hxy + by^2 = 1$ with $px + qy = 1$.

10. Find the equations of the pair of straight lines joining the origin to the points of intersection of $7x^2 - 3xy = 1$ and $x + y = 1$.

11. Find the equations of the pair of straight lines joining the origin to the points of intersection of $8x^2 + 12xy + 5y^2 = 1$ with $3x + 2y = 1$.

12. Find the condition that the lines joining the origin to the points of intersection of $3x^2 + xy - y^2 = 1$ with $px + qy = 1$ should be perpendicular.

Exercise 25.6: Miscelleneous

1. Show that the points of intersection of
$$3x^2 + 2y^2 + 4x + 2y - 4 = 0 \quad \text{and} \quad 2x^2 + y^2 = 1$$
lie on a circle and find its radius.

2. Show that the points of intersection of
$$3x^2 + 2y^2 + 4x + 2y + 4 = 0 \quad \text{and} \quad 6x^2 + 4y^2 = 1$$
lie on a line.

3. Show that the points of intersection of
$$ax^2 + by^2 + 2gx + 2fy + c = 0$$
and
$$px^2 + qy^2 = 1$$
lie on a line if $aq = bp$ and that otherwise they are concyclic.

4. Show that $S + kll' = 0$ where $S = 0$ is a conic and $l = 0$ and $l' = 0$ are straight lines in a conic passing through the four points of intersection of S with l and l'.

5. The lines $\quad 2x + 3y = 1 \quad$ and $\quad 2x - 3y = 1$
   meet the conic $\qquad x^2 + 2y^2 = 4$
   at A, B, C and D. Show that the points A, B, C and D are concyclic.

6. Find the equation of the rectangular hyperbola which passes through the points of intersection of the lines $2x + 3y = 1$ and $2x - 3y = 1$ with $x^2 + 4y^2 = 4$.

7. Show that every conic through the points of intersection of $x^2 - y^2 = 4$ and $xy = 8x$ is a rectangular hyperbola.

8. Find the equation of the pair of lines through the origin parallel to the lines $x^2 - xy - 2y^2 + 2x - y + 1 = 0$.

9. Find the equation of the ellipse which has $(4, 0)$ and $(-4, 0)$ as foci and passes through the point $(4, \frac{10}{3})$.

10. Find the equation of the hyperbola which has $(5, 0)$ and $(-5, 0)$ as foci and passes through the point $(5, 2\frac{1}{4})$.

11. Given that the circle $x^2 + y^2 + 2gx + 2fy + c = 0$ cuts the parabola $y^2 = 4x$ in four real points, show that a parabola with axis parallel to the y-axis may be drawn through the four points.

12. Find the equation of the parabola whose focus is the origin and whose directrix is $px + qy = 1$.

13. Find the equation of the axis of the parabola defined in question 12.

14. Find the coordinates of the vertex of the parabola defined in question 12.

15. Find the equation of the directrix of the parabola whose focus is $(0, 0)$ and whose vertex is $(1, 1)$.

16. Find the equation of the parabola whose focus is $(0, 0)$ and whose vertex is $(1, 1)$.

17. Show that the circle $x^2 + y^2 = 15$ meets the hyperbola $xy = 5$ in four points which form a rectangle of sides $x + y = \pm 5, x - y = \pm \sqrt{5}$.

18. Prove that the product of the perpendiculars from the foci of the ellipse $\dfrac{x^2}{a^2} + \dfrac{y^2}{b^2} = 1$ to the line $\dfrac{x \cos \alpha}{a} + \dfrac{y \sin \alpha}{b} = 1$ is b^2.

19. Prove that the product of the perpendiculars from a focus of the hyperbola $\dfrac{x^2}{a^2} - \dfrac{y^2}{b^2} = 1$ to the line $y = mx + \sqrt{(a^2m^2 - b^2)}$ is b^2.

20. Prove that the foot of the perpendicular from the focus of the parabola $y^2 = 4ax$ to the line $y = mx + \dfrac{a}{m}$ lies on the tangent at the vertex.

21. Prove that the lines $my = m^2x + a$ and $my + x = -am^2$ meet on the directrix of the parabola $y^2 = 4ax$.

22. Prove that the foot of the perpendicular from a focus of the ellipse $\dfrac{x^2}{a^2} + \dfrac{y^2}{b^2} = 1$ to the line $\dfrac{x \cos \alpha}{a} + \dfrac{y \sin \alpha}{b} = 1$ lies on the circle which has the major axis of the ellipse as diameter.

23. Find the coordinates of the points in which the rectangular hyperbola through the points of intersection of
$$x^2 + y^2 + 4x + 2y - 1 = 0 \quad \text{and} \quad x^2 - xy - 2y = 0$$
meets the x-axis.

24. Show that the pair of straight lines joining the points of intersection of the circle $x^2 + y^2 + 2gx + 2fy + c = 0$ with the line $px + qy = 1$ to the origin are
$$x^2 + y^2 + (2gx + 2fy)(px + qy) + c(px + qy)^2 = 0.$$

25. Find the equation of the pair of lines joining the points of intersection of the circle $x^2 + y^2 - 3x + 2y - 1 = 0$ and $x + 2y = 1$ to the origin.

26. The line $x + y = 4$ meets the pair of straight lines $x^2 - xy - y^2 = 0$ at the points A and B. Show that
$$x^2 - xy - y^2 + (px + qy)(x + y - 4) = 0$$
is a conic circumscribing the triangle OAB.

27. Find the equation of the rectangular hyperbola
$$\sqrt{3}(y^2 - x^2) - 2xy = 1$$
referred to axes rotated through an angle of 60° anticlockwise. Hence deduce the equations of the asymptotes of the original hyperbola.

28. Find the equation of the rectangular hyperbola with focus $(0, 0)$ and corresponding directrix $x + y = 1$.

29. Find the centre of the rectangular hyperbola whose focus is $(0, 0)$ and whose corresponding directrix is $x + y = 1$. Find also the lengths of the axes.

30. Find the equation of the hyperbola in question 28 referred to axes through the origin parallel to the axes of the hyperbola.

26 Parametric Forms

Revision

Parameters

We saw in *Additional Pure Mathematics* that any point on the parabola $y^2 = 4ax$ may be expressed as $(at^2, 2at)$, where t is called a *parameter*. Any value of t gives a point on the parabola, and every point on the parabola corresponds to one value of t. Thus when $t = -1$, the point is $(a, -2a)$; when $t = 4$, the point is $(16a, 8a)$ and the point $(9a, 6a)$ corresponds to the value $t = 3$.

Many other curves can be expressed in parametric form. Points (t, t^3) always lie on $y = x^3$, points (t^2, t^3) lie on $y^2 = x^3$, points $(a \cos^3 t, a \sin^3 t)$ lie on the astroid $x^{\frac{2}{3}} + y^{\frac{2}{3}} = a^{\frac{2}{3}}$.

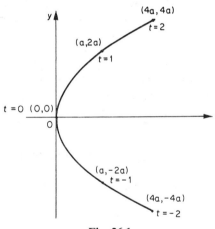

Fig. 26.1

The parabola

Any point on the parabola $y^2 = 4ax$ may be expressed as $(at^2, 2at)$ since $(2at)^2 = 4a(at^2)$. This is a very convenient form for the coordinates of a point on the parabola and is usually used in dealing with problems on the parabola.

Let us now find the equation of the chord joining the points with parameters m and t, i.e. $(am^2, 2am)$ and $(at^2, 2at)$.

The gradient of the chord is

$$\frac{2at - 2am}{at^2 - am^2} \quad \text{or} \quad \frac{2a(t - m)}{a(t + m)(t - m)} \quad \text{or} \quad \frac{2}{t + m}.$$

The equation of the chord is

$$\frac{y - 2am}{x - am^2} = \frac{2}{m + t}$$

or
$$(m + t)y - 2am^2 - 2amt = 2x - 2am^2$$

or
$$(m + t)y - 2x = 2amt.$$

N.B. The equation must obviously be symmetrical between m and t which gives a check on the working.

Equation of the tangent

If we know the equation of the chord joining two points m and t, we can deduce the equation of the tangent, for as the point m moves closer and closer to the point t, the chord becomes closer to the tangent. Putting $m = t$ in the equation of the chord, we see that the equation of the tangent is

$$ty = x + at^2.$$

Generally we shall not know the equation of the chord, and so we shall have to find the equation of the tangent by first differentiating to obtain the gradient. We have two methods; we can differentiate the equation of the parabola, i.e. if $y^2 = 4ax$, $2y\dfrac{dy}{dx} = 4a$, whence $\dfrac{dy}{dx} = \dfrac{2a}{y}$. When $y = 2at$, $\dfrac{dy}{dx} = \dfrac{1}{t}$. The tangent is the straight line through $(at^2, 2at)$ with gradient $\dfrac{1}{t}$, so its equation is

$$y - 2at = \frac{1}{t}(x - at^2),$$

i.e.
$$ty = x + at^2.$$

In the other method, we use the parameteric form $x = at^2$, $y = 2at$ even to find the gradient of the tangent. For if

$$x = at^2, \frac{dx}{dt} = 2at \quad \text{and if} \quad y = 2at, \frac{dy}{dt} = 2a.$$

Now
$$\frac{dy}{dx} = \frac{dy/dt}{dx/dt} = \frac{2a}{2at} = \frac{1}{t},$$

as before, and we find the equation of the tangent as in the previous paragraph.

Equation of normal

The normal at $(at^2, 2at)$ is perpendicular to the tangent at that point, so since the gradient of the tangent is $\dfrac{1}{t}$, the gradient of the normal is $-t$. Thus the equation of the normal is

$$y - 2at = -t(x - at^2),$$

i.e.
$$y + tx = 2at + at^3.$$

Intersection of two tangents

To find the point of intersection of the tangents at the points m and t, the equations of the tangents are

$$my = x + am^2,$$
$$ty = x + at^2.$$

Solving simultaneously, $y = a(m + t)$, $x = amt$, so that the two tangents meet at the point $\{amt, a(m + t)\}$.

Normals through a given point (*h, k*)

The normal at the point t is $tx + y = at^3 + 2at$. This goes through a given point (h, k) if $th + k = at^3 + 2at$, which can be written as a cubic in t

$$at^3 + t(2a - h) - k = 0.$$

A cubic may have three distinct roots, two equal roots and a third distinct root, or only one real root, so that we can either have three normals through a given point (if two of these coincide, that corresponds to the two equal roots) or we can have only one normal through a given point.

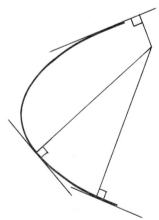

Fig. 26.2

Example 1. *A chord PQ of a parabola passes through the focus. Show that the tangents at P and Q meet on the directrix.*

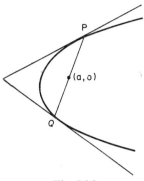

Fig. 26.3

Let P be $(ap^2, 2ap)$, Q be $(aq^2, 2aq)$. Then the equation of the chord PQ is
$$y(p + q) - 2x = 2apq$$
Since this passes through the focus $(a, 0)$,
$$-2a = 2apq,$$
i.e. $$pq = -1.$$
But we have shown that the point of intersection of the tangents is $\{apq, a(p + q)\}$ so that the x coordinate is $-a$, i.e. the tangents always meet on the line $x = -a$, the directrix.

Example 2. *The tangents at points P and Q to the parabola $y^2 = 4ax$ meet at an angle of 45°. Find the locus of their point of intersection R.*

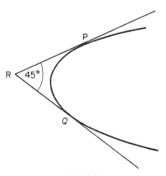

Fig. 26.4

Taking the points P as $(ap^2, 2ap)$ and Q as $(aq^2, 2aq)$, the tangents are
$$py = x + ap^2$$
$$qy = x + aq^2$$
and their point of intersection R has coordinates $\{apq, a(p + q)\}$ as before.

The angle θ between two straight lines gradients m_1, m_2 is given by

$$\tan \theta = \frac{m_1 - m_2}{1 + m_1 m_2}.$$

Since the gradients of the tangents are $\dfrac{1}{p}$, $\dfrac{1}{q}$ and the angle is $45°$

$$\tan 45° = \frac{\dfrac{1}{p} - \dfrac{1}{q}}{1 + \dfrac{1}{pq}}$$

i.e. $$1 = \frac{q - p}{pq + 1}$$

i.e. $$pq + 1 = q - p. \qquad (1)$$

Taking the coordinates of R as (X, Y) where $X = apq$, $Y = a(p + q)$, we want to find the equation between X and Y, using (1) to eliminate p and q. Now

$$(q - p)^2 = (q + p)^2 - 4pq$$

so that $$(pq + 1)^2 = (q + p)^2 - 4pq$$

i.e. $$\left(\frac{X}{a} + 1\right)^2 = \left(\frac{Y}{a}\right)^2 - 4\frac{X}{a},$$

the locus is $$y^2 - 4ax = (x + a)^2.$$

Exercise 26.1

1. (i) Write down the value of the parameter t corresponding to each of the points on the parabola $x = at^2$, $y = 2at$:
   $$(a, 2a), \ (\tfrac{1}{4}a, a), \ (9a, -6a).$$

   (ii) Write down the coordinates of the points with parameter t on the parabola $x = 2t^2$, $y = 2t$:
   $$t = 1; \quad 0; \quad \tfrac{1}{2}; \quad -1.$$

2. Find a parametric form for points on each of the following parabolas:

   (i) $y = 8x$.   (ii) $y^2 = 8(x - 1)$.
   (iii) $(y - 1)^2 = 8x$.   (iv) $(y - 1)^2 = 8(x + 1)$.

3. Find the equation of the chord joining the points $(4a, 4a)$ and $(a, 2a)$ on $y^2 = 4ax$.

4. Find the equation of the chord joining the points $(9a, 6a)$ and $(4a, 4a)$ on $y^2 = 4ax$.

5. Find the equation of the tangent at the point $(9a, 6a)$ on the parabola $y^2 = 4ax$.

6. Find the meet of the tangents at the points $(4a, 4a)$ and $(a, 2a)$ to the parabola $y^2 = 4ax$.

7. The line $px + qy = 1$ passes through the points $(am^2, 2am)$ and $(at^2, 2at)$. Show that $amtp = -1$.

8. The chord joining P $(ap^2, 2ap)$ and Q $(aq^2, 2aq)$ passes through the foot of the directrix, i.e. the point $(-a, 0)$. Show that $pq = 1$.

9. The tangent at a point P of a parabola meets the axis at the point T. If S is the focus, show that SP = ST.

10. Using the result of question 9, show that the tangent at a point P of a parabola bisects the angle between the axis and PS.

   It follows that a ray of light from the focus, when reflected by the parabola, is parallel to the axis of the parabola. This is the basis of parabolic reflectors, used in lights, fires and radio telescopes.

11. Find the equation of the normal at the point $(am^2, 2am)$ to the parabola.

12. Find the coordinates of the meet of the normals to the parabola at the points $(am^2, 2am)$ and $(at^2, 2at)$.

13. The tangents at the points P and Q on the parabola $y^2 = 4ax$ meet at the point $(6a, 5a)$. Find the coordinates of P and Q.

14. Find the equation of the normal at the point $(a, 2a)$ on the parabola $y^2 = 4ax$, and find also the coordinates of the other point at which it meets the parabola.

15. Write down the equation of the normal at the point $(at^2, 2at)$ to the parabola $y^2 = 4ax$ and find the parameter of the other point at which it meets the parabola.

16. P is the point $(at^2, 2at)$ on the parabola $y^2 = 4ax$. The line through the focus of the parabola parallel to the tangent at P meets the normal at P in Q. Find the coordinates of P and Q and the length of the line PQ.

17. Three points P $(ap^2, 2ap)$, Q $(aq^2, 2aq)$ and R $(ar^2, 2ar)$ lie on the parabola $y^2 = 4ax$. The tangents at P and Q meet at Z, the tangents at P and R meet at Y and the tangents at Q and R meet at X. If X is the midpoint of YR, prove that ZX is parallel to PR.

18. A chord PQ of the parabola $y^2 = 4ax$ passes through the fixed point $(c, 0)$. Taking P as $(ap^2, 2ap)$ and Q as $(aq^2, 2aq)$ write down the coordinates of the midpoint of PQ in terms of p and q, and show that for all positions of P and Q the midpoint of PQ lies on the parabola.

19. Two tangents are drawn from the point (h, k) to the parabola $y^2 = 4ax$. These meet the tangent at the vertex in O at points X and Y. Prove that OX × OY is independent of k.

20. PQ is a variable chord of the parabola $y^2 = 4ax$ such that PXQ is a right angle, where X is the point $(a, 2a)$. Prove that the locus of the midpoint of PQ is the parabola.

$$(y + a)^2 = 2a(x - \tfrac{9}{2}a).$$

21. PQ is a chord of the parabola $y^2 = 4ax$, passing through the focus $(a, 0)$. Prove that the length of PQ is $a\left(t + \dfrac{1}{t}\right)^2$.

22. Two tangents to the parabola $y^2 = 4ax$ meet an angle of 60°. Prove that the locus of the point of intersection of these tangents is $y^2 = 3x^2 + 10ax + 3a^2$.

23. PQ is a chord of the parabola $y^2 = 4ax$ such that PQ is perpendicular to OQ, where O is the vertex of the parabola. Prove that the locus of the midpoint of PQ is

$$y^2 = 2a(x - 4a).$$

24. The normal at a point P on the parabola $y^2 = 4ax$ meets the curve again at Q. The tangents at P and Q meet at R. Prove that as P varies on the curve, R always lies on

$$y^2(x + 2a) + 4a^3 = 0.$$

Sketch both curves to illustrate the relation between them.

The rectangular hyperbola $xy = c^2$

The point $\left(ct, \dfrac{c}{t}\right)$ lies on the rectangular hyperbola $xy = c^2$ for all values of t, and so any point can be taken in this parametric form.

Chord joining two points

Take the two points in the parametric form $\left(ct, \dfrac{c}{t}\right)$, $\left(cs, \dfrac{c}{s}\right)$. Then the equation of the straight line through P and Q is

$$\frac{y - \dfrac{c}{t}}{\dfrac{c}{s} - \dfrac{c}{t}} = \frac{x - ct}{cs - ct}$$

i.e. $-sty + cs = x - ct,$

i.e. $x + sty = c(s + t).$

Tangent at point $(ct, c/t)$

Proceeding as with the parabola, we write $t = s$, and the equation of the tangent is seen to be

$$x + t^2 y = 2ct.$$

Alternatively, we can use calculus to find the gradient of the tangent, for if

$$x = ct, \quad y = \frac{c}{t},$$

$$\frac{dx}{dt} = c, \quad \frac{dy}{dt} = -\frac{c}{t^2},$$

$$\frac{dy}{dx} = \frac{\dfrac{dy}{dt}}{\dfrac{dx}{dt}} = -\frac{1}{t^2}.$$

$\therefore$ the equation of the tangent at $\left(ct, \dfrac{c}{t}\right)$ is

$$y - \frac{c}{t} = -\frac{1}{t^2}(x - ct)$$

i.e. $x + t^2 y = 2ct.$

Equation of the normal at (*ct, c/t*)

Since the normal is perpendicular to the tangent at $\left(ct, \dfrac{c}{t}\right)$, the gradient of the normal is t^2, so the equation of the normal is

$$y - \frac{c}{t} = t^2(x - ct),$$

i.e. $ty - t^3 x = c(1 - t^4).$

Example 1. *The tangents at points P and Q on the rectangular hyperbola* $xy = c^2$ *meet the line* $y = 0$ *at X and Y respectively. Prove that PQ passes through the midpoint of XY.*

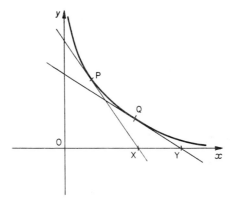

Fig. 26.5

Let P be $\left(cp, \dfrac{c}{p}\right)$, Q be $\left(cq, \dfrac{c}{q}\right)$. Then the tangent at P is $x + p^2 y = 2cp$ and this meets the line $y = 0$ at $(2cp, 0)$. Similarly the coordinates of Y are $(2cq, 0)$ so the coordinates of the midpoint of PQ are $\{c(p + q), 0\}$. The equation of the chord PQ is $x + pqy = c(p + q)$, and this is satisfied by $x = c(p + q)$, $y = 0$. Thus the midpoint of XY lies on PQ.

Example 2. *P, Q, R and S are four points of parameters p, q, r and s on the rectangular hyperbola* $xy = c^2$, *such that RS is perpendicular to PQ. Show that* $pqrs = -1$ *and hence find the coordinates of the orthocentre of the triangle PQR.*

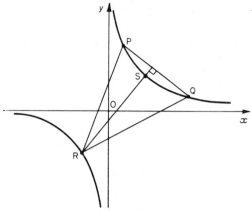

Fig. 26.6

The gradient of RS $= \dfrac{\dfrac{c}{r} - \dfrac{c}{s}}{cr - cs} = -\dfrac{1}{rs}.$

The gradient of PQ is $-\dfrac{1}{pq}.$

Since these two lines are perpendicular, $pqrs = -1$.

By the symmetry of this condition, it follows that PS is perpendicular to RQ and that QS is perpendicular to PR.

Therefore S is the orthocentre of the triangle PQR. The coordinates of S are $\left(cs, \dfrac{c}{s}\right)$ or $\left(-\dfrac{c}{pqr}, -cpqr\right)$. This point is the orthocentre of the triangle formed by the points p, q and r.

N.B. The orthocentre of a triangle inscribed in a rectangular hyperbola always lies on the rectangular hyperbola.

Exercise 26.2

1. (i) Write down the value of the parameter t corresponding to each of these points on the curve $xy = c^2$:

$$(-c, -c), \quad (2c, \tfrac{1}{2}c), \quad \left(c\sqrt{2}, \dfrac{c}{\sqrt{2}}\right).$$

   (ii) Write down the coordinates of the points with parameter t on the curve $xy = 1$:

$$t = \dfrac{1}{\sqrt{2}}; \quad t = -1; \quad t = \tfrac{1}{2}.$$

2. Find parametric forms for points on each of the following rectangular hyperbolas:

   (i) $xy = 4$.   (ii) $xy = \tfrac{1}{4}$.
   (iii) $(x - 1)y = c^2$.   (iv) $(x - 1)(y + 1) = 1$.

3. Find the equation of the tangent at $(2, \tfrac{1}{2})$ to the curve $xy = 1$.

4. Find the equation of the tangent and normal at $(1, 4)$ to the curve $xy = 4$.

5. Find the equation of the tangent and normal to the curve $xy = c^2$ at the point $(2c, \frac{1}{2}c)$.

6. Find the equation of the chord joining the points $(2c, \frac{1}{2}c)$, (c, c) on the rectangular hyperbola $xy = c^2$.

7. Find the equation of the tangent to the rectangular hyperbola $xy = c^2$ that passes through $(\frac{2}{3}c, 0)$.

8. Find the equation of the normal at the point $\left(t, \dfrac{1}{t}\right)$ on the rectangular hyperbola $xy = 1$. Find the two possible values of t if the normal passes through the point $(3, -3)$.

9. Find the coordinates of the point of intersection of the tangents at $\left(ct, \dfrac{c}{t}\right)$, $\left(cs, \dfrac{c}{s}\right)$ to the rectangular hyperbola $xy = c^2$.

10. Find the equation of the normal at the point $(4, 1)$ to the rectangular hyperbola $xy = 4$. This normal meets the hyperbola again at the point Q. Find the length PQ.

All the remaining questions in this exercise refer to the rectangular hyperbola $xy = c^2$.

11. Show that no two tangents to a rectangular hyperbola can be perpendicular.

12. T is the midpoint of a chord PQ of the rectangular hyperbola. Show that PQ and OT are equally inclined to the coordinate axes, O being the origin of coordinates.

13. Find the equations of the tangents to the hyperbola that make an angle of $45°$ with the axes.

14. T is the midpoint of a chord PQ of the rectangular hyperbola. PQ meets the x-axis at X. Show that TX = CT.

15. T is the midpoint of the chord PQ of the rectangular hyperbola. If PQ meets the x-axis at X and the y-axis at Y, show that T is the midpoint of XY.

16. Tangents TP, TQ are drawn from the point T $(c, \frac{1}{2}c)$ to the rectangular hyperbola. Find the equation of the chord PQ.

17. If the chord joining two variable points P and Q on the rectangular hyperbola always passes through $(2c, \frac{1}{2}c)$, show that the tangents to the hyperbola at P and Q always meet on the line $x + 4y = 4c$.

18. Points P and Q are taken on the rectangular hyperbola. X is the foot of the perpendicular from P onto Ox, and Y is the foot of the perpendicular from Q onto Oy. If PY is the tangent at P, show that QX is the tangent at X.

19. The normal to the rectangular hyperbola at a point P meets the curve again at Q. The line joining P to the origin O when produced meets the curve again at R. Prove that PQR is always a right angle.

20. The tangent at a point P to the hyperbola meets the x-axis at X and the y-axis at Y. QX is a line parallel to the y-axis meeting the curve at Q; RY is a line parallel to the x-axis meeting the curve at R. Show that, as P varies, the locus of the midpoint of PQ is the same rectangular hyperbola as the locus of the midpoint of PR, and find the locus of the midpoint of QR.

The circle $x^2 + y^2 = 1$

Any point on this circle can be written in the parametric form $x = \cos t, y = \sin t$. The point P at which the circle meets the positive x-axis has parameter 0, the point Q at which it meets the positive y-axis has parameter $\dfrac{\pi}{2}$, and so on.

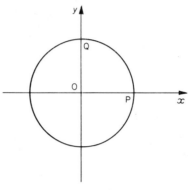

Fig. 26.7

The tangent at the point (cos t, sin t)

Since $x = \cos t, \dfrac{dx}{dt} = -\sin t$; since $y = \sin t, \dfrac{dy}{dt} = \cos t,$

$$\therefore \quad \frac{dy}{dx} = \frac{\dfrac{dy}{dt}}{\dfrac{dx}{dt}} = \frac{\cos t}{-\sin t} = -\cot t.$$

The equation of the tangent at $(\cos t, \sin t)$ is therefore
$$y - \sin t = -\cot t(x - \cos t),$$
i.e. $\qquad x \cos t + y \sin t = 1, \quad$ using $\cos^2 t + \sin^2 t = 1$.

The semi-cubical parabola $y^2 = x^3$

Any point on this semi-cubical parabola can be written in the form $x = t^2, y = t^3$. Since $x = t^2$, the curve only exists when x is positive. For any two values of t, say $t = \alpha$ and $t = -\alpha$, there are two points on the curve whose x coordinates are equal and whose y coordinates are equal and opposite, so that the curve is symmetrical about the x-axis.

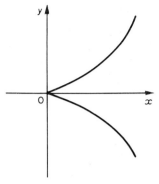

Fig. 26.8

The tangent at (t^2, t^3)

Since $x = t^2$, $\dfrac{dx}{dt} = 2t$; since $y = t^3$, $\dfrac{dy}{dt} = 3t^2$.

$$\therefore \quad \frac{dy}{dx} = \frac{\dfrac{dy}{dt}}{\dfrac{dx}{dt}} = \frac{3t^2}{2t} = \frac{3t}{2}.$$

The equation of the tangent at (t^2, t^3) is therefore

$$y - t^3 = \tfrac{3}{2}t(x - t^2),$$

i.e. $$2y = 3tx - t^3.$$

Example. *The tangent at the point P on the curve $x = t^2$, $y = t^3$ meets the curve again at Q. Find the coordinates of Q.*

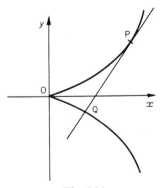

Fig. 26.9

The equation of the tangent at P we have found to be
$$2y = 3tx - t^3.$$
This meets the curve again at Q, so that we can take Q to be (q^2, q^3). Since Q lies on the tangent at P,
$$2q^3 - 3tq^2 + t^3 = 0.$$
This is a cubic in q, but we know that it has two equal roots $q = t$, since the point of contact P corresponds to two equal roots of the equation. Factorising, we see that
$$2q^3 - 3tq^2 + t^3 = (q - t)(q - t)(2q + t)$$
so that $q = t$ (twice) or $q = -\frac{1}{2}t$, the coordinates of Q are $(\frac{1}{4}t^2, -\frac{1}{8}t^3)$.

Exercise 26.3

1. The tangent to the circle $x = \cos t$, $y = \sin t$ at any point P meets the coordinate axes at points $(h, 0)$ and $(0, k)$. Find the locus of the point (h, k), and give a sketch to show its relation to the original circle.

2. The tangent at the point $t = \alpha$ on the circle $x = \cos t$, $y = \sin t$ meets the tangent at the point $t = \beta$ at the point T. Find the coordinates of T.

3. Find the equation of the chord through the two points $t = \alpha$, $t = \beta$, on the circle $x = \cos t$, $y = \sin t$.

4. Find a suitable parametric form for any point on the curve $y = x^3$. Find the equation of the tangent at P (α, α^3), and the coordinates of the point at which this tangent meets the curve again.

5. P and Q are points on the curve $x = t^2$, $y = t^3$ such that POQ is a right angle, O being the origin. Find the locus of the point of intersection of the tangents to the curve at P and Q.

The ellipse

Consider the circle drawn on the major axis of an ellipse as diameter as shown in Fig. 26.10. This is called the **auxiliary circle** of the ellipse.

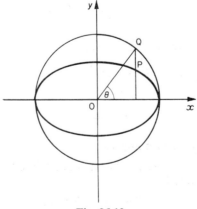

Fig. 26.10

Draw a radius CQ of this circle making an angle θ with the major axis. Then CQ $= a$ and the coordinates of Q are $(a \cos \theta,\ a \sin \theta)$. Draw the perpendicular from Q to the major axis to meet the ellipse at P. The x-coordinate of P is also $a \cos \theta$ and since P lies on

$$\frac{x^2}{a^2} + \frac{y^2}{b^2} = 1,$$

$$\cos^2 \theta + \frac{y^2}{b^2} = 1.$$

$$\therefore\quad y^2 = b^2(1 - \cos^2 \theta) = b^2 \sin^2 \theta$$

and
$$y = \pm b \sin \theta.$$

The coordinates of the point P shown in the diagram are $(a \cos \theta,\ b \sin \theta)$. The angle θ is called the eccentric angle of the point P and $x = a \cos \theta$, $y = b \sin \theta$ are the parametric equations of the ellipse.

The gradient of the chord joining the points $(a \cos \alpha, b \sin \alpha)$ and $(a \cos \beta, b \sin \beta)$ is

$$\frac{b(\sin \beta - \sin \alpha)}{a(\cos \beta - \cos \alpha)} \quad \text{or} \quad \frac{2b \cos \frac{1}{2}(\alpha + \beta) \sin \frac{1}{2}(\beta - \alpha)}{2a \sin \frac{1}{2}(\alpha + \beta) \sin \frac{1}{2}(\alpha - \beta)}$$

or
$$-\frac{b \cos \frac{1}{2}(\alpha + \beta)}{a \sin \frac{1}{2}(\alpha + \beta)}.$$

The equation of the chord joining the two points is

$$\frac{y - b \sin \alpha}{x - a \cos \alpha} = -\frac{b \cos \frac{1}{2}(\alpha + \beta)}{a \sin \frac{1}{2}(\alpha + \beta)}$$

or $\quad ay \sin \dfrac{\alpha + \beta}{2} + bx \cos \dfrac{\alpha + \beta}{2}$

$$= ab\left(\sin \alpha \sin \frac{\alpha + \beta}{2} + \cos \alpha \cos \frac{\alpha + \beta}{2} \right)$$

$$= ab \cos \frac{\alpha - \beta}{2}.$$

The equation of the chord is therefore

$$\frac{x}{a} \cos \frac{\alpha + \beta}{2} + \frac{y}{b} \sin \frac{\alpha + \beta}{2} = \cos \frac{\alpha - \beta}{2}.$$

The equation of the tangent

If β is put equal to α, we get the equation of the tangent at the point $(a \cos \alpha, b \sin \alpha)$ which is

$$\frac{x \cos \alpha}{a} + \frac{y \sin \alpha}{b} = 1.$$

The meet of the tangents at the points whose eccentric angles are α and β

The equations of the tangents at these points are

$$\frac{x \cos \alpha}{a} + \frac{y \sin \alpha}{b} = 1$$

and

$$\frac{x \cos \beta}{a} + \frac{y \sin \beta}{b} = 1.$$

Eliminating y from these equations

$$\frac{x}{a}(\cos \alpha \sin \beta - \cos \beta \sin \alpha) = \sin \beta - \sin \alpha.$$

$$\therefore \quad \frac{x}{a} \sin (\beta - \alpha) = 2 \sin \tfrac{1}{2}(\beta - \alpha) \cos \tfrac{1}{2}(\beta + \alpha)$$

or

$$\frac{x}{a}(2 \sin \tfrac{1}{2}(\beta - \alpha) \cos \tfrac{1}{2}(\beta - \alpha)) = 2 \sin \tfrac{1}{2}(\beta - \alpha) \cos \tfrac{1}{2}(\beta + \alpha)$$

and so

$$x = a \frac{\cos \tfrac{1}{2}(\alpha + \beta)}{\cos \tfrac{1}{2}(\beta - \alpha)}.$$

Eliminating x from the equations,

$$\frac{y}{b}(\sin \alpha \cos \beta - \sin \beta \cos \alpha) = \cos \beta - \cos \alpha.$$

$$\therefore \quad \frac{y}{b} \sin (\alpha - \beta) = 2 \sin \tfrac{1}{2}(\alpha - \beta) \sin \tfrac{1}{2}(\alpha + \beta)$$

and

$$y = b \frac{\sin \tfrac{1}{2}(\alpha + \beta)}{\cos \tfrac{1}{2}(\alpha - \beta)}.$$

Since $\cos \tfrac{1}{2}(\alpha - \beta) = \cos \tfrac{1}{2}(\beta - \alpha)$, the point of intersection of the tangents is

$$\left(a \frac{\cos \tfrac{1}{2}(\alpha + \beta)}{\cos \tfrac{1}{2}(\alpha - \beta)}, \, b \frac{\sin \tfrac{1}{2}(\alpha + \beta)}{\cos \tfrac{1}{2}(\alpha - \beta)} \right).$$

Example. *The chord PQ of an ellipse passes through the focus* $(ae, 0)$. *Show that the meet of the tangents at P and Q lies on the directrix* $x = \dfrac{a}{e}$.

Suppose $P = (a \cos \alpha, b \sin \alpha)$ and $Q = (a \cos \beta, b \sin \beta)$. The equation of PQ is

$$\frac{x}{a} \cos \tfrac{1}{2}(\alpha + \beta) + \frac{y}{b} \sin \tfrac{1}{2}(\alpha + \beta) = \cos \tfrac{1}{2}(\alpha - \beta).$$

This passes through $(ae, 0)$ and so

$$e \cos \tfrac{1}{2}(\alpha + \beta) = \cos \tfrac{1}{2}(\alpha - \beta).$$

The meet of the tangents at P and Q is

$$\left(a\, \frac{\cos \frac{1}{2}(\alpha + \beta)}{\cos \frac{1}{2}(\alpha - \beta)},\, b\, \frac{\sin \frac{1}{2}(\alpha + \beta)}{\cos \frac{1}{2}(\alpha - \beta)} \right).$$

The x coordinate is $a\, \dfrac{\cos \frac{1}{2}(\alpha + \beta)}{\cos \frac{1}{2}(\alpha - \beta)}$ or $\dfrac{a}{e}$.

Exercise 26.4

1. If P is the point of eccentric angle θ and Q of eccentric angle $\dfrac{\pi}{2} + \theta$, show that $CP^2 + CQ^2 = a^2 + b^2$.

2. Find the equation of the tangent at the point $\left(\dfrac{a}{\sqrt{2}}, \dfrac{b}{\sqrt{2}} \right)$ to the ellipse $\dfrac{x^2}{a^2} + \dfrac{y^2}{b^2} = 1$.

3. Find the meet of the tangents of the ellipse at the points whose eccentric angles are θ and $\dfrac{\pi}{2} + \theta$.

4. If P is the point of eccentric angle θ and Q the point of eccentric angle $\dfrac{\pi}{2} + \theta$, show that the tangent at Q is parallel to CP.

5. Express a point on the ellipse $\dfrac{(x - 1)^2}{a^2} + \dfrac{(y - 2)^2}{b^2} = 1$ parametrically.

6. If the tangents at the points whose eccentric angles are θ and φ are perpendicular, show that $\tan \theta \tan \varphi = -\dfrac{b^2}{a^2}$.

7. Find the equation of the normal to the ellipse at the point $(a \cos \varphi, b \sin \varphi)$.

8. The tangent and normal to the ellipse at a point P cut the major axis at K and L. Show that $CK \cdot CL = a^2 e^2$.

9. At what point is $3x + 8y = 50$ a tangent to $\dfrac{x^2}{100} + \dfrac{y^2}{25} = 1$?

10. The tangent at the point $(a \cos \alpha, b \sin \alpha)$ to an ellipse meets the axes at P and Q. Find the area of the triangle OPQ.

11. By comparing $x + y = c$ with $\dfrac{x \cos \alpha}{a} + \dfrac{y \sin \alpha}{b} = 1$, find the condition that $x + y = c$ should be a tangent to $\dfrac{x^2}{a^2} + \dfrac{y^2}{b^2} = 1$.

12. Find the equation of the tangent at the point $(2, 3)$ to the ellipse $4x^2 + 3y^2 = 43$.

The hyperbola

A point on the hyperbola $\dfrac{x^2}{a^2} - \dfrac{y^2}{b^2} = 1$ may be expressed as $(a \sec \alpha,$ $b \tan \alpha)$ or as $(a \cosh \beta, b \sinh \beta)$, since

$$\sec^2 \alpha - \tan^2 \alpha = 1 \quad \text{and} \quad \cosh^2 \beta - \sinh^2 \beta = 1.$$

These parameters are sometimes useful but often lead to heavy trigonometry.

The algebraic form $\left\{ \dfrac{a}{2}\left(t + \dfrac{1}{t}\right), \dfrac{b}{2}\left(t - \dfrac{1}{t}\right) \right\}$ is possibly of greater value but, here again, the algebra involved may be cumbersome and the hyperbola does not lend itself to parametric representation as readily as the parabola and ellipse.

That the point $\left\{ \dfrac{a}{2}\left(t + \dfrac{1}{t}\right), \dfrac{b}{2}\left(t - \dfrac{1}{t}\right) \right\}$ always lies on the hyperbola is easily seen since

$$\frac{(t + 1/t)^2}{4} - \frac{(t - 1/t)^2}{1} = \frac{4}{4} = 1.$$

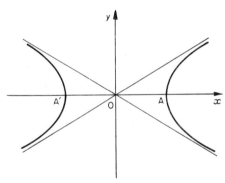

Fig. 26.11

When $t = 1$, the point is $(a, 0)$, i.e. A.

When t lies between 1 and ∞, both x and y are positive, so as t increases from 1 to ∞, the point moves from A to infinity along the hyperbola in the first quadrant (see Fig. 26.11).

When $t = 0$, both x and y are infinite and when t lies between 0 and 1, x is positive and y negative. So as t decreases from 1 to 0, the point describes that part of the hyperbola from A to infinity in the fourth quadrant.

When $t = -1$, the point is $(-a, 0)$, i.e. A'.

When t is between 0 and -1, x is negative and y is positive. So as t

increases from -1 to 0, the point describes that part of the hyperbola from A' to infinity in the second quadrant.

As t decreases from -1 to $-\infty$, the point describes that part of the curve from A' to infinity in the third quadrant.

The tangent

The gradient of the chord joining the points of parameters m and t on the hyperbola is

$$\frac{\frac{1}{2}b(t - 1/t - m + 1/m)}{\frac{1}{2}a(t + 1/t - m - 1/m)} = \frac{b[mt(t - m) + (t - m)]}{a[mt(t - m) - (t - m)]}$$

$$= \frac{b(mt + 1)}{a(mt - 1)}.$$

The equation of the chord is

$$\frac{y - \frac{1}{2}b(m - 1/m)}{x - \frac{1}{2}a(m + 1/m)} = \frac{b(mt + 1)}{a(mt - 1)}$$

or $\quad ay(mt - 1) - \dfrac{ab}{2}\left(m - \dfrac{1}{m}\right)(mt - 1) =$

$$bx(mt + 1) - \frac{ab}{2}\left(m + \frac{1}{m}\right)(mt + 1).$$

This reduces to

$$\frac{x}{a}(mt + 1) - \frac{y}{b}(mt - 1) = m + t.$$

By putting $t = m$, we get the equation of the tangent at the point m which is

$$\frac{x}{a}(m^2 + 1) - \frac{y}{b}(m^2 - 1) = 2m.$$

The asymptotes

The points at infinity on the hyperbola are given by $m = 0$ and $m = \infty$. The tangents at these points are the asymptotes.

Putting $m = 0$, we have $\dfrac{x}{a} + \dfrac{y}{b} = 0$, which is one of the asymptotes.

Putting the equation of the tangent in the form

$$\frac{x}{a}\left(1 + \frac{1}{m^2}\right) - \frac{y}{b}\left(1 - \frac{1}{m^2}\right) = \frac{2}{m}$$

and putting $m = \infty$, we have the equation of the other asymptote which is $\dfrac{x}{a} - \dfrac{y}{b} = 0$.

The two asymptotes of the hyperbola $\dfrac{x^2}{a^2} - \dfrac{y^2}{b^2} = 1$ are $\dfrac{x}{a} = \pm\dfrac{y}{b}$.

Example. *The tangent at the point P of a hyperbola meets the asymptotes at L and M. Show that P is the mid-point of LM.*

Let P be $\left\{\dfrac{a}{2}\left(t+\dfrac{1}{t}\right), \dfrac{b}{2}\left(t-\dfrac{1}{t}\right)\right\}$

The tangent at P is

$$\frac{x}{a}(t^2+1) - \frac{y}{b}(t^2-1) = 2t.$$

This meets $\dfrac{x}{a} = \dfrac{y}{b}$ where

$$\frac{x}{a}(t^2+1) - \frac{x}{a}(t^2-1) = 2t$$

i.e. $\dfrac{2x}{a} = 2t$ or $x = at$.

The coordinates of L are (at, bt).

The tangent meets $\dfrac{x}{a} = -\dfrac{y}{b}$ where

$$\frac{x}{a}(t^2+1) + \frac{x}{a}(t^2-1) = 2t$$

i.e. $\dfrac{x}{a}(2t^2) = 2t$ or $x = \dfrac{a}{t}$.

The coordinates of M are $\left(\dfrac{a}{t}, -\dfrac{b}{t}\right)$.

The mid-point of LM is $\left\{\dfrac{a}{2}\left(t+\dfrac{1}{t}\right), \dfrac{b}{2}\left(t-\dfrac{1}{t}\right)\right\}$ or P.

N.B. Since LPM is a straight line, it would be sufficient to prove that the sum of the x-coordinates of L and M is double that of P. There is no need to consider both coordinates and this is a tip for saving time in more complicated examples.

Exercise 26.5

1. Write down the equations of the asymptotes of $x^2 - y^2 = a^2$.

2. What is the angle between the asymptotes of $\dfrac{x^2}{a^2} - \dfrac{y^2}{b^2} = 1$? What is the condition for this to be a right angle?

3. Find the equations of the asymptotes of the hyperbola.
$$4x^2 - 8x - y^2 - 2y = 0.$$
   [*Hint:* first find the centre.]

4. Find the equations of the asymptotes of the hyperbola $x^2 - 9y^2 - 4x + 18y = 6$.

5. Show that the point $\left\{\dfrac{a(1+t^2)}{1-t^2}, \dfrac{2bt}{1-t^2}\right\}$ always lies on the hyperbola $\dfrac{x^2}{a^2} - \dfrac{y^2}{b^2} = 1$.

6. Prove that the product of the lengths of the perpendiculars from any point of a hyperbola to its asymptotes is equal to $\dfrac{b^2}{e^2}$.

7. P is a point on the hyperbola $x^2 - y^2 = a^2$. The tangent at P meets the asymptotes at L and M. Show that $CP = PL = PM$.

8. Find the equations of the asymptotes of the hyperbola $\dfrac{x^2}{a^2} - \dfrac{y^2}{b^2} = k^2$.

9. Find the equation of the hyperbola which passes through the point $(1, 1)$ and has as asymptotes $y = \pm 2x$.

10. Find the centre of the hyperbola which has $y = x + 1$ and $y + x = 2$ as asymptotes.

11. Find the equation of the hyperbola which passes through the origin and has as asymptotes $y = x + 1$ and $y + x = 2$.

12. Find the eccentricity of the hyperbola defined in question 11.

Exercise 26.6: Miscellaneous

1. P and Q are points on the parabola $y^2 = 4ax$ such that POQ is a right angle, O being the vertex of the parabola. The normals at P and Q to the parabola meet at R. Find the locus of R as P and Q move on the parabola.

2. P is any point on the parabola $y^2 = 4ax$. The normal at P to the parabola meets the curve again at Q. Find the locus of the midpoint of PQ.

3. With the data of Q.2, if S is the point on PQ such that $PS:SQ = 3:1$, find the locus of S.

4. P is any point on the parabola $y^2 = 4ax$, origin O, focus S. PO produced meets the directrix of the parabola in the point Q. Prove that SQ is parallel to the tangent at P to the parabola.

5. PQ is any chord of P is any point on the parabola $y^2 = 4ax$. The straight line through P parallel to a given straight line meets the curve again in Q. Prove that the normals at P and Q to the parabola always meet on a fixed straight line.

6. By comparing $lx + my + n = 0$ with the equation of the tangent at the point $(at^2, 2at)$ to the parabola $y^2 = 4ax$, find the condition that $lx + my + n = 0$ is a tangent to the parabola.

7. If the normals at the points with parameters p, q and r on the parabola $x = at^2$, $y = 2at$ are concurrent, show that $p + q + r = 0$.

8. P is any point on the rectangular hyperbola $x = ct$, $y = \dfrac{c}{t}$. The coordinates of a focus S of the hyperbola are $(c\sqrt{2}, c\sqrt{2})$ and the equation of the corresponding directrix is $x + y = c\sqrt{2}$. If M is the foot of the perpendicular from P onto the directrix, find the ratio PM:PS.

9. The normal at any point P on the rectangular hyperbola $x = ct$, $y = \dfrac{c}{t}$ meets the curve again at Q. If O is the origin of coordinates, prove that $c^2 PQ = OP^3$.

10. The tangent at a point P on the hyperbola $x = ct$, $y = \dfrac{c}{t}$ meets the coordinate axes in Q and R. PO produced meets the curve again at S. Prove that, as P varies, SQ and SR are always tangents to another rectangular hyperbola $3xy = -c^2$.

11. Find the condition that the straight line $lx + my + n = 0$ is a tangent to the rectangular hyperbola $xy = c^2$.

12. Find the equation of the tangent at the point $(\cos t, \sin t)$ to the circle $x^2 + y^2 = 1$. Hence find the equations of the two tangents to this circle that pass through the point $(3, -1)$.

13. Find the equation of the circle which has the points $(1, 2)$, $(5, 3)$ as the end points of a diameter. Find also the coordinates of the points at which this circle meets the circle $x = 2 \cos t$, $y = 2 \sin t$.

14. Find the equation of the tangent at the point $t = \alpha$ to the cycloid $x = a(t + \sin t)$, $y = a(1 - \cos t)$. Find also the length of the perpendicular from the origin onto this tangent.

15. The tangent at any point P on the astroid $x = \cos^3 t$, $y = \sin^3 t$ meets the coordinate axes in Q and R. Prove that QR is always of unit length.

16. P and Q are points on an ellipse with coordinates $(a \cos \theta, \ b \sin \theta)$, $(a \cos \varphi, \ b \sin \varphi)$ respectively. If P varies, but the direction of PQ is always constant, show that $\theta + \varphi$ is constant.

17. PQ is a chord of the ellipse $x = a \cos \theta$, $y = b \sin \theta$. If the tangent at the point R is always parallel to PQ, show that $\alpha + \beta = 2\gamma$, where α, β and γ are the parameters of P, Q and R respectively.

18. The circle $x^2 + y^2 + 2gx + 2fy + c = 0$ meets the parabola $y^2 = 4ax$ in four points P, Q, R and S. If $P = (ap^2, 2ap)$ and the co-ordinates of the other points are similarly defined, show that $p + q + r + s = 0$.

19. Four points with parameters p, q, r and s lie on the rectangular hyperbola given by $x = ct$, $y = \dfrac{c}{t}$. If the four points are concyclic, show that $pqrs = 1$.

20. From a point P on the hyperbola $\dfrac{x^2}{a^2} - \dfrac{y^2}{b^2} = 1$, the perpendicular is drawn to one of the asymptotes to meet this asymptote at X and the other asymptote at Y. Show that $PX \cdot PY = \dfrac{a^2 b^2}{a^2 - b^2}$.

27 Coordinate Geometry in Three Dimensions

(*The methods of this chapter may be compared with those of Chapter 21*)

Coordinates

To specify the position of a point in a plane using cartesian coordinates requires two axes and two coordinates. To specify a point in space requires three axes and so three coordinates. The axes used in this chapter will be mutually perpendicular, and are conventionally called the axes of x, y and z. They are chosen in such a way that corkscrewing along the axis of z rotates from the x-axis to the y-axis. These axes are called 'right-handed', and shown in Fig. 27.1.

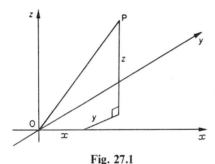

Fig. 27.1

If the coordinates of a point P are (x, y, z), the position vector of P relative to O can be written $x\mathbf{i} + y\mathbf{i} + z\mathbf{k}$ or

$$\begin{pmatrix} x \\ y \\ z \end{pmatrix}.$$

If points P_1, P_2 have coordinates (x_1, y_1, z_1), (x_2, y_2, z_2) respectively, the vector $\overrightarrow{P_1P_2}$ is $(x_2 - x_1)\mathbf{i} + (y_2 - y_1)\mathbf{j} + (z_2 - z_1)\mathbf{k}$.

Point dividing P_1P_2 in a given ratio

Let us find the coordinates (x, y, z) of the point P dividing the join of P_1P_2 in a given ratio $\lambda:\mu$.

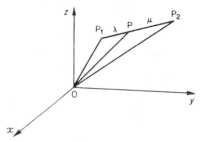

Fig. 27.2

From Fig. 27.2, using vectors
$$\overrightarrow{OP} = \overrightarrow{OP_1} + \overrightarrow{P_1P}$$

$$\therefore \quad x\mathbf{i} + y\mathbf{j} + z\mathbf{k} = x_1\mathbf{i} + y_1\mathbf{j} + z_1\mathbf{k} + \frac{\lambda}{\lambda + \mu}\, \overrightarrow{P_1P_2}$$

$$= x_1\mathbf{i} + y_1\mathbf{j} + z_1\mathbf{k}$$
$$+ \frac{\lambda}{\lambda + \mu}\{(x_2 - x_1)\mathbf{i} + (y_2 - y_1)\mathbf{j} + (z_2 - z_1)\mathbf{k}\}$$

$$= \frac{\mu x_1 + \lambda x_2}{\lambda + \mu}\mathbf{i} + \frac{\mu y_1 + \lambda y_2}{\lambda + \mu}\mathbf{i} + \frac{\mu z_1 + \lambda z_2}{\lambda + \mu}\mathbf{k}.$$

This gives us the coordinates of the point P.

If P is outside the join of $P_1 P_2$, so that P divides $P_1 P_2$ externally, the ratio $\lambda : \mu$ must be negative.

Special case: the mid point of $P_1 P_2$

When $\lambda = \mu$, the coordinates of the midpoint of $P_1 P_2$ are
$$\left(\frac{x_1 + x_2}{2}, \frac{y_1 + y_2}{2}, \frac{z_1 + z_2}{2}\right).$$

Example 1. *Find the points of trisection of the join of*
$$P_1(1, 2, 4) \quad and \quad P_2(2, 3, -1).$$
For the point of trisection nearer P_1, $\lambda = 1$ and $\mu = 2$.
The point is $\left(\dfrac{2 + 2}{3}, \dfrac{4 + 3}{3}, \dfrac{8 - 1}{3}\right)$ or $(\frac{4}{3}, \frac{7}{3}, \frac{7}{3})$.
For the point of trisection nearer P_2, $\lambda = 2$ and $\mu = 1$.
The point is $\left(\dfrac{1 + 4}{3}, \dfrac{2 + 6}{3}, \dfrac{4 - 2}{3}\right)$ or $(\frac{5}{3}, \frac{8}{3}, \frac{2}{3})$.

Example 2. *The points P_1 and P_2 have coordinates $(2, 3, 5)$ and $(3, 4, -2)$ respectively. P is the point on $P_1 P_2$ produced such that $P_2 P = \frac{1}{2} P_1 P_2$. Find the coordinates of P.*

The ratio $\dfrac{P_1P}{PP_2} = -\dfrac{3}{1}$.

Put $\lambda = 3$ and $\mu = -1$.

P is $\left(\dfrac{-2+9}{2}, \dfrac{-3+12}{2}, \dfrac{-5-6}{2}\right)$ or $(\tfrac{7}{2}, \tfrac{9}{2}, -\tfrac{11}{2})$.

Distance between two points

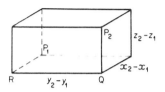

Fig. 27.3

Suppose that P_1 and P_2 have coordinates (x_1, y_1, z_1) and (x_2, y_2, z_2) respectively.

Draw lines through P_1 and P_2 parallel to the axes to form a box as shown in Fig. 27.3. The lengths of the sides of the box are $x_2 - x_1$, $y_2 - y_1$ and $z_2 - z_1$.

$$\begin{aligned}
P_1P_2{}^2 &= P_1Q^2 + QP_2{}^2 \\
&= P_1R^2 + RQ^2 + QP_2{}^2 \\
&= (x_2 - x_1)^2 + (y_2 - y_1)^2 + (z_2 - z_1)^2.
\end{aligned}$$

The length of the line P_1P_2 is

$$\sqrt{\{(x_2 - x_1)^2 + (y_2 - y_1)^2 + (z_2 - z_1)^2\}}.$$

The length of the line joining P to the origin is

$$\sqrt{(x^2 + y^2 + z^2)}.$$

If the point P moves so that its distance from the origin is a constant r, then $x^2 + y^2 + z^2 = r^2$. This equation therefore represents a sphere, centre the origin and radius r.

The equation of the sphere centre (x_1, y_1, z_1) and radius r is

$$(x - x_1)^2 + (y - y_1)^2 + (z - z_1)^2 = r^2.$$

Direction cosines

The direction cosines of the line P_1P_2 are defined as the cosines of the angles which the line P_1P_2 makes with the positive directions of the axes. They are usually denoted by the letters l, m and n. In Fig. 27.3, l is the cosine of the angle between P_1P_2 and P_1R.

$$\therefore \quad l = \frac{x_2 - x_1}{P_1P_2}.$$

Similarly $$m = \frac{y_2 - y_1}{P_1P_2} \quad \text{and} \quad n = \frac{z_2 - z_1}{P_1P_2}.$$

Notice that

$$l^2 + m^2 + n^2 = \frac{(x_2 - x_1)^2 + (y_2 - y_1)^2 + (z_2 - z_1)^2}{P_1P_2{}^2}$$

$$= \frac{P_1P_2{}^2}{P_1P_2{}^2} = 1.$$

$$\therefore \quad l^2 + m^2 + n^2 = 1.$$

Very often the ratios of the direction cosines are sufficient. Notice that these ratios are $x_2 - x_1 : y_2 - y_1 : z_2 - z_1$.

Example. *If the direction cosines of a line are in the ratios 4:5:7, find the actual direction cosines of the line.*

If the actual direction cosines are $4K, 5K, 7K$, since the sum of their squares is unity,

$$K^2(16 + 25 + 49) = 1.$$

$$\therefore \quad K = \frac{1}{\sqrt{90}} = \frac{1}{3\sqrt{10}}.$$

The actual direction cosines are $\dfrac{4}{3\sqrt{10}}, \dfrac{5}{3\sqrt{10}}, \dfrac{7}{3\sqrt{10}}.$

In general, if the direction cosines of a line are proportional to m and n, the actual direction cosines are

$$\frac{l}{\sqrt{(l^2 + m^2 + n^2)}}, \frac{m}{\sqrt{(l^2 + m^2 + n^2)}}, \frac{n}{\sqrt{(l^2 + m^2 + n^2)}}.$$

Coordinates of point distant r from P_1 along P_1P_2

Suppose that P is the point distant r from P_1 along the line P_1P_2.

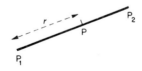

Fig. 27.4

If α is the angle P_1P_2 makes with the x-axis, the increase in the x-coordinate between P_1 and P is $r\cos\alpha$ or rl.

$$\therefore \quad x = x_1 + rl.$$

Similarly $$y = y_1 + rm \quad \text{and} \quad z = z_1 + rm$$

$$\therefore \quad \frac{x - x_1}{l} = \frac{y - y_1}{m} = \frac{z - z_1}{n}.$$

In these equations the actual values of the direction cosines are not necessary. These are, in fact, the equation of the line through P_1 with direction cosines proportional to l, m, n. Notice that in three dimensional work a line is represented by two equations. We shall see later that a plane is represented by a linear equation and a line as the intersection of two planes.

Example. *Find the direction cosines of the line joining* $(1, 2, 2)$ *to* $(2, 3, -1)$.
  The direction cosines are proportional to $(2 - 1, 3 - 2, -1 - 2)$ or to $(1, 1, -3)$.
  The actual direction cosines are $\dfrac{1}{\sqrt{11}}$, $\dfrac{1}{\sqrt{11}}$, $-\dfrac{3}{\sqrt{11}}$.

Angle between two lines

Suppose two lines pass through the origin and have direction cosines (l, m, n) and (l', m', n'). Suppose the angle between them is θ and the angle between parallel lines through a point other than the origin will be the same.
  Any point P_1 on the first line distant r from O is (rl, rm, rn).

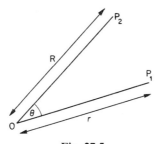

Fig. 27.5

Any point P_2 on the second line distant R from O is (Rl', Rm', Rn').
$$P_1P_2{}^2 = OP_1{}^2 + OP_2{}^2 - 2OP_1 . OP_2 \cos \theta.$$
$$\therefore \quad (Rl' - rl)^2 + (Rm' - rm)^2 + (Rn' - rn)^2$$
$$= r^2l^2 + r^2m^2 + r^2n^2 + R^2l'^2 + R^2m'^2 + R^2n'^2 - 2rR \cos \theta.$$
$$\therefore \quad 2rR \cos = 2Rr(ll' + mm' + nn').$$
$$\therefore \quad \cos \theta = ll' + mm' + nn'.$$

If the direction cosines are only proportional to (l, m, n) and (l', m', n'), then
$$\cos \theta = \frac{ll' + mm' + nn'}{\sqrt{\{(l^2 + m^2 + n^2)(l'^2 + m'^2 + n'^2)\}}}.$$

The condition for two lines to be perpendicular is that $\cos \theta = 0$ or $ll' + mm' + nn' = 0$ and in this equation actual direction cosines need not be used.

For two lines to be parallel their direction cosines must be proportional, i.e.

$$\frac{l}{l'} = \frac{m}{m'} = \frac{n}{n'}.$$

Example 1. *Find the angle between the lines joining the points $(0, 0, 0)$ and $(1, 2, 3)$ and the points $(1, 1, -1)$ and $(2, 2, 1)$.*

The direction cosines of the lines are proportional to $(1, 2, 3)$ and $(1, 1, -2)$.

$$\therefore \quad \cos \theta = \frac{1(1) + 2(1) + 3(-2)}{\sqrt{\{(1^2 + 2^2 + 3^2)(1^2 + 1^2 + 2^2)\}}}$$

$$= -\frac{3}{\sqrt{(14)(6)}} = -\frac{3}{\sqrt{84}}.$$

Example 2. *A line makes angles of $60°$ and $45°$ with the positive directions of the x- and y-axis respectively. Find the angle it makes with the positive direction of the z-axis.*

$$l = \cos 60° = \tfrac{1}{2}; \quad m = \cos 45° = \frac{1}{\sqrt{2}}.$$

$$l^2 + m^2 + n^2 = 1.$$
$$\therefore \quad n^2 = 1 - \tfrac{1}{4} - \tfrac{1}{2} = \tfrac{1}{4}.$$
$$\therefore \quad n = \pm\tfrac{1}{2}.$$
$$\therefore \quad \cos \gamma = \pm\tfrac{1}{2} \quad \text{and} \quad \gamma = 60° \quad \text{or} \quad 120°.$$

Exercise 27.1

1. Find the length of the line joining the points $(1, 3, 2)$ and $(5, 1, 3)$.
2. Find the direction cosines of the line defined in question 1.
3. Find the length of the line joining $(1, 2, 4)$ and $(2, 5, 7)$.
4. Find the direction cosines of the line joining $(1, 2, 5)$ and $(2, 6, 8)$.
5. Show that the points $(3, 3, 3)$ and $(5, 1, 1)$ are equidistant from the origin.
6. Find the mid-point of the line joining $(1, 2, 3)$ to $(3, -6, 1)$.
7. Show that the lines with direction cosines proportional to $(1, 1, 4)$ and $(-3, 3, 0)$ are perpendicular.
8. If $P = (5, 2, 3)$, $Q = (6, 3, 7)$ and $R = (2, 5, 3)$ show that the angle QPR is a right angle.
9. Find the points of trisection of the line joining $(-1, 1, 1)$ and $(2, 4, 5)$.
10. If $P = (2, 1, 1)$, $Q = (3, 2, 2)$ and $R = (4, 3, 2)$, find $\cos$ QPR.
11. Find the equations of the line through the origin which makes angles of $45°$, $60°$ and $60°$ with the axes.
12. Find the equations of the line through the point $(1, 1, 1)$ with direction cosines proportional to $(2, 3, 4)$.

13. Find the ratio in which the yz plane (i.e. $x = 0$) divides the join of $(1, 1, 1)$ and $(2, 3, 4)$.

14. Find the ratio in which the xz plane divides the join of $(2, 1, 1)$ and $(5, 3, 2)$.

15. If α, β, γ are the angles made by a line with the axes, show that $\sin^2 \alpha + \sin^2 \beta + \sin^2 \gamma = 2$.

16. The lengths of the projections of a line on the three axes are 2, 3 and 6. Find the length of the line.

17. Find the direction cosines of a line that makes equal angles with the three axes.

18. If $P = (2, 3, -2)$ and $Q = (1, 4, 2)$, find the angle between OP and OQ.

19. Show that the lines with direction cosines proportional to $(2, 3, 4)$ and $(1, -2, 1)$ are perpendicular.

20. Find the angle between two of the diagonals of a cube.

21. Find the direction cosines of a line given that they are proportional to $(-1, 2, -3)$.

22. Write down the equation of the sphere, centre $(1, 0, 1)$ and radius 1.

23. Find the centre and radius of the sphere
$$x^2 + y^2 + z^2 - 2x - 4y - 2z + 2 = 0.$$

24. Find the centre and radius of the sphere
$$x^2 + y^2 + z^2 - 4x - 2z = 11.$$

25. The line through the origin with direction cosines proportional to $(2, 3, 4)$ meets the sphere $x^2 + y^2 + z^2 = 4x$ at the point P. Find the length of OP.

Equation of a plane

Let us find the equation of a plane which is such that the perpendicular from the origin to the plane is of length p and has direction cosines l, m, n.

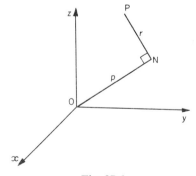

Fig. 27.6

Suppose that N is the foot of the perpendicular in Fig. 27.6 and let P be any point on a line NP which is perpendicular to ON. Since NP is perpendicular to ON, P is any point in the plane whose equation we wish to find. Let NP be of length r and suppose the direction cosines of NP are l', m' and n'.

The coordinates of N are (pl, pm, pn). Since P is at a distance r along a line of direction cosines l', m', n', the coordinates of P are $(pl + rl', pm + rm', pn + rn')$.

$$\therefore \quad x = pl + rl', \quad y = pm + rm', \quad z = pn + rn',$$

where (x, y, z) is any point in the required plane.

Since ON is perpendicular to NP,

$$ll' + mm' + nn' = 0.$$

Substituting for l', m' and n' gives

$$l(x - pl) + m(y - pm) + n(z - pn) = 0,$$

or $$lx + my + nz = p(l^2 + m^2 + n^2).$$

But $l^2 + m^2 + n^2 = 1$ and so the equation of the plane is

$$lx + my + nz = p.$$

The general linear equation $Ax + By + Cz = D$ therefore represents a plane. Provided $D \neq 0$, this equation can always be put in the form $A'x + B'y + C'z = 1$, which shows that the equation of a plane contains three arbitrary constants. A plane may therefore be found to pass through any given three points.

The plane $Ax + By + Cz = D$ may also be expressed as

$$\frac{A}{\sqrt{(A^2 + B^2 + C^2)}} x + \frac{B}{\sqrt{(A^2 + B^2 + C^2)}} y$$
$$+ \frac{C}{\sqrt{(A^2 + B^2 + C^2)}} z = \frac{D}{\sqrt{(A^2 + B^2 + C^2)}}$$

in which the sum of the squares of the coefficients of x, y and z is unity. This corresponds to $lx + my + nz = p$ and so the plane $Ax + By + Cz = D$ is such that the perpendicular from the origin is of length

$$\frac{D}{\sqrt{(A^2 + B^2 + C^2)}}$$

and has direction cosines

$$\frac{A}{\sqrt{(A^2 + B^2 + C^2)}}, \frac{B}{\sqrt{(A^2 + B^2 + C^2)}} \text{ and } \frac{C}{\sqrt{(A^2 + B^2 + C^2)}}.$$

The direction cosines of a normal to the plane

$$Ax + By + Cz = D$$

are therefore proportional to A, B, C.

Example 1. *Find the equation of the plane through the points $(1, 0, 0)$, $(1, 1, 1)$ and $(2, -1, 2)$.*

Suppose the plane is $Ax + By + Cz = 1$. Then by substitution,

$$A = 1;$$
$$A + B + C = 1;$$
$$2A - B + 2C = 1.$$
$$\therefore \quad B + C = 0 \quad \text{and} \quad -B + 2C = -1,$$

from which $\qquad A = 1; \quad B = \tfrac{1}{3}; \quad C = -\tfrac{1}{3}.$

The equation of the plane is $3x + y - z = 3$.

Example 2. *Find the equation of the plane through the point* $(1, 1, 1)$ *such that a normal to it had direction cosines proportional to 1, 2 and 3.*

Any plane such that a normal to it has direction cosines proportional to 1, 2, 3, is $x + 2y + 3z = k$.

Since the plane passes through the point $(1, 1, 1)$,

$$1 + 2 + 3 = k$$

and the equation of the plane is

$$x + 2y + 3z = 6.$$

Angle between two planes

The angle between two planes $Ax + By + Cz = D$ and $A'x + B'y + C'z = D'$ is equal to the angle between normals to the two planes. The direction cosines of the normals are proportional to A, B, C and A', B', C'.

$$\therefore \quad \cos \theta = \frac{AA' + BB' + CC'}{\sqrt{\{(A^2 + B^2 + C^2)(A'^2 + B'^2 + C'^2)\}}}.$$

The planes are perpendicular if $AA' + BB' + CC' = 0$.

Equations of a line

We have already seen that the equations of a line through the point (x', y', z') with direction cosines proportional to l, m, n are

$$\frac{x - x'}{l} = \frac{y - y'}{m} = \frac{z - z'}{n}.$$

A line is the intersection of two planes. Therefore the equations $Ax + By + Cz = D$ and $A'x + B'y + C'z = D'$ are the equations of a line. How do we find the direction cosines of this line?

The line will obviously have the same direction cosines as the intersection of parallel planes through the origin, i.e.

$$Ax + By + Cz = 0$$
and $$A'x + B'y + C'z = 0.$$

Solving these equations for the ratios $x:y:z$ gives

$$\frac{x}{BC' - CB'} = \frac{y}{A'C - C'A} = \frac{z}{AB' - BA'}.$$

The direction cosines of the line are proportional to

$$BC' - CB', \quad A'C - C' - C'A, \quad AB' - BA'.$$

To put the equation of the line in the direction cosine form, all that remains is to find a particular point on the line. This is done by giving one of x, y, z a particular value and solving for the other two variables as is shown in the following example.

Example. *Put in direction cosine form the line*

$$x + y + z = 2, \quad 2x + 3y + 5z = 8.$$

The line is parallel to

$$x + y + z = 0,$$
$$2x + 3y + 5z = 0.$$

From these

$$\frac{x}{2} = \frac{y}{-3} = \frac{z}{1}$$

and so the direction cosines are proportional to 2, -3 and 1. Put $x = 0$ in the original equations.

Then $\qquad\qquad y + z = 2 \quad$ and $\quad 3y + 5z = 8,$

from which $\qquad\qquad y = 1 \quad$ and $\quad z = 1.$

So $(0, 1, 1)$ is a point on the line and the line may be written as

$$\frac{x}{2} = \frac{y-1}{-3} = \frac{z-1}{1}.$$

This is called the **normal form** of the line.

Any point on the line may be put in the form $(2\lambda, 1 - 3\lambda, \lambda + 1)$.

Exercise 27.2

1. Find the equation of the plane which makes intercepts of 1, 2 and 4 on the axes.
2. Find the equation of the plane which passes through the origin and the points $(1, 1, 1)$ and $(2, 3, -1)$.
3. Find the equation of the plane which passes through the points $(1, 0, 0)$, $(1, 1, 1)$ and $(3, 5, -2)$.
4. Find the equations of the line through the origin perpendicular to the plane $3x - y - z = 8$.
5. Find the equations of the line through the point $(1, 2, 1)$ perpendicular to the plane $5x + y + 2z = 7$.
6. Find the length of the perpendicular from the origin to the plane $2x + 3y + 6z = 14$.
7. Find the equation of the plane through the point $(1, 2, 0)$ parallel to $3x + 5y + z = 8$.
8. Find the equation of the plane through the point $(1, 1, 2)$ parallel to the plane $x - y - z = 4$.
9. Find the equation of the plane through the point (x', y', z') parallel to $Ax + By + Cz = D$.

10. If P is the point $(1, 2, 3)$, find the equation of the plane through P perpendicular to OP.

11. Find the equation of the plane through P $(1, 1, -1)$ perpendicular to OP.

12. Find the cosine of the angle between the planes
$$x + y + z = 8 \quad \text{and} \quad x + y - z = 4.$$

13. Find the cosine of the angle between the planes
$$x - y + 2z = 7 \quad \text{and} \quad x + 2y + 3z = 15.$$

14. Find the equation of the plane through the points $(2, 2, 0)$, $(2, 4, 2)$ and $(-4, 4, -2)$.

15. Show that the four points $(0, -3, 0)$, $(6, 3, -3)$, $(3, 3, 3)$ and $(9, 9, 0)$ are coplanar.

16. Find the equation of the plane through the point $(1, 1, 1)$ parallel to $2x + 3y + 6z = 18$. Hence find the length of the perpendicular from $(1, 1, 1)$ to the plane.

17. Find the equation of the plane through the point (x', y', z') parallel to $Ax + By + Cz + D = 0$. Hence find the length of the perpendicular from (x', y', z') to the plane.

18. Put into normal form the line
$$x + y + z = 1, \quad x + 3y + 4z = 4.$$

19. Put into normal form the line
$$x + 2y + z = 4, \quad x + 5y + 6z = 12.$$

20. Find the equation of the plane through the origin normal to the join of $(3, 4, 1)$ and $(2, 2, 2)$.

21. Find the equation of the plane through the point $(1, 1, 1)$ normal to the join of $(1, 2, 3)$ and $(3, 4, 1)$.

22. Prove that the line $\dfrac{x - 3}{2} = \dfrac{y - 4}{3} = \dfrac{z - 5}{4}$ is parallel to the plane $8x + 8y - 10z = 15$.

23. Show that if $L = 0$ and $L' = 0$ are the equations of two planes, $L + kL' = 0$ is the equation of a plane passing through the line of intersection of $L = 0$ and $L' = 0$.

24. Find the equation of the plane passing through $(1, 1, 1)$ and containing the line $\dfrac{x}{2} = \dfrac{y - 1}{3} = \dfrac{z - 2}{4}$.

25. Find the equation of the plane which passes through the origin and contains the line $\dfrac{x - 1}{2} = \dfrac{y - 3}{1} = \dfrac{z - 4}{3}$.

Problems

Geometrical or trigonometrical problems may often be solved by the methods of coordinate geometry as in the following examples.

Example 1. *Show that the lines joining each vertex of a tetrahedron to the centre of gravity of the opposite face are concurrent.*

Suppose the tetrahedron is $P_1P_2P_3P_4$ and let P_1 be (x_1, y_1, z_1) etc. (One vertex could be taken as $(0, 0, 0)$. This eases the algebra but destroys the symmetry.)

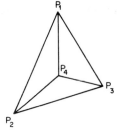

Fig. 27.7

The mid-point of P_2P_4 is

$$\left(\frac{x_2 + x_4}{2}, \frac{y_2 + y_4}{2}, \frac{z_2 + z_4}{2}\right).$$

The centre of gravity of the face $P_2P_3P_4$ is

$$\left(\frac{x_2 + x_3 + x_4}{3}, \frac{y_2 + y_3 + y_4}{3}, \frac{z_2 + z_3 + z_4}{3}\right).$$

Any point on the line joining this point to P_1 (x_1, y_1, z_1) has as its x-coordinate $\dfrac{\frac{1}{3}(x_2 + x_3 + x_4) + \lambda x_1}{1 + \lambda}$.

We must choose λ so that this expression is symmetrical.

Putting $\lambda = \frac{1}{3}$ gives $\dfrac{x_1 + x_2 + x_3 + x_4}{4}$ for the x-coordinate.

All four lines therefore pass through the point $\left(\dfrac{\Sigma x}{4}, \dfrac{\Sigma y}{4}, \dfrac{\Sigma z}{4}\right)$ which is the centre of gravity of the tetrahedron.

Example 2. *ABCD is a face of a cube of which AA', BB', CC' and DD' are parallel edges. Show that the line DB' is perpendicular to the plane ACD'.*

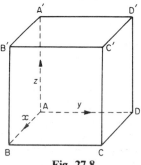

Fig. 27.8

Take AB, AD and AA' to be the axes of x, y and z. Let the side of the cube be of length one unit.

The coordinates of the points D, B', C and D' are:
$$D = (0, 1, 0); \quad B' = (1, 0, 1); \quad C = (1, 1, 0); \quad D' = (0, 1, 1).$$

The direction cosines of DB' are proportional to $1, -1, 1$.

The plane ACD' passes through the origin. Suppose its equation is $Ax + By + Cz = 0$.

Then
$$A + B = 0 \quad \text{and} \quad B + C = 0.$$
$$\therefore \quad A = -B = C.$$

The equation of the plane ACD' is $x - y + z = 0$.

The direction cosines of a normal to this plane are proportional to $1, -1, 1$.
$$\therefore \quad \text{DB' is perpendicular to the plane ACD'.}$$

Exercise 27.3: Miscellaneous

1. Find the coordinates of the point in which the join of $(1, 1, 1)$ and $(2, 3, -1)$ meets the plane $x + y + 2z = 5$.

2. Show that the join of $(2, 1, -2)$ to $(0, 0, 1)$ meets the join of $(3, 2, -4)$ and $(2, 4, -5)$.

3. Find the point of intersection of the lines in question 2.

4. Find the equation of the plane which contains the line $x = 2y = 3z$ and passes through the point $(1, 1, 1)$.

5. Find the equation of the plane which contains the line $x = y = z$ and passes through the point $(2, 3, 1)$.

6. Find the point common to three planes $x + y = 4$, $z - y + 5 = 0$, $x = y + z$.

7. Find the angle between the planes $x + y = A$ and $z - y = B$.

8. Find the angle between the planes $x + y = A$ and $x - y - z = B$.

9. Find the condition that the three planes $x = y + az$, $y = bx + z$ and $z = x + cy$ have a common line.

10. Show that the lines
$$\frac{x - 1}{2} = \frac{y - 2}{3} = \frac{z - 3}{4} \quad \text{and} \quad \frac{x - 2}{1} = \frac{y - 3}{2} = \frac{z - 4}{3}$$
intersect and find their point of intersection.

11. Find the point of intersection of the lines
$$\frac{x - 2}{3} = \frac{y + 1}{2} = \frac{z - 1}{5} \quad \text{and} \quad \frac{x - 3}{2} = 2 - y = z - 5.$$

12. Find the equation of the plane containing the two lines of question 11.

13. ABCD is a face of a cube of which AA', BB', CC' and DD' are parallel edges. Show that the planes AD'C and A'BC' are parallel.

14. Show that the two planes defined in question 13 trisect the line DB'.

15. If two pairs of opposite edges of a tetrahedron are perpendicular prove that the third pair are also perpendicular.

16. If the opposite edges of a tetrahedron are perpendicular, prove that the sums of the squares of opposite edges are equal.

17. Prove that the points $(2, 1, 3)$, $(3, 4, 1)$, $(4, 7, -1)$ and $(1, -2, 5)$ are collinear.

18. If the edges of a rectangular parallelepiped are of lengths, a, b and c find the cosine of the angle between two of the diagonals.

19. Find the ratio in which the plane $Ax + By + Cz + D = 0$ divides the join of (x_1, y_1, z_1) and (x_2, y_2, z_2).

20. Find the normal form of the line $x = ay + 1$, $z = cy + 1$.

21. A is the point $(a, 0, 0)$ and A' the point $(-a, 0, 0)$. Find the equation of the set of points P such that $AP^2 + A'P^2 = 4a^2$.

22. A is the point $(a, 0, 0)$ and A' the point $(-a, 0, 0)$. Find the equation of the set of points P such that APA' is a right angle.

23. Show that the equations of two skew lines may be taken as $y = z = 0$ and $y = kz$, $x = a$.

24. Find the cosine of the angle between the lines
$$\frac{x-1}{2} = \frac{y-1}{3} = \frac{z-2}{6} \quad \text{and} \quad \frac{x-2}{3} = \frac{y-1}{-2} = \frac{z-4}{1}.$$

25. Q is any point of the sphere $x^2 + y^2 + z^2 = 4$ and A is the fixed point $(1, 2, 3)$. If P is the mid-point of AQ, find the equation of the set P.

26. Find the centre and radius of the sphere
$$x^2 + y^2 + z^2 - 2x + 2y = 2.$$

27. Find the centre and radius of the sphere
$$x^2 + y^2 + z^2 - 6x + 4y - 2z = 11.$$

28. Find the centre of the circle which is the intersection of the plane $x + y + z = 3$ with the sphere $x^2 + y^2 + z^2 = 6$.

29. Find the centre of the circle which is the intersection of the plane $x + 2y + 3z = 14$ with the sphere $x^2 + y^2 + z^2 = 20$.

30. Find the coordinates of the other end of the diameter of the sphere $x^2 + y^2 + z^2 - 2x = 1$ through the point $(0, -1, 0)$.

31. Show that the equation $x^2 + y^2 + 2xy - z^2 + 2z - 1 = 0$ represents two planes.

32. Show that the equation $x^2 - y^2 - z^2 - 2yz + 2y + 2z - 1 = 0$ represents two planes.

33. A line is drawn through the point $(1, 1, 1)$ with direction cosines proportional to 2, 3, 1. Find the coordinates of the points in which the line meets the sphere $x^2 + y^2 + z^2 = 5$.

34. A line is drawn through the point $(0, 1, 1)$ with direction cosines proportional to 2, 3, 4. Find the coordinates of the point in which this line meets the plane $x + y + z = 11$.

35. A line is drawn through the point $(1, 2, 1)$ with direction cosines proportional to 1, -1, 1. Find the coordinates of the point in which this line meets the plane $x + 2y + 3z = 12$.

36. Show that the mid-point of the line joining the points $(1, 2, 3)$ and $(3, 1, -2)$ lies on the plane $x + 2y + 2z = 6$.

37. Show that the plane $x = y$ trisects the join of the points (1, 2, 1) and (3, 1, −2).

38. Find the direction cosines of the line $x = y$, $x + y + z = 2$.

39. A tetrahedron is formed by joining the origin to the points A $(a, 0, 0)$, B $(0, b, 0)$ and C $(0, 0, c)$. Find the coordinates of N, the foot of the perpendicular from O to the plane ABC.

40. In question 39, show that CN is perpendicular to AB.

41. In a tetrahedron, show that the lines joining the mid-points of opposite edges meet and bisect each other.

42. Show that the point of intersection in question 41 is the centre of gravity of the tetrahedron.

43. OD is a diagonal of the box whose edges OA, OB and OC lie along the axes and are of lengths, a, b and c. If G is the centre of gravity of the tetrahedron OABC, show that $OG = \frac{1}{4}OD$.

44. Show that the plane $x + y = z - 1$ contains the line

$$\frac{x - 1}{2} = y = \frac{z - 2}{3}.$$

45. Show that the plane $mnx + lny - 2lmz = amn + bln - 2clm$ contains the line

$$\frac{x - a}{l} = \frac{y - b}{m} = \frac{z - c}{n}.$$

Revision Paper E1

1. The points $(-1, -3)$, $(2, 1)$ and $(6, 4)$ are three vertices of a rhombus. Find the coordinates of the fourth vertex, the equations of the diagonals, and the area of the rhombus. (L.)

2. Find the centre and radius of the circle.
$$x^2 + y^2 - 2x - 8y + 8 = 0.$$
Show by calculation that the point $(2.9, 6.4)$ lies outside this circle and calculate the length of the tangent to the circle from this point. (C.)

3. Find the equation of the tangent to the parabola $y^2 = \frac{1}{2}x$ at the point $(2t^2, t)$.
Hence, or otherwise, find the equations of the common tangents of the parabola $y^2 = \frac{1}{2}x$ and the ellipse $5x^2 + 20y^2 = 4$.
Draw a sketch to illustrate the results.

4. The parabola S has the equation $y^2 = 4ax$, and the parabola S' has the equation $y^2 = 16a(x + 4a)$. A variable point of S is P $(at^2, 2at)$, and the origin is O. Verify that one of the points in which the line through P perpendicular to OP meets S' is $(a(t^2 - 4), 4at)$. Show also that this line is normal to S' at this point.

5. Show that, for all values of t, the point P given by $x = at(t + 2)$, $y = 2a(t + 1)$ lies on the curve $y^2 = 4ax + 4a^2$ and find the equation of the normal to the curve at P.
If this normal meets the x-axis at G and N is the foot of the perpendicular from P to the x-axis, prove that $NG = 2a$. (J.M.B.)

6. A variable tangent to the parabola $y^2 = 4ax$ meets the circle $x^2 + y^2 = r^2$ at P and Q. Prove that the locus of the mid-point of PQ is
$$x(x^2 + y^2) + ay^2 = 0. \qquad \text{(J.M.B.)}$$

7. Prove that the centroid of the triangle whose vertices are (x_1, y_1), (x_2, y_2), (x_3, y_3) is the point
$$\left(\frac{x_1 + x_2 + x_3}{3}, \frac{y_1 + y_2 + y_3}{3} \right).$$
P is the point $(at^2, 2at)$ on the curve $y^2 = 4ax$. The tangent and normal at P meet the x-axis at T and G respectively. Show that, as t varies, the centroid of the triangle PGT describe the curve $9y^2 = 12ax - 8a^2$. (L.)

8. Find the equations of the tangent and normal to the rectangular hyperbola $xy = c^2$ at the point P $\left(ct, \dfrac{c}{t} \right)$.
If the tangent at P meets the axes of x and y at X and Y respectively, and the normal at P meets the lines $y = x$, $y = -x$ at L and M respectively, prove that LYMX is a rhombus. (Assume that t^2 is not equal to 1.) (C.)

9. Express in normal form the line $2x + 3y + z = 6$, $3x - y - z = 1$.

10. Find the cosine of the angle between the planes $2x + 3y + z = 6$ and $3x - y - z = 1$.

Revision Paper E2

1. A is the point $(4, 4)$, B is $(5, 3)$ and C is $(6, 0)$. Find the equations of the perpendicular bisectors of AB and BC. Hence calculate the coordinates of the circumcentre and the length of the circumradius of the triangle ABC.
(L.)

2. The perpendicular from the point P $(-1, 2)$ to the straight line $3x + 2y = 14$ meets the line at L and is produced to Q so that $LQ = 2PL$. Find the coordinates of Q.

If R and S are two points on the given straight line such that the areas of the triangles PLR and PLS are each equal numerically to 13 calculate the coordinates of R and S.
(C.)

3. A variable chord through the focus of the parabola $y^2 = 4ax$ cuts the curve at P and Q. The straight line joining P to $(0, 0)$ cuts the straight line joining Q to $(-a, 0)$ at R. Prove that the equation of the locus of R is
$$y^2 + 8x^2 + 4ax = 0.$$
(J.M.B.)

4. Show that the tangent at the point P, with parameter t, on the curve $x = 3t^2$, $y = 2t^3$ has equation $y = tx - t^3$. Prove that this tangent will cut the curve again in the point Q with coordinates $\left(\dfrac{3t^2}{4}, -\dfrac{t^3}{4} \right)$.

Find the coordinates of the possible positions of P if the tangent to the curve at P is the normal to the curve at Q.
(L.)

5. The line joining the points (x_1, y_1) and (x_2, y_2) is a diameter of a circle. Show that the equation of the circle is
$$(x - x_1)(x - x_2) + (y - y_1)(y - y_2) = 0.$$
The points A, B and C have coordinates $(0, -14)$, $(-5, 1)$ and $(7, -5)$ respectively. The perpendicular from A to BC meets BC at L. Find
(i) the equation of the circle through A, L and C,
(ii) the ratio $\triangle ALC : \triangle ALB$.

Find also, the exact value of the tangent of the angle between the line BC and the tangent at L to the circle through A, L and C.
(A.E.B.)

6. Any point P $(at^2, 2at)$ is taken on the parabola $y^2 = 4ax$. S is the focus of the parabola and a straight line through S perpendicular to SP meets the tangent to the parabola at P in the point L. Prove that L lies on the directrix of the parabola.

Show also that the area of the triangle PSL is $\dfrac{a^2(1 + t^2)^2}{2t}$.
(C.)

7. The tangent and normal at the point P $\left(ct, \dfrac{c}{t} \right)$ of the hyperbola $xy = c^2$ meet the x-axis at Q and R. Find the equation of the circle on QR as diameter (which, of course, passes through P).

If this circle passes through the point of the hyperbola with parameter $-t$, prove that $t^4 = \frac{1}{3}$, and that the circle then passes also through the points with parameters $\dfrac{1}{t}$ and $-\dfrac{1}{t}$.
(O.)

8. The curves $y^2 = 4ax$ and $xy = c^2$ intersect at right angles. Prove that (i) $c^4 = 32a^4$ and (ii) if the tangent and normal to either curve at the point of intersection meet the x-axis at T and G, then $TG = 6a$,   (C.)

9. Find the equation of the plane which contains the line $x = 0$, $y + z = 4$ and passes through the point $(1, 1, 1)$.

10. Find the point of intersection of the planes $x + y + z = 4$, $2x + y - z = 1$, $x + 2y + 3z = 9$.

Revision Paper E3

1. The coordinates of the points A, B, C are $(-2, 1)$, $(2, 7)$, $(5, 5)$ respectively. Prove that these points form three corners of a rectangle and that $AB = 2BC$.

   If D is the fourth corner of the rectangle, calculate the distance of C from the diagonal BD. (C.)

2. If the tangent at the point P (at^2, at^3) on the curve $ay^2 = x^3$ meets the curve again at Q, find the coordinates of Q.

   If N is the foot of the perpendicular from P to the x-axis, R is the point where the tangent at P cuts the y-axis, and O is the origin, prove that OQ and RN are equally inclined to the x-axis. (L.)

3. The points P $(2, 3)$, Q $(-11, 8)$, R $(-4, -5)$ are vertices of a parallelogram PQRS which has PR as a diagonal. Find the coordinates of S.

   Determine also the area of the parallelogram. (J.M.B.)

4. Obtain the equation of the locus of a point P which moves so that PB $= 2PA$, where A, B are respectively the points $(1, 0)$ and $(-1, 0)$. Show that the locus is a circle and determine the radius and the coordinates of the centre.

   Verify that $y = \frac{4}{3}$ is a tangent to the circle and determine the equation of the other tangent that passes through the point $(-1, \frac{4}{3})$. (J.M.B.)

5. The coordinates of a point on a curve are given parametrically by $x = a(t - \sin t)$, $y = a(1 - \cos t)$.

   Find $\frac{dy}{dx}$ in terms of t. Deduce that the tangent at the point on the curve where $t = T$ makes an angle $\frac{1}{2}T$ with the y-axis.

   Hence, or otherwise, sketch the curve in the neighbourhood of the origin. (A.E.B.)

6. Given that $a^2 + b^2 = c^2$, show that the two circles $x^2 + y^2 + ax + by = 0$ and $x^2 + y^2 = c^2$ touch each other and find the coordinates of the point of contact.

   Two circles, which pass through the origin and the point $(1, 0)$, touch the circle $x^2 + y^2 = 4$. Find the coordinates of the points of contact. Find also the equation of the circle which has these points of contact as the ends of a diameter. (L.)

7. Find the equation of the tangent to the curve $xy = c^2$ at the point P $\left(cp, \dfrac{c}{p}\right)$.

   Show that the tangents at P and Q $\left(cq, \dfrac{c}{q}\right)$ can never be perpendicular and that when they are parallel the line PQ passes through the origin, O.

   Find the coordinates of R, the point of intersection of the tangents at P and Q, and show that the line RO, produced if necessary, passes through the mid-point of PQ. (A.E.B.)

8. Find the equation of the tangent to the rectangular hyperbola $xy = c^2$ at the point $P\left(ct, \dfrac{c}{t}\right)$.

The tangent at P meets the line $y = x$ at T, and N is the foot of the perpendicular from P to this line. If O is the origin, prove that
$$OT.ON = 2c^2. \qquad \text{(C.)}$$

9. Find the point of intersection of the line $\dfrac{x}{2} = \dfrac{y-1}{3} = \dfrac{z-1}{4}$ with the plane $x + y + z = 11$.

10. Find the equation of the locus of points P equidistant from the points $(1, -1, 1)$ and $(2, 1, 3)$.

Revision Paper E4

1. The gradients of two straight lines are respectively m and m'. If the lines enclose an angle of $45°$, show that either $m' = \dfrac{1 + m}{1 - m}$ or $m' = \dfrac{m - 1}{m + 1}$.

   The two opposite vertices of a square are $(-1, 2)$ and $(5, 6)$. Calculate the coordinates of the other two vertices. (C.)

2. Verify by calculation that the circles
$$x^2 + y^2 + 8x + 4y - 5 = 0$$
and
$$x^2 + y^2 - 7x - 16y + 20 = 0$$
touch one another externally at the point $(-1, 2)$.

   The line joining the centres of the two circles is produced in both directions to meet the circles again at P and Q. Find the equation of the circle having PQ as diameter. (C.)

3. A variable tangent to the hyperbola $xy = a^2$ meets the hyperbola $xy = b^2$ in points P, Q. Prove that the area between the chord PQ and the arc of the second hyperbola is constant. (J.M.B.)

4. Show that, if (x_1, y_1) is a point on the circle $x^2 + y^2 = a^2$, then for any value of k the equation
$$x^2 + y^2 - a^2 + k(xx_1 + yy_1 - a^2) = 0$$
represents a circle which touches the circle $x^2 + y^2 = a^2$ at the point (x_1, y_1).

   Determine the equation of the circle C which passes through the point $(5, 1)$ and touches the circle $x^2 + y^2 = 2$ at the point $(1, 1)$, and find the equations of the tangents to C that are parallel to the line $y = x$. (J.M.B.)

5. Two sides of a parallelogram lie along the lines
$$x - y + 1 = 0, \quad 2x + 3y - 6 = 0$$
and the diagonals meet at the point $(1, \frac{1}{2})$. Find the coordinates of the vertices of the parallelogram and the equations of the other two sides. (L.)

6. Prove that the circle which has as a diameter the common chord of the two circles
$$x^2 + y^2 + 2x - 5y = 0, \quad x^2 + y^2 + 6x - 8y = 1$$
touches the axes of coordinates. (L.)

7. Find the equation of the tangent to the curve $y^2 = x^3$ at the point (t^2, t^3).

   Prove that the maximum number of tangents to the curve which pass through a given point (X, Y) is three.

   If there are three such tangents, prove that the centroid of the triangle formed by their points of contact is $(2X, -2Y)$. (O. & C.)

8. Write down the equation of a parabola whose axis is the x-axis, but whose vertex is not, in general, the origin.

Two parabolas have perpendicular axes and intersect in four points. Prove that the centre of any conic through the four points lies on a certain rectangular hyperbola whose asymptotes are the axes of the two parabolas. (O. & C.)

9. Find the angles of the triangle with vertices $(1, 3, 2)$, $(2, 4, 6)$, $(3, 5, 4)$.

10. Find the equation of the plane passing through the line of intersection of the planes $x + y + z + 2 = 0$, $2x - z + 6 = 0$ and perpendicular to the plane $4x - y - 2z = 12$.

Answers

Exercise 1.1 (p. 3)

1. 6840.
2. $\dfrac{23!}{3!}$.
3. 360.
4. 120.

5. 9.
6. 120.
7. 7999; 800.
8. 480.

9. 120; 72.
10. 72.
11. 3; 1.
12. 3; 1.

13. $^{20}C_{10}$.
14. 15.
15. 1260.
16. 10.

17. 280.
18. 6.
19. 2187; 14.
20. $\left[\dfrac{13!}{6!\,7!}\right]^2$.

Exercise 1.2 (p. 4)

1. 10.
2. 1260.
3. 20.
4. 32.

5. 140.
6. 60; 20.
7. 20 160.
8. $\dfrac{11!}{4}$.

9. $\dfrac{10!}{2}$.
10. 60.
11. 20.
12. None.

13. 560.
14. 35.
15. 56.
16. 4.

17. 15.
18. 5.
19. $12 \times 7!$.
20. 7!.

Exercise 1.3 (p. 7)

1. 159.
2. 29.
3. 20.
4. 127.

5. 64.
6. 71.
7. 12; 60.
8. 13.

9. 28.
10. 5; 5.

Exercise 1.4 (p. 8)

1. 198.
2. 21
3. 24; 12.
4. 24; 64.

5. 23.
6. 120.
7. 8.
8. 34.

9. 60.
10. 800.
11. 3.
12. 10; 15.

13. 105.
14. $\dfrac{(2m)!}{2^m(m!)}$.
15. 15.
16. 7!; 7! 4!; $(4!)^3$.

17. 4.
18. 56.
19. 200.
20. $\frac{1}{2}n(n-3)$. No.

21. 104.
22. 17.

Exercise 2.1 (p. 12)

1. (i) $\frac{799}{7999}$; (ii) $\frac{2667}{7999}$.
3. (i) $\frac{1}{5}$; (ii) $\frac{1}{5}$; (iii) 1.
5. $\frac{1}{3}$.
7. $\frac{1}{3}$.
9. $\frac{11}{20}$.

2. (i) $\frac{1}{2}$; (ii) $\frac{1}{12}$.
4. (i) $\frac{10}{21}$; (ii) $\frac{1}{21}$; (iii) $\frac{10}{21}$.
6. $\frac{3}{5}$.
8. (i) $\frac{1}{81}$; (ii) $\frac{16}{81}$; (iii) $\frac{32}{81}$.
10. $\frac{20}{119}$.

Exercise 2.2 (p. 14)

1. (i) 0.9; (ii) 0.75; (iii) 0.86.
3. (i) 0.8; (ii) 0.6; (iii) 0.8; Yes.
6. (i) 0.3; (ii) 0.7; (iii) 0.43.
8. (i) 1; (ii) 0.875; No.
10. 0.72.

2. (i) 0.45; (ii) 0.75; (iii) 0.56.
4. (i) 0.71; (ii) 1; No.
7. (i) 0.24; (ii) 0.7; (iii) 0.44.
9. (i) 0.75; (ii) 0.86.

Exercise 2.3 (p. 17)

1. 0.77.
2. 0.61.
3. 0.6.
4. (i) 0.33, 0.25, 0.42; (ii) 0.1.
5. 0.2, 0.92.
6. 0.57, 0.31.

Exercise 2.4 (p. 17)

1. $\frac{1}{6}$.
2. $\frac{5}{72}$.
3. $\frac{5}{324}$.
4. $\frac{1}{6}$, $\frac{5}{72}$, $\frac{5}{324}$.
5. 0.51; Second.
6. 0.32.
7. 10^{-7}.
8. (i) $\frac{1}{36}$; (ii) $\frac{25}{36}$; (iii) $\frac{11}{36}$; (iv) $\frac{5}{36}$.
9. (a) $\frac{5}{18}$, $\frac{5}{36}$; (b) $\frac{6}{11}$.
10. $\frac{11}{12}$.
11. (i) 0.57; (ii) 0.38.
13. (i) 0.15; (ii) 0.17; (ii) 0.98.
14. (i) 0.125; (ii) 0.14; (iii) 0.21; (iv) 0.375.
15. (i) 0.042; (ii) 0.375.
16. (i) 0.083; (ii) 0.37.
17. (i) 0.89; (ii) 0.8.
18. (i) 0.105; (ii) 0.395; (iii) 0.11.
19. (i) 0.67; (ii) 0.75; (iii) 0.33.
20. (i) $\frac{1}{6}$.

Exercise 3.1 (p. 24)

1. (i) $\sum_{1}^{n+1} (2r-1)$; (ii) $\sum_{1}^{n} \{a+(r-1)d\}$; (iii) $\sum_{1}^{n} (2r-1)^3$;
   (iv) $\sum_{1}^{n} \tan r\theta$; (v) $\sum_{1}^{n} \tan \{\alpha + (r-1)\beta\}$.

Exercise 3.3 (p. 32)

1. (i) $n(n + 2)$; (ii) $(n + 2)(n + 3)$; (iii) $n(n + 3)$; (iv) $2(3n - 2)(n + 1)$; (v) $2n(n + 1)^2$.

2. (i) $\frac{1}{6}n(n + 1)(2n + 7)$; (ii) 385; (iii) 2485; (iv) 166 650; (v) 1296; (vi) 43 316; (vii) $\frac{1}{6}m(2m + 1)(7m + 1)$; (viii) $\frac{1}{4}m^2(5m + 3)(3m + 1)$; (ix) $\frac{1}{12}n(n + 1)(n + 2)(3n + 5)$; (x) $\frac{1}{12}(n + 1)(n + 2)(n + 3)(3n + 8)$.

3. (i) $\frac{1}{3}n(n + 1)(n + 2)$; (ii) $\frac{4}{3}n(n + 1)(n + 2)$; (iii) $\frac{1}{3}n(n + 1)(4n - 1)$; (iv) $\frac{1}{3}n(4n^2 + 6n - 1)$; (v) $\frac{1}{3}n(n + 1)(4n + 5)$.

4. 14.   5. $\frac{1}{6}n(n - 1)(4n + 1)$.

6. $\frac{1}{12}n(n + 1)(3n^2 + 35n + 106)$.   7. $\frac{1}{3}n(n^2 + 9n + 26)$.

8. 8, 22, 42.   9. 2, 10, 24.

10. 1, 7, 19.   11. $\frac{1}{4}n(n + 1)(n + 4)(n + 5)$.

12. $\frac{1}{12}n(n + 1)(3n^2 + 23n + 46)$.

Exercise 3.4 (p. 34)

5. $\frac{1}{2}n(n + 1)$.   8. $1 + 2^n(n - 1)$.   9. $\frac{1}{4}\{1 + 3^n(2n - 1)\}$.

10. $[\frac{1}{2}n(n + 1)]^2$.   11. $-n(2n + 1)$.   14. $n^2(2n^2 - 1)$.

15. $2r - 1$.   16. $3r^2 - 3r + 1$.

17. $\frac{1}{12}k(k - 1)(3k^2 + 5k + 8)$.

20. $2\dfrac{1 - x^n}{1 - x} + \dfrac{1 - (3x)^n}{1 - 3x}$. 22. $\frac{2}{3}m(m + 1)(2m + 1)$. 23. $2m^2(m + 1)^2$.

26. 3^n, 1.   30. $\dfrac{n(n + 1)(n + 2)}{6}$.

Exercise 4 (p. 42)

1. (a) No; (b) Odd.   2. $y \mapsto \log_2 y$.   3. 2, 2.

4. (a) $\mathbb{R}_+$; (b) $\{y: -1 \leqslant y \leqslant 1\}$; (c) $\{y: -1 \leqslant y \leqslant 1\}$; (d) $\{y: e^{-1} \leqslant y \leqslant e^1\}$.

5. Only (i); (i) $\mathbb{R}$; (ii) $\{y: -1 \leqslant y\}$; (iii) $\{y: 0 < y \leqslant \frac{1}{2}\}$.

6. (i) $f^{-1}: y \mapsto \sqrt{y}$; (ii) $f^{-1}: y \mapsto \sqrt{(y - 1)}$; (iii) $f^{-1}: y \mapsto \sqrt{(y + 1)}$; (iv) If domain is $\{x: x \geqslant 1\}, f^1: y \mapsto 1 + \sqrt{y}$; (v) If domain is $\{x: x \geqslant 1\}, f^{-1}: y \mapsto 1 + \sqrt{(y + 1)}$.

8. $h: x \mapsto 3 \sin x$, $H: x \mapsto \sin 3x$.

If $\left\{x: -\dfrac{\pi}{6} \leqslant x \leqslant \dfrac{\pi}{6}\right\}$, $h^{-1}: y \mapsto \text{inv} \sin \dfrac{y}{3}$, $H^{-1}: y \mapsto \frac{1}{3} \text{inv} \sin y$.

9. $h: x \mapsto \dfrac{\pi}{4} + \cos x$, $H: x \mapsto \cos\left(x + \dfrac{\pi}{4}\right)$.

If $\left\{x: 0 \leqslant x \leqslant \dfrac{3\pi}{4}\right\}$, $h^{-1}: y \mapsto \text{inv} \cos\left(y - \dfrac{\pi}{4}\right)$, $H^{-1}: y \mapsto -\dfrac{\pi}{4} + \text{inv} \cos y$.

10. (i) π; (ii) $\dfrac{\pi}{2}$; (iii) $\dfrac{\pi}{2}$; (iv) $\dfrac{\pi}{2}$; (v) 2π; (vi) $\dfrac{\pi}{2}$.

11. (iv) $\{y: -\sin 1 \leqslant y \leqslant \sin 1\}$, period 2π.

12. 2; even.

13. (ii) even; (iii) odd; (iv) odd, π; (v) even, 2π; (vi) even, 2π.

14. $2\pi, \pi; \pi, 2\pi; \{y: -1 \leqslant y \leqslant 1\}, \{y: -\tan 1 \leqslant y \leqslant \tan 1\}$.

15. (i) onto, bijective; (ii) into, injective; (iii) into, bijective; (iv) into, surjective; (v) onto, surjective; (vi) into.

Exercise 5.1 (p. 50)

1. (i) -1; (ii) 1; (iii) ∞; (iv) 0.   **2.** (i) 1; (ii) 2; (iii) ∞; (iv) 0.

3. $\dfrac{3a}{2}$.   **4.** 0.   **5.** $2\pi r$.   **6.** $4\pi r^2$.   **7.** $\sqrt{e}$.   **8.** e^3.

9. $e^{x/2}$.   **10.** e^{2x}.   **11.** (i) $3\cos 3x$; (ii) $-4\sin 4x$; (iii) $\dfrac{1}{2\sqrt{x}}$.

13. 3.   **14.** 0.   **15.** 1.   **16.** 2.   **17.** 3.   **18.** n.

19. $n-1$.   **20.** $n.2^{n-3}$.

Exercise 5.2 (p. 53)

1. (i) $\frac{2}{3}$; (ii) $\frac{1}{2}$; (iii) $-\sqrt{3}$; (iv) 0; (v) 2; (vi) na^{n-1}; (vii) ∞; (viii) na^{n-2}.

2. (i) 6.083; (ii) 1.002; (iii) 5.013; (iv) 0.099; (v) 2.013; (vi) 0.0003; (vii) 0.0015; (viii) 0.5013.

Exercise 5.3 (p. 53)

1. 12.   **2.** $\frac{3}{2}, \frac{4}{3}$.   **3.** $\frac{3}{2}$.   **4.** 3.   **5.** $2\sec^2 2x$.

6. e^4.   **7.** $e^{\frac{1}{3}}$.   **8.** $15(1+3x)^4$.   **9.** $\frac{3}{4}$.   **10.** $\frac{3}{4}$.

11. $\frac{4}{5}$.   **12.** $\frac{2}{5}$.   **13.** $\dfrac{a}{1-r}$.   **14.** n.   **15.** $\frac{1}{2}$.

16. $-\frac{1}{2}$.   **17.** $\frac{1}{3}$.   **18.** 4.02.   **19.** 1.0003.   **20.** 0.

Exercise 6.1 (p. 59)

1. $n\pi + (-1)^n \dfrac{\pi}{6}$.   **2.** $2n\pi \pm \dfrac{\pi}{4}$.   **3.** $n\pi + \dfrac{\pi}{3}$.

4. $n\pi + (-1)^n \dfrac{\pi}{3}$.   **5.** $2n\pi \pm \dfrac{\pi}{3}$.   **6.** $n\pi + \dfrac{\pi}{6}$.

7. $n\pi + (-1)^{n+1} \dfrac{\pi}{6}$.   **8.** $2n\pi \pm \dfrac{3\pi}{4}$.   **9.** $n\pi - \dfrac{\pi}{3}$.

10. $180n° + (-1)^n 36.9°$.   **11.** $360n° \pm 36.9°$.

12. $180n° + 21.8°$.   **13.** $180n° + (-1)^{n+1} 53.1°$.

14. $360n° \pm 126.9°$.   **15.** $180n° - 26.6°$.

16. $\dfrac{(4n-1)\pi}{2}$ or $\dfrac{(4n+1)\pi}{6}$.   **17.** $\dfrac{(4n+1)\pi}{2}$ or $\dfrac{(4n-1)\pi}{6}$.

18. $\dfrac{(2n+1)\pi}{6}$.

19. $n\pi - \dfrac{\pi}{2}$.

20. $\dfrac{(4n+1)\pi}{2}$ or $\dfrac{(4n-1)\pi}{10}$.

21. $(2n+1)\dfrac{\pi}{2}$.

22. $\dfrac{n\pi}{3}$.

23. $\dfrac{n\pi}{2}$.

24. $\dfrac{(4n-1)\pi}{12}$.

25. $\dfrac{(4n-1)\pi}{8}$.

26. $\dfrac{(2n+1)\pi}{2}$.

27. $\dfrac{(2n+1)\pi}{12}$.

28. $\dfrac{(2n+1)\pi}{4}$.

29. $2n\pi$ or $\dfrac{(2n+1)\pi}{3}$.

30. $\dfrac{(2n+1)\pi}{4}$.

Exercise 6.2 (p. 60)

1. $2n\pi + \dfrac{\pi}{4}$.

2. $2n\pi + \dfrac{\pi}{6}$ or $2n\pi + \dfrac{\pi}{3}$.

3. $360n° + 16.3°$ or $360n° + 90°$.

4. $360n° + 107.1°$ or $360n° + 27.7°$.

5. $360n° + 107°$ or $360n° + 16.8°$.

Exercise 6.3 (p. 62)

1. $n\pi \pm \dfrac{\pi}{3}$.

2. $\dfrac{n\pi}{4}$.

3. $\dfrac{n\pi}{4}$.

4. $n\pi + \dfrac{\pi}{4}$.

5. $n\pi \pm \dfrac{\pi}{6}$.

6. $n\pi \pm \dfrac{\pi}{3}$.

7. $2n\pi \pm \dfrac{\pi}{3}$.

8. $n\pi + (-1)^n \dfrac{\pi}{6}$.

9. $180n° + 45°$ or $180n° - 26.6°$.

10. $n\pi + \dfrac{\pi}{4}$.

Exercise 6.4 (p. 63)

1. $\dfrac{n\pi}{3}$ or $n\pi \pm \dfrac{\pi}{6}$.

2. $(2n+1)\dfrac{\pi}{6}$ or $n\pi \pm \dfrac{\pi}{6}$.

3. $(2n+1)\dfrac{\pi}{6}$ or $\dfrac{n\pi}{2} + (-1)^n \dfrac{\pi}{12}$.

4. $\dfrac{n\pi}{3}$ or $\dfrac{n\pi}{2} + (-1)^n \dfrac{\pi}{12}$.

5. $\dfrac{n\pi}{4}$ or $n\pi \pm \dfrac{\pi}{6}$.

6. $\dfrac{(2n+1)\pi}{8}$ or $\dfrac{n\pi}{2} + (-1)^n \dfrac{\pi}{12}$.

7. $\dfrac{(2n+1)\pi}{8}$ or $n\pi \pm \dfrac{\pi}{6}$.

8. $\dfrac{n\pi}{4}$ or $\dfrac{n\pi}{2} + (-1)^n \dfrac{\pi}{12}$.

9. $4n\pi$ or $\dfrac{(2n+1)\pi}{3}$.

10. $(2n+1)\pi$ or $\dfrac{2n\pi}{3}$.

11. $\dfrac{2n\pi}{3}$.

12. $\dfrac{(2n+1)\pi}{3}$.

13. $\dfrac{n\pi}{3}$.

14. $(2n+1)\dfrac{\pi}{6}$.

15. $\dfrac{n\pi}{3}$.

16. $\dfrac{(2n+1)\pi}{6}$ or $\dfrac{2n\pi}{3}$.

17. $\dfrac{n\pi}{4}$.

18. $\dfrac{(2n+1)\pi}{4}$.

19. $\dfrac{n\pi}{4}$.

20. $\dfrac{(2n+1)\pi}{8}$ or $\dfrac{n\pi}{2}$.

Exercise 6.5 (p. 63)

1. (i) $2n\pi \pm \dfrac{2\pi}{3}$; (ii) $n\pi \pm \dfrac{\pi}{3}$.

2. $2n\pi + \cos^{-1}\frac{1}{3}$.

3. $360n° - 68°$ or $360° + 248°$.

4. $n\pi,\ n\pi \pm \dfrac{\pi}{4}$.

5. $2 - \sqrt{3}$.

6. $\tan\dfrac{\pi}{4}, \tan\dfrac{7\pi}{12}, \tan\dfrac{11\pi}{12}$.

7. $360n° + 140.2°, 360n° + 7.3°$.

8. $(2n+1)\dfrac{\pi}{4}, 2n\pi \pm \dfrac{2\pi}{3}$.

9. $\dfrac{b}{a}$.

10. $\dfrac{a^2 - b^2}{a^2 + b^2}$.

11. $180n° + 100°$.

12. $180n° + 170.3°, 180n° + 28.6°$.

13. $360n° + 53.1°$

14. $360n° + 126.9°$.

15. $n\pi + \dfrac{\pi}{4}$.

16. $2n\pi, 2n\pi + \dfrac{\pi}{2}$.

17. $\tan\theta$ where $\theta = \dfrac{\pi}{16}, \dfrac{5\pi}{16}, \dfrac{9\pi}{16}, \dfrac{13\pi}{16}$.

20. $\dfrac{(4n+1)\pi}{2} \pm (B + C)$.

21. $\dfrac{(4n-1)\pi}{2} \pm (B + C)$.

22. $\tan\theta$ where $\theta = \dfrac{\pi}{24}, \dfrac{5\pi}{24}, \dfrac{13\pi}{24}, \dfrac{17\pi}{24}$.

24. $\dfrac{(4n+1)\pi}{6}$.

25. $\dfrac{(2n+1)\pi}{3}$.

26. $n\pi - \dfrac{\pi}{4}$ or $\dfrac{n\pi}{2} + (-1)^n \dfrac{\pi}{12}$.

27. $n\pi - \dfrac{\pi}{4}, \dfrac{n\pi}{2} + (-1)^n \dfrac{\pi}{12}$.

28. $\dfrac{2n\pi}{3} \pm \alpha;\ \cos\alpha,\ \cos\left(\dfrac{2\pi}{3} + \alpha\right),\ \cos\left(\dfrac{4\pi}{3} + \alpha\right)$.

29. $\dfrac{n\pi}{3} + (-1)^n\alpha;\ \sin\alpha;\ \sin\left(\dfrac{\pi}{3} - \alpha\right),\ \sin\left(\dfrac{4\pi}{3} + \alpha\right)$.

30. $\dfrac{(4n+1)\pi}{16}$.

Revision Paper A.1 (p. 65)

1. $1 + 8x + 28x^2 + 56x^3$; $0.016\,000\,112$.

2. (i) $3p$; (ii) $\dfrac{1}{p}$; (iii) $\dfrac{1}{p} - 1$; (iv) $\dfrac{p}{1 - p}$; (v) $\dfrac{7p}{3(1 - p)}$.

3. $\dfrac{\pi}{6}, \dfrac{5\pi}{6}, \dfrac{3\pi}{2}$.   4. $\{x : 2 < x < 4\}$.

5. 2000.   6. $\frac{4}{3}$.

7. 5; $(x + 2)(2x + 3)$.   8. $6, -5$.

9. (i) -3; (ii) $54 \pm 12\sqrt{19}$.

Revision Paper A.2 (p. 66)

1. $5 - c$; $\frac{1}{2} < c < \frac{9}{2}$.   3. $9, 27$.

4. 2.130.   5. $-\frac{7}{18}$; $1 + 20x + 163x^2$.

6. $a = 27$, $r = \frac{1}{3}$ and $a = 54$, $r = -\frac{1}{3}$.

7. $\sqrt{74}$; $74°$; $\frac{11}{39}$.

8. All pass through $(2, 1, 3)$; (iii) lies in (ii); (i) perpendicular to (ii).

9. $149.2°, 329.2°$.

10. (i) $201°, 339°$; (ii) $30°, 150°, 270°$; (iii) $97°, 217°$.

Revision Paper A.3 (p. 68)

1. 6188.   2. $\frac{1}{45}$.   3. Yes.

4. (i) $n\pi + (-1)^n \dfrac{\pi}{6}$, $n\pi - (-1)^n \sin^{-1}\left(\frac{3}{4}\right)$; (ii) $(2n + 1)\dfrac{\pi}{2}$ or $\dfrac{(4n + 1)\pi}{10}$.

5. $-\frac{405}{16}, \frac{8505}{32}$.   6. 105; 20.

7. $1 + 6x + 9x^2 - 20x^3 - 90x^4$; 1.1234.

8. (i) $45°, 60°, 135°, 225°, 300°, 315°$; (ii) $20.3°, 86°$.

9. 2.

Revision Paper A.4 (p. 69)

1. (i) $\frac{1}{21}$; (ii) $\frac{2}{7}$; (iii) $\frac{4}{9}$; (iv) $\frac{5}{42}$; (v) 1.

2. (i) 0.35; (ii) $\frac{4}{13}$.

3. (i) $0.007\,66$, 0.115; (ii) $\frac{5}{12}$.

5. $\dfrac{n}{m}$.   6. 100, 32.

8. (i) $95.8°, 174.2°, 185.8°, 264.2°$; (ii) $-45°, 135°$.

9. $(4k + 1)\dfrac{\pi}{10}$, $(4k - 1)\dfrac{\pi}{2}$; ± 1, $-\sin\dfrac{3\pi}{10}$; $\frac{1}{4}(\sqrt{5} + 1)$.

10. f neither; g, h even. Period of G is 6π; H not periodic.

Revision Paper A.5 (p. 71)

1. (i) $\frac{2}{3}$; (ii) $\frac{1}{6}$; (iii) $\frac{5}{18}$; (iv) $\frac{1}{4}$; (v) $\frac{2}{5}$.

2. (i) 0.28; (ii) 0.58; (iii) 0.7; (iv) 0.48, not independent.

3. $\dfrac{1}{3}, \dfrac{2}{9}, \dfrac{2^4}{3^5}, \dfrac{2^5}{3^5}$, 75p; $(\frac{2}{3})^4$; 0.177.

5. 0.776.   **6.** 15 600, 26^3, 6300.

10. Only $g^{-1}f$ exists, 0.67.

Exercise 7.1 (p. 77)

(Constants are omitted for brevity.)

1. $\dfrac{3x^2}{x^3 + 1}$.   **2.** $\cot x$.   **3.** $-\cot x$.

4. $\dfrac{nx^{n-1}}{1 + x^n}$.   **5.** $\dfrac{4x + 3}{2x^2 + 3x + 1}$.   **6.** $\dfrac{2}{x}\log_{10} e$.

7. $\dfrac{3}{x}\log_a e$.   **8.** $\dfrac{-3}{1 - x}$.   **9.** $\dfrac{1}{(1 + 2x)}$.

10. $\dfrac{1}{-3(1 - x)}$.   **11.** $\frac{1}{2}\cot x$.   **12.** $-\frac{1}{2}\tan x$.

13. $\dfrac{2x + 1}{2(x^2 + x + 1)}$.   **14.** $\dfrac{b}{a + bx}$.   **15.** $\dfrac{2\ln x}{x}$.

16. $\dfrac{3}{x}(\ln x)^2$.   **17.** $\dfrac{1}{2x\sqrt{\ln x}}$.   **18.** $\dfrac{1}{-x(\ln x)^2}$.

19. $\dfrac{2}{-x(\ln x)^3}$.   **20.** $2\cot x \ln(\sin x)$.   **21.** $\ln(x + 1)$.

22. $\frac{1}{2}\ln(2x + 1)$.   **23.** $\frac{1}{3}\ln(3x + 2)$.   **24.** $-\ln(1 - x)$.

25. $-\frac{1}{3}\ln(1 - 3x)$.   **26.** $\frac{1}{4}\ln(x^4 + 1)$.   **27.** $\frac{1}{2}\ln(x^2 + 2x + 5)$.

28. $\frac{1}{2}\ln \sec 2x$.   **29.** $\ln \sin(x + 1)$.   **30.** $-\frac{1}{2}\ln \sec(1 - 2x)$.

31. $\frac{1}{2}\ln(x^2 + 4x + 1)$.   **32.** $\ln \dfrac{x}{x + 1}$.   **33.** $x - \ln(1 - x)$.

34. $\frac{1}{2}\ln(x^2 + 1)$.   **35.** $\ln(1 + \sin x)$.   **36.** $\ln(\ln x)$.

37. $x - 2\ln(x + 1)$.   **38.** $\ln(1 - \cos x)$.   **39.** $\ln \frac{3}{2}$.

40. $\frac{1}{2}\ln 2$.

Exercise 7.2 (p. 79)

1. $\dfrac{e^{\sqrt{x}}}{2\sqrt{x}}$.   **2.** $-\sin x\, e^{\cos x}$.   **3.** $\sec^2 x\, e^{\tan x}$.

4. $5\,e^{5x}$.   **5.** $(x + 1)\,e^x$.   **6.** $e^x(\sin x + \cos x)$.

7. $\dfrac{e^x(x - 1)}{x^2}$.   **8.** $e^{4x}(4x + 1)$.   **9.** $e^{\sin x}(x \cos x + 1)$.

10. $(x + 2)\,e^x$.   **11.** $4\ln a \cdot a^{4x}$.   **12.** $\cos x \ln a \cdot a^{\sin x}$.

13. $3^x \ln 3$.

14. $-\sin x \cdot 3^{\cos x} \ln 3$.

15. $e^x \left(\ln x + \dfrac{1}{x} \right)$.

16. $e^x (x \ln x + \ln x + 1)$.

17. $-e^{1-x}$.

18. $-b\, e^{a-bx}$.

19. $e^{-x} (2x - x^2)$.

20. $e^{-x} (\cos x - \sin x)$.

21. $\frac{1}{4} e^{4x}$.

22. $\dfrac{1}{a} e^{ax+b}$.

23. $-e^{-x}$.

24. $-e^{1-x}$.

25. $\frac{1}{3} e^{x^3+1}$.

26. $2\, e^{\sqrt{x}}$.

27. $e^{\tan x}$.

28. $\dfrac{4^x}{\ln 4}$.

29. $\dfrac{a^x}{\ln a}$.

30. $-\dfrac{4^{1-x}}{\ln 4}$.

31. $\frac{1}{2} e^{x^2 + 2x}$.

32. x.

33. $\frac{1}{5} e^{5x-3}$.

34. $\frac{1}{2} e^{x^2}$.

35. $-e^{1/x}$.

36. $\frac{1}{2} e^2 (e^2 - 1)$.

37. $\frac{1}{2} e^4 (e^5 - 1)$.

Exercise 7.3 (p. 80)

1. $\dfrac{2}{(x + 1)^2}$.

2. $\dfrac{1}{(x - 1)^{\frac{1}{2}}(x + 1)^{\frac{3}{2}}}$.

3. $\dfrac{4x}{(x^2 + 1)^2}$.

4. $\dfrac{2x}{(x^2 - 1)^{\frac{1}{2}}(x^2 + 1)^{\frac{3}{2}}}$.

5. $\dfrac{x^2 - 6x + 7}{(x - 3)^2}$.

6. $\dfrac{x^2 - 6x + 7}{2(x - 1)^{\frac{1}{2}}(x - 2)^{\frac{1}{2}}(x - 3)^{\frac{3}{2}}}$.

7. $(1 + \ln x)x^x$.

8. $(2 \ln x)x^{\ln x - 1}$.

9. $\left(\ln \ln x + \dfrac{1}{\ln x} \right)(\ln x)^x$.

10. $\left(\dfrac{1}{x} - 1 - \ln x \right)x^{1-x}$.

Exercise 7.4 (p. 81)

1. $\dfrac{1}{e}$.

3. $e^{ax} (a \sin bx + b \cos bx)$.

4. $(1 + x)\{1 + 2 \log (1 + x)\}$.

9. $(\ln \sin x + x \cot x)(\sin x)^x$.

10. $e^{ax} \{(a + b) \cos bx + (a - b) \sin bx\}$.

11. $\dfrac{1}{\sqrt{(x^2 + 1)}}$.

15. $-\ln (\cos x - \sin x)$.

18. 5 minutes.

19. $\dfrac{1}{2} \left(e^2 - \dfrac{1}{e^2} \right)$.

20. 1 or 3.

21. e.

22. $\frac{1}{2}$, $-\frac{1}{2}$; $\frac{1}{2}(\sin x - \cos x)\, e^x$.

23. $\frac{1}{4}(e + 1)$.

24. $\dfrac{(5x + 9)(x + 1)}{(x + 3)^4}$.

25. $\frac{2}{27}$.

26. $(1 + ax + bx \cot x)\, e^{ax} \sin bx$.

27. $c^2 \ln 2$.

28. $x\, e^x$; $(x - 1)\, e^x$.

29. $-2, 2$; $(x^2 - 2x + 2)\, e^x$.

30. $\dfrac{1}{e - 1}$.

Exercise 8.1 (p. 85)

1. $\dfrac{3}{x-3} - \dfrac{3}{x-2}$.

2. $\dfrac{3}{x-3} - \dfrac{2}{x-2}$.

3. $\dfrac{7}{x-3} - \dfrac{5}{x-2}$.

4. $\dfrac{3}{x-2} - \dfrac{2}{x-1}$.

5. $\dfrac{2}{x+1} - \dfrac{1}{x-1}$.

6. $\dfrac{1}{2(x-1)} - \dfrac{2}{x-2} + \dfrac{3}{2(x-3)}$.

7. $\dfrac{-2}{x} + \dfrac{3}{2(x-1)} + \dfrac{1}{2(x+1)}$.

8. $\dfrac{1}{4x} - \dfrac{3}{8(x+2)} + \dfrac{1}{8(x-2)}$.

9. $\dfrac{13}{6(x-2)} + \dfrac{5}{6(x+4)}$.

10. $\dfrac{1}{x+1} - \dfrac{6}{x+2} + \dfrac{6}{x+3}$.

11. $1 - \dfrac{1}{x-1} + \dfrac{4}{x-2}$.

12. $1 - \dfrac{3}{2(x-1)} + \dfrac{13}{2(x-3)}$.

13. $\dfrac{3}{4(2x-3)} - \dfrac{1}{4(2x-1)}$.

14. $\dfrac{1}{2(x-1)} - \dfrac{4}{x-2} + \dfrac{9}{2(x-3)}$.

15. $5 + \dfrac{3}{2x-1} - \dfrac{2}{3x+1}$.

Exercise 8.2 (p. 87)

1. $\dfrac{1}{x} - \dfrac{x-3}{x^2+1}$.

2. $\dfrac{x+4}{5(x^2+4)} - \dfrac{1}{5(x+1)}$.

3. $\dfrac{1}{4x} - \dfrac{x-4}{4(x^2+4)}$.

4. $\dfrac{x+1}{x^2+2} - \dfrac{1}{x+1}$.

5. $\dfrac{x}{x^2+1} - \dfrac{1}{x+2}$.

6. $\dfrac{1}{x} - \dfrac{x}{x^2+x+1}$.

7. $\dfrac{1}{x-1} - \dfrac{x+1}{x^2+2}$.

8. $\dfrac{1}{x-2} - \dfrac{x}{x^2+3}$.

9. $\dfrac{1}{x-1} - \dfrac{x-1}{x^2+x+1}$.

10. $\dfrac{1}{x-1} - \dfrac{x}{x^2-x+1}$.

11. $\dfrac{x+1}{x^2-x+1} - \dfrac{1}{x+1}$.

12. $\dfrac{1}{x-1} - \dfrac{x+2}{x^2+x+1}$.

Exercise 8.3 (p. 90)

1. $\dfrac{1}{x-1} + \dfrac{1}{(x-1)^2}$.

2. $\dfrac{1}{2(x+1)} - \dfrac{1}{2(x-1)} + \dfrac{2}{(x-1)^2}$.

3. $\dfrac{x}{2(x^2+1)} - \dfrac{1}{2(x-1)} + \dfrac{1}{2(x-1)^2}$.

4. $\dfrac{1}{(x-1)^2} + \dfrac{1}{(x-1)^3}$.

5. $\dfrac{1}{8(x+1)} - \dfrac{1}{8(x-1)} + \dfrac{1}{4(x-1)^2} + \dfrac{1}{2(x-1)^3}$.

6. $-\dfrac{1}{9(x+2)} + \dfrac{1}{9(x-1)} - \dfrac{2}{3(x-1)^2}$.

7. $\dfrac{1}{(x-2)^2} + \dfrac{6}{(x-2)^3} + \dfrac{12}{(x-2)^4} + \dfrac{8}{(x-2)^5}$.

8. $\dfrac{3}{4(x-1)} + \dfrac{1}{4(x+1)} - \dfrac{1}{2(x+1)^2}$.

9. $\dfrac{1}{(x+1)^2} - \dfrac{2}{(x+1)^3} + \dfrac{1}{(x+1)^4}$.

10. $\dfrac{1}{4(x-1)} - \dfrac{1}{4(x+1)} + \dfrac{1}{2(x+1)^2} - \dfrac{1}{(x+1)^3}$.

Exercise 8.4 (p. 92)

1. $\ln(x-1) + 2\ln(x-2)$.

2. $\ln(x-1) - \ln(2x-1)$.

3. $x + 2\ln(x-1) - \dfrac{1}{x-1}$.

4. $\tfrac{1}{2}\ln(2x-1) + \tfrac{1}{3}\ln(3x-1)$.

5. $\ln x + \tfrac{1}{2}\ln(2x+1)$.

6. $\tfrac{1}{2}\ln(x^2+1) + \ln(x+1)$.

7. $\tfrac{1}{2}\ln\dfrac{x^2+1}{x^2+2}$.

8. $\ln(x^2-x+1) + 2\ln(x+1)$.

9. $\ln(x-2) - \dfrac{2}{x-2}$.

10. $3\ln\dfrac{x-1}{2x-1}$.

11. $\dfrac{1}{4} - \dfrac{1}{2(n+1)} + \dfrac{1}{2(n+2)}; \tfrac{1}{4}$.

12. $\dfrac{n}{2n+1}; \tfrac{1}{2}$.

13. $\dfrac{3}{4} - \dfrac{1}{2(n+1)} - \dfrac{1}{2(n+1)}; \tfrac{3}{4}$.

14. $\dfrac{n(n+2)}{(n+1)^2}; 1$.

15. $\dfrac{n+1}{n(2n+1)}; 0$.

Exercise 8.5 (p. 93)

1. $-2\ln(1+x) + \tfrac{1}{2}\ln(1-2x) + c$.

2. $\ln\tfrac{6}{5}$.

3. $\ln\tfrac{16}{15}$.

4. $\dfrac{n}{2(3n+2)}$.

5. $\ln\tfrac{4}{3}$.

6. $3\ln\dfrac{x+1}{x+2} + \dfrac{2}{x+1}$.

7. $-\dfrac{3}{(x+1)^2} + \dfrac{4}{(x+1)^3} + \dfrac{3}{(x+2)^2}$.

8. $\dfrac{n(n^2+3n+3)}{(n+1)^3}$.

9. $\dfrac{1}{(y-1)^3} + \dfrac{1}{(y-1)^4}$.

10. $-\dfrac{1}{2(x-1)^2} - \dfrac{1}{3(x-1)^3}$.

11. $\dfrac{1}{12} - \dfrac{1}{8(2n+1)} + \dfrac{1}{8(2n+3)}$.

12. $\tfrac{1}{12}$.

13. $\ln\tfrac{4}{3} - \tfrac{1}{6}$.

14. $\ln (1 - x) - \frac{1}{2} \ln (1 - 2x)$.

15. $\ln \dfrac{x}{x + 1} + \dfrac{1}{x + 1} + \dfrac{1}{2(x + 1)^2}$.

16. $-\dfrac{1}{x} + \frac{1}{2} \ln (1 + x^2)$.

17. $\dfrac{1}{4} - \dfrac{1}{2(n + 1)(n + 2)}$.

18. (i) $\dfrac{x^2}{2} - x + \ln (x + 1)$; (ii) $x - 2 \ln (x + 1)$.

19. $\dfrac{1}{x + 2} + \dfrac{1}{x - 1} + \dfrac{1}{(x - 1)^2}$.

20. $\ln \frac{5}{2} + \frac{1}{2}$.

Exercise 9.1 (p. 96)

1. $2 \tan x \sec^2 x$.

2. $2 \sec^2 x \tan x$.

3. $-\cos \frac{1}{2}x \sin \frac{1}{2}x$.

4. $2 \tan \left(x + \dfrac{\pi}{3}\right) \sec^2 \left(x + \dfrac{\pi}{3}\right)$.

5. $-2 \operatorname{cosec}^2 \left(2x + \dfrac{\pi}{6}\right)$.

6. $\sin x + x \cos x$.

7. $2 \cot 2x$.

8. $2 \cot x$.

9. $2 \cot x \ln \sin x$.

10. $\operatorname{cosec} x$.

11. $-\frac{1}{2} \cot 2x + C$.

12. $-\frac{1}{2} \cot 2x - x + C$.

13. $\frac{1}{4} \ln \sin 4x + C$.

14. $-\cot \left(x + \dfrac{\pi}{3}\right) - x + C$.

15. $\frac{1}{2} \ln \sin \left(2x + \dfrac{\pi}{6}\right) + C$.

16. $\frac{1}{2} \tan^2 x + C$.

17. $\frac{1}{8} \sin^4 2x + C$.

18. $-\frac{1}{2} \cos (x^2) + C$.

19. $\ln (1 - \cos x) + C$.

20. $\frac{1}{4} \ln (1 + 2 \sin 2x) + C$.

Exercise 9.2 (p. 101)

1. (i) $n\pi$, $2n\pi + \dfrac{\pi}{2}$, $2n\pi - \dfrac{\pi}{2}$; (ii) $2n\pi + \dfrac{\pi}{2}$, $2n\pi$, $(2n + 1)\pi$;

(iii) $n\pi$, $n\pi + \dfrac{\pi}{3}$, $n\pi - \dfrac{\pi}{3}$.

2. 0, $\dfrac{\pi}{2}$, $-\dfrac{\pi}{2}$; (ii) $\dfrac{\pi}{2}$, 0, π; (iii) 0, $\dfrac{\pi}{3}$, $-\dfrac{\pi}{3}$.

3. $\dfrac{\pi}{2} - x$.

6. $\frac{2}{9}$.

9. $\frac{56}{33}$.

10. $\dfrac{2\pi}{3}$.

11. $\frac{4}{5}$.

13. $\dfrac{1}{\sqrt{(1 + x^2)}}$.

14. $\dfrac{1 - x^2}{1 + x^2}$.

16. $\frac{5}{3}$.

17. $\dfrac{\pi}{4}$.

18. $\dfrac{2x}{1 - x^2}$.

20. $\dfrac{1}{\sqrt{3}}$.

Exercise 9.3 (p. 104)

1. $\dfrac{3}{\sqrt{(1-9x^2)}}$.

2. $\dfrac{-4}{\sqrt{(1-16x^2)}}$.

3. $\dfrac{5}{1+25x^2}$.

4. $\dfrac{1}{\sqrt{(9-x^2)}}$.

5. $\dfrac{-1}{\sqrt{(16-x^2)}}$.

6. $\dfrac{-5}{1+25x^2}$.

7. $\dfrac{1}{\sqrt{(2x-x^2)}}$.

8. $\dfrac{-1}{\sqrt{(2x-x^2)}}$.

9. $\dfrac{1}{\sqrt{(x(1-x))}}$.

10. $\dfrac{1}{2(x+1)\sqrt{x}}$.

11. $\dfrac{2x}{1+x^4}$.

12. $\dfrac{1}{2+2x+x^2}$.

13. $\dfrac{e^x}{1+e^{2x}}$.

14. $\dfrac{\cos x}{1+\sin^2 x}$.

15. -1.

16. $\dfrac{-1}{1+x^2}$.

17. $\dfrac{-1}{1+x^2}$.

18. $\dfrac{1}{2\sqrt{x(1-x)}}$.

19. $\dfrac{2x}{\sqrt{(1-x^4)}}$.

20. $\dfrac{2\sin^{-1}x}{\sqrt{(1-x^2)}}$.

21. $\sin^{-1}x+\dfrac{x}{\sqrt{(1-x^2)}}$.

22. $\tan^{-1}x+\dfrac{x}{1+x^2}$.

23. $2x\tan^{-1}x+\dfrac{x^2}{1+x^2}$.

24. -1.

25. $\dfrac{2(x^2+2)}{4+x^4}$.

26. $\dfrac{1}{x[1+(\ln x)^2]}$.

27. $\dfrac{1}{\tan^{-1}x(1+x^2)}$.

28. $\dfrac{-1}{\sqrt{(4x-3-x^2)}}$.

29. $\dfrac{1}{2\sqrt{(x-x^2)}}$.

30. $\cos^{-1}(1-x)+\dfrac{x}{\sqrt{(2x-x^2)}}$.

Exercise 9.4 (p. 107)

(Constants of integration are omitted for brevity.)

1. $\frac{1}{2}\tan^{-1}2x$.

2. $\frac{1}{2}\tan^{-1}\left(\dfrac{x}{2}\right)$.

3. $\frac{1}{2}\sin^{-1}2x$.

4. $\sin^{-1}\left(\dfrac{x}{2}\right)$.

5. $\frac{1}{10}\tan^{-1}\dfrac{5x}{2}$.

6. $\frac{1}{5}\sin^{-1}\dfrac{5x}{2}$.

7. $\frac{1}{12}\tan^{-1}\dfrac{4x}{3}$.

8. $\frac{1}{4}\sin^{-1}\dfrac{4x}{3}$.

9. $\sin^{-1}(x-1)$.

10. $\frac{1}{2}\log\dfrac{x}{x+2}$.

11. $\tan^{-1}(x+1)$.

12. $\sin^{-1}\dfrac{x-4}{4}$.

13. $\tan^{-1}(x+2)$.

14. $\tan^{-1}(x+3)$.

15. $\sin^{-1}(x-2)$.

16. $\frac{1}{3}\tan^{-1}(3x+1)$.

17. $\tan^{-1}(x^2)$.

18. $\frac{1}{2}\sin^{-1}(x^2)$.

19. $\frac{1}{3}\sin^{-1}(x^3)$.

20. $\tan^{-1}(\ln x)$.

Exercise 9.5 (p. 107)

1. $\dfrac{\pi}{2}$. 2. $-\sin^{-1}\left(\dfrac{1}{x}\right) + C$. 4. 1.

5. $\sin^{-1}\dfrac{x+2}{3} + C$. 6. $\dfrac{\pi}{4}$. 7. $-\frac{1}{3}$.

8. $\dfrac{\pi^2}{32}$. 9. $\pm\frac{1}{4}$. 11. $\dfrac{\pi}{3}$.

15. $\dfrac{\pi}{4}$. 16. $\dfrac{\pi}{6}$. 17. $\dfrac{\pi}{12}$.

19. $\frac{2}{3}\pi a^2$. 21. $-\dfrac{1}{\sqrt{(1-x^2)}}$. 22. $\dfrac{\pi}{12\sqrt{3}}$.

24. 0. 25. $\dfrac{\pi}{4}$. 26. $-\dfrac{1}{1+x^2}$.

28. $2x\tan^{-1}x$. 29. $\tan^{-1}x$. 30. $\sin^{-1}x$.

Exercise 10.1 (p. 113)

1. (i) $\frac{3}{2}$; (ii) $\frac{5}{4}$; (iii) $\frac{4}{5}$; (iv) $\frac{10}{11}$; (v) $\frac{10}{9}$; (vi) $\frac{8}{3}$; (vii) $10\,\dfrac{10}{99}$; (viii) $\dfrac{10^9}{999}$; (ix) $\frac{3}{5}$; (x) 10.

2. (i) 4; (iii) $\frac{5}{9}$; (iv) $\dfrac{100}{19}$.

3. (i) $1 - 4x + 10x^2 - 20x^3$; (ii) $1 + 4x + 12x^2 + 32x^3$;
   (iii) $1 - 6x + 27x^2 - 108x^3$; (iv) $1 - \frac{1}{2}x - \frac{1}{8}x^2 - \frac{1}{16}x^3$;
   (v) $1 + x + \frac{3}{2}x^2 + \frac{5}{2}x^3$; (vi) $1 + 3x + \frac{3}{2}x^2 - \frac{1}{2}x^3$;
   (vii) $1 - x + \frac{3}{4}x^2 - \frac{1}{2}x^3$; (viii) $1 - x - x^2 - \frac{5}{3}x^3$;
   (ix) $1 + x + \frac{5}{2}x^2 + \frac{15}{2}x^3$; (x) $1 - 2x + 4x^2 - 8x^3$;
   (xi) $\dfrac{1}{2} - \dfrac{x^2}{16} + \dfrac{3}{256}x^4 - \dfrac{5}{2048}x^6$; (xii) $\dfrac{1}{3} - \dfrac{x^2}{9} + \dfrac{x^4}{27} - \dfrac{x^6}{81}$;
   (xiii) $2 + \dfrac{1}{4}x^2 - \dfrac{x^4}{64} + \dfrac{x^6}{512}$; (xiv) $2 + \dfrac{9}{4}x - \dfrac{81}{64}x^2 + \dfrac{729}{512}x^3$;
   (xv) $2 + \dfrac{x}{12} - \dfrac{x^2}{288} + \dfrac{10}{81}\left(\dfrac{x}{8}\right)^3$; (xvi) $x + \frac{1}{2}x^3 - \frac{1}{8}x^5 + \frac{1}{16}x^7$;
   (xvii) $x + 2x^2 + 4x^3 + 8x^4$; (xviii) $x^2 - 3x^3 + 9x^4 - 27x^5$;
   (xix) $1 + nx + \frac{1}{2}n(n+1)x^2 + \frac{1}{6}(n+1)(n+2)x^3$;
   (xx) $1 + nx^2 + \frac{1}{2}n(n+1)x^4 + \frac{1}{6}n(n+1)(n+2)x^6$.

4. (i) $-1 < x < 1$; (ii) $-\frac{1}{2} < x < \frac{1}{2}$; (iii) $-\frac{1}{3} < x < \frac{1}{3}$; (iv) $-1 \leqslant x \leqslant 1$;
   (v) $-\frac{1}{2} \leqslant x < \frac{1}{2}$; (vi) $-\frac{1}{2} \leqslant x \leqslant \frac{1}{2}$; (vii) $-2 < x < 2$;
   (viii) $-\frac{1}{3} \leqslant x \leqslant \frac{1}{3}$; (ix) $-\frac{1}{4} \leqslant x \leqslant \frac{1}{4}$; (x) $-\frac{1}{2} < x < \frac{1}{2}$.

5. (i) $(-1)^r \dfrac{(r+1)(r+2)(r+3)}{6}$; (ii) $2^r(r+1)$; (iii) $(-3)^r(r+1)$;
   (iv) $-\dfrac{(2r-3)!}{r!(r-2)!2^{2r-2}}$; (v) $\left(\dfrac{1}{2}\right)^{r-1}\dfrac{(2r-1)!}{(r-1)!r!}$; (vi) $3\dfrac{(-1)^r(2r-5)!}{2^{r-3}(r-3)!r!}$, $r \geqslant 3$;

(x) $(-2)^r$; (xii) $-\left(\dfrac{-1}{3}\right)^{r/2+1}$ if r even; 0 if r odd;

(xix) $\dfrac{(n+r-1)!}{r!(n-1)!}$; (xx) $\dfrac{1}{k!}\dfrac{(n+k-1)!}{(n-1)!}$ if $n=2k$, $k \in \mathbb{Z}$, 0 if n odd.

6. $-\frac{1}{16}$.   **7.** Only one.

8. (i) $\dfrac{1}{x} - \dfrac{1}{x^2} + \dfrac{1}{x^3}$; (ii) $-\dfrac{1}{8x^3} - \dfrac{3}{16x^4} - \dfrac{3}{16x^5}$; (iii) $\dfrac{1}{9x^2} - \dfrac{2}{27x^3} + \dfrac{1}{27x^4}$;

(iv) $\dfrac{1}{4x^2} - \dfrac{1}{16x^4} + \dfrac{1}{64x^6}$; (v) $\dfrac{1}{x^2} - \dfrac{4}{x^4} + \dfrac{16}{x^6}$.

9. $1 - x + x^3 - x^4$.   **10.** $1 + x - x^3 - x^4$.

11. $-1 - x - \frac{1}{2}x^2$.

Exercise 10.2 (p. 117)

1. (i) $1 + 2x + 2x^2 + \frac{4}{3}x^3$; (ii) $1 - \frac{1}{2}x + \frac{1}{8}x^2 - \frac{1}{48}x^3$;

(iii) $1 + x^2 + \frac{1}{2}x^4 + \frac{1}{6}x^6$; (iv) $2\left(x - \dfrac{x^3}{3!} + \dfrac{x^5}{5!} \cdots\right)$;

(v) $1 + x \ln 3 + \dfrac{x^2(\ln 3)^2}{2!} + \dfrac{x^3(\ln 3)^3}{3!}$;

(vi) $1 - x \ln 2 + \dfrac{x^2(\ln 2)^2}{2!} - \dfrac{x^3(\ln 2)^3}{3!}$;

(vii) $1 - 2 + \dfrac{4}{2!} - \dfrac{8}{3!}$;

(viii) $1 + \dfrac{1}{2} + \dfrac{1}{2!}\left(\dfrac{1}{2}\right)^2 + \dfrac{1}{3!}\left(\dfrac{1}{2}\right)^3$;

(ix) $2\left(1 + \dfrac{1}{2!} + \dfrac{1}{4!} + \dfrac{1}{6!} \cdots\right)$;

(x) $1 + \frac{1}{2}\ln 2 + \dfrac{1}{2!}(\frac{1}{2}\ln 2)^2 + \dfrac{1}{3!}(\frac{1}{2}\ln 2)^3 \ldots$.

2. 0.3679.   **3.** $1 - x + \frac{3}{2}x^2 - \frac{7}{6}x^3$.

4. $\frac{2}{3}$.   **5.** $\dfrac{4\,\mathrm{e}}{3}$.

6. $\mathrm{e}^3\left(1 - x + \dfrac{x^2}{2}\right)$.   **7.** $\frac{1}{6}(\ln 10)^3$.

8. 1.   **9.** 2.

10. $\dfrac{1}{n!} + \dfrac{1}{(n-1)!} + \dfrac{1}{(n-2)!}$.   **11.** $1\frac{1}{2}$.

12. 4, 1.   **13.** $1 - 6x + 10x^2$.

14. $\dfrac{2^n + 1}{n!}$.   **15.** $\dfrac{\mathrm{e}^x}{\mathrm{e}^x - 1}$.

16. $-\frac{3}{2}x + \frac{1}{8}x^2 - \frac{23}{48}x^3$.   **17.** $x - \frac{10}{3}x^3$.

19. $y - \dfrac{y^2}{2} + \dfrac{y^3}{3} - \ldots$; $-1 < y \leqslant 1$.   **20.** $\dfrac{2^r(1-r)}{r!}$.

Exercise 10.3 (p. 121)

1. (i) $1 + 2x + 2x^2$; (ii) $1 + x^2$; (iii) kx; (iv) ax; (v) $1 + \dfrac{x^2}{2}$; (vi) $x^2 - \frac{1}{3}x^4$;

   (vii) $x^2 - \dfrac{x^6}{6}$; (viii) $x + x^2 + \dfrac{x^3}{2}$; (ix) $x + \frac{1}{6}x^3$; (x) $x - \dfrac{x^3}{3}$.

2. (i) $1 - x + x^2$; (ii) $1 - 2x + 4x^2$; (iii) $\dfrac{1}{2} - \dfrac{x}{4} + \dfrac{x^2}{8}$; (iv) $1 - \frac{1}{2}x + \frac{3}{8}x^2$;

   (v) $1 - 6x + 27x^2$.

3. $2x^2$.   4. $1 + x + \dfrac{x^2}{2}$.

6. $\sin x + h \cos x - \dfrac{h^2}{2} \sin x - \dfrac{h^3}{6} \cos x$.

7. $e^x + h e^x + \dfrac{h^2}{2} e^x + \dfrac{h^3}{6} e^x$.

8. $\cos x - h \sin x - \dfrac{h^2}{2} \cos x + \dfrac{h^3}{6} \sin x$.

12. 0.5003.   13. 0.4995.

Exercise 10.4 (p. 124)

1. 1.099.   3. $-\frac{1}{6}$.   4. $-1 - \dfrac{1}{x} \ln (1 - x)$.

5. $x + \frac{1}{2}x^2 + \frac{5}{6}x^3$.

6. If $n = 0$, $\ln 2$ otherwise $-\dfrac{(-2)^{-n}}{n}$.

7. 0.0198.   8. -0.2007.   9. 0.2877.

10. $3x - \dfrac{3x^2}{2} + x^3$.   11. $3x - \frac{5}{2}x^2 + 3x^3$.   12. $-x + \frac{3}{2}x^2 - \frac{1}{3}x^3$.

13. $x + \dfrac{x^2}{2} - \dfrac{2x^3}{3} + \dfrac{x^4}{4}$.   14. 1.   15. 3.

Exercise 10.5 (p. 125)

1. $\dfrac{e^k - 1}{k}$.   2. $\dfrac{\pi}{2k} (e^{2k} - 1)$.

3. $-\frac{1}{6}$.   4. $mx + \dfrac{m^3 x^3}{6}$.

5. $-3x - \frac{5}{2}x^2 - 3x^3$; $-\dfrac{(2^r + 1)}{r}$; $-\frac{1}{2} \leqslant x < \frac{1}{2}$.

6. $mx + \frac{1}{6}m(1 - m^2)x^3$.   7. $4x + 5x^2 + \frac{22}{3}x^3$.

8. $x + x^2 + 2x^3$.   9. $-\dfrac{\alpha^n + \beta^n + \gamma^n}{n}$.

10. 1.099.

12. $x - \dfrac{x^2}{2} + \dfrac{x^3}{6}.$

14. $2x - 4x^2 + \frac{8}{3}x^3.$

17. 2.

20. $\dfrac{2^{n/2}\cos(n\pi/4)}{n!}.$

22. $\frac{1}{5}.$

24. $\frac{2}{3}.$

29. 3.141 60.

11. $x - \frac{7}{2}x^2 + \frac{19}{3}x^3.$

13. $\dfrac{x+1}{x}\log(1+x) - 1.$

15. $-\frac{1}{2}x^2 - \frac{1}{12}x^4.$

19. $x - x^2.$

21. $\frac{1}{2}.$

23. $x^2 - \frac{1}{3}x^4 + \frac{2}{45}x^6.$

27. 1.3956.

30. $1 + x + x^2.$

Exercise 11.4 (p. 139)

1. $(1, 2)$ min.; $(-1, -2)$ max.

2. $(4, 1\frac{1}{2})$ min.

3. $(1, -3)$ min.

4. $(1, 0)$ max; $(\frac{7}{3}, -\frac{32}{27})$ min.

5. $(1, 0)$ pt. inflexion; $(\frac{5}{2}, -\frac{27}{16})$ min.

6. $(-2, 4\,e^{-2})$ max; $(0, 0)$ min.

7. $x = 2n\pi + \dfrac{\pi}{4}$ gives max; $(2n + 1)\pi + \dfrac{\pi}{4}$ gives min.

8. $(0, 0)$ pt. inflexion; $(\frac{3}{4}, -\frac{27}{256})$ min.

9. $(0, 0)$ max; $(\frac{4}{5}, -\frac{256}{3125})$ min.

10. $x = 2n\pi - \dfrac{\pi}{4}$ gives min.; $x = (2n + 1)\pi - \dfrac{\pi}{4}$ gives max.

Exercise 11.5 (p. 142)

1. (a) $y = 4x$; (b) $y = 3x$; (c) $x = 0$; (d) $y + x = 0.$

2. (a) $y = \pm 2x$; (b) $x = 0$; (c) $4y = \pm 3x$; (d) $x^2 + y^2 = 0$; origin is isolated point.

Exercise 11.7 (p. 146)

1. $x > -2.$

2. $x < -2.$

3. $x < -2$ or $x > 2.$

4. $-3 < x < 3.$

5. $x < 1$ or $x > 5.$

6. $-1 < x < 2.$

7. $1 < x < 3.$

8. $x < -1$ or $x > 5.$

9. $x < 3.$

10. $x > 3.$

11. $1 < x < 3.$

12. $x < -1$ or $x > 0.$

13. $0 \leqslant x \leqslant 2$ or $x \geqslant 3.$

14. $x < 0$ or $2 \leqslant x \leqslant 3.$

15. $-5 \leqslant x < 0$ or $x \geqslant 2.$

16. $\frac{1}{2} \leqslant x \leqslant 1$ or $x \geqslant \frac{3}{2}.$

17. $x < \frac{1}{2}$ or $x > 1.$

18. $\frac{1}{2} < x < 1.$

19. $3 < x < 5.$

20. $x < 1$ or $x > 3.$

Exercise 11.8 (p. 147)

4. $-\frac{1}{3}, -3$.
6. $x < 1, 2 < x < 3, x > 4$.
7. $x > 1$.
8. $1 < x < 2$.
9. $x > 3$.
10. $3 < x < 5$.

13. 1 min, $2\,e^{-\frac{1}{2}}$ max.
23. $\dfrac{1}{\sqrt{3}}$ max, $-\dfrac{1}{\sqrt{3}}$ min.

Exercise 12.1 (p. 152)

1. 1.91. **2.** 1.03. **3.** 3.01. **4.** 1.94.
5. 2.04. **6.** 0.91. **7.** 1.046. **8.** 0.80.
9. 1.260 **10.** 1.328. **11.** 2.095. **12.** 1.382
13. 1.146, -1.841. **14.** 1.114, 2.773. **15.** 4.405.

Exercise 12.2 (p. 155)

1. 2.09. **2.** 2.89, $-0.125, -2.76$. **3.** 2.24.
4. 2.05, 0.594, no further roots. **5.** 0.567
6. $x_{r+1} = \ln\left(\dfrac{10}{x_r}\right)$; 1.74. **7.** 3.91.
8. 1.50. **9.** -1.75. **10.** 0.243.

Exercise 12.3 (p. 159)

1. $\frac{7}{20}, -\frac{3}{8}$. **2.** $\lambda, \frac{1}{2}(1 - 5\lambda)$. **3.** No solutions.
4. 0 or 4, $2\lambda, -5\lambda$ or $\lambda, \frac{1}{2}(8 - 5\lambda)$.
5. $\dfrac{\lambda - 40}{\lambda^2 - 16}, \dfrac{5 - 2\lambda}{\lambda^2 - 16}$.
6. 1, -1, 2, three planes meeting in a point.
7. No solutions, three planes meeting only in pairs.
8. $\lambda, 7 - 4\lambda, 3\lambda - 6$, three planes meeting in a straight line.
9. No solution, two parallel planes.
10. $x = 1 - \lambda - 3\mu, y = \lambda, z = \mu$, three coincident planes.
11. No solution, two parallel planes.
12. $(\lambda, 1 - \lambda, 0)$, two coincident planes.
13. $a = 1, (-2 - 9\lambda, 1 + 2\lambda, 2 + 5\lambda), a = 2, (2 - 9\lambda, 2\lambda, 5\lambda)$.
14. (i) $(\frac{1}{5}, \frac{3}{5}, \frac{2}{5})$; three planes meeting in a point.
   (ii) $(\frac{1}{5}, \lambda + \frac{1}{5}, \lambda)$; three planes meeting in a line.
   (iii) no solution; planes form a prism.
15. $a = -1, (3\lambda, 4\lambda, -9\lambda); a = 3, (\lambda, 0, \lambda)$.

Exercise 12.4 (p. 160)

1. $1\frac{2}{7}$; 1.421. 2. 1.44. 3. 1.44.
4. $x_{r+1} = \frac{1}{4}(1 - x_r^3)$; 0.236. 5. 0.236.
6. 1.896. 7. 0.842; 0.779. 8. ± 2.19, ± 0.459.
9. 3.146, 3.146. 10. 4.02. 12. 4.93.
13. 2.03. 14. 1.17. 18. 3.01.
19. 1.92. 20. 6; 1.43. 21. 1.26.
22. 0.818. 23. $f'(x) = 0$ at $x = \pm 1$; 0.35 is a root.
24. $y = 3z$. 25. $x = -\frac{1}{2}$, $y = 3(z - \frac{1}{2})$.
26. (i) $x = 2$, $y = -3$, $z = 4$; (ii) $z = 1 - y = x + 2$; (iii) Equations are inconsistent.
28. (i) 1; (ii) 3; (iii) 1. 29. All roots lie between 6 and -5.
30. (i) $k = 4$; (ii) No real k; (iii) No real k; (iv) $k = 2$.

Revision Paper B1 (p. 163)

1. 0, 1, 2, 3, 4.
2. $1 - 6x + 24x^2 - 80x^3$, $|x| < \frac{1}{2}$, 8.500×10^{-6}.
3. 2, $1 < x < 2$ or $4 < x$.
4. 3.065.
6. (i) $\dfrac{x + 1}{2(x^2 + x + 1)} - \dfrac{x - 1}{2(x^2 - x + 1)}$;
   (ii) $1 - x + x^3 - x^4 + x^6 - x^7 \ldots$
7. (a) $1 - \dfrac{x}{\sqrt{(1 - x^2)}} \sin^{-1} x$; (b) $\dfrac{2 \tan x \sec^2 x}{\tan^2 x - 1}$; (c) $x^x(1 + \ln x)$.
10. $\dfrac{4}{x - 1} - \dfrac{6}{2x - 1}$.

Revision Paper B2 (p. 165)

1. (i) $\dfrac{2(x^2 + x - 5)}{(2x + 1)^2}$, (ii) $13 \cos 3x\, e^{2x}$, (iii) $-\dfrac{1}{\sqrt{(x^2 - a^2)}}$.
2. $x^x(1 + \ln x) + (\ln x)^x \left[\ln(\ln x) + \dfrac{1}{\ln x} \right]$.
3. $(\ln \frac{1}{2}, 2)$; $\left(\frac{1}{2} \ln \frac{1}{2}, \dfrac{8}{3\sqrt{2}} \right)$. 4. 98.5.
5. (i) $x > \frac{1}{2}$ or $x < -3$; (ii) $1 < x < 2$; (iii) $x > 3$ or $-1 < x < 0$.
6. $\alpha = -\frac{7}{3}$, $x = -\dfrac{17}{27} - \dfrac{k}{3}$, $y = \dfrac{22}{27} - \dfrac{4k}{3}$, $z = k$,
   $\alpha = 2$, $x = \dfrac{1}{3} - \dfrac{k}{3}$, $y = \dfrac{1}{3} - \dfrac{4k}{3}$, $z = k$.
7. 2.06.
8. $9x^2 \sin^{-1} x$.

Revision Paper B3 (p. 167)

1. (a) (i) $x < -6$ or $-2 < x < \frac{2}{3}$; (ii) $1 \leqslant x \leqslant 3$; (b) (i) 1; (ii) $-\sqrt{2}$.

2. 0.290.

3. $x^x(1 + \ln x) + \dfrac{1}{x^2}(1 - \ln x)x^{1/x}$.

5. (i) $\dfrac{2}{x - 3} - \dfrac{1}{x - 2}$, (ii) $\dfrac{1}{x - 2} - \dfrac{1}{x - 3} + \dfrac{2}{(x - 3)^2}$,

(iii) $\dfrac{1}{5(x - 2)} - \dfrac{x - 3}{5(x^2 + 1)}$.

6. $(-2, 5, 4)$; -6, $(-1, 1, 1)$, $(-t, t, t)$; $(1, 2, 1)$, $(2 - t, 1 + t, t)$.

7. (a) $2^{n+1} + n^2 - 2$; (b) -2, -1, $\frac{73}{74}$.

9. $e^{-\pi}$.

Revision Paper B4 (p. 169)

2. $x = -\frac{4}{3}$, $y = \frac{4}{3}$ or $x = \frac{4}{3}$, $y = 4$.

4. (a) (i) $-\dfrac{5}{(1 + 2x)^2}$, (ii) $6\left(x^4 - \dfrac{1}{x^2}\right)^2\left(2x^3 + \dfrac{1}{x^3}\right)$, (iii) $-\operatorname{cosec} x$.

5. (i) $\dfrac{3}{3x - 1} - \dfrac{1}{x + 1} + \dfrac{1}{(x + 1)^2}$; $n(-1)^n - 3^{n+1}$;

(ii) $1 - \frac{1}{3000} - \frac{1}{9} . 10^{-6}$; 3.332222.

7. $1, -3$.   **8.** $\frac{1}{8}$.   **9.** 2.65.

10. $\dfrac{1}{e}$. Two, none.

Revision Paper B5 (p. 171)

1. $3, 1, \lambda, -1 - \lambda$.   **2.** (a) $x < -1$ or $3 < x < 5$.

6. (i) $\ln 2$; (ii) $\frac{1}{2}(e^x + e^{-x})$.

7. (i) $(r + 1)(2r + 1)$; (ii) $\dfrac{1}{x - 2} - \dfrac{1}{x + 1} + \dfrac{2}{(x + 1)^2}$;

$\frac{1}{2} - 3\frac{1}{4}x + 4\frac{7}{8}x^2 - 7\frac{1}{16}x^3$, $-1 < x < 1$.

8. $32x^5 + 240x^4 + 720^3 + 1080x^2 + 810x + 243$,

$8x^3 - 36x^2 + 54x - 27$, 768.

9. (i) $\dfrac{\cos \sqrt{x}}{2\sqrt{x}}$; (ii) $\dfrac{\cos x}{2\sqrt{\sin x}}$; (iii) $(2 \ln 10)10^{2x}$.

10. (iii) 2.094.

Exercise 13.2 (p. 176)

1. $\operatorname{sech}^2 x$.

2. $-\operatorname{sech} x \tanh x$.

3. $-\operatorname{cosech} x \coth x$.

4. $-\operatorname{cosech}^2 x$.

5. $5 \cosh 5x$.

5. $4 \sinh 4x$.

7. $2 \sinh x \cosh x$.

8. $\sinh 2x + 2x \cosh 2x$.

9. $\sinh x + \cosh x$.

10. $\cosh x - \sinh x$.

11. $\coth x$.

12. $\tanh x$.

13. $9 \sinh^2 3x \cosh 3x$.

14. $4 \cosh 2x \sinh 2x$.

15. $4 \cosh x \sinh x$.

16. $\ln \cosh x$.

17. $\ln \sinh x$.

18. $\frac{1}{3} \cosh 3x$.

19. $\frac{1}{4} \sinh 4x$.

20. $\frac{1}{2} \ln \cosh 2x$.

21. $\frac{1}{5} \ln \sinh 5x$.

22. $\sinh x + \cosh x$.

23. $\cosh x - \sinh x$.

24. $\frac{1}{2} \sinh^2 x$.

25. $\frac{1}{2}x + \frac{1}{4} \sinh 2x$.

26. $\dfrac{(e-1)^2}{2}$.

27. $\dfrac{e^2 - 1}{2e}$

28. $\ln \dfrac{e^2 + 1}{2e}$.

29. $\dfrac{1}{2} \ln \dfrac{e^2 + 1}{2e}$.

30. $e - 1$.

Exercise 13.3 (p. 181)

1. $\dfrac{1}{\sqrt{(x^2 + 2x + 2)}}$.

2. $\dfrac{2}{\sqrt{(4x^2 - 1)}}$.

3. $\dfrac{3}{\sqrt{(9x^2 + 1)}}$.

4. $\dfrac{1}{\sqrt{(x^2 + 2x)}}$.

5. $\dfrac{2}{\sqrt{(4x^2 + 4x + 2)}}$.

6. $\dfrac{1}{\sqrt{(x^2 + x)}}$.

7. $\sinh^{-1} x + \dfrac{x}{\sqrt{(x^2 + 1)}}$.

8. $2x \cosh^{-1} x + \dfrac{x^2}{\sqrt{(x^2 - 1)}}$.

9. $-\dfrac{1}{x\sqrt{(x^2 + 1)}}$.

10. $-\dfrac{1}{x\sqrt{(1 - x^2)}}$.

11. $\dfrac{1}{2\sqrt{x(x + 1)}}$.

12. $\dfrac{1}{2\sqrt{x(x - 1)}}$.

13. $\frac{1}{2} \sinh^{-1} 2x$.

14. $\frac{1}{2} \cosh^{-1} 2x$.

15. $\sinh^{-1} (x + 2)$.

16. $\cosh^{-1} (x + 2)$.

17. $\sinh^{-1} (x + 3)$.

18. $\cosh^{-1} (x + 3)$.

19. $\sinh^{-1} (x + 4)$.

20. $\cosh^{-1} (x + 4)$.

21. $\ln \dfrac{2 + \sqrt{5}}{1 + \sqrt{2}}$.

22. $\ln \dfrac{3 + \sqrt{8}}{2 + \sqrt{3}}$.

23. $\ln \dfrac{2 + \sqrt{5}}{1 + \sqrt{2}}$.

24. $\ln (2 + \sqrt{3})$.

25. $\frac{1}{2} \ln (2 + \sqrt{5})$.

26. $\frac{1}{2} \ln \dfrac{6 + \sqrt{35}}{4 + \sqrt{15}}$.

27. $\ln \dfrac{3 + \sqrt{10}}{2 + \sqrt{5}}$.

28. $\ln \dfrac{3 + \sqrt{8}}{2 + \sqrt{3}}$.

29. $\frac{1}{2} \ln \dfrac{5 + \sqrt{26}}{3 + \sqrt{10}}$.

30. $\frac{1}{2} \ln \dfrac{5 + \sqrt{24}}{3 + \sqrt{8}}$.

Exercise 13.4 (p. 182)

1. $x \sinh x - \cosh x$.   **2.** $x \cosh x - \sinh x$.   **3.** $x + \dfrac{x^2}{2} + \dfrac{x^3}{3}$.

4. $\frac{1}{2} \operatorname{sech} x$.   **5.** $\ln \dfrac{1 + \sqrt{10}}{3}$.   **6.** $\operatorname{sech} x$.

7. $-\sqrt{3}$.   **8.** $\ln 2$.   **10.** $\cosh nx + \sinh nx$.

11. $\pm \frac{4}{3},\ \pm \frac{4}{5}$.   **12.** $\dfrac{1}{1 - x^2}$.   **13.** $-\dfrac{1}{x \sqrt{(1 - x^2)}}$.

15. $\frac{1}{2} \ln 3$.   **17.** $\pm \frac{5}{4}$.

19. $\frac{1}{2} x \sqrt{(1 + x^2)} + \frac{1}{2} \sinh^{-1} x$.   **20.** $\ln (2 + \sqrt{3})$.

21. $\sinh^{-1} (x - 1)$.   **22.** $\cosh^{-1} (x - 2)$.   **26.** $\frac{3}{4}$.

27. $\frac{5}{3}$.   **28.** $\frac{1}{2}$.   **38.** $\dfrac{2}{1 - x^2}$.

39. $\frac{1}{2} \cosh^{-1} \dfrac{2x + 1}{a}$.   **40.** $\frac{1}{3} \sinh^{-1} \dfrac{3x + 1}{b}$.   **41.** $2 \tan^{-1} (e^x)$.

42. $\ln \dfrac{e^x - 1}{e^x + 1}$.   **46.** $\sqrt{5}$.   **48.** $\frac{1}{4} e^{2x} + \frac{1}{2} x$.

49. $\frac{1}{4} e^{2x} - \frac{1}{2} x$.   **50.** $\frac{1}{4} \sinh 2x + \dfrac{x}{2}$.

Exercise 14.1 (p. 186)

2. $\frac{1}{2} a^2,\ \frac{1}{4} a^4,\ \frac{1}{4} a^4 + \frac{1}{3} a^3$.   **2.** $\frac{1}{2} a^2 + a,\ a^3 + a,\ a^4 + \frac{1}{2} a^2 + a$.

3. 0.0035.

Exercise 14.2 (p. 189)

4. 1.1.   **7.** Overestimates.

Exercise 14.3 (p. 195)

1. $\dfrac{\theta}{2} - \dfrac{\sin 2\theta}{4} + c$.   **2.** $\frac{1}{2} a^2 \sin^{-1} \dfrac{x}{a} + \dfrac{x}{2} \sqrt{(a^2 - x^2)} + c$.

3. $\frac{1}{2} \ln (\sec 2\theta + \tan 2\theta) + c$.   **4.** $\frac{1}{2} \ln (\operatorname{cosec} 2\theta - \cot 2\theta) + c$.

5. $2 \ln \left(\sec \dfrac{x}{2} + \tan \dfrac{x}{2} \right) + c$.   **6.** $2 \ln \left(\operatorname{cosec} \dfrac{x}{2} - \cot \dfrac{x}{2} \right) + c$.

7. $\dfrac{1}{n} \ln (\sec nx + \tan nx) + c.$ **8.** $\dfrac{1}{n} \ln (\operatorname{cosec} nx - \cot nx) + c.$

9. $\dfrac{x}{2} \sqrt{(x^2 - a^2)} - \dfrac{a^2}{2} \cosh^{-1} \dfrac{x}{a} + c.$ **10.** $\ln (\sinh x + 1) + c.$

11. $\tan \dfrac{x}{2} + c.$ **12.** $-\cot \dfrac{x}{2} + c.$

13. $\dfrac{2}{\sqrt{15}} \tan^{-1} \left(\sqrt{\tfrac{5}{3}} \tan \dfrac{x}{2} \right) + c.$

14. $\dfrac{1}{\sqrt{2}} \ln \left\{ \sec \left(x - \dfrac{\pi}{4} \right) + \tan \left(x - \dfrac{\pi}{4} \right) \right\} + c.$

15. $-\cosh^{-1} \left(\dfrac{1}{x} \right) + c.$ **16.** $-\sinh^{-1} \left(\dfrac{1}{x} \right) + c.$

17. $-\sqrt{\left(\dfrac{x + 2}{x} \right)} + c.$ **18.** $\sqrt{\left(\dfrac{x - 2}{x} \right)} + c.$

19. $\dfrac{2}{\sqrt{63}} \tan^{-1} \left(\dfrac{8 \tan \frac{1}{2}x - 1)}{\sqrt{63}} \right) + c.$ **20.** $\ln \left(1 + \tan \dfrac{x}{2} \right) + c.$

21. $\dfrac{\pi}{4}.$ **22.** $\dfrac{\pi}{4}.$ **23.** $\dfrac{\pi}{8}.$

24. $\dfrac{\pi}{8}.$ **25.** $\tfrac{1}{2} \ln 3.$ **26.** $\ln (2 + \sqrt{3}).$

27. $\tfrac{1}{3}a^3.$ **28.** $\cos^{-1} \tfrac{3}{5}.$ **29.** $\sqrt{2}.$

30. $\sqrt{6} - \dfrac{4}{\sqrt{3}}.$ **31.** $\dfrac{\pi}{4}.$ **32.** $\tfrac{2}{3} \tan^{-1} 3.$

33. $\tfrac{1}{3} \ln 2.$ **34.** $\dfrac{\pi}{3}.$ **35.** $\dfrac{\pi}{20}.$

36. $\tfrac{1}{3}.$ **37.** $\dfrac{1}{\sqrt{2}}.$ **38.** $\dfrac{\pi}{2} + 1.$

39. $\tfrac{1}{4} \ln 2.$

Exercise 14.4 (p. 201)

1. $(\sin x - x \cos x) + c.$ **2.** $e^x (x^2 - 2x + 2) + c.$

3. $\dfrac{x^2}{2} \ln x - \dfrac{x^2}{4} + c.$

4. $x^2 \sin x + 2x \cos x - 2 \sin x + c.$

5. $-x^2 \cos x + 2x \sin x + 2 \cos x + c.$

6. $x(\ln x)^2 - 2x \ln x + 2x + c.$ **7.** $x \tan^{-1} x - \tfrac{1}{2} \ln (1 + x^2) + c.$

8. $-e^{-x} (x + 1) + c.$ **9.** $-e^{-x} (x^2 + 2x + 2) + c.$

10. $\dfrac{e^x (\sin x - \cos x)}{2} + c.$ **11.** $-\dfrac{e^{-x} (\sin x + \cos x)}{2} + c.$

12. $\dfrac{e^x (\cos x + \sin x)}{2} + c.$ **13.** $\dfrac{e^{-x} (\sin x - \cos x)}{2} + c.$

14. $\dfrac{e^{ax} (a \cos bx + b \sin bx)}{a^2 + b^2} + c.$

15. $\frac{1}{2} x \sqrt{(x^2 - 1)} - \frac{1}{2} \ln \{x + \sqrt{(x^2 - 1)}\} + c.$

16. $\frac{1}{2} x \sqrt{(x^2 + 4)} + 2 \ln \{x + \sqrt{(x^2 + 4)}\} + c.$

17. $-\frac{1}{2} \operatorname{cosec} x \cot x + \frac{1}{2} \ln (\operatorname{cosec} x - \cot x) + c.$

18. $\dfrac{x^6}{6} \ln x - \dfrac{x^6}{36} + c.$

19. $\dfrac{x^{n+1}}{n+1} \ln x - \dfrac{x^{n+1}}{(n+1)^2} + c.$

20. $-x^3 \cos x + 3x^2 \sin x + 6x \cos x - 6 \sin x + c.$

Exercise 14.5 (p. 205)

1. $\frac{8}{15}.$ **2.** $\dfrac{3\pi}{16}.$ **3.** $1.$ **4.** $\dfrac{5\pi}{32}.$ **5.** $\frac{8}{15}.$ **6.** $\dfrac{\pi}{4}.$

7. $\dfrac{35\pi}{256}.$ **8.** $\dfrac{35\pi}{256}.$ **9.** $0.$ **10.** $\dfrac{3\pi}{8}.$ **11.** $\frac{32}{35}.$ **12.** $\dfrac{5\pi}{16}.$

13. $\frac{16}{15}.$ **14.** $-\frac{8}{15}.$ **15.** $\dfrac{9\pi}{16}.$ **16.** $\frac{16}{15}.$ **17.** $\dfrac{3\pi}{8}.$ **18.** $\dfrac{\pi}{32}.$

19. $\dfrac{\pi}{8}.$ **20.** $\dfrac{3\pi}{32}.$

Exercise 14.6 (p. 206)

1. $\frac{1}{4} \sin^4 x - \frac{1}{6} \sin^6 x + c.$ **2.** $\sin x - \frac{1}{3} \sin^3 x + c.$

3. $-\cos x + \frac{2}{3} \cos^3 x - \dfrac{\cos^5 x}{5} + c.$ **4.** $(m + n)I_{m,n} = (n - 1)I_{m,n-2}.$

5. $\frac{1}{24}.$ **6.** $1.$

7. $\pi - 2, \dfrac{\pi}{96} (\pi^2 + 6).$ **8.** $\dfrac{\pi}{2} - 1.$

9. $\dfrac{\pi^2 + 4}{16}.$ **11.** $\pi.$

13. $\dfrac{\pi}{32}.$ **14.** $\frac{1}{2}.$

15. $1.$ **16.** $\frac{1}{252}.$

17. $\dfrac{\pi}{3}.$ **18.** $\dfrac{e^x (\sin 2x - 2 \cos 2x)}{5} + c.$

19. $\dfrac{x}{2} \sqrt{(4 + x^2)} + 2 \ln (x + \sqrt{(4 + x^2)}) + c.$

20. $\dfrac{e^{2x}}{4} + \dfrac{x}{2}.$

21. $I_n + I_{n-2} = \dfrac{\tan^{n-1} x}{n-1}; \dfrac{\tan^2 x}{2} - \ln \sec x.$

23. $\dfrac{x^4(\ln x)^2}{4} - \dfrac{x^4 \ln x}{8} + \dfrac{x^4}{32}.$

24. $I_n + nI_{n-1} = x^n e^x; e^x (x^5 - 5x^4 + 20x^3 - 60x^2 + 120x - 120) + c.$

25. $I_n + I_{n-2} = -\dfrac{\cot^{n-1} x}{n-1}; -\dfrac{\cot^3 x}{3} + \cot x + x + c.$

26. $\sin (\ln x) + c.$ **28.** $\dfrac{2}{\sqrt{5}} \tan^{-1} \left(\sqrt{5} \tan \dfrac{x}{2} \right) + c.$

29. $\frac{2}{15}.$ **30.** $\dfrac{\pi}{8}.$

31. $\dfrac{\pi^2}{4}; \left(\dfrac{\pi^2 + 4}{4\pi}, 0 \right).$ **32.** $\pi^2 - 4.$

33. $3 \ln 3 - 2 \ln 2 - 1.$

34. $\ln 4 - 1; \left\{ \dfrac{\ln 4 - \frac{3}{4}}{\ln 4 - 1}, \dfrac{(\ln 2)^2 - 2\ln 2 + 1}{\ln 4 - 1} \right\}.$

35. $(2n + 1)I_n = 2na^2 I_{n-1}.$ **36.** $\frac{1}{2} \tan^{-1} \frac{1}{2}.$

37. $\frac{2}{5}(e^\pi - 1).$

38. $\dfrac{x^4}{4} \tan^{-1} x - \dfrac{x^3}{12} + \dfrac{x}{4} - \dfrac{1}{4} \tan^{-1} x + c.$

39. $x \tan x - \ln \sec x + c.$ **40.** $\dfrac{1}{(n+1)(n+2)}.$

41. $\dfrac{\pi}{2}.$ **42.** $x \ln (x^2 - 4) - 2x - 2 \ln \dfrac{x-2}{x+2}.$

43. $\frac{1}{8}(10 - 3\pi).$ **44.** $\dfrac{x^5}{5} (\ln x)^2 - \dfrac{2}{25} x^5 \ln x + \dfrac{2x^5}{125}.$

46. $\dfrac{e^x}{x+2}.$ **47.** $\dfrac{e^{ax}}{2a} + \dfrac{e^{ax} (a \cos 2bx + 2b \sin 2bx)}{2(a^2 + 4b^2)}.$

48. $\frac{16}{315}, \frac{32}{315}.$

Exercise 15.1 (p. 214)

1. $\ln (2 + x) + c.$ **2.** $\frac{1}{2} \ln (1 + 2x) + c.$

3. $x - 2 \ln (2 + x) + c.$ **4.** $\frac{1}{2}x^2 - 2x + 4 \ln (2 + x) + c.$

5. $\frac{1}{2}x^2 + x + \ln (x - 1) + c.$ **6.** $\frac{1}{2} \tan^{-1} (2x) + c.$

7. $\frac{1}{2} \ln (4 + x^2) + c.$ **8.** $x - 2 \tan^{-1} \dfrac{x}{2} + c.$

9. $-\frac{1}{2} \ln (4 - x^2) + c.$ **10.** $\frac{1}{3} \tan^{-1} \dfrac{x}{3} - \frac{1}{2} \ln (9 + x^2) + c.$

11. $\frac{1}{8} \ln (1 + 4x^2) + c.$

12. $\frac{1}{4} \ln \left(\dfrac{1 + 2x}{1 - 2x} \right) + c.$

13. $-\frac{1}{8} \ln (1 - 4x^2) + c.$

14. $-x + \ln \left(\dfrac{2 + x}{2 - x} \right) + c.$

15. $\sin^{-1} \left(\dfrac{x}{2} \right) + c.$

16. $\frac{1}{2} \sin^{-1} (2x) + c.$

17. $\frac{1}{2} \sin^{-1} \left(\dfrac{2x}{3} \right) + c.$

18. $- \sqrt{(4 - x^2)} + c.$

19. $\frac{1}{2} \sin^{-1} x + \frac{1}{2} x \sqrt{(1 - x^2)} + c.$

20. $-\frac{1}{3}(1 - x^2)^{\frac{3}{2}} + c.$

21. $\tan^{-1} (e^x) + c.$

22. $\frac{1}{2} \ln \left(\dfrac{1 + e^x}{1 - e^x} \right) + c.$

23. $\ln (1 + e^x) + c.$

24. $x - \ln (1 + e^x) + c.$

25. $\frac{1}{2} \tan^{-1} (x^2) + c.$

26. $\frac{1}{4} \ln \left(\dfrac{1 + x^2}{1 - x^2} \right) + c.$

27. $\frac{1}{3}x^3 - \frac{1}{2}x^2 + x - \ln (x + 1) + c.$

28. $\ln [x + \sqrt{(x^2 + 4)}] + c.$

29. $\ln [x + \sqrt{(x^2 - 4)}] + c.$

30. $(x^2 - 4)^{\frac{1}{2}} + c.$

31. $x - \ln (x + 2) + c.$

32. $\dfrac{x^2}{2} - 3x + 10 \ln (x + 3) + c.$

33. $\ln \dfrac{x - 2}{x - 1} + c.$

34. $\ln \dfrac{(x - 2)^2}{x - 1} + c.$

35. $\dfrac{x^2}{3} + 3x - \ln (x - 1) + 8 \ln (x - 2) + c.$

36. $\dfrac{1}{\sqrt{5}} \ln \dfrac{2x - 3 - \sqrt{5}}{2x - 3 + \sqrt{5}} + c.$

37. $\frac{1}{2} \ln (x^2 - 3x + 1) + \dfrac{3}{2\sqrt{5}} \ln \dfrac{2x - 3 - \sqrt{5}}{2x - 3 + \sqrt{5}} + c.$

38. $x + \frac{3}{2} \ln (x^2 - 3x + 1) + \dfrac{7}{2\sqrt{5}} \ln \dfrac{2x - 3 - \sqrt{5}}{2x - 3 + \sqrt{5}} + c.$

39. $\ln (x - \frac{3}{2} + \sqrt{(x^2 - 3x + 1)}) + c.$

40. $\sqrt{(x^2 - 3x + 1)} + \frac{3}{2} \ln (x - \frac{3}{2} + \sqrt{(x^2 - 3x + 1)}) + c.$

41. $\sin^{-1} \dfrac{x - 2}{2} + c.$

42. $\frac{1}{4} \ln \dfrac{x}{4 - x} + c.$

43. $\frac{1}{2} \ln (x + \frac{3}{4} + \sqrt{(x^2 + \frac{3}{2}x)}) + c.$

44. $\frac{1}{4} \sqrt{(4x^2 + 6x)} - \frac{3}{8} \ln (x + \frac{3}{4} + \sqrt{(x^2 + \frac{3}{2}x)}) + c.$

45. $\frac{1}{2} \sin^{-1} \dfrac{8x + 1}{\sqrt{17}} + c.$

46. $-\frac{1}{4} \sqrt{(1 - x - 4x^2)} + \frac{7}{16} \sin^{-1} \dfrac{8x + 1}{\sqrt{17}} + c.$

47. $\ln \dfrac{\sqrt{(1 + x^2)} - 1}{x} + c.$

48. $\ln \dfrac{1 - \sqrt{(1 - x^2)}}{x} + c.$

49. $\dfrac{1}{2}\sqrt{\dfrac{x-4}{x}} + c.$

50. $\sqrt{(x^2-1)} - \ln(x + \sqrt{(x^2-1)}) + c.$

Exercise 15.2 (p. 217)

1. $\sin\theta - \frac{1}{3}\sin^3\theta + c.$

2. $-\cos\theta + \frac{1}{3}\cos^3\theta + c.$

3. $-\frac{1}{4}\cos 2\theta + c.$

4. $\frac{1}{3}\sin^3\theta - \frac{1}{5}\sin^5\theta + c.$

5. $\frac{1}{4}\sin^4\theta - \frac{1}{6}\sin^6\theta + c.$

6. $\sec\theta + c.$

7. $\frac{3}{8}\theta + \frac{1}{4}\sin 2\theta + \frac{1}{32}\sin 4\theta + c.$

8. $\frac{3}{8}\theta - \frac{1}{4}\sin 2\theta + \frac{1}{32}\sin 4\theta + c.$

9. $\frac{1}{8}\theta - \frac{1}{32}\sin 4\theta + c.$

10. $-\frac{1}{8}\cos^8\theta + c.$

11. $\frac{2}{3}.$ **12.** $\frac{4}{3}.$ **13.** $\frac{1}{2}.$ **14.** $0.$ **15.** $0.$

16. $\sqrt{2} - 1.$ **17.** $\dfrac{3\pi}{16}.$ **18.** $\dfrac{3\pi}{32} - \dfrac{1}{4}.$ **19.** $\dfrac{\pi}{16}.$ **20.** $0.$

Exercise 15.3 (p. 217)

1. $\dfrac{2}{\sqrt{3}}\tan^{-1}\dfrac{2x+1}{\sqrt{3}} + c.$

2. $\ln\dfrac{x+1}{x} - \dfrac{1}{x} + c.$

4. $\frac{16}{3}.$

5. $\left(\dfrac{3\pi}{16}, \dfrac{1}{5}\right).$

6. $\frac{1}{3}\sin^3\theta - \frac{3}{5}\sin^5\theta + \frac{3}{7}\sin^7\theta - \frac{1}{9}\sin^9\theta + c.$

7. $\frac{16}{315}.$

8. $2 - \dfrac{\pi}{2}.$

9. $\frac{10}{3}.$

10. $-\frac{1}{3}.$

11. $\frac{1}{2}\sin 2\theta,\ \theta,\ \frac{1}{2}\theta + \frac{1}{4}\sin 2\theta,\ \frac{1}{2}\theta - \frac{1}{4}\sin 2\theta + c.$ **12.** $\pi.$

13. $-\sqrt{\dfrac{x+2}{x}} + c.$

14. $2\ln(\sqrt{x} - 1) + c.$

15. $-\sqrt{\dfrac{1-x}{1+x}} + c.$

16. $0.$

17. $\sin^2 t.$

18. $\frac{1}{2}.$

19. $\frac{2}{3}.$

20. $6\pi.$

21. $x - \ln(x+3) + c.$

22. $\frac{1}{2} - \frac{1}{2}\log 2.$

23. $-\frac{1}{2}.$

24. $a^2\left(\dfrac{\pi}{2} - 1\right).$

25. $\dfrac{\pi a^2}{2}.$

26. $\left(\dfrac{\pi}{2}, \dfrac{3}{8}\right).$

27. $\frac{1}{3}(2x+1)^{3/2} + (2x+1)^{1/2} + c.$ **28.** $\pi(\pi - 2).$

29. $\frac{8}{15}.$

30. $\frac{8}{105}.$

Exercise 16.1 (p. 222)

1. $\frac{1}{2}$.   **2.** $\frac{1}{3}$.   **3.** 1.   **4.** $\frac{4}{3}$.

5. 0.   **6.** $\frac{1}{2}$.   **7.** 0.   **8.** $\frac{1}{2}$.

9. 0.   **10.** $\dfrac{2}{\pi}$.   **11.** $\frac{1}{2}$.   **12.** $\frac{1}{2}$.

13. 1, $\frac{4}{3}$.   **14.** 0, 0.   **15.** $\frac{1}{2}$, $\dfrac{4}{\pi}$.

Exercise 16.2 (p. 228)

1. $\frac{3}{4}$ way down.   **2.** $\dfrac{2r}{\pi}$.   **3.** $\frac{1}{2}a\pi$.

4. $\left(\dfrac{2a}{\pi}, \dfrac{2a}{\pi}\right)$.   **5.** $56\pi^2$ cm^3.   **7.** $2\sqrt{2}a$.

8. $\dfrac{20\sqrt{2}\pi a^2}{3}$.   **9.** $\left\{\dfrac{a\sin 2\alpha}{2\alpha}, \dfrac{a(1-\cos 2\alpha)}{2\alpha}\right\}$.

10. $2\pi a^2 \sin 2\alpha$.   **12.** $6a$.   **13.** $\frac{8}{27}\{(\frac{13}{4})^{\frac{3}{2}} - 1\}$.

15. $\frac{12}{5}\pi a^2$.   **16.** $(\frac{2}{3}a, 0)$.   **17.** $\left(0, \dfrac{6}{\pi}\right)$; 8π.

Exercise 16.3 (p. 229)

1. $\frac{1}{2}ka^2$.   **2.** $\frac{2}{3}a$.

3. $\frac{1}{2}r$ from centre.   **4.** $(\frac{2}{3}a, 0)$.

5. $(\frac{5}{7}, 0)$.   **6.** $\dfrac{6h^2 + 8rh + 3r^2}{4(2r + 3h)}$ from base.

7. $\frac{3}{4}a$.   **8.** $4a\sqrt{5} + 2a \ln (2 + \sqrt{5})$.

9. $(\frac{2}{3}a, 0)$.   **10.** $\frac{2}{15}\pi$.

11. $(\frac{5}{8}, 0)$.   **13.** $\frac{4}{3}\pi ab^2$.

14. πka^4.   **15.** $\dfrac{kl}{2}(l + 2)$.

16. $\frac{4}{3}$.   **17.** $\frac{3}{4}\pi$.

20. $4\pi a^2(\pi + 1)$.

Exercise 17.1 (p. 233)

1. $\dfrac{5\sqrt{5}}{2}$.   **2.** $10\sqrt{5}$.   **3.** $5\sqrt{10}$.   **4.** $\dfrac{5\sqrt{5}}{2}$.

5. $\dfrac{3\sqrt{3}}{2}$.   **6.** $\dfrac{5\sqrt{5}}{4}$.   **7.** $\dfrac{5\sqrt{10}}{3}$.   **8.** $\dfrac{13\sqrt{13}}{6}$.

9. $\dfrac{(1601)^{\frac{3}{2}}}{38}$.   **10.** $\dfrac{(1 + e^2)^{\frac{3}{2}}}{e}$.   **11.** $\cosh^2 c$.   **12.** $2a$.

13. $\dfrac{17\sqrt{17}}{18}$.   **14.** $\dfrac{5\sqrt{10}}{3}$.   **15.** $2\sqrt{2}$.   **16.** $\dfrac{5\sqrt{5}}{3}$.

17. 2.   **18.** $\dfrac{13\sqrt{26}}{4}$.   **19.** $2\sqrt{2}$.   **20.** $\dfrac{7\sqrt{7}}{4}$.

Exercise 17.2 (p. 235)

1. $2a$.   **2.** a.   **3.** $\dfrac{(a^2+b^2)^{\frac{3}{2}}}{2\sqrt{2ab}}$.   **4.** $\dfrac{b^2}{a}$.

5. $c\sqrt{2}$.   **6.** 4.   **7.** 16.   **8.** $\dfrac{80\sqrt{10}}{3}$.

9. $4a$.   **10.** 0.   **11.** $\dfrac{5\sqrt{5}}{2}$.   **12.** ∞.

13. $\frac{1}{2}$.   **14.** $\frac{1}{2}$.   **15.** 1.

Exercise 17.3 (p. 239)

1. $\frac{1}{4}$.   **2.** $\frac{1}{6}$.   **3.** $\dfrac{5\sqrt{5}}{2}$.   **4.** ∞.   **5.** 2.   **6.** 2.

7. 1.   **8.** $\frac{1}{2}$.   **9.** $2\sqrt{2}$.   **10.** $\dfrac{5\sqrt{5}}{2}$.   **11.** ∞.   **12.** 1.

13. 0.   **14.** 0.   **15.** 0.   **16.** ∞.   **17.** ∞.   **18.** $\dfrac{5\sqrt{5}}{2}$.

19. $\dfrac{17\sqrt{17}}{2}$.   **20.** $\dfrac{5\sqrt{10}}{3}$.

Exercise 17.4 (p. 239)

1. $\frac{1}{2}$.   **2.** 1.   **3.** 2.

4. $\frac{1}{2}$.   **5.** $\frac{1}{2}a^2$.   **6.** $4a\cos\dfrac{\theta}{2}$.

7. $3a\cos t \sin t$.   **8.** $\dfrac{2}{ab}(ax+by)^{\frac{3}{2}}$.

9. $\dfrac{(a^2\sin^2\theta + b^2\cos^2\theta)^{\frac{3}{2}}}{ab}$.   **10.** $a(\cosh^2\theta + \sinh^2\theta)^{\frac{3}{2}}$.

11. $\dfrac{c(t^4+1)^{\frac{3}{2}}}{2t^3}$.   **13.** $4a\cos\dfrac{\theta}{2}$.   **14.** $c\cosh^2\dfrac{x}{c}$.

16. $\dfrac{\sqrt{x}}{6}(4+9x)^{\frac{3}{2}}$.   **17.** $x^2+y^2=4x$.   **18.** $x^2+y^2=2x+2y$.

19. $x^2+y^2=2x+2y$.   **21.** $(2a+3am^2, -2am^3)$.

22. $2a\sqrt{2}$.   **23.** $\dfrac{1}{2a^2}$.   **24.** $\dfrac{1}{2a^2}$.

25. $\dfrac{a^2}{b}$ and $\dfrac{b^2}{a}$.   **26.** $3(axy)^{\frac{1}{3}}$.   **27.** $\dfrac{a}{2}$.

28. -1.   **29.** $-a$.   **30.** $\sqrt{2}\cosh^2 t$.

Exercise 18.1 (p. 242)

1. 1st.   **2.** 1st.   **3.** 2nd.

4. 2nd.   **5.** 3rd.   **6.** $y = x\dfrac{dy}{dx}$.

7. $\dfrac{d^2y}{dx^2} = 0$.   **8.** $x\left(\dfrac{dy}{dx}\right)^2 - y\dfrac{dy}{dx} + 1 = 0$.

9. $(\sin x - x\cos x)\dfrac{d^2y}{dx^2} = x\sin x\dfrac{dy}{dx} - y\sin x$.

10. $\dfrac{d^2y}{dx^2} = n^2y$.   **11.** $\dfrac{d^2y}{dx^2} = n^2y$.

12. $x\dfrac{d^2y}{dx^2} + \dfrac{dy}{dx} = 0$.   **13.** $\sin^{-1}x\dfrac{dy}{dx} = \dfrac{y}{\sqrt{(1-x^2)}}$.

14. $\tan^{-1}x\dfrac{dy}{dx} = \dfrac{y}{1+x^2}$.   **15.** $\dfrac{d^2y}{dx^2} = \dfrac{dy}{dx}$.

16. $\dfrac{dy}{dx} = y + \dfrac{1}{x} - \ln x$.   **17.** $y\dfrac{d^2y}{dx^2} + \left(\dfrac{dy}{dx}\right)^2 = 1$.

18. $y + 2 = x\dfrac{dy}{dx} - x^2$.   **19.** $(1 + x^2)\dfrac{dy}{dx} = xy$.

20. $y - x\dfrac{dy}{dx} = (1 + x^2)\dfrac{d^2y}{dx^2}$.

Exercise 18.2 (p. 244)

1. $y = \tan(x + A)$.   **2.** $y = \sin(x + A)$.

3. $y(x + A) + 1 = 0$.   **4.** $\ln Ay = -\dfrac{1}{x}$.

5. $3y^2 + 2x^3 = A$.   **6.** $\cos y = \cos x + A$.

7. $e^y - e^x = A$.   **8.** $y = Ax^2$.

9. $y = A(x + 1)$.   **10.** $\dfrac{1}{y} - \dfrac{1}{x} = A$.

11. $y = \tan x$.   **12.** $y = \sin\left(x + \dfrac{\pi}{4}\right)$.

13. $y(x - 2) + 1 = 0$.   **14.** $\ln y + 1 = -\dfrac{1}{x}$.

15. $3y^2 + 2x^3 = 19$.

16. $\cos y = \cos x - 1$.

17. $e^y - e^x = e - 1$.

18. $y = 4x^2$.

19. $y = 2(x + 1)$.

20. $\dfrac{1}{y} - \dfrac{1}{x} = 1$.

Exercise 18.3 (p. 246)

1. $\sin^{-1} \dfrac{y}{x} = \ln x + C$.

2. $y + \sqrt{(x^2 + y^2)} = Kx^2$.

3. $\dfrac{y}{x} = \ln x + C$.

4. $\dfrac{y}{x} = 2 \ln x + C$.

5. $\ln x + \dfrac{x}{y - x} = C$.

6. $\dfrac{y^2}{x^2} = 2 \ln x + C$.

7. $\dfrac{y^2}{2x^2} + \ln y = C$.

8. $\dfrac{y}{x} + \ln y = C$.

9. $\dfrac{y^2}{2x^2} + \dfrac{y}{x} + \ln \dfrac{(y - x)^2}{x} = C$.

10. $\dfrac{x}{y} + \ln x = C$.

11. $\sin^{-1} \dfrac{y}{x} = \ln x + \dfrac{\pi}{2}$.

12. $y + \sqrt{(x^2 + y^2)} = x^2$.

13. $\dfrac{y}{x} = \ln x + 2$.

14. $\dfrac{y}{x} = 2 \ln x + 3$.

15. $\ln x + \dfrac{x}{y - x} = 1$.

16. $\dfrac{y^2}{x^2} = 2 \ln x + 1$.

17. $\dfrac{y^2}{2x^2} + \ln y = 2$.

18. $\dfrac{y}{x} + \ln y = 2 + \ln 2$.

19. $\dfrac{y^2}{2x^2} + \dfrac{y}{x} + \ln \dfrac{(y - x)^2}{x} = 4$.

20. $\dfrac{x}{y} + \ln x = 2$.

Exercise 18.4 (p. 248)

1. $y = x^2 - 2x + 2 + C e^{-x}$.

2. $y e^x = x + C$.

3. $xy = \frac{1}{3}x^3 + C$.

4. $y \sin x - x = C$.

5. $y \sin x + x \cos x - \sin x = C$.

6. $y(1 + x^2) = \tan^{-1} x + C$.

7. $y = \frac{1}{4} e^{2x} + C e^{-2x}$.

8. $y(1 + x^3) = x + C$.

9. $y = \dfrac{x^2}{4} + \dfrac{C}{x^2}$.

10. $y = C(1 + x)^2 - \dfrac{1}{3(1 + x)}$.

11. $y = x^2 - 2x + 2$.

12. $y e^x = x + 1$.

13. $3xy = x^3 - 1$.

14. $x = y \sin x$.

15. $y \sin x + x \cos x = \sin x$.

16. $y(1 + x^2) - 1 = \tan^{-1} x$.

17. $4y = e^{2x}$.

18. $y(1 + x^3) = x + 1$.

19. $y = \dfrac{x^2}{4} + \dfrac{5}{4x^2}$.

20. $y = \frac{2}{3}(1 + x)^2 - \dfrac{1}{3(1 + x)}$.

Exercise 18.5 (p. 254)

1. $y = A e^{3x} + B e^{-3x}$.
2. $y = \frac{3}{2}x^3 + Ax + B$.
3. $y = A \cos 3x + B \sin 3x$.
4. $y = -\frac{3}{2}x^3 + Ax + B$.
5. $y = A e^{3x} + B e^{-3x} - 1$.
6. $y = A \cos 3x + B \sin 3x + 1$.
7. $y = A e^{3x} + B e^{-3x} - x - 2$.
8. $y = A \cos 3x + B \sin 3x + x + 2$.
9. $y = A e^x + B e^{-x} - x$.
10. $y = A \cos x + B \sin x + x$.
11. $A e^x + B e^{-x} - x^2 - 2$.
12. $y = A \cos x + B \sin x + x^2 - 2$.
13. $y = A e^x + B e^{-x} - \frac{1}{5} \cos 2x$.
14. $y = A \cos x + B \sin x - \frac{1}{3} \cos 2x$.
15. $y = A e^x + B e^{-x} - \frac{1}{5} \sin 2x$.
16. $y = A \cos x + B \sin x - \frac{1}{3} \sin 2x$.
17. $y = A e^{2x} + B e^{-2x} - \frac{1}{5}(\cos x + \sin x)$.
18. $y = A \cos 2x + B \sin 2x + \frac{1}{3}(\cos x + \sin x)$.
19. $y = A e^{2x} + B e^{-2x} - \frac{1}{4}x^2 - \frac{1}{4}x - \frac{1}{8}$.
20. $y = A \cos 2x + B \sin 2x + \frac{1}{4}x^2 - \frac{1}{4}x - \frac{1}{8}$.
21. $y = 2x$.
22. $y = 2x + 1$.
23. $y = x$.
24. $y = x - 1$.
25. $y = \frac{1}{3}x^2 + \frac{2}{9}$.
26. $y = \frac{1}{3}x^2 + x + \frac{2}{9}$.
27. $y = \frac{1}{6} \sin x$.
28. $y = \frac{1}{6} \cos x$.
29. $y = \frac{1}{6}(\cos x - \sin x)$.
30. $y = \frac{1}{5}(3 \sin 2x - 2 \cos 2x)$.

Exercise 18.6 (p. 257)

1. $x^2(1 - y) = C(1 + y)$.
2. $y + b = C(x + a)$.
3. $x \tan y = C$.
4. $x \cos y = C$.
5. $y = A \ln x - x + B$.
6. $y = A - \ln(\alpha - ax)$.
7. $(2x - y)^3(2x + y) = C$.
8. $\ln y = \dfrac{x^2}{2y^2} + C$.
9. $y - x^2 = Cx$.
10. $y e^x - x = C$.
11. $y + 1 = C e^{\frac{1}{2}x^2}$.
12. $C(x + 2) = e^{\frac{1}{2}y^2}$.
13. $ax^2 + 2hxy + by^2 + 2gx + 2fy + C = 0$.
14. $x^2 y = \frac{1}{4}x^4 + C$.
15. $y = Ax + B - \frac{1}{4} \sin 2x$.
16. $y = A e^{3x} + B e^{-3x}$.
17. $y = Ax^2 + B$.
18. $y = A \log x + B$.
19. $y = A e^{3x} + B$.
20. $y = \frac{1}{3}(2x + A)^{\frac{3}{2}} + B$.
21. $y = A \sin 2x + B \cos 2x$.
22. $y = A \log x + \frac{1}{4}x^2 + B$.
23. $y = A e^{2x} + B e^{-2x} + 2$.
24. $y = A \sin 2x + B \cos 2x + 2$.
25. $y = A \sin 2x + B \cos 2x + x - 2$.
26. $y = A e^x + B e^{-x} - \sin 3x$.
27. $y = A \sin x + B \cos x + \frac{1}{2} e^x$.
28. $y = A \sin 2x + B \cos 2x + \frac{1}{5} e^x$.

29. $y = A \sin 4x + B \cos 4x + x^2 - \frac{1}{8}$.

30. $y = A\,\mathrm{e}^{4x} + B\,\mathrm{e}^{-4x} - x^2 - \frac{1}{8}$.

31. 4 m.   **32.** $\dfrac{\pi}{12}$ s.   **33.** π s.

34. $\left(2\,\mathrm{e} - \dfrac{2}{\mathrm{e}}\right)$ m.   **35.** $\left(2\,\mathrm{e} + \dfrac{2}{\mathrm{e}}\right)$ m.   **37.** 30°C.

38. 11.9 min.   **41.** 2.303.   **42.** $\frac{1}{10}$.

44. $(\mathrm{e}^t - \mathrm{e}^{-2t})$ m.   **45.** $\left(\mathrm{e} + \dfrac{2}{\mathrm{e}^2}\right)$ m/s.   **47.** $\mathrm{e}^{-3t} \sin 2t$ metres.

49. $3g$ m/s.   **50.** $(3 \log 3)$ s.

Revision Paper C1 (p. 259)

1. $y = \dfrac{x^3}{3} - x^2 + \dfrac{4}{3}$; $\frac{4}{3}$, max; 0 min.

2. $7\frac{4}{27}$ max; 7 min.

3. $(0, 0)$ and $(5, -125)$ min; $(2, 64)$ max.

4. (ii) $\ln 2 + \frac{1}{2}x + \frac{1}{8}x^2$.   **5.** $\frac{1}{4}(\sqrt{5} + 1)$.

9. $\dfrac{x}{2}\,\sqrt{(4 + x^2)} + 2 \ln \{x + \sqrt{(4 + x^2)}\}$;

  (ii) $-\mathrm{e}^{-2x}\left(\dfrac{x^3}{2} + \dfrac{3}{4}x^2 + \dfrac{3}{4}x + \dfrac{3}{8}\right)$.

10. (i) $xy = 2(x - 1)$; (ii) $4y = (2x + \sin 2x) \cos^n x$.

Revision Paper C2 (p. 260)

1. (a) (i) $\dfrac{-2(x + 5)\sqrt{(1 - x)}}{3}$, (ii) $\dfrac{\sin^4 x}{4} - \dfrac{\sin^6 x}{6}$; (b) $\frac{1}{3}$.

2. (a) $-\dfrac{1}{4(2x + 1)^2}$; (b) $-\dfrac{1}{2(x^2 + 1)}$; (c) $\dfrac{\sqrt{2} - 1}{3}$.

5. $x = \pm \dfrac{1}{\sqrt{3}}; 4.$

6. (i) $\frac{10}{3}$; (ii) $\frac{1}{2}\tan^{-1}(2\tan^{-1}x)$.

9. (i) $\frac{1}{2}\ln\dfrac{1-y}{1+y} + \dfrac{1}{1+x} = C;$

   (ii) $y\sqrt{(1+x^2)} = \dfrac{x}{2}\sqrt{(1+x^2)} + \frac{1}{2}\sinh^{-1}x + C.$

10. $Ay = 2 + B\,e^{4x}; y = C.$

Revision Paper C3 (p. 262)

1. (i) $y^2 = 2(x-1)$; (ii) $y^2 = \tan^2 x + 4\tan x - 1$.

2. $\left(\dfrac{\pi}{4} + \dfrac{1}{\pi}, 0\right)\cdot$

4. $(1, 40), (-1, 40); 9.$

6. $\dfrac{\pi}{4}\cdot$

7. $\dfrac{x^3}{3} - \dfrac{3x^2}{2} + 2x; \frac{5}{6}\max; \frac{2}{3}\min.$

8. $\dfrac{\pi}{8}\cdot$

9. $\dfrac{\pi}{2}\cdot$

Revision Paper C4 (p. 264)

1. $2 - \dfrac{\pi}{2}\cdot$

5. (i) $\tan\frac{1}{2}x + x\tan\frac{1}{2}x - 2\ln\sec\frac{1}{2}x.$

$\ln\dfrac{x}{\sqrt{(x^2+1)}} - \dfrac{1}{x} - \tan^{-1}x$; (ii) $\frac{27}{140}$.

6. $A = 1, B = \frac{4}{5}, C = -\frac{4}{5}.$

8. (i) $y = A\,e^x\sin x$ (ii) $y = 2 + A\sin(3x + B).$

10. $1 - \dfrac{2}{e}\cdot$

Revision Paper C5 (p. 266)

1. $\dfrac{x^4}{4}\tan^{-1}x - \dfrac{x^3}{12} + \dfrac{x}{4} - \dfrac{1}{4}\tan^{-1}x.$

2. $\left(\dfrac{3\pi a}{16}, \dfrac{a}{5}\right); \dfrac{2\pi a^3}{15}.$

3. (i) $\pi\left(1 - \dfrac{\pi}{4}\right)$; (ii) $\dfrac{\pi^2}{3} - \pi.$

4. $\left(\dfrac{\pi}{4} + \dfrac{1}{\pi}, 0\right)\cdot$

5. (a) $\ln\dfrac{1+x}{x} - \dfrac{1}{x}$; (b) $\frac{1}{4}\ln 3.$

6. $3, 12, -2$ or $-2, 12, 3.$

8. (i) $\dfrac{\pi}{8}$; (ii) $\frac{1}{4}\ln\frac{432}{125}$; (iv) $\dfrac{\pi}{8}\cdot$

9. $-2, \frac{3}{4}, -\frac{1}{2}, \frac{11}{4}\ln\frac{3}{2} + \frac{3}{4}\ln 2 - \frac{7}{6}.$

10. (ii) $x(\ln x - 1), \frac{1}{5}e^x(\sin 2x - 2\cos 2x)$; (iii) $\frac{2}{15}$.

Exercise 19.2 (p. 274)

1. $r(\cos\theta + \sin\theta) = 1.$
2. $r^2\cos\theta\sin\theta = c^2.$
3. $r\cos\theta = 4.$
4. $r\sin\theta = 2.$
5. $r(3\cos\theta + 4\sin\theta) = 5.$
6. $r = 2\cos\theta.$
7. $r\cos^2\theta = \sin\theta.$
8. $r^2(4\cos^2\theta + \sin^2\theta) = 1.$
9. $3\cos\theta\sin\theta = 1.$
10. $r^2 = \cos\theta\sin\theta.$
11. $x^2 + y^2 = 4a^2.$
12. $x^2 + y^2 - 2x - 1 = 0.$
13. $x^2 + y^2 + 2y - 3 = 0.$
14. $x + 2y = 1.$
15. $xy = 2.$
16. $x^2 - y^2 = 1.$
17. $(x^2 + y^2)^2 = x^2 - y^2.$
18. $(x^2 + y^2)^2 = 2a^2xy.$
19. $y = x.$
20. $(x^2 + y^2)^3 = x^2 - y^2.$

Exercise 19.3 (p. 278)

1. $\frac{1}{2}a^2(e^2 - 1).$
2. $4a.$
3. $\sec\alpha(r_1 - r_2).$

5. $\dfrac{20a^2}{3}.$
6. $\dfrac{r\sin\alpha}{\alpha}.$
7. $\dfrac{2r\sin\alpha}{3\alpha}.$

8. $a^2.$
9. $\dfrac{64\pi a^2}{3}.$
10. $\pi a^2.$

11. $2\pi a.$
12. $\dfrac{\pi a^2}{8}.$
13. $\frac{3}{2}\pi a^2.$

14. $8a.$
15. $\dfrac{a^2}{\pi}.$
16. $a^2.$

17. $\left(\dfrac{256a}{105\sqrt{2\pi}}, 0\right).$
18. $\dfrac{4\pi a^3(9 - 8\sqrt{2})}{105}.$
19. $\sqrt{2}a(e^\pi - 1).$

20. $\frac{1}{4}\pi.$

Exercise 19.4 (p. 279)

3. $(x - a)^2(x^2 + y^2) = b^2x^2.$
4. $r = \pm\cos\theta.$
5. $r\cos\theta = 1 - \tan^2\theta.$
6. $r = \pm 2a\cos\theta.$

11. $\pi ab.$
12. $\frac{1}{2}a^2$
13. $\dfrac{c^2}{4}\ln 3.$

15. $2\pi + \dfrac{3\sqrt{3}}{2}.$
16. $\dfrac{\pi a}{4\sqrt{2}}.$

Exercise 20.1 (p. 282)

1. (i) 3; (ii) $3 - 4i$; (iii) $3 + i$; (iv) $-6 + 4i$; (v) $-15 + 36i$; (vi) $3 - 2i$; (vii) $\frac{1}{3}$; (viii) $\frac{1}{5}(1 + 3i)$; (ix) $\frac{1}{2}(1 - 3i)$; (x) $\frac{1}{13}(1 - 8i)$; (xi) $\frac{1}{25}(2 - 11i)$; (xii) $\frac{1}{169}(-3 - 41i).$

2. (i) $-2 \pm 4i$; (ii) $-2 \pm i\sqrt{3}$; (iii) $\pm 5i$; (iv) $-i \pm 1$; (v) $i(-1 \pm \sqrt{3}).$

3. (i) $x^2 + 16 = 0$; (ii) $x^2 - 10x + 41 = 0$; (iii) $x^2 - 4x + 7 = 0$;
(iv) $x^2 - (3 + i)x + 4 + 3i = 0$.

4. i.　　　　　　　**5.** $\frac{1}{13}$.　　　　　　　**6.** $1, -1$.

7. $3, -2$.　　　　　**10.** $-1, \dfrac{1 \pm \sqrt{3}i}{2}$.　　　**11.** $+1, \dfrac{-1 \pm \sqrt{3}i}{2}$.

13. $3, \dfrac{-1 \pm 3\sqrt{3}i}{2}$.　　**14.** $(1, 2)$.　　　　　**15.** $(-3, -1)$.

16. $\cos\theta - i\sin\theta$.　　**17.** 1.　　　　　　　**18.** $2\cos\theta, 2i\sin\theta$.

21. $\cos\theta \pm i\sin\theta$.　　**22.** $2, 1$.　　　　　　**23.** $2, 3$.

24. $2 + 3i$.　　　　　**25.** $4 - 3i$.　　　　　**26.** -16.

27. $2\cos\theta$.　　　　　**30.** $2\cos 2\theta$.

Exercise 20.2 (p. 287)

2. $\frac{5}{2}$; (b) 13; (c) 17.　　　　　**3.** (a) $45°$; (b) $-59° 2'$; (c) $-123° 41'$.

4. $\dfrac{5}{\sqrt{2}}$.　　　**5.** $-15°$.　　　**7.** $2, 30°$.　　　**8.** $3, -70°$.

9. $\pm 90°$.　　　**10.** $\dfrac{3\pi}{4}$.　　　**11.** $\dfrac{\pi}{2} + \theta$.　　　**12.** $|z|$.

13. $1 + i, 45°$.　　**14.** $45°$.　　　**15.** $2\sqrt{2}$.　　　**16.** $75°$.

17. 5.

18. Circle, centre origin, radius 1.

19. Circle, centre origin, radius 2.

20. Circle, centre $(1, 0)$, radius 1.

Exercise 20.3 (p. 290)

1. $\frac{1}{5}$.　　　**2.** 1.　　　**3.** $\sqrt{\frac{2}{13}}$.　　　**4.** 15.　　　**5.** $\pi/4$.

6. $\pi/12$.　　　**7.** i.　　　**8.** -1.　　　**9.** -1.　　　**10.** i.

11. $\cos\theta + i\sin\theta$.　　　**12.** $\cos\theta + i\sin\theta$.　　　**13.** $\cos\theta + i\sin\theta$.

14. 1.　　　　　　**15.** i.　　　　　　**16.** $-8i$.

17. $\cos^4\theta - 6\cos^2\theta\sin^2\theta + \sin^4\theta, 4\cos^3\theta\sin\theta - 4\sin^3\theta\cos\theta$.

18. $16\sin^5\theta - 20\sin^3\theta + 5\sin\theta$.　　**20.** 3 and 1.

Exercise 20.4 (p. 294)

2. Circle, centre $(2, 0)$, radius 3.

3. Interior of a circle, centre $(1, -2)$, radius 3.

4. Perpendicular bisector of $(1, 0)$ and $(-1, 0)$.

6. Circle.　　　　　　**7.** Exterior of a circle.

8. $22° 36', 78° 42', 78° 42'$.　　　**9.** $(1, 2)$; 5.

13. Semi-line through origin. **14.** Semi-line through $(1, 0)$.

15. Exterior of a circle. **17.** $\frac{1}{3}(z_1 + z_2 + z_3)$.

18. $2, \dfrac{\pi}{2}$. **19.** 3. **20.** $\sqrt{10} - 2$.

Exercise 20.5 (p. 295)

3. (a) $\sqrt{29}$, 1.2 rad; (b) $2, -\dfrac{2\pi}{3}$; (c) $4, \dfrac{\pi}{2}$; (d) $1, \dfrac{\pi}{4}$.

6. $-\cos\theta \pm i\sin\theta$.

7. (a) $1 - i$; (b) $\dfrac{3 - i}{10}$; (c) $\dfrac{7 + i}{10}$; (d) $\frac{1}{2} - \frac{1}{2}i\tan\dfrac{\theta}{2}$.

8. 25. **10.** $x^3 - 8x^2 + 37x - 50 = 0$.

11. $\cos^5\theta - 10\cos^3\theta\sin^2\theta + 5\cos\theta\sin^4\theta$.

12. $\cos 2\theta + i\sin 2\theta$.

13. (a) $\cos(-\theta) + i\sin(-\theta)$; $2(\cos 2\theta + i\sin 2\theta)$;

$\cos\left(-\dfrac{\pi}{3}\right) + i\sin\left(-\dfrac{\pi}{3}\right)$. **14.** $0, -2$.

15. $16\cos^4\dfrac{\theta}{2}(\cos 2\theta + i\sin 2\theta)$. **16.** $3x^2 + 3y^2 + 10x + 3 = 0$.

22. $\cos\dfrac{2r\pi}{5} + i\sin\dfrac{2r\pi}{5}$, $r = 0$ to 4.

23. $\cos\dfrac{2r\pi}{7} + i\sin\dfrac{2r\pi}{7}$, $r = 0$ to 6.

24. $\cos\dfrac{(4r + 1)\pi}{8} + i\sin\dfrac{(4r + 1)\pi}{8}$, $r = 0$ to 3.

Exercise 21.1 (p. 301)

1. 17, 17. **2.** 7, 4.4. **3.** 7.5, 2.8. **4.** 24, 25.

5. $\sqrt{5}$, $\sqrt{116}$, $\sqrt{257}$; $\sqrt{101}$, $\sqrt{73}$, $\sqrt{216}$.

6. $\sqrt{2}$, $\sqrt{14}$, $\sqrt{50}$; $\sqrt{14}$, $\sqrt{24}$, $\sqrt{38}$. **7.** 5.

8. $5\mathbf{i} - 3\mathbf{j}$, $7\mathbf{i} - 7\mathbf{j}$.

9. $5\mathbf{i} - 3\mathbf{j} - 2\mathbf{k}$, $8\mathbf{i} - 6\mathbf{j} - 5\mathbf{k}$; $3\mathbf{i} - \mathbf{j}$, $2\mathbf{j} + 3\mathbf{k}$.

10. $\mathbf{i} + \mathbf{j}$, $2\mathbf{i} + \mathbf{j} + \mathbf{k}$; $14\mathbf{i} + \mathbf{j} + 13\mathbf{k}$, $-11\mathbf{i} + \mathbf{j} - 12\mathbf{k}$.

13. No. **14.** Yes. **15.** Angle A; greater.

Exercise 21.2 (p. 303)

1. (i) $2t\mathbf{i}$, $2\mathbf{i}$; (ii) $2t\mathbf{i} + 2t\mathbf{j}$, $2\mathbf{i} + 2\mathbf{j}$;
(iii) $\cos t\mathbf{i}$, $-\sin t\mathbf{j}$; (iv) $e^t(\mathbf{i} + \mathbf{j})$, $e^t(\mathbf{i} + \mathbf{j})$.

3. $-c\sin t\mathbf{i} + c\cos t\mathbf{j} + b\mathbf{k}$, $-c\cos t\mathbf{i} - c\sin t\mathbf{j}$; helix.

Exercise 21.3 (p. 308)

2. $\dfrac{1}{\sqrt{2}}$.

4. $\pm\frac{1}{5}(4\mathbf{i} + 3\mathbf{j})$.

5. $\pm\frac{1}{3}(2\mathbf{i} - 2\mathbf{j} + \mathbf{k})$.

6. $\frac{1}{4}(\sqrt{2} \pm \sqrt{6})\mathbf{i} + \frac{1}{4}(\sqrt{2} \mp \sqrt{6})\mathbf{j}$.

7. $\mathbf{r} = 3\mathbf{i} + \mathbf{j} + \lambda(2\mathbf{i} + 5\mathbf{j})$.

8. $\mathbf{r} = \mathbf{i} + 2\mathbf{k} + \lambda(2\mathbf{i} - 2\mathbf{j} - 3\mathbf{k})$.

9. $\mathbf{r}.(4\mathbf{i} + \mathbf{j} - 2\mathbf{k}) = 1$.

10. $\mathbf{r}.(7\mathbf{i} + 19\mathbf{j} + 3\mathbf{k}) = -1$.

11. $\dfrac{10}{3}\sqrt{3}$.

12. $\frac{4}{5}$, $2.04\mathbf{i} - 4\mathbf{j} - 2.28\mathbf{k}$.

13. 11; $-4\mathbf{i} - 5\mathbf{j} + 8\mathbf{k}$.

14. $\dfrac{1}{\sqrt{13}}$.

15. 2; $\frac{1}{5}(17\mathbf{i} - 6\mathbf{j})$.

16. $\mathbf{r}.(3\mathbf{i} + 4\mathbf{j}) = 1$; $\mathbf{r}.(4\mathbf{i} - 3\mathbf{j}) = 18$.

17. 1.

18. $\mathbf{r}.(4\mathbf{i} - \mathbf{j}) = 11$.

19. Same.

20. $\arccos\left(\dfrac{18}{5\sqrt{13}}\right)$.

21. ± 1.

22. $2\mathbf{i} + \mathbf{j}$.

23. $\frac{2}{5}(3\mathbf{i} + 4\mathbf{j})$.

24. $\frac{9}{2}$; $\frac{15}{2}$.

25. $\frac{1}{2}\sqrt{3}$; $\frac{5}{6}$.

26. $\frac{22}{3}$.

27. Yes; $\frac{1}{3}$.

28. $(\mathbf{r} - \mathbf{i} - \mathbf{j}).(\mathbf{r} - 4\mathbf{i} + 2\mathbf{j}) = 0$.

30. $\dfrac{5}{\sqrt{84}}$.

Exercise 21.4 (p. 311)

1. $2\mathbf{m} - \mathbf{a}$.

2. $3\mathbf{p} - 2\mathbf{a}$.

3. $3\mathbf{g} - \mathbf{a}$.

4. $3\mathbf{g} - \mathbf{a} - \mathbf{b}$.

5. $\mathbf{b} - \mathbf{a}$.

6. $\mathbf{b} - 2\mathbf{a}$.

7. $\frac{1}{3}(2\mathbf{a} + \mathbf{b})$; $\frac{1}{6}(2\mathbf{a} + \mathbf{b})$; $\frac{1}{4}\mathbf{b}$.

9. $4\mathbf{a} - 3\mathbf{b}$.

12. $\frac{1}{3}(\mathbf{b} + 2\mathbf{c})$.

14. Mid-point of XT, where T lies in YZ and $YT:TZ = 1:4$.

15. H is in plane ABC; $(lm + mk + kl)(\alpha, \beta, \gamma) = (lm, mk, kl)$.

Exercise 21.5 (p. 317)

1. (i) $-\mathbf{i} + 7\mathbf{j} - 5\mathbf{k}$; (ii) $\mathbf{i} - 3\mathbf{j} + 3\mathbf{k}$; (iii) $2\mathbf{j} - 2\mathbf{k}$.

2. (i) $6\mathbf{j} - 4\mathbf{k}$; (ii) $-6\mathbf{j} + 4\mathbf{k}$; (iii) $6\mathbf{j} - 4\mathbf{k}$.

3. $\frac{1}{2}\sqrt{174}$.

4. $\frac{1}{2}\sqrt{150}$.

5. $\sqrt{2}$.

6. $\sqrt{\frac{54}{5}}$.

7. $\frac{1}{2}\sqrt{26}$.

8. $\sqrt{13}$.

9. $\frac{1}{3}$.

10. 4.

11. $\mathbf{r}.(-4\mathbf{i} + 3\mathbf{j} + \mathbf{k}) = 0$.

12. $\mathbf{r}.(7\mathbf{i} - 2\mathbf{j} + 2\mathbf{k}) = 7$.

13. $\mathbf{r}.(2\mathbf{i} + 3\mathbf{j} - 3\mathbf{k}) = 10$.

14. $\mathbf{r}.(\mathbf{i} - 2\mathbf{j} + \mathbf{k}) = 0$.

15. $\mathbf{r}.(\mathbf{i} + \mathbf{j} - \mathbf{k}) = 0$.

Exercise 21.6 (p. 317)

4. $\mathbf{r} = \lambda(\sqrt{2}\mathbf{i} + \mathbf{j} + \mathbf{k})$.

5. (i) Circle, centre origin, radius a;
   (ii) Straight line through origin, parallel to $\mathbf{a}$;
   (iii) Straight line perpendicular to $\mathbf{a}$, distance $\frac{1}{2}a$ from origin;
   (iv) Straight line perpendicular to $\mathbf{a}$, distance a from origin;
   (v) Circle through origin, diameter $\mathbf{a}$.

6. (i) Sphere, centre origin, radius a;
   (ii) Straight line through origin parallel to $\mathbf{a}$;
   (iii) Plane, perpendicular to $\mathbf{a}$, distance $\frac{1}{2}a$ from origin;
   (iv) Plane, perpendicular to $\mathbf{a}$, distance a from origin;
   (v) Sphere through origin, diameter $\mathbf{a}$.

7. $\dfrac{1}{\sqrt{15}}$.   **8.** $\frac{3}{2}$.

11. $4\mathbf{i} + 5\mathbf{j}$; $\sqrt{41}$; $12\mathbf{i}$.   **13.** $\pm\dfrac{1}{\sqrt{2}}(\mathbf{i} - \mathbf{j})$.

14. $\frac{1}{3}(-\mathbf{i} + 2\mathbf{j} - 2\mathbf{k})$.   **15.** (i) $-\frac{1}{2}$; (ii) 1 or 7.

16. $\mathbf{r}.(2\mathbf{i} + 2\mathbf{j} + \mathbf{k}) = 4$; $2x + 2y + z = 4$.

17. $\dfrac{1}{\sqrt{3}}(\mathbf{i} + \mathbf{j} - \mathbf{k})$.

18. $a = \frac{1}{2}(\sqrt{3} - 1)$, $b = \frac{1}{2}(\sqrt{3} + 1)$; $p = \dfrac{1 - \sqrt{3}}{2\sqrt{3}}$, $q = \dfrac{1 + \sqrt{3}}{2\sqrt{3}}$, $r = \dfrac{2}{\sqrt{3}}$.

19. $-\dfrac{1}{3\sqrt{11}}, \dfrac{7}{\sqrt{2}}$.

20. $\dfrac{1}{3\sqrt{3}}, \frac{1}{2}\sqrt{26}, \frac{1}{3}\sqrt{26}$.

24. (i) 8; (ii) $\mathbf{r}.(16\mathbf{i} + 24\mathbf{j} - 5\mathbf{k}) = 48$; (iii) $\dfrac{48}{\sqrt{857}}(16\mathbf{i} + 24\mathbf{j} - 5\mathbf{k})$.

27. (iv) $\dfrac{k}{a^2}$.

28. $\lambda = \mu = \frac{2}{3}$; $19\frac{1}{2}°$.

29. $30°$, $\mathbf{r} = \mathbf{i} - \mathbf{k} + \lambda(\mathbf{i} + \mathbf{j} + \mathbf{k})$, $(2, 1, 0)$.

30. Yes, $\sqrt{5}$.

31. (i) $-30\mathbf{i} - 15\mathbf{j} + 8\mathbf{k}$; (ii) $\frac{1}{5}(3\mathbf{i} + 4\mathbf{k})$, $\frac{1}{13}(12\mathbf{i} + 5\mathbf{j})$;
   (iii) $\frac{36}{65}$; (iv) $\frac{4}{5}$, $\alpha = -\frac{36}{169}$, $75x - 180y + 676z = 0$.

32. (i) $\mathbf{r}.(6\mathbf{i} + 3\mathbf{j} + 2\mathbf{k}) = 6$; (ii) $\mathbf{r} = \lambda(6\mathbf{i} + 3\mathbf{j} + 2\mathbf{k})$;
   (iii) $\frac{6}{49}(6\mathbf{i} + 3\mathbf{j} + 2\mathbf{k})$.

33. $\mathbf{r}.(\mathbf{i} - \mathbf{k}) = 1$, E and F.

35. (i) $x + 2y + z = 0$; (ii) $(-3, 2, -1), (-4, 3, -2), (1, 1, -3)$;
   (iii) $(-3, 1, 1)$.

38. (iii) (v) true.   **39.** c.

40. Two circles on sphere centre O radius OA.

Exercise 22.1 (p. 328)

1. $1; 0; 0; 0; 0; \begin{pmatrix} 3 & -4 \\ -2 & 3 \end{pmatrix}$.

2. (i) Parallelogram, vertices $(0, 0)$, $(3, 2)$, $(7, 5)$, $(4. 3)$;
   (ii) Segment of $3y = 2x$ between $(0, 0)$ and $(9, 6)$;
   (iii) Segment of $y = 0$ between $(0, 0)$ and $(4, 0)$;
   (iv) Segment of $y = 0$ between $(0, 0)$ and $(3, 0)$;
   (v) The point $(0, 0)$.

3. (i) The line $7y = 5x$; (ii) The line $3y = 2x$; (iii) The line $y = 0$;
   (iv) The line $y = 0$; (v) The point $(0, 0)$.

4. (i) The line $2y = x + 1$; (ii) The point $(3, 2)$; (iii) The line $y = 0$;
   (iv) The line $y = 0$; (v) The point $(0, 0)$.

5. $5y = 4x - 2$.

6. The point $(2, 4)$; the point $(3, 6)$.

8. (i) $\lambda = 3$ or 4, $\begin{pmatrix} 1 \\ -1 \end{pmatrix}, \begin{pmatrix} -2 \\ 3 \end{pmatrix}$; (ii) $\begin{pmatrix} -2 \\ 1 \end{pmatrix}, \begin{pmatrix} 1 \\ -2 \end{pmatrix}$; (iii) $\begin{pmatrix} 1 \\ 0 \end{pmatrix}, \begin{pmatrix} -2 \\ 5 \end{pmatrix}$;
   (iv) $\begin{pmatrix} 1 \\ 0 \end{pmatrix}, \begin{pmatrix} 0 \\ 1 \end{pmatrix}$; (v) $\begin{pmatrix} -3 \\ 1 \end{pmatrix}, \begin{pmatrix} 4 \\ 3 \end{pmatrix}$.

9. $12; 10; 6; 6; -30$.

Exercise 22.2 (p. 334)

1. (ii), (iv).

2. (i) $\dfrac{1}{18} \begin{pmatrix} -5 & 1 & 7 \\ 1 & 7 & -5 \\ 7 & -5 & 1 \end{pmatrix}$; (ii) $\dfrac{1}{18} \begin{pmatrix} -5 & 7 & 1 \\ 1 & -5 & 7 \\ 7 & 1 & -5 \end{pmatrix}$;

   (iii) $\begin{pmatrix} \frac{1}{2} & \frac{1}{2} & -\frac{1}{2} \\ \frac{1}{2} & -\frac{1}{2} & \frac{1}{2} \\ -\frac{1}{2} & \frac{1}{2} & \frac{1}{2} \end{pmatrix}$; (iv) $\dfrac{1}{5} \begin{pmatrix} -5 & 5 & 5 \\ 13 & -14 & -10 \\ -6 & 8 & 5 \end{pmatrix}$;

   (v) $\dfrac{1}{4} \begin{pmatrix} -11 & 2 & 7 \\ -19 & 6 & 11 \\ 9 & -2 & -5 \end{pmatrix}$;

3. $1, -1, 2$.

4. $-2, 1, 1$.

9. All points on the plane $x + z = 0$.

10. $\dfrac{1}{16} \begin{pmatrix} 12 & -9 & -1 \\ -4 & 7 & -1 \\ -4 & -1 & 7 \end{pmatrix}$.

Exercise 22.3 (p. 336)

1. $2, -1$.

2. (i) $\dfrac{1}{10}\begin{pmatrix} 3 & 4 \\ -1 & 2 \end{pmatrix}$; (ii) Singular; (iii) $\frac{1}{4}$ (1); (iv) Not square;

(v) $\dfrac{1}{3}\begin{pmatrix} 3 & 6 & -4 \\ 0 & -3 & 2 \\ 0 & 0 & 1 \end{pmatrix}$; (vi) $\begin{pmatrix} 1 & 0 & 0 \\ 0 & \frac{1}{2} & 0 \\ 0 & 0 & \frac{1}{3} \end{pmatrix}$;

(vii) $\begin{pmatrix} 0 & 0 & -1 \\ -1 & 0 & 0 \\ 0 & -1 & 0 \end{pmatrix}$; (viii) Singular.

3. Each line $3y = x$ and $3y = -x$ is mapped into itself.

5. 0, 1 or 2.

11. $(4, 6, 2), (1, -1, 1)$.

12. $\begin{pmatrix} 0 & 0 & 0 \\ 0 & 0 & 0 \\ 0 & 0 & 0 \end{pmatrix}$. Both are singular.

13. $\begin{pmatrix} -3 & 0 & 0 \\ 0 & -3 & 0 \\ 0 & 0 & -3 \end{pmatrix}$.

14. $\begin{pmatrix} 1 \\ 2 \\ 3 \end{pmatrix}, \begin{pmatrix} 5 \\ -4 \\ -5 \end{pmatrix}$

15. Direction-ratios $-2:1:3$; $y = 0$.

16. (i) $(1, 0, 0)$; (ii) $3(\lambda - 1), 2\lambda - 1, \lambda$.

17. $\begin{pmatrix} 1 & 0 & 0 \\ 0 & 1 & 0 \\ -2 & 0 & 1 \end{pmatrix}$; $\begin{pmatrix} 1 & -1 & 0 \\ 0 & 1 & 0 \\ 0 & 0 & 1 \end{pmatrix}$;

$\begin{pmatrix} 1 & 0 & 0 \\ 0 & 1 & -2 \\ 0 & 0 & 1 \end{pmatrix}$; $\begin{pmatrix} 1 & -1 & 0 \\ 4 & 1 & -2 \\ -2 & 0 & 1 \end{pmatrix}$.

18. Both $n \times n$ matrices, $\mathbf{X} = \begin{pmatrix} a & b \\ 0 & a \end{pmatrix}$.

19. (i) $(-1, 3, 4); (1, -3, 16)$;

(ii) $\begin{pmatrix} 1 & 2 & -1 \\ 0 & 1 & -1 \\ 0 & 0 & 1 \end{pmatrix}$; (iii) $\begin{pmatrix} -1 \\ 3 \\ 4 \end{pmatrix}$; (iv) $\begin{pmatrix} 1 & 2 & -1 \\ -4 & -9 & 5 \\ 3 & 9 & -2 \end{pmatrix}$.

20. $(9, 18, 18)$; ratio $1:9$; $(2\lambda, -2\lambda, \lambda)$; $k = 3$; $(2\lambda, \lambda, -2\lambda)$.

21. $\begin{pmatrix} 1 & 0 & 0 \\ 0 & 1 & -3 \\ 0 & 0 & 1 \end{pmatrix}, \begin{pmatrix} 1 & 0.4 & 0 \\ 0 & 1 & 0 \\ 0 & 0 & 1 \end{pmatrix}$, 46.

22. $-2, 0, 3$.

23. $-1, 0.7, -5.7$; ± 0.8.

24. $(\alpha, \alpha, -\alpha)$, $(\alpha, \alpha, -2\alpha)$, $(0, \alpha, -\alpha)$.

Eigenvectors are $\begin{pmatrix} 1 \\ 1 \\ -1 \end{pmatrix}, \begin{pmatrix} 1 \\ 1 \\ -2 \end{pmatrix}, \begin{pmatrix} 0 \\ 1 \\ -1 \end{pmatrix}$.

30. $\dfrac{1}{24}\begin{pmatrix} 12 & -4 & -4 \\ 0 & 8 & -10 \\ 0 & 0 & 6 \end{pmatrix}$.

33. $\begin{pmatrix} 0 & 1 & 0 \\ 0 & 0 & 1 \\ 1 & 0 & 0 \end{pmatrix}; \begin{pmatrix} a \\ b \\ c \end{pmatrix}$.

34. $\begin{pmatrix} \frac{2}{3} & \frac{1}{2} \\ \frac{1}{3} & \frac{1}{2} \end{pmatrix}; \begin{pmatrix} \frac{1}{2} & 1 \\ \frac{1}{2} & 0 \end{pmatrix}; \frac{8}{13}$.

35. (i) 0.2401; (ii) 0; (iii) 0.12; (iv) 0.31.

36. $\frac{5}{9}$.

37. $2ax + b$; 0, equal to $\dfrac{d^3 f}{dx^3}$.

38. $\dfrac{1}{8}\begin{pmatrix} 1 & 16 & 19 \\ 2 & -8 & 10 \\ -3 & 0 & 1 \end{pmatrix}$; $(0, 0, 0)$, $(0, 1, -1)$, $(-1, 3, -3)$.

39. $34:1$.

40. $\begin{pmatrix} 1 + \dfrac{R_3}{R_2} & -R_1 - R_3 - \dfrac{R_1 R_3}{R_2} \\ -\dfrac{1}{R_2} & 1 + \dfrac{R_1}{R_2} \end{pmatrix}$.

Revision Paper D1 (p. 344)

1. $65.4°$, $114.6°$.   **2.** a^2.   **3.** (v).

7. $\mathbf{r}.(6\mathbf{i} + 3\mathbf{j} + 2\mathbf{k}) = 6$; $\mathbf{r} = \lambda(6\mathbf{i} + 3\mathbf{j} + 2\mathbf{k})$;
$\frac{6}{49}(6\mathbf{i} + 3\mathbf{j} + 2\mathbf{k})$.

Revision Paper D2 (p. 346)

1. $\dfrac{3\pi}{16}a^2$.

2. $(e^{2\pi} - 1)\sqrt{2}$.

3. (i) $\arctan\left(\frac{4}{3}\right)$; (ii) 5; (iii) $-4 + 3i$; (iv) $3 - 4i$.

4. $\pm\dfrac{1}{\sqrt{2}}(1 + i)$; $\pm 1 \pm i$; $\sqrt{2}$; $\dfrac{\pi}{4}, \dfrac{3\pi}{4}, \dfrac{5\pi}{4}, \dfrac{7\pi}{4}$; $(z^2 - 2z + 2)(z^2 + 2z + 2)$.

5. (i) $1 + \frac{1}{2}i$, $-1 \pm \dfrac{1}{\sqrt{2}}(1 + i)$; (ii) $2 \pm \frac{3}{2}i$.

6. 3, 2.

7. $\frac{2}{3}\mathbf{i} + \frac{2}{3}\mathbf{j} + \frac{1}{3}\mathbf{k}$; 1.5.

8. AB parallel to $A'B'$.

9. 1, -1, 1.

10. $\pi_0 = \beta/(\alpha + \beta)$; $\pi_1 = \alpha/(\alpha + \beta)$.

Revision Paper D3 (p. 348)

2. $z = w = \frac{1}{5}(-1 + 2i)$.

4. (a) $2 - 11i$; (b) $4 + i$; (c) $\pm(1 - i)$; $2 + i$, $1 + 2i$; coefficients not real.

5. (i) (a) $2\sqrt{10}$; (b) 10; (c) $\frac{1}{5}\sqrt{10}$; (ii) $4\left[\cos\left(-\dfrac{2\pi}{3}\right) + i\sin\left(-\dfrac{2\pi}{3}\right)\right]$;

(iii) $\dfrac{5t - 10t^3 + t^5}{1 - 10t^2 + 5t^4}$, where $t = \tan\alpha$.

6. $\frac{3}{2}\mathbf{b} - \frac{1}{2}\mathbf{c}$.

8. (i) $-\frac{4}{9}$; (ii) $\frac{1}{2}\sqrt{65}$; (iii) $-\dfrac{6}{\sqrt{65}}, -\dfrac{2}{\sqrt{65}}, \dfrac{5}{\sqrt{65}}$; (iv) $\frac{1}{6}$.

9. -1, 3; $3{:}4{:}-9$, $1{:}0{:}1$.

10. $\alpha = 1$, $x = 1 + 4z$, $y = -3z$; $\alpha = -\frac{3}{5}$, $x = \frac{17}{5} + 4z$, $y = -\frac{48}{25} - 3z$.

Revision Paper D4 (p. 351)

1. $r = 1.62$, $\theta = 51.8°$ or $308.2°$.

2. (i) $\dfrac{1}{2}\left(\dfrac{3\pi}{4} \pm 2\right)a^2$; (ii) $\frac{4}{15}\pi a^3$.

3. 0 or -22.

5. 1, -4; -3, $1 \pm i$.

6. $1 - 3i$, $-3 + 4i$.

7. (i) $-\mathbf{i} + \mathbf{j} + 3\mathbf{k}$; (ii) $-3\lambda\mathbf{j} + \lambda\mathbf{k}$ for any λ; (iii) $125°$; (iv) $35°$.

8. 1:4.

10. $\frac{2}{3}\pi$.

Revision Paper D5 (p. 353)

3. $c^7 - 21c^5s^2 + 35c^3s^4 - 7cs^6$; $7c^6s - 35c^4s^3 + 21c^2s^5 - s^7$.

5. $(\frac{5}{3}, 0)$, $\frac{4}{3}$.

6. (i) $(1 - k^2)(x^2 + y^2 + a^2) + 2(1 + k^2)ax = 0$; (ii) $\dfrac{x^2}{b^2} + \dfrac{y^2}{b^2 - a^2} = 1$;

(iii) $\dfrac{x^2}{c^2} + \dfrac{y^2}{a^2 - c^2} = 1$.

8. (i) $\pm\dfrac{1}{\sqrt{6}}(-\mathbf{i} + 2\mathbf{j} + \mathbf{k})$; (ii) $2\sqrt{6}$; (iii) $\mathbf{i} + 7\mathbf{j} - 2\mathbf{k}$.

9. $\lambda = 1, 3$; $\mu = 1, 3^n$.

Exercise 23.1 (p. 357)

1. $3x + 4y = 1$; $4x - 3y = 18$.

2. 5. **3.** $\frac{11}{8}$. **4.** $(5, -3)$; $(7, -7)$.

5. 1. **6.** $y = 4x - 11$.

7. $y - x + 5 = 0$; $y + x + 3 = 0$.

8. $2\frac{2}{5}$. **9.** Same. **10.** $(6, 7)$.

11. $\tan^{-1} \frac{1}{18}$. **12.** $x = 4y$. **13.** ± 1.

14. $(2, 1)$. **15.** $(\frac{6}{5}, \frac{8}{5})$. **16.** $2\frac{4}{5}$.

17. $(-3, 2)$ or $(3, -2)$. **18.** $1:1$. **19.** $4y - 2x = 11$.

Exercise 23.2 (p. 361)

1. $(14x + 112y - 25)(64x - 8y - 105) = 0$.

2. $\tan^{-1} \frac{1}{7}$. **3.** $x - 8y + 1 = 0$.

4. $(3x - y - 2)(19x + 7y - 26) = 0$.

5. $x^2 - 2xy - 2y^2 = 0$. **6.** $\sqrt{10}$.

7. $x + 2y = 3$.

8. $(9x + 28y - 44)(21x + 12y - 76) = 0$.

9. $(x - 2y + 3)(x - 3y + 5) = 0$.

10. $(2x + y - 3)(3x + y - 4) = 0$.

11. $(4x + 3y)(x + 2y) = 0$. **12.** $\dfrac{\sqrt{41}}{3}$.

14. $(1, 1)$. **15.** $\pm\frac{1}{5}$.

16. $x \cos \alpha + y \sin \alpha - p = \pm(x \cos \beta + y \sin \beta - q)$.

17. $(x - y)(x + y - 2) = 0$. **18.** No.

19. No. **20.** 8; $\frac{16}{65}$.

Exercise 23.3 (p. 362)

1. $x + 4y = 0$.

2. $(y - x - 4)(y - x + 4) = 0$.

3. $5x - 5y = 9$.

4. $\left(-a, \dfrac{a(m + t)}{mt}\right)$.

6. $1:2$.

7. $x = 2y$.

8. $x - 6y + 12 = 0$.

9. $-3:7$.

10. $y = x + 4$.

11. $C = (0, 6)$ or $(6, 2)$; $D = (-2, 3)$ or $(4, -1)$.

12. No; $-1:2$.

13. $4x + a = 0$.

15. $\left(2 + \dfrac{1}{\sqrt{3}}, 2 - \dfrac{1}{\sqrt{3}}\right)$ and $\left(2 - \dfrac{1}{\sqrt{3}}, 2 + \dfrac{1}{\sqrt{3}}\right)$.

16. $(1, 10)$ and $(9, 4)$.

17. $3x^2 + 3y^2 - 18x - 8y - 13 = 0$.

18. $x^2 + y^2 - 3x - 4y + 5 = 0$.

19. 1.

20. $(\frac{4}{5}, \frac{13}{5})$.

21. $\frac{36}{7}$.

22. $(-\frac{1}{3}, \frac{5}{3})$.

23. $-\frac{9}{8}$.

24. $(\frac{53}{6}, \frac{1}{6})$.

25. 2.

26. $2(bp - cd)$.

27. $2ax + 2by = a^2 + b^2$; $\dfrac{(a^2 + b^2)^{\frac{3}{2}}}{2ab}$.

28. $\frac{25}{9}$.

29. $-\dfrac{al + bm + n}{l \cos \theta + m \sin \theta}$.

30. $(lr - np)x + (mr - nq)y = 0$.

Exercise 24.1 (p. 367)

1. $x^2 + y^2 - 2x - 4y = 0$.

2. $5x^2 + 5y^2 - 29x - 20y + 20 = 0$.

4. $x^2 + y^2 - 4x - 4y + 7 = 0$.

5. $x^2 + y^2 - 5y = 0$.

7. $x = 7y + 25$; $(4, -3)$ and $(-3, 4)$.

8. $x^2 + y^2 - 4x + 2y - 20 = 0$.

9. $x - 3y = 7$.

13. $(0, -1)$ and $(0, -4)$.

14. $x^2 + y^2 - 4x + 3y = 0$.

15. $x^2 + y^2 + 3x - 5y = 0$.

16. $3x + 4y = 22$; $3x + 4y = -8$.

17. $c(x^2 + y^2) - c(a + b)x - (ab + c^2)y + cab = 0$.

18. 5.

20. $4\sqrt{6}$.

Exercise 24.2 (p. 368)

1. $x^2 + y^2 - ax - by = 0$; $ax + by = a^2 + b^2$.

2. $(7, 9)$ and $(9, -5)$; $x^2 + y^2 - 14x - 18y + 30 = 0$, $x^2 + y^2 - 18x + 10y + 6 = 0$.

3. $3x^2 + 3y^2 - 10x - 10y - 28 = 0$.

4. $x^2 + y^2 - 12x - 13y + 36 = 0$; $(0, 9)$.

5. $\sqrt{(x_1 x_2 + y_1 y_2)}$.

6. $5x^2 + 5y^2 - 2x - 4y - 78 = 0$.

7. $(l^2 + m^2)(x^2 + y^2) - 2lx - 2my + 2 - r^2(l^2 + m^2) = 0$.

8. $x^2 + y^2 + 11x + 19y = 0$.

9. $13x^2 + 13y^2 - 38x + 43y - 31 = 0$.

10. 7 or $-\frac{23}{7}$.

11. -5; $(-\frac{2}{9}, \frac{2}{9})$, $\frac{1}{9}\sqrt{35}$.

12. $(\pm 1, +1)$.

13. $5x^2 + 5y^2 + 2x(9G - 4g) + 2y(9F - 4f) + 9C - 4c = 0$.

14. 12.   **15.** $(0, 1)$ and $(0, \frac{17}{8})$.

16. $x + y = 7$.

17. $x(a - p) + y(b - q) + p^2 + q^2 - ap - bq = 0$.

18. $x^2 + y^2 - 2ax - 2by + \frac{1}{2}(a^2 + b^2) = 0$.

19. $-g \pm \sqrt{(g^2 - c)}$.   **20.** $x^2 + y^2 = 2r^2$.

21. $x^2 - y^2 = a^2 - b^2$.   **22.** $gF = fG$.

23. $(x^2 + y^2 - x)^2 = x^2 + y^2$.   **23.** $2x + 4y + 1 = 0$.

25. $(\frac{8}{3}, 0)$.   **26.** $(10, 0)$.

28. $hk = -a^2$.

29. $\left(x - \dfrac{l - m^2}{l^2 + m^2}\right)^2 + \left(y - \dfrac{m + ml}{l^2 + m^2}\right)^2 = 4 - \dfrac{(1 + l)^2}{l^2 + m^2}$.

30. $x^2 + y^2 = 13$.

Exercise 25.1 (p. 372)

1. $(y - 3)^2 = \pm 4(x - 2)$.   **2.** $(2, 0)$, $(4, 0)$.

3. $(0, 0)$.   **4.** $(0, 4)$, $(0, 8)$.

5. $(0, 0)$.   **6.** $(y - 3)^2 = 16(x - 2)$.

7. $(x - 3)^2 = -8(y - 4)$.   **8.** 4.

Exercise 25.2 (p. 373)

1. $\frac{1}{3}\sqrt{5}$.   **2.** $(\pm 4, 0)$.   **3.** $(6, 3)$ and $(-2, 3)$.

4. $\frac{2}{3}$.   **5.** $(1, 0)$ and $(1, 4)$.   **6.** $(1, 1)$.

7. $\frac{13}{5}$ and $\frac{37}{5}$.   **8.** $\dfrac{x^2}{9} + \dfrac{y^2}{5} = 1$.   **9.** $\dfrac{7x^2}{64} + \dfrac{y^2}{4} = 1$.

Exercise 25.3 (p. 376)

1. $\frac{1}{2}\sqrt{5}$.   **2.** $(\pm 5, 0)$.   **3.** $(7, 3)$, $(-3, 3)$.

4. $\frac{5}{3}$.   **5.** $(6, 2)$, $(-4, 2)$.   **6.** $(1, -1)$.

7. $\frac{13}{3}$ and $\frac{37}{3}$.   **12.** $3(x - 5)^2 - y^2 = 3$.

Exercise 25.4 (p. 377)

1. $(\pm \sqrt{2c}, \pm \sqrt{2c})$. 2. $(1, 2)$. 3. $(-2, -3)$.
4. $x = -1; y = 2$. 6. $x + y = \pm 2$. 7. $(\pm 2, \pm 2)$.
8. $xy = 2$. 9. $8, 8$. 10. $6, 6$.
12. $\left(4t - 1, \dfrac{4}{t} + 1\right)$.

Exercise 25.5 (p. 379)

1. $(x - y)^2 = 0$. 2. $x^2 + 16y^2 = 20$.
3. $3x^2 - 10xy + 3y^2 = 0$. 4. $x^2 + y^2 = 3$.
5. No. 6. $x^2 = x - y$.
7. $x^2 = y + 1$ and $x^2 + 2xy + y^2 = x$.
8. $x = 0, x = 2y$. 10. $y = x, y = -6x$.
11. $x = \pm y$. 12. $p^2 + q^2 = 2$.

Exercise 25.6 (p. 380)

1. $2\sqrt{2}$. 6. $5x^2 - 5y^2 - 4x = 3$.
8. $x^2 - xy - 2y^2 = 0$. 9. $\dfrac{x^2}{36} + \dfrac{y^2}{20} = 1$.
10. $\dfrac{x^2}{16} - \dfrac{y^2}{9} = 1$.
12. $q^2x^2 - 2pqxy + p^2y^2 + 2px + 2qy - 1 = 0$.
13. $qx = py$. 14. $\left(\dfrac{p}{2(p^2 + q^2)}, \dfrac{q}{2(p^2 + q^2)}\right)$.
15. $x + y = 4$.
16. $x^2 - 2xy + y^2 + 8x + 8y - 16 = 0$.
23. $(2 \pm \sqrt{3}, 0)$. 25. $3x^2 + 8xy - y^2 = 0$.
27. $4xy = 1; y = \sqrt{3}x, y\sqrt{3} + x = 0$.
28. $2xy - 2x - 2y + 1 = 0$. 29. $(1, 1); 2$ and 2.
30. $x^2 - y^2 - 2\sqrt{2}x + 1 = 0$.

Exercise 26.1 (p. 386)

1. (i) $1, \frac{1}{2}, -3$; (ii) $(2, 2), (0, 0), (\frac{1}{2}, 1), (2, -2)$.
2. (i) $(2t^2, 4t)$; (ii) $(2t^2 + 1, 4t)$; (iii) $(2t^2, 4t + 1)$; (iv) $(2t^2 - 1, 4t + 1)$.
3. $3y - 2x = 4a$. 4. $5y - 2x = 12a$.
5. $3y = x + 9a$. 6. $(2a, 3a)$.
11. $y + mx = 2am + am^3$.
12. $\{2a + a(m^2 + mt + t^2), -amt(m + t)\}$.
13. $(4a, 4a), (9a, 6a)$. 14. $(9a, -6a)$.
15. $-2\left(t + \dfrac{2}{t}\right)$. 16. $\{a(1 + t^2), at\}, A\sqrt{(1 + t^2)}$.

Exercise 26.2 (p. 390)

1. (i) $-1, 2, \sqrt{2}$; (ii) $\left(\dfrac{c}{\sqrt{2}}, c\sqrt{2}\right)$, $(-c, -c)$, $(\tfrac{1}{2}c, 2c)$.

2. (i) $\left(2t, \dfrac{2}{t}\right)$; (ii) $\left(\tfrac{1}{2}t, \dfrac{1}{2t}\right)$; (iii) $\left(ct + 1, \dfrac{c}{t}\right)$; (iv) $\left(t + 1, \dfrac{1}{t} - 1\right)$.

3. $x + 4y = 4$.

4. $4x + y = 8$, $x - 4y + 15 = 0$.

5. $x + 4y = 4c$, $8x - 2y = 15c$.

6. $x + 2y = 3c$.   7. $9x + y = 6c$.

8. $1 \pm \sqrt{2}$.   9. $\left\{\dfrac{2cst}{s + t}, \dfrac{2c}{s + t}\right\}$.

10. $\tfrac{17}{4}\sqrt{17}$.   13. $x + y = \pm 2c$.

16. $x + 2y = 4c$.   20. $8xy = 9c^2$.

Exercise 26.3 (p. 394)

1. $(x^2 - 1)(y^2 - 1) = 1$.   2. $\dfrac{\cos \tfrac{1}{2}(\alpha + \beta)}{\cos \tfrac{1}{2}(\alpha - \beta)}, \dfrac{\sin \tfrac{1}{2}(\alpha + \beta)}{\cos \tfrac{1}{2}(\alpha - \beta)}$.

3. $x \cos \tfrac{1}{2}(\alpha + \beta) + y \sin \tfrac{1}{2}(\alpha + \beta) = \cos \tfrac{1}{2}(\alpha - \beta)$.

4. $(-\tfrac{1}{2}\alpha, -\tfrac{1}{8}\alpha^3)$.   5. $4y^2 + 1 = 3x$.

Exercise 26.4 (p. 397)

2. $\dfrac{x}{a} + \dfrac{y}{b} = \sqrt{2}$.

3. $\{a(\cos \theta - \sin \theta), b(\cos \theta + \sin \theta)\}$.

5. $(1 + a \cos \theta, 2 + b \sin \theta)$.

7. $ax \sin \varphi - by \cos \varphi = (a^2 - b^2) \cos \varphi \sin \varphi$.

9. $(6, 4)$.   10. $ab \operatorname{cosec} 2\alpha$.

11. $c^2 = a^2 + b^2$.   12. $8x + 9y = 43$.

Exercise 26.5 (p. 400)

1. $x = \pm y$.   2. $2 \tan^{-1} \dfrac{b}{a}$; $a = b$.

3. $2x + y = 1$, $2x - y = 3$.   4. $3y - x = 1$, $3y + x = 5$.

8. $\dfrac{x}{a} = \pm \dfrac{y}{b}$.   9. $4x^2 - y^2 = 3$.

10. $(\tfrac{1}{2}, \tfrac{3}{2})$.   11. $y^2 - x^2 - 3y + x = 0$.

12. $\sqrt{2}$.

Exercise 26.6 (p. 401)

1. $y^2 = 16a(x - 2a)$.

2. $2a(xy^2 - 2a^3) = (y^2 + 2a^2)^2$.

3. $y^2 = a(x - 3a)$.

6. $ln = am^2$.

8. $\sqrt{2}:1$.

11. $n^2 = 4c^2lm$.

12. $3x + 4y = 5, y = -1$.

13. $(1.12, 1.66); (1.83, 0.8)$.

14. $a\alpha \sin \dfrac{\alpha}{2}$.

Exercise 27.1 (p. 408)

1. $\sqrt{21}$.

2. $\dfrac{1}{\sqrt{21}}(4, -2, 1)$.

3. $\sqrt{19}$.

4. $\dfrac{1}{\sqrt{26}}(1, 4, 3)$.

6. $(2, -2, 2)$.

9. $(0, 2, \tfrac{7}{3})$ and $(1, 3, \tfrac{11}{3})$.

10. $\dfrac{5}{3\sqrt{3}}$.

11. $\dfrac{x}{\sqrt{2}} = y = z$.

12. $\dfrac{x - 1}{2} = \dfrac{y - 1}{3} = \dfrac{z - 1}{4}$.

13. $-1:2$.

14. $-1:3$.

16. 7.

17. $\pm\dfrac{1}{\sqrt{3}}$.

18. $\cos^{-1}\dfrac{10}{\sqrt{357}}$.

20. $\cos^{-1}\tfrac{1}{3}$.

21. $-\dfrac{1}{\sqrt{14}}, \dfrac{2}{\sqrt{14}}, -\dfrac{3}{\sqrt{14}}$.

22. $(x - 1)^2 + y^2 + (z - 1)^2 = 1$.

23. $(1, 2, 1); 2$.

24. $(2, 0, 1); 4$.

25. $\tfrac{1}{8}\sqrt{29}$.

Exercise 27.2 (p. 412)

1. $x + \tfrac{1}{2}y + \tfrac{1}{4}z = 1$.

2. $4x - 3y - z = 0$.

3. $7x - 2y + 2z = 7$.

4. $\dfrac{x}{3} = -y = -z$.

5. $\dfrac{x - 1}{5} = \dfrac{y - 2}{1} = \dfrac{z - 1}{2}$.

6. 2.

7. $3x + 5y + z = 13$.

8. $x - y - z = -2$.

9. $Ax + By + Cz = Ax' + By' + Cz'$.

10. $x + 2y + 3z = 14$.

11. $x + y - z = 3$.

12. $\tfrac{1}{3}$.

13. $\dfrac{5}{\sqrt{84}}$.

14. $2x + 3y - 3z = 10$.

16. $2x + 3y + 6z = 11; 1$.

17. $\dfrac{Ax' + By' + Cz' + D}{\sqrt{(A^2 + B^2 + C^2)}}$.

18. $x = -\dfrac{y}{3} = \dfrac{z - 1}{2}$.

19. $\dfrac{x-1}{7} = \dfrac{y-1}{-5} = \dfrac{z-1}{3}.$　　　　**20.** $x + 2y - z = 0.$

21. $x + y - z = 1.$　　　　　　　　**24.** $x - 2y + z = 0.$

25. $x + y - z = 0.$

Exercise 27.3 (p. 415)

1. $(0, -1, 3).$　　　　　　　　　**3.** $(\tfrac{16}{5}, \tfrac{8}{5}, -\tfrac{19}{5}).$

4. $x - 4y + 3z = 0.$　　　　　　　**5.** $2x = y + z.$

6. $(1, 3, -2).$　　　　　　　　　**7.** $60°.$

8. $90°.$　　　　　　　　　　　**9.** $a + b + c + abc = 0.$

10. $(3, 5, 7).$　　　　　　　　　**11.** $(5, 1, 6).$

12. $x + y = z.$　　　　　　　　　**18.** $\dfrac{a^2 + b^2 - c^2}{a^2 + b^2 + c^2}.$

19. $-\dfrac{Ax_1 + By_1 + Cz_1 + D}{Ax_2 + By_2 + Cz_2 + D}.$　　**20.** $\dfrac{x-1}{a} = y = \dfrac{z-1}{c}.$

21. $x^2 + y^2 + z^2 = a^2.$　　　　　**22.** $x^2 + y^2 + z^2 = a^2.$

24. $\dfrac{6}{7\sqrt{14}}.$

25. $(2x - 1)^2 + (2y - 2)^2 + (2z - 3)^2 = 4.$

26. $(1, -1, 0); 2.$　　　　　　　　**27.** $(3, -2, 1); 5.$

28. $(1, 1, 1).$　　　　　　　　　**29.** $(1, 2, 3).$

30. $(2, 1, 0).$　　　　　　　　　**33.** $(-1, -2, 0)$ and $(\tfrac{9}{7}, \tfrac{10}{7}, \tfrac{8}{7}).$

34. $(2, 4, 5).$　　　　　　　　　**35.** $(3, 0, 3).$

38. $\dfrac{1}{\sqrt{6}}, \dfrac{1}{\sqrt{6}}, -\dfrac{2}{\sqrt{6}}.$

39. $\left(\dfrac{\lambda}{a}, \dfrac{\lambda}{b}, \dfrac{\lambda}{c}\right)$ where $\lambda = \dfrac{1}{a^2} + \dfrac{1}{b^2} + \dfrac{1}{c^2}.$

Revision Paper E1 (p. 418)

1. $(3, 0); x - y = 2, x + y = 3; 7.$　　**2.** $(1, 4), 3; 0.6.$

3. $x - 4ty + 2t^2 = 0; x \pm 4y + 2 = 0.$

5. $y + x(t + 1) = a(t + 1)(t^2 + 2t + 2).$

9. $\dfrac{x-1}{2} = \dfrac{y-1}{-5} = \dfrac{z-3}{11}.$　　　　**10.** $\dfrac{2}{\sqrt{154}}.$

Revision Paper E2 (p. 419)

1. $x - y = 1, x - 3y = 1; (1, 0), 5.$

2. $(8, 8), (-2, 10), (6, -2).$

4. $(6, 4\sqrt{2})$ or $(6, -4\sqrt{2}).$

5. (i) $x^2 + y^2 + 5x + 13y - 14 = 0;$ (ii) $5:1; 1.$

9. $2x + y + z = 4.$　　　　　　　　**10.** $(1, 1, 2).$

Revision Paper E3 (p. 421)

1. $\sqrt{\frac{52}{5}}$.   2. $(\frac{1}{4}at^2, -\frac{1}{8}at^3)$.   3. $(9, -10)$; 134.

4. $3x^2 + 3y^2 - 10x + 3 = 0$; $(\frac{5}{3}, 0)$; $\frac{4}{3}$; $3y + 4x = 0$.

6. $(-1, -\sqrt{3})$, $(-1, \sqrt{3})$; $x^2 + y^2 + 2x - 2 = 0$.

9. $(2, 4, 5)$.   10. $2x + 4y + 4z = 11$.

Revision Paper E4 (p. 423)

1. $(0, 7)$ and $(4, 1)$.   2. $x^2 + y^2 - x - 8y - 140 = 0$.

4. $x^2 + y^2 - 6x - 6y + 10 = 0$; $y - x + 4 = 0$, $y = x + 4$.

5. $(\frac{3}{5}, \frac{8}{5})$, $(-\frac{2}{5}, \frac{3}{5})$, $(\frac{7}{5}, -\frac{3}{5})$, $(\frac{12}{5}, \frac{2}{5})$; $y - x + 2 = 0$, $2x + 3y = 1$.

7. $2y - 3tx + t^3 = 0$.   9. $90°$, $54.7°$, $35.3°$.

10. $8x + 10y + 11z + 14 = 0$.

Index